A Resource and Strategies Guide for Biology

www.apstrategies.org

Acknowledgments

Funding for the *Laying the Foundation* series was provided through a grant from the O'Donnell Foundation.

Advanced Placement* Strategies gratefully acknowledges the tireless efforts of the following educators to write and edit the *Laying the Foundation* series.

Project Directors

René McCormick
AP* Strategies, Inc.
Dallas, Texas

Lisa McGaw
AP* Strategies, Inc.
Dallas, Texas

Authors

Carol Brown
Saint Mary's Hall
San Antonio, Texas

Hugh Henderson
Plano Senior High School
Plano, Texas

Jason Hook
Kealing Junior High
Austin, Texas

Lynn Kirby
Kealing Junior High
Austin, Texas

Carol Leibl
James Madison High School
San Antonio, Texas

René McCormick
AP Strategies, Inc.
Dallas, Texas

Lisa McGaw
AP* Strategies, Inc.
Dallas, Texas

Mary Payton
AP Strategies, Inc.
Dallas, Texas

Debbie Richards
Bryan High School
Bryan, Texas

Editor

Mary Payton
Editor In Chief

Contributing Authors

Randy Baskin
Rider High School
Wichita Falls, Texas

Adrian Carrales
Kealing Junior High
Austin, Texas

Andrew Cordell
Fort Worth Country Day School
Fort Worth, Texas

Judy Cordell
Nolan High School
Fort Worth, Texas

Ron Esman
Plano Senior High School
Plano, Texas

Jeff Funkhouser
Northwest High School
Justin, Texas

Brian Kaestner
Saint Mary's Hall
San Antonio, Texas

René Moses
Carroll High School
Southlake, Texas

Mary Anne Potter
Micron Systems
Dallas, Texas

Other Contributors and Reviewers

Pat Chriswell
Fort Bend Baptist Academy High School
Sugar Land, Texas

Kristen Jones
A&M Consolidated High School
College Station, Texas

Dennis Ruez, Jr.
UT Austin, Department of Geology
Austin, Texas

Charlotte Taggart
Abilene High School
Abilene, Texas

Syllabi Contributors

Rhonda Alexander
Robert E. Lee High School
Tyler, Texas

Carol Brown
St. Mary's Hall
San Antonio, Texas

Tom Campbell
Keeling Junior High
Austin, Texas

Lynn Cook
Putnam City Schools
Oklahoma City, Oklahoma

Luiz DeCarvalho
Carroll High School
Southlake, Texas

Denise DeMartino
Westlake High School
Austin, Texas

Chuy Garcia
Hyde Park Baptist
Austin, Texas

Lawanna Jenkins
Hodges Bend Middle School
Houston, Texas

Sharon Hamilton
Fort Worth Country Day
Fort Worth, Texas

Nancy Nixon
Covington Middle School
Austin, Texas

Patti O'Conner
James Madison High School
San Antonio, Texas

Camie Fillpot
O'Henry Middle School
Austin, Texas

Nancy Ramos
Northside Health Careers High School
San Antonio, Texas

Jackie Snow
Troy High School
Troy, Texas

Charlotte Taggart
Abilene High School
Abilene, Texas

Production

Sonya Pullen
AP* Strategies, Inc.
Dallas, Texas

Table of Contents

Introduction to the Laying the Foundation Series

The Laying the Foundation Series in Science is designed to support classroom teachers in better preparing students for Advanced Placement* science courses. We believe this goal is readily accomplished through well-designed science programs that begin in the middle grades. These guide books are also designed to assist a school or school district in building a strong science vertical team. Each guide is designed to provide the teacher with insight into the process skills, content skills, and assessment strategies that will better prepare students as they pursue Advanced Placement science courses and other advanced coursework.

Each guide begins with a set of Foundation Lessons. The Foundation Lessons target the process skills needed to provide a solid foundation for further scientific study. These lessons should serve as a spring board for establishing the basic expectations for a science vertical team and should be reinforced at each grade level.

Pre-AP* teachers often say, "If I just knew what to teach, I would teach it!" Content skills specific to each course are outlined in the appropriate LTF guide. The Pre-AP course should have a greater depth and breadth of content. Therefore, a course scope along with sample syllabi from successful Pre-AP teachers is provided to aid teachers in designing their course. It is also our belief that connections between math and science should be demonstrated and emphasized to students from an early age. The middle grades content has been divided into two LTF guides, one for life and earth sciences and one for chemistry and physics. Some middle schools have found an integrated chemistry and physics course offered to students in Algebra I to be very successful. Middle grade teachers with an integrated science course covering all four disciplines should utilize both of the middle school guides. The remaining three guides in the series focus on first-year courses in biology, chemistry and physics.

Currently, there are no Pre-AP science textbooks. The lessons found in the LTF guides model how to add the fullness to each course that is currently lacking in most widely adopted textbooks. Teacher pages included with each lesson provide correlations to the TEKS and the National Science Standards as well as a connection to the relevant AP course outline. In addition, these pages provide helpful hints for setting up laboratory activities and insightful teaching strategies. Finally, the teacher pages offer content assistance for the lessons dealing with topics that are not typically found in the on-level science textbook.

We hope that you will use these guides to enhance instruction in your classroom, formulate strong horizontal and vertical teams, and better prepare students to succeed on AP science exams. It is also our hope that you use the lessons from the guides with all of your students. Ultimately, we believe student achievement depends upon the strong expectation that all of your students are preparing for Advanced Placement science classes or advanced course work.

— René McCormick and Lisa McGaw

Overview of Laying the Foundation in Biology

Biology is experiencing a golden era of expansive growth and discovery. Through collaborative efforts such as the Human Genome Project and through innovations in technology in the field of molecular research, the 21st century has seen an exponential rise in new scientific information. These are exciting times to be in the biology classroom, guiding the students who will be the scientists of tomorrow.

The first year of biology serves as a foundational course in a student's academic development in high school, and, in Texas, the course is required for graduation. The amount of content covered in biology can be overwhelming to both student and teacher yet is innately interesting to most students. The teacher continually faces decisions regarding the issue of breadth versus depth of concept coverage. With exponential growth in biology expected to continue, decisions regarding the scope of the course will remain an issue.

Teachers face the challenge of preparing students to function effectively in a world where biological information is increasing at a rapid rate. By focusing on the development of learning skills, the teacher empowers the students to be lifelong learners. Teachers can employ Pre-AP strategies to ensure students have a strong fundamental understanding of biological concepts. Using these strategies affords teachers the opportunity to present a foundational course in a manner that is academically challenging and one that focuses on the development of analytical skills. Acquisition of the appropriate knowledge and possession of these investigative skills is pivotal to student's success in AP science courses.

The teacher plays a multifaceted role in preparing students for success in AP Biology. One facet is to provide a course that is rigorous and intellectually challenging. Additionally, the teacher should provide students with hands-on laboratory experiences that focus on development of analytical skills required for AP Biology. Through collaboration, the teacher should ensure that the course is vertically aligned with other science courses in order to provide a highly effective AP science program.

The ultimate purpose of the *Laying the Foundation* series is to provide resources for the teacher desiring to fully implement Pre-AP strategies in the classroom. This guide contains samples of learning activities designed to address biological concepts known to be difficult for students to grasp. Also included are laboratory experiences that target specific skill development and contain analysis questions that elevate the content to an appropriate level of rigor. Assessment items are included and can be used by the teacher as sample questions. This guide is not intended to be an all-inclusive curriculum guide but rather a valuable resource to the teacher in the development of a course that prepares the student for AP Biology.

We hope this series will serve as a stepping stone in the process of establishing an AP program, providing access for all students, preparing them for the challenges ahead.

— Debbie Richards and Carol Leibl

Process Skills Progression Chart

PROCESS SKILLS PROGRESSION CHART

	Factual Knowledge	Conceptual Understanding	Reasoning and Analysis
Acquire Data By Experimentation and Observation	Identify scientific equipment, instruments, and technology Know and observe safety precautions Follow a procedure	Choose appropriate equipment and technology	Work collaboratively to obtain scientific data
Record and Manipulate Data	Measure and record data in SI units Make and record observations	Determine variables to be measured Estimate and approximate quantities Solve mathematical equations using data	Design a data table or chart as appropriate Create appropriate graphical representations of data Analyze error Apply statistical analysis such as standard deviation, percent error, and chi square
Graph and Analyze Data	Plot data points Label the axes Title the graph	Translate graph into words Scale axes Calculate slope, area, and intercepts Construct line of best fit, curve fits, regression equations	Evaluate line of best fit, curve fit, and regression equation Detect patterns in data Interpret physical meaning of slope, area, and intercepts Interpolate, extrapolate and predict from a graph Transform data into linear form Recognize cause and effect relationships Draw appropriate conclusions Apply conclusions to new situations and further investigations

	Factual Knowledge	Conceptual Understanding	Reasoning and Analysis
Communicate and Share Results		Translate data into words Read and understand scientific articles	Defend results and conclusions in both written and oral format Relate concepts to unifying themes
Design Experiments	State the purpose Practice identifying variables	Design and use models to explain scientific concepts Understand the importance of controls Apply steps of scientific method to solve a problem Formulate a feasible and practical procedure	Formulate testable questions and hypotheses Critique experimental designs Predict outcomes Make environmentally friendly choices when designing experiments
Demonstrate Mathematical Problem-solving Skills	Identify relevant given information	Substitute values into an equation and solve Use dimensional analysis Estimate reasonable answers	
Use Technology	Recognize useful data tools such as graphing calculators, probes, data collection device and computers	Use data collection tools such as graphing calculators, probes, data collection device and computers	

Foundation Lessons

The Scientific Method
Exploring Experimental Design

Unit Overview

OBJECTIVE
Students will identify and apply the steps of the scientific method.

LEVEL
All

NATIONAL STANDARDS
UCP.1, UCP.2, UCP.3, A.1, A.2, G.2

TEKS
6.1(A), 6.2(A), 6.2(B), 6.2(C), 6.2(D), 6.2(E), 6.3(A)
7.1(A), 7.2(A), 7.2(B), 7.2(C), 7.2(D), 7.2(E), 7.3(A)
8.1(A), 8.2 (A), 8.2(B), 8.2(C), 8.2(D), 8.2(E), 8.3(A)
IPC: 1(A), 2(A), 2(B), 2(C), 2(D), 3(A)
Biology: 1(A), 2(A), 2(B), 2(C), 2(D), 3(A)
Chemistry: 1(A), 2(A), 2(B), 2(C), 2(D), 2(E), 3(A)
Physics: 1(A), 2(A), 2(B), 2(C), 2(D), 2(E), 2(F), 3(A)

CONNECTIONS TO AP
AP Science courses all contain a laboratory component where the scientific method will be used.

TIME FRAME
Two 45 minute class periods

MATERIALS

Come Fly With Us student pages
Penny Test Lab student pages
Scientific Method Practice 1 student pages
Scientific Method Practice 2 student pages

TEACHER NOTES

Modern scientific inquiry or science (from *scientia*, Latin for knowledge) is generally attributed to the historical contributions of Galileo Galilei and Roger Bacon, though some historians believe that their practices were inspired by earlier Islamic tradition. In spite of the rich human tradition of scientific inquiry, there is, today, no single or universal method of performing science. According to the National Science Teachers Association, science is "characterized by the systematic gathering of information through various forms of direct and indirect observations and the testing of this information by methods including, but not limited to, experimentation." Although this definition is helpful to explain the process of science, it does not specify a list of experimental steps that one should logically progress through to perform an experiment. (An experiment can be defined as an organized series of steps used to test a probable solution to a problem, commonly called a hypothesis, or educated guess.) Despite the absence of a *standard* scientific method, there is a generally agreed upon model that describes how science operates.

Steps of the Scientific Method

1. State the problem: What is the problem? This is typically stated in a question format.
   - *EXAMPLE: Will taking one aspirin per day for 60 days decrease blood pressure in females ages 12-14?*

2. Research the problem: The researcher typically will gather information on the problem. They may read accounts and journals in the subject or be involved in communications with other scientists.
   - *EXAMPLE: Some people relate stories to doctors that they feel relief from high blood pressure after taking one aspirin per day. It is not scientific if the idea is untested or if one person reports this (called anecdotal evidence).*

3. Form a probable solution, or hypothesis, to your problem. Make an educated guess as to what will solve the problem. Ideally this should be written in an *if-then* format.
   - *EXAMPLE: If a female aged 12-14 takes one aspirin per day for 60 days, then it will decrease her blood pressure.*

4. Test your hypothesis: **Do an experiment**.
   - *EXAMPLE: Test 100 females, ages 12-14, to see if taking one aspirin a day for 60 days lowers blood pressure in those females.*

   Independent Variable (I.V.): The variable you change, on purpose, in the experiment. To help students remember it suggest the phrase "**I**" change it" emphasizing the **I**ndependent variable.
   - *EXAMPLE: In this described experiment, taking an aspirin or not would be the independent variable. This is what the experimenter changes between his groups in the experiment.*

Dependent Variable (D.V.): The response to the I.V.

- *EXAMPLE: The blood pressure of the individuals in the experiment, which may change from the administration of aspirin.*

Control: The group, or experimental subject, which does not receive the I.V.

- *EXAMPLE: The group of females that does not get a dose of aspirin.*

Constants: Conditions that remain the same in the experiment.

- *EXAMPLE: In this scenario some probable constants would include: only females were used, only females at around the same age, the same dosage of aspirin was given to all the individuals in the experimental group for the same defined time interval—60 days, the same brand of aspirin was given, the same type of diet was ideally given to the members of the experimental group as well as the same activity level prescribed.*

5. Recording and analyzing the data: What sort of results did you get? Typically data is organized into data tables. The data is then graphed for ease of understanding and visual appeal.
   - *EXAMPLE: Out of 100 females, ages 12-14 yrs., 76 had lower blood pressure readings after taking one aspirin per day for 60 days.*

6. Stating a conclusion: What does all the data mean? Is your hypothesis correct?
   - *EXAMPLE: It appears that taking one aspirin per day for 60 days decreases blood pressure in 76% of the tested females ages 12-14, therefore the original hypothesis has been verified, that taking aspirin can decrease blood pressure.*

7. Repeating the work: Arguably, the most important part of scientific inquiry! When an experiment can be repeated and the same results obtained by different experimenters, that experiment is validated.

Included in this unit is a hands-on lab, the *Penny Test Lab*, that can be modified for use at any level (although it was initially designed for middle school use), to teach the steps of the scientific method. Students are given the simple task of determining the number of drops that can fit on the "Lincoln" side of a penny. As the lab is designed, the students quickly learn that even the most simple of experiments can contain many hidden variables that decrease the validity of the experiment.

Another student-centered activity has been included called *Come Fly with Us*. This activity makes a great first day activity to get kids warmed up to the scientific method. They will examine what happens to the spin direction of a paper helicopter when you fold the blades in different directions. Students construct a paper helicopter to test their hypothesis about how the helicopter will fly upon folding the blades in different directions.

Suggested Teaching Procedure

Day 1

1. Present notes on the steps of the scientific method as you see fit. Although this part is teacher-directed, ideally the steps should be presented as more of a discussion. Some questions to ask during your discussion are:
   - "What is the variable that the scientist changes?"
   - "What makes a valid experiment?"
   - "Why is it important to have detailed procedures for other scientists to repeat your experiment?"
   - "Why is the control such an important part of the experiment?"

   Also, students can be asked to imagine a scientific problem while the teacher asks students, "What is the independent variable in your problem?" and so on. An example of a scientific question was just presented in these teacher notes. You can use this example or make up another example to illustrate the prescribed steps. Students should record the steps in their notebooks.

2. After students take notes, pass out the student activity pages for *Come Fly With Us*.

3. Students should read the directions and perform the prescribed tasks in the procedure, applying new-found scientific method knowledge to the activity. Students should complete and turn in *Come Fly with Us* before leaving.

4. Assign *Scientific Method Practice 1* reading and questions for homework. Students are to return the completed questions the following class period.

Day 2

5. Use the answers that follow to review *Scientific Method Practice 1* after collecting the students' papers.

6. Pass out the student activity pages for the *Penny Test Lab*. Students should read the instructions and perform the lab during class.

7. After completing the lab, students should turn in a lab write-up at the end of the period.

8. Assign *Scientific Method Practice 2* reading and questions for homework. Students should answer questions and return the completed assignment the following class period.

Day 3

9. After collecting the students' papers, use the answers that follow to review *Scientific Method Practice 2* with students.

10. At this point you can begin an introduction to *Can Mosquitoes Transmit HIV Roleplay*, a complex student inquiry-based activity also found in this *Laying the Foundation* guide.

The Scientific Method
Exploring Experimental Design
Come Fly With Us

OBJECTIVE
Students will practice applying the steps of the scientific method to a problem.

LEVEL
All levels

NATIONAL STANDARDS
UCP.1, UCP.2, UCP.3, A.1, A.2, G.2

TEKS
6.1(A), 6.2(A), 6.2(B), 6.2(C), 6.2(D), 6.2(E), 6.3(A)
7.1(A), 7.2(A), 7.2(B), 7.2(C), 7.2(D), 7.2(E), 7.3(A)
8.1(A), 8.2 (A), 8.2(B), 8.2(C), 8.2(D), 8.2(E), 8.3(A)
IPC: 1(A), 2(A), 2(B), 2(C), 2(D), 3(A)
Biology: 1(A), 2(A), 2(B), 2(C), 2(D), 3(A)
Chemistry: 1(A), 2(A), 2(B), 2(C), 2(D), 2(E), 3(A)
Physics: 1(A), 2(A), 2(B), 2(C), 2(D), 2(E), 2(F), 3(A)

CONNECTIONS TO AP
Using the scientific method by acquiring data through experimentation and design of experiments are all fundamental skills needed for the AP Science courses.

TIME FRAME
45 minutes

MATERIALS

28 models of helicopter (provided)
28 pens or pencils
28 pairs of scissors

TEACHER NOTES
Come Fly With Us is an effective way for students to experimentally test a variable in a simple activity. This activity is designed to be the first activity that students do after learning the steps of the scientific method. The students can apply their newfound knowledge in a meaningful way.

Students cut out and fold a paper helicopter according to the instructions on the lab. After constructing the simple helicopter, students are instructed to fold the blades of the helicopter in opposing directions. Students generate a hypothesis as to how they think it will affect the direction of spin. The students then test their hypothesis and fly the helicopter after folding the blades in each direction. The students will discover that folding the blade one way will produce a clockwise spin of the helicopter. Folding the blades in the opposite direction will produce a counterclockwise spin of the helicopter. The students will ideally discover that applying the independent variable (folding the blades in opposing directions) causes the dependent variable to change (the direction of spin clockwise or counterclockwise). The students must also take into consideration the constants in their experiment: holding the helicopter at the same initial height, maintaining a stable wind environment, no other external forces acting on the helicopter, and holding the helicopter at the T each time. Although a control setup is not at first apparent, it is illustrated later.

The control is best illustrated in the second half of *Come Fly With Us*. A fictitious student, Bonita, believes that adding mass (paper clips) will stabilize her paper helicopter and increase the flight time. The independent variable is the presence or absence of the added mass. The control, by definition, does not receive the independent variable. Therefore, the control in Bonita's experiment is a paper helicopter with no paper clips added. The students can typically clearly envision the idea of a control. Further discussion of a control can describe how the experimental subject can only be truly tested when the results of the control setup are compared to the results of the experimental setup. Then the effect of the independent variable upon the dependent variable can clearly be seen. An extension of this lab could be to have the students actually try testing the extra weight and seeing how it affects the flight time.

POSSIBLE ANSWERS TO THE CONCLUSION QUESTIONS

1. In the helicopter experiment, what was the independent variable?
   - Folding the blades in different directions, with the black circle up and the white square down, or with the black circle down and the white square up.

2. What was the dependent variable?
   - The dependent variable is the direction of spin, clockwise or counterclockwise.

3. List three things you should try to keep constant each time you try this experiment.
   - There are many correct answers for this question. Possible answers include:
     - holding the helicopter in the same place (on the body versus the wing)
     - holding it at the same height
     - making sure there is no cross breeze each time
     - using the same helicopter
     - adding no extra force when letting it go each time

4. What is the problem question in Bonita's experiment?
   - Will adding extra mass in the form of paper clips to the helicopter stabilize it, making it stay in the air longer?

5. What is Bonita's hypothesis?
   - If additional paperclips are added to the helicopter, then the helicopter will be stabilized resulting in a longer flight time.

6. What is her independent variable?
   - Bonita's independent variable is the addition of paper clips (weight) to the helicopter.

7. What is her dependent variable?
   - Bonita's dependent variable is the amount of time the helicopter stays in the air.

8. What should her constants be?
   - Her constants should be the same as those listed in #3, plus: use the same size paper clips, attach the paper clips to the same place on the helicopter each time, etc…

9. What can she use for a control?
   - Her control is the same helicopter with no added mass.

10. Why should Bonita retest her experiment between 5-10 times?
    - Bonita should retest to make sure her results are reasonable and valid.

The Scientific Method
Exploring Experimental Design

Scientific Method Practice 1

POSSIBLE ANSWERS TO THE CONCLUSION QUESTIONS
NOTE: Problem, hypothesis and conclusion should all match in wording!

1. What was Erika's problem? [The problem should be stated as a question.]
   - Is the oven heating to the correct temperature? OR
   - Why didn't the cake rise?

2. What was Erika's hypothesis? [This is an answer to your problem question.]
   - No, the oven is not heating to the correct temperature. OR
   - The cake did not rise because the oven was not heating to the correct temperature.

3. What was Erika's conclusion? [This states whether your hypothesis was correct.]
   - The oven is heating to the correct temperature. OR
   - The oven was heating to the correct temperature and therefore could not have been the cause of the cake's failure to rise.

4. Which step in the scientific method do you think Erika should do next? Explain your reasoning.
   - Form a new hypothesis OR gather more information OR repeat the experiment.

5. List two other hypotheses which might explain why the cake did not rise.
   - Answers will vary

The Scientific Method
Exploring Experimental Design
Penny Test Lab

OBJECTIVE
Students will learn about controls and variables in an experiment. Additionally, they will learn what constitutes valid experimental procedure.

LEVEL
All levels

NATIONAL STANDARDS
UCP.1, UCP.2, UCP.3, A.1, A.2, G.2

TEKS
6.1(A), 6.2(A), 6.2(B), 6.2(C), 6.2(D), 6.2(E), 6.3(A)
7.1(A), 7.2(A), 7.2(B), 7.2(C), 7.2(D), 7.2(E), 7.3(A)
8.1(A), 8.2 (A), 8.2(B), 8.2(C), 8.2(D), 8.2(E), 8.3(A)
IPC: 1(A), 2(A), 2(B), 2(C), 2(D), 3(A)
Biology: 1(A), 2(A), 2(B), 2(C), 2(D), 3(A)
Chemistry: 1(A), 2(A), 2(B), 2(C), 2(D), 2(E), 3(A)
Physics: 1(A), 2(A), 2(B), 2(C), 2(D), 2(E), 2(F), 3(A)

CONNECTIONS TO AP
Using the scientific method by acquiring data through experimentation and design of experiments are all fundamental skills needed for the AP Science courses.

TIME FRAME
50 minutes

MATERIALS

28 pennies
28 eyedroppers
28 small beakers of water
28 paper towel
28 pencils or pens
28 calculators
28 pieces of graph paper (in appendix)
28 metric rulers
28 pieces of notebook paper

TEACHER NOTES

The *Penny Test Lab* takes a simple problem, how many drops of water will fit onto the "Lincoln" side of a penny, and expands it into an excellent lab that can be used to study the steps of the scientific method. To summarize, students use an eyedropper to determine how many drops of water will fit onto the penny before it spills over. This seemingly simple task generates many diverse results. By definition, a valid experiment is one that can be repeated by anyone else with the same results obtained. The lack of similar student results verifies that there are hidden variables that are unaccounted for in the procedure. This lab procedure is designed to show the students what an invalid experiment looks like.

Some of the hidden variables include pennies of different ages and conditions and different droppers (some plastic, some glass). Also, no exact procedure is given to the students about how to hold the dropper, how much pressure to put on the dropper, how to make a drop, how to drop it onto the penny, or from what height the drop should be released.

Before class, draw on the chalkboard or the overhead a data table with three rows and as many columns as there are students in the classroom. The first row should be labeled "student initials". The second row will be labeled "predicted" and the bottom row be labeled "observed".

One of the first steps of the procedure is for students to make a prediction about the number of drops they believe will fit on the "Lincoln" side of a penny. If students have never done a lab like this before or have no knowledge of the cohesive properties of water, they tend to underestimate the number of drops that will actually fit. Have students write their initials and their predicted number of drops on the chalkboard. Students then perform three trials, take an average from these three trials, and round it to the nearest whole number. Once they have completed this, they should write their average whole number of drops in the space provided on the class data table.

student initials	jh	hs	if	hg	sc	br
predicted #	12	8	13	20	26	11
actual #	23	16	35	12	22	13

A partial data table is shown here.

After everyone has completed their trials, students will analyze the class data by graphing the frequency of ranges of drops. Together as a class, you and the students will count the number of people that averaged 0-10 drops. Repeat this procedure for the ranges of 11-20, 21-30, 31-40, 41-50, etc. Instruct students to make a bar graph (technically a histogram since the intervals are equivalent) showing the number of people on the *y*-axis versus the range of drops on the *x*-axis.

Here is an example of a possible student histogram.

Frequency of Actual Number of Drops Put on a Penny

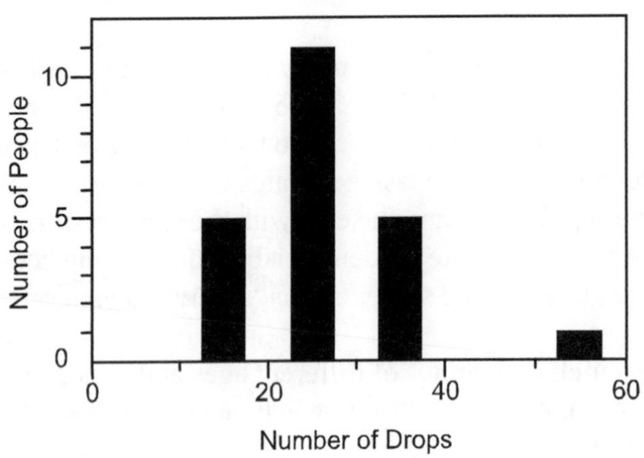

Before the students answer the questions, lead a discussion with students regarding what is considered a valid experiment versus an invalid experiment. Most students come to the conclusion that this is an invalid experiment due to the diverse results. Also, the discussion can include student ideas of hidden variables. These will include: different droppers, different pennies, no exact procedure for dropping, no definition of "drop," unstable table, etc. You can reveal to the students that this lab was purposefully designed to produce invalid results so that students could begin to understand that even in a simple task there can be many hidden variables.

POSSIBLE ANSWERS TO THE CONCLUSION QUESTIONS AND SAMPLE DATA

A typical data table for the student's 3 trials:

	Trial #1	Trial #2	Trial #3	Average
Number of Water Drops	______	______	______	______

1. Using your bar graph, determine if the average number of drops for each experimenter is about the same?
   - No, the results are not the same.

2. List four reasons why the actual number of drops for each experimenter was similar or dissimilar.
   - Student answers will vary
   - Four possible reasons:
     a. different types pennies
     b. no standard way of administering drops
     c. the table could be uneven
     d. each dropper is physically different and delivers drops of varying volume

3. Are the results of this experiment "valid"? Why or why not? Be sure to think about what makes an experiment valid.
   - Results are not valid in this experiment. To make an experiment valid, the results should be repeatable regardless of experimenter.

4. In this experiment, there were a limited number of constants. Name two of them.
   - Water (as opposed to alcohol or some other fluid)
   - Using pennies (as opposed to using nickels and pennies, etc…)

5. What was the independent variable in this experiment?
   - Student answers will vary. Some variation or factor that could affect the outcome (the dependent variable) could be accepted as the independent variable: height of dropper, size of dropper hole, pressure used when squeezing the dropper, size of drops, and so on.

6. What was the dependent variable in this experiment?
   - The dependent variable is the number of drops that fit on the head side of a penny.

7. Is it possible to state definitively how many drops of water will fit on the "Lincoln" side of a penny with this lab procedure? Why or why not?
   - Using this procedure it is not possible to state exactly how many drops fit onto a penny. This is not a valid experiment. There are too many hidden variables.

The Scientific Method
Exploring Experimental Design

Scientific Method Practice 2

POSSIBLE ANSWERS TO THE CONCLUSION QUESTIONS

1. State the problem in the form of a question.
   - What causes fresh water to freeze at a higher temperature than sea water?

2. Form a hypothesis to answer the problem question above based on the fact that fresh water does not contain salt.
   - The salt in sea water lowers the temperature at which water freezes.

3. According to the data table above, at what temperature did the experiment begin?
   - The experiment began at 25ºC.

4. At what time intervals were the temperature measurements taken?
   - The time intervals were 5 minutes.

5. What conclusions can you draw from these graphs about the effect of salt on the freezing point of water?
   - Salt lowers the freezing point of water.

6. What can you say about the rate at which the temperature in the fresh water container dropped compared to the rate at which the temperature in the salt water container dropped?
   - The rate at which the temperature in the fresh water container dropped was the same as the rate at which the temperature in the salt water container dropped.

7. What was the independent variable in Stephanie and Amy's experiment?
   - The independent [manipulated] variable was the addition of salt.

8. What was the dependent variable?
   - The dependent [responding] variable was the temperature at which the water froze.

9. Explain why detailed, step-by-step written procedures are an essential part of any scientific experiment.
   - When a scientist writes a report on his or her experiment, it must be detailed enough so that scientists throughout the world can repeat the experiment for themselves. In many cases, it is only when an experiment has been repeated by scientists worldwide that it is considered to be accurate.

10. The following hypothesis is suggested to you: Water will heat up faster when placed under the direct rays of the sun than when placed under indirect, or angled, rays of the sun. Design an experiment to test this hypothesis. Be sure to number each step of your procedure. Identify your independent variable, dependent variable and control. Identify those things which will remain constant during your experiment.
    - Answers will vary.

The Scientific Method
Exploring Experimental Design
Overview

PURPOSE
Through this series of activities you will identify and apply the steps of the scientific method.

MATERIALS

Come Fly With Us	*Scientific Method Practice 1*
Penny Test Lab	*Scientific Method Practice 2*

PROCEDURE
Day 1

1. Take notes in your notebook from your teacher's discussion about the steps of the scientific method.
2. Do the *Come Fly With Us* activity in class. Turn in at the end of the period.
3. Do the *Scientific Method Practice 1* activity for homework. Be ready to turn in the write-up at the beginning of the next period.

Day 2

4. Turn in *Scientific Method Practice 1* to your teacher at the beginning of class. Your teacher will review the correct answers.
5. Begin *Penny Test Lab* after collecting your materials.
6. Turn in the *Penny Test Lab* write-up to your teacher after completing it.
7. Do the *Scientific Method Practice 2* activity for homework. Be ready to turn in the write-up at the beginning of the next period.

Day 3

8. Turn in *Scientific Method Practice 2* to your teacher at the beginning of class. Your teacher will review the correct answers.

The Scientific Method
Exploring Experimental Design

Come Fly With Us

This assignment is intended to be a quick and easy guide to the methods scientists use to solve problems. It should also give you information about how to "wing your way" through your own experiments. You are going to start by making a model helicopter with the attached instructions. You will be given a problem question, and it is your job to write a suitable hypothesis. Remember, your hypothesis should be a possible answer to the problem question and it should be based upon what you already know about a topic.

GLOSSARY OF WORDS USED IN CONDUCTING EXPERIMENTS

- **problem**: scientific question that can be answered by experimentation.
- **hypothesis**: an educated prediction about how the independent variable will affect the dependent variable stated in a way that is testable. This should be an "If…then…" statement.
- **variable**: a factor in an experiment that changes or could be changed
- **independent variable**: the variable that is changed on purpose.
- **dependent variable**: the variable that responds to the independent variable.
- **control**: the standard for comparison in an experiment; the independent variable is not applied to the control group.
- **constant**: a factor in an experiment that is kept the same in all trials.
- **repeated trials**: the number of times an experiment is repeated for each value of the independent variable.

PURPOSE
In this assignment you will practice applying the steps of the scientific method to a problem by experimentation.

MATERIALS

model of helicopter (provided)
scissors
pen

PROCEDURE

1. Find the section labeled Hypothesis on your student answer page. Read the problem question and respond with an appropriate hypothesis. Remember to use an "If…then…" format.

2. Once you have made your hypothesis, you should test it for accuracy. Stand on a chair and hold your helicopter by the "T" at shoulder level.

3. Drop the helicopter and note whether it spins clockwise or counterclockwise. Repeat this test several times.

4. Refold the blades so that the square on section Y shows when you look down on top of the helicopter.

5. Stand on a chair and hold your helicopter by the top of the "T" at shoulder level. Drop the helicopter and note whether it spins clockwise or counterclockwise.

6. Repeat this test several times.

Name ______________________________

Period ______________________________

The Scientific Method
Exploring Experimental Design

Come Fly With Us

PROBLEM

How will changing the direction that the paper helicopter blades are folded affect the "flight" of the helicopter?

HYPOTHESIS

ANALYSIS

You have just performed an experiment. Experiments involve changing something to see what happens. In this case, you refolded the helicopter blades. You made this change on purpose to learn about its effect on the flight of the helicopter. The parts of an experiment that change are called *variables*.

When designing an experiment, you should choose one variable that you will purposely change. You will measure the effect of this *independent variable* on another variable that you think will respond to the change. The responding variable is called the *dependent variable*.

If you kept every variable except the folds the same in each test, you were making it a fair test. Why? Only the variable you changed could be causing the dependent variable to change because everything else was kept constant.

To have a fair test, you also need a *control*, or a standard for comparison. A control for the helicopter experiment would be an "unchanged" helicopter against which you could compare the results. You could make another helicopter as your standard for comparison and not refold its blades.

It is important to note that in some experiments, it is impossible to have a control that is completely unchanged. For example, let's say you are trying to determine the effect of light from different light sources on plant growth. The control plant needs some kind of light in order to live through the experiment. So, you have to choose one light source — any one say, normal sunlight — to be the standard of comparison.

After you refolded the blades of the helicopter, you dropped the helicopter several times and observed the results. These repeated trials enable you to be more confident of your results. If you conducted your experiment only once, the results could be due to an error or a chance event, such as a draft. But, when you repeat your experiment many times and each time achieve similar results, you can be more confident that your findings are not due to an error or chance.

Read the following paragraph and then answer the conclusion questions that follow using complete sentences:

> Bonita wanted to know if adding mass to her paper helicopter would affect how long it would stay in the air. She predicted that adding some mass would help to stabilize the helicopter and keep it in the air longer than a helicopter without extra mass. She experimented with different numbers of paper clips attached to her helicopter.

CONCLUSION QUESTIONS

1. In the helicopter experiment, what was the independent variable?

2. What was the dependent variable?

3. List three things you should try to keep constant each time you try this experiment.
   a.
   b.
   c.

4. What is the problem question in Bonita's experiment?

5. What is Bonita's hypothesis?

6. What is her independent variable?

7. What is her dependent variable?

8. What should her constants be?

9. What can she use for a control?

10. Why should Bonita retest her experiment between 5-10 times?

PAPER HELICOPTER MODEL

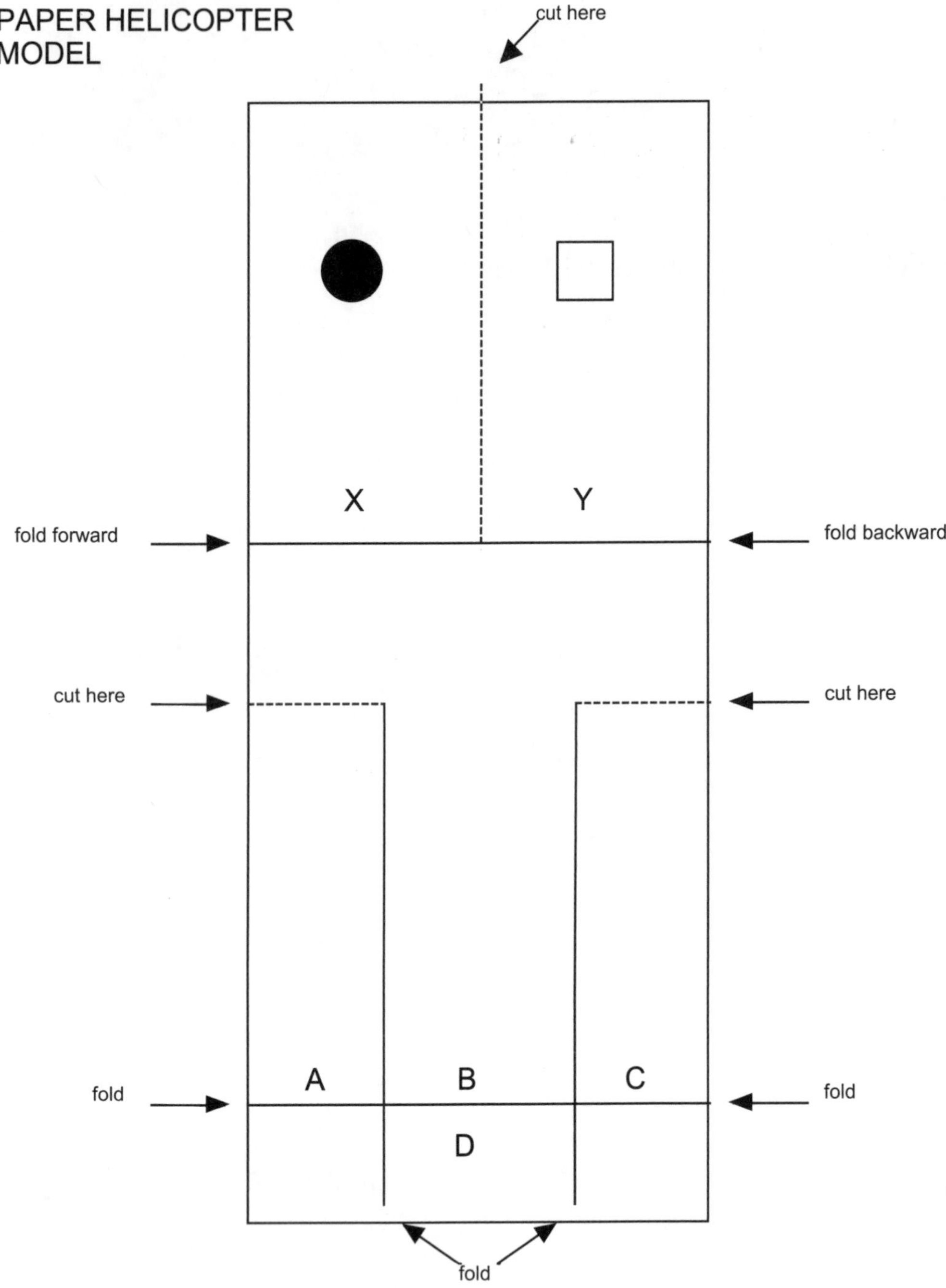

INSTRUCTIONS:

1. Cut out the rectangular helicopter (above).
2. Now cut along dotted lines.
3. Fold along the solid lines: section C behind section B, section A behind section B, and section D behind section B.
4. Complete the helicopter by folding blade X with the dot up and blade Y in the opposite direction with the square down.

Name ____________________

Period ____________________

The Scientific Method
Exploring Experimental Design

Scientific Method Practice 1

DIRECTIONS: *Read the following paragraphs and then answer the questions that follow on a separate sheet of paper. Use complete sentences to answer all questions. Be certain to restate the question in your answer.*

Science differs from other subject areas in the way it seeks to answer questions. This approach to problem solving is called the scientific method. The scientific method is a systematic approach to problem solving. The basic steps, in no particular order, of the scientific method are:

- Stating the problem
- Gathering information on the problem
- Forming a hypothesis
- Performing experiments to test the hypothesis
- Recording and analyzing data
- Stating a conclusion
- Repeating the work

Erika baked a cake for her mother's birthday. When the cake was taken from the oven, Erika noticed that the cake had not risen. She guessed that the oven had not heated to the correct temperature. She set up the following experiment to test her hypothesis.

First, Erika put a thermometer in the oven. She then turned the oven dial to 375ºF. She noticed that the preheating light came on when she turned the oven on. She waited until the preheating light went out, indicating that the oven was up to temperature. Erika then read the thermometer within the oven. It read 400ºF. Erika concluded that the oven was heating properly.

CONCLUSION QUESTIONS

1. What was Erika's problem? [The problem should be stated as a question.]

2. What was Erika's hypothesis? [This is an answer to your problem question.]

3. What was Erika's conclusion? [This states whether your hypothesis was correct.]

4. Which step in the scientific method do you think Erika should do next? Explain your reasoning.

5. List two other hypotheses which might explain why the cake did not rise.

Name ______________________________

Period ______________________________

The Scientific Method
Exploring Experimental Design

Penny Test Lab

PURPOSE
In this activity you will learn about controls and variables in an experiment. You will also learn what constitutes valid experimental procedure.

MATERIALS

penny
eyedropper
water
paper towel
calculator (optional)
graph paper
ruler
pen

DEFINITIONS
- **variable**: things in an experiment that change or could be changed.
- **independent variable**: variable that is changed on purpose.
- **dependent variable**: variable that responds to the independent variable.
- **constant**: things in an experiment that are kept the same in all trials.

PROCEDURE
1. Answer each of the following questions using complete sentences. For fill-in-the blank statements, copy the entire sentence.

2. Copy the lab purpose onto your paper.

3. Your task is to guess how many drops of water will fit on the "Lincoln" side of a penny.

   [Copy the following statement.] PROBLEM: How many drops of water will fit onto the "Lincoln" side of a penny?

4. [Copy the following statement and make a prediction by filling in the blank.] HYPOTHESIS: I predict that _________ drops of water will fit on the head side of a penny.

5. After you have made your hypothesis and have written it down on your lab paper, you will write it on the chalkboard under the heading "Predicted Number of Drops."

6. Copy the following chart onto your paper. Be neat and use a ruler!

TEST RESULTS:

	Trial #1	Trial #2	Trial #3	Average
Number of Water Drops	______	______	______	______

7. Test to see if your hypothesis is correct. Place your penny on a paper towel and, using the eyedropper, add water to the "Lincoln" side of the penny, one drop at a time, counting each drop until the water spills over. Do not count the drop that causes the water to spill over. Write the number of drops you counted under Trial #1 on your chart. Repeat this procedure two more times, filling in the number of drops you counted for each trial under the appropriate heading on your Test Results chart.

8. Find the average of your three trials, round your answer to a whole number (no decimals), and write the average number of drops on your Test Results chart. Then write your average on the chalkboard under the heading "Actual Average".

9. Write a sentence that will serve as your conclusion for this experiment. Remember that your conclusion should state whether your hypothesis was correct.

10. Make a bar graph of the class test results using the data from "Actual Average" on the chalkboard. The x-axis (horizontal line) should be titled "Average Number of Drops" and the y-axis (vertical line) should be titled "Number of Tests." Before graphing, you will need to organize the class data into ranges — make a chart that shows how many people got averages between 0-10, 11-20, 21-30, etc. When you have finished your bar graph, give it an appropriate title.

Answer the conclusion questions on your paper. Be sure to use complete sentences.

CONCLUSION QUESTIONS

1. Using your bar graph, determine if the average number of drops for each experimenter is about the same.

2. List four reasons why the actual number of drops for each experimenter was similar or dissimilar.

3. Are the results of this experiment "valid"? Why or why not? Be sure to think about what makes an experiment valid.

4. In this experiment, there were a limited number of constants. Name two of them.

5. What was the independent variable in this experiment?

6. What was the dependent variable in this experiment?

7. Is it possible to state definitively how many drops of water will fit on the "Lincoln" side of a penny with this lab procedure? Why or why not?

Name ________________________________

Period ________________________________

The Scientific Method
Exploring Experimental Design

Scientific Method Practice 2

DIRECTIONS: *Answer these questions on a separate sheet of paper using a black or dark blue ink pen. Use complete sentences to answer all questions. Be certain to restate the question in your answer!*

Stephanie and Amy were vacationing in Canada. Bundled up in warm clothing, they walked along the beach. Glistening strips of ice hung from the roofs of the beach houses. Only yesterday, Stephanie commented, these beautiful icicles had been a mass of melting snow. Throughout the night, the melted snow had continued to drip, freezing into lovely shapes. Near the ocean's edge, Amy spied a small pool of sea water. Surprisingly, she observed, it was not frozen as were the icicles on the roofs. What could be the reason, they wondered?

A scientist might begin to solve the problem by gathering information. The scientist would first find out how the sea water in the pool differs from the fresh water on the roof. This information might include the following facts: The pool of sea water rests on sand, while the fresh water drips along a tar roof. The sea water is exposed to the cold air for less time than the fresh water. The sea water is saltier than the fresh water.

Using all of the information that has been gathered, the scientist might be prepared to suggest a possible solution to the problem. A proposed solution to a scientific problem is called a hypothesis. A hypothesis almost always follows the gathering of information about a problem. Sometimes, however, a hypothesis is a sudden idea that springs from a new and original way of looking at a problem.

A scientist (or a science student) does not stop once a hypothesis has been suggested. In science, evidence that either supports a hypothesis or does not support it must be found. This means that a hypothesis must be tested to show whether it is correct. Such testing is usually done by performing experiments.

Experiments are performed according to specific rules. By following these rules, scientists can be confident that the evidence they uncover will clearly support or not support a hypothesis. For the problem of the sea water and freshwater, a scientist would have to design an experiment that ruled out every factor but salt as the cause of the different freezing temperatures. Stephanie and Amy, being excellent science students, set up their experiment in the following as follows.

First, they put equal amounts of fresh water into two identical containers. Then Stephanie added salt to only one of the containers. [The salt is the variable. In any experiment, only one variable should be tested at a time. In this way, scientists can be fairly certain that the results of the experiment are caused by one and only one factor — in this case the variable of salt.] To eliminate the possibility of hidden or unknown variables, Stephanie and Amy conducted a control experiment. A control experiment is set up exactly like the one that contains the variable. The only difference is that the control experiment does not contain the variable. Scientists compare the results of an experiment to a control experiment.

In the control experiment, Stephanie and Amy used two containers of the same size with equal amounts of water. The water in both containers was at the same starting temperature. The containers were placed side by side in the freezing compartment of a refrigerator and checked every five minutes. But only one container had salt in it. In this way, they could be fairly sure that any differences that occurred in the two containers were due to the single variable of salt. In such experiments, the part of the experiment with the variable is called the experimental setup. The part of the experiment with the control is called the control setup.

Stephanie and Amy collected the following data: the time intervals at which the containers were observed, the temperatures of the water at each interval, and whether the water in either container was frozen or not. They recorded the data in the tables below and then graphed their results.

WATER (control setup)

Time (min)	0	5	10	15	20	25	30
Temperature (°C)	25	20	15	10	5	0*	-10

*Asterisk means liquid has frozen

WATER WITH SALT (experimental setup)

Time (min)	0	5	10	15	20	25	30
Temperature (°C)	25	20	15	10	5	0	-10*

Stephanie and Amy might be satisfied with their conclusion after just one test. For a scientist, however, the results from a single experiment are not enough to reach a conclusion. A scientist would want to repeat the experiment many times to be sure the data were reproducible. So, a scientific experiment must be able to be repeated. And before the conclusion of a scientist can be accepted by the scientific community, other scientists must repeat the experiment and check the results. Consequently, when a scientist writes a report on his or her experiment, that report must be detailed enough so that scientists throughout the world can repeat the experiment for themselves. In most cases, it is only when an experiment has been repeated by scientists worldwide that it is considered to be accurate and worthy of being included in new scientific research.

By now it might seem as if science is a fairly predictable way of studying the world. After all, you state a problem, gather information, form a hypothesis, run an experiment, and determine a conclusion. Well, sometimes it isn't so neat and tidy.

In practice, scientists do not always follow all the steps in the scientific method. Nor do the steps always follow the same order. For example, while doing an experiment a scientist might observe something unusual or unexpected. That unexpected event might cause the scientist to discard the original hypothesis and suggest a new one. In this case, the hypothesis actually followed the experiment.

As you already learned, a good rule to follow is that all experiments should have only one variable. Sometimes, however, scientists run experiments with several variables. Naturally, the data in such experiments are much more difficult to analyze. For example, suppose scientists want to study lions in their natural environment in Africa. It is not likely they will be able to eliminate all the variables in the environment and concentrate on just a single lion. So, although a single variable is a good rule and you will follow this rule in almost all of the experiments you design or perform, it is not always practical in the real world.

There is yet another step in the scientific method that cannot always be followed. Believe it or not, many scientists search for the truths of nature without ever performing experiments. Sometimes the best they can rely on are observations and natural curiosity. Here is an example. Charles Darwin is considered the father of the theory of evolution, how living things change over time. Much of what we know about evolution is based on Darwin's work. Yet Darwin did not perform a single controlled evolutionary experiment! He based his hypotheses and theories on his observations of the natural world. Certainly it would have been better had Darwin performed experiments to prove his theory of evolution. But as the process of evolution generally takes thousands, even millions of years, performing an experiment would be a bit too time consuming.

CONCLUSION QUESTIONS

1. State Stephanie and Amy's problem in the form of a question.

2. Form a hypothesis (to answer the problem question above) based on the fact that fresh water does not contain salt.

3. According to the data table above, at what temperature did the experiment begin?

4. At what time intervals were the temperature measurements taken?

5. What conclusions can you draw from these graphs about the effect of salt on the freezing point of water?

6. What can you say about the rate at which the temperature in the fresh water container dropped compared to the rate at which the temperature in the salt water container dropped?

7. What was the independent variable in Stephanie and Amy's experiment?

8. What was the dependent variable?

9. Explain why detailed, step-by-step written procedures are an essential part of any scientific experiment.

10. The following hypothesis is suggested to you: Water will heat up faster when placed under the direct rays of the sun than when placed under indirect, or angled, rays of the sun. Design an experiment to test this hypothesis. Be sure to number each step of your procedure. Identify your independent variable, dependent variable and control. Identify those things which will remain constant during your experiment.

Numbers in Science
Exploring Measurements, Significant Digits, and Dimensional Analysis

OBJECTIVE
Students will be introduced to correct measurement techniques, correct use of significant digits, and dimensional analysis.

LEVEL
All

NATIONAL STANDARDS
UCP.1, UCP.3, A.1, G.2

TEKS
6.1(A), 6.2(A), 6.2(B), 6.2(C), 6.2(D), 6.4(A)
7.1(A), 7.2(A), 7.2(B), 7.2(C), 7.2(D), 7.4(A)
8.1(A), 8.2 (A), 8.2(B), 8.2(C), 8.2(D), 8.4(A)
IPC: 1(A), 2(A), 2(B), 2(C), 2(D)
Biology: 1(A), 2(A), 2(B), 2(C), 2(D)
Chemistry: 1(A), 2(A), 2(B), 2(C), 2(E)
Physics: 1(A), 2(A), 2(B), 2(C), 2(D), 2(F)

CONNECTIONS TO AP
Students are expected to report measurements and perform calculations with the correct number of significant digits.

TIME FRAME
180 minutes, depending on level

MATERIALS
small cube
metric ruler
200 mL beaker
large graduated cylinder
spherical object
tweezers
flexible tape measure
balance

TEACHER NOTES
Small wooden alphabet blocks or dice should be inexpensive and easy to obtain. Cubic shaped ice could also be used. Be sure to find a cube/graduated cylinder combination that ensures total submersion of the cube since its volume will be determined by water displacement.

Spherical objects might be a large marble or small rubber ball. Again, be sure to check the sphere/cylinder size to ensure that total submersion of the sphere is possible.

For the flexible tape measure, photocopy the metric side of a tape measure and have students cut it out on paper. Or, provide students with a length of string and metric ruler. The string can be wrapped around the sphere, marked, and then removed and measured.

This lesson is designed to introduce or reinforce accurate measurement techniques, correct usage of significant digits, and dimensional analysis. Dimensional analysis is also called the Factor-Label method or Unit-Label method and is a technique for setting up problems based on unit cancellations. Lecture as well as guided and independent practice of these topics should precede this activity. Students should be provided with reference tables containing metric and English conversion factors.

The purpose of significant digits is to communicate the accuracy of a measurement as well as the measuring capacity of the instrument used. Remind students repeatedly to take measurements including an estimated digit and to perform their calculations with the correct number of significant digits. Emphasize that points will be deducted for answers containing too many or too few significant digits. The correct number of significant digits to be reported by your students will depend entirely upon your equipment.

POSSIBLE ANSWERS TO CONCLUSION QUESTIONS AND SAMPLE DATA

Introduction

Left: 5.75 mL

Middle: 3.0 mL

Right: 0.33 mL

DATA AND OBSERVATIONS

Data Table			
Cube			
Mass: 15.05 g (4sd)			
Dimensions	length: 3.68 cm (3sd)	width: 3.65 cm (3 sd)	height: 3.67 cm (3 sd)
Volume	Beaker initial volume: 100 mL (1sd)	Beaker Final volume: 150 mL (2 sd)	
	Graduated cylinder initial volume: 175.0 mL (4 sd)	Graduated cylinder final volume: 225.1 mL (4 sd)	
Sphere			
Mass: 19.38 g (4sd)			
Dimensions	Circumference: 7.62 cm (3sd)		
Volume	Beaker initial volume: 100 mL (1sd)	Beaker final volume: 110 mL (2sd)	
	Graduated cylinder initial volume: 175.0 mL (4sd)	Graduated cylinder final volume: 182.3 mL (4sd)	
Formula for calculating the volume of a cube:	V = length x width x height		
Formula for calculating the circumference of a circle:	$C = \pi d$		
Formula for calculating the diameter of a circle:	$d = 2r$		
Formula for calculating the volume of a sphere:	$V = \frac{4}{3}\pi r^3$		

ANALYSIS

- Remember to follow the rules for reporting all data and calculated answers with the correct number of significant digits.
- You may need tables of metric and English conversion factors to work some of these problems.

1. For each of the measurements you recorded above, go back and indicate the number of significant digits in parentheses after the measurement. Ex: 15.7 cm (3sd)
   - The number of significant digits will be determined by the equipment you are using.

2. Use dimensional analysis to convert the mass of the cube to (a) mg and (b) ounces.

(a) $15.05\,\cancel{g} \times \frac{1000\,\text{mg}}{1\,\cancel{g}} = 15{,}050\,\text{mg}$

(b) $15.05\,\cancel{g} \times \frac{1\,\cancel{lb}}{454\,\cancel{g}} \times \frac{16\,\text{oz}}{1\,\cancel{lb}} = 0.5304\,\text{oz}$

3. Calculate the volume of the cube in cm^3.
   - $V = l \times w \times h$

   $V = 3.68\,\text{cm} \times 3.65\,\text{cm} \times 3.67\,\text{cm} = 49.3\,\text{cm}^3$

4. Use dimensional analysis to convert the volume of the cube from cm^3 to m^3.

- $$49.3\,\cancel{cm}^3 \times \frac{1\,m}{100\,\cancel{cm}} \times \frac{1\,m}{100\,\cancel{cm}} \times \frac{1\,m}{100\,\cancel{cm}} = 4.93 \times 10^{-5}\,m^3$$

5. Calculate the volume of the cube in mL as measured in the beaker. Convert to cm^3 knowing that $1\ cm^3 = 1$ mL.

- $V = V_{final} - V_{initial}$

  $V = 150\,mL - 100\,mL$

  $V = 50\,mL = 50\,cm^3$

6. Calculate the volume of the cube in mL as measured in the graduated cylinder. Convert to cm^3 knowing that $1\ cm^3 = 1$ mL.

- $V = V_{final} - V_{initial}$

  $V = 225.1\,mL - 175.0\,mL$

  $V = 50.1\,mL = 50.1\,cm^3$

7. Using the density formula $D = \frac{mass}{volume}$, calculate the density of the cube as determined by the (a) ruler (b) beaker (c) graduated cylinder.

(a) $$D = \frac{15.05\,g}{49.3\,cm^3}$$

$$D = 0.305\,\frac{g}{cm^3}$$

(c) $$D = \frac{15.05\,g}{50.1\,cm^3}$$

$$D = 0.300\,\frac{g}{cm^3}$$

(b) $$D = \frac{15.05\,g}{50\,cm^3}$$

$$D = 0.3\,\frac{g}{cm^3}$$

8. Use dimensional analysis to convert these three densities into kg/m^3.

(a) $$0.305\,\frac{\cancel{g}}{\cancel{cm}^3} \times \frac{1\,kg}{1000\,\cancel{g}} \times \frac{100\,\cancel{cm}}{1\,m} \times \frac{100\,\cancel{cm}}{1\,m} \times \frac{100\,\cancel{cm}}{1\,m} = 305\,\frac{kg}{m^3}$$

(b) $$0.3\,\frac{\cancel{g}}{\cancel{cm}^3} \times \frac{1\,kg}{1000\,g} \times \frac{100\,\cancel{cm}}{1\,m} \times \frac{100\,\cancel{cm}}{1\,m} \times \frac{100\,\cancel{cm}}{1\,m} = 300\,\frac{kg}{m^3}$$

(c) $$0.300\,\frac{\cancel{g}}{\cancel{cm}^3} \times \frac{1\,kg}{1000\,\cancel{g}} \times \frac{100\,\cancel{cm}}{1\,m} \times \frac{100\,\cancel{cm}}{1\,m} \times \frac{100\,\cancel{cm}}{1\,m} = 30\bar{0}\,\frac{kg}{m^3}$$

TEACHER PAGES

- The bar above the last zero of the number 300 communicates it is a significant zero transforming the recorded answer from one significant digit to three. It is equally appropriate to teach your students to use scientific notation to effectively communicate three significant digits. The number would be correctly written as 3.00×10^2. Another way to communicate a number accurate to the ones position is to use a decimal at the end of the number. The number could be written as 300. representing that this measurement is accurate to the last digit.

9. Convert the mass of the sphere to (a) kg and (b) lbs.

(a) $19.38\,\cancel{g} \times \frac{1\,\text{kg}}{1000\,\cancel{g}} = 0.01938\,\text{kg}$

(b) $19.38\,\cancel{g} \times \frac{1\,\cancel{\text{lb}}}{454\,\cancel{g}} = 0.04269\,\text{lbs}$

10. Using the measured circumference, calculate the diameter of the sphere.

- $C = \pi d$

  $d = \frac{C}{\pi}$

  $d = \frac{7.62\,\text{cm}}{3.14} = 2.43\,\text{cm}$

11. Calculate the radius of the sphere.

- $d = 2r$

  $r = \frac{d}{2}$

  $r = \frac{2.43\,\text{cm}}{2} = 1.22\,\text{cm}$

12. Calculate the volume of the sphere from its radius.

- $V = \frac{4}{3}\pi r^3$

  $V = \frac{4}{3}(\pi)(1.22)^3$

  $V = 7.61\,\text{cm}^3$

13. Calculate the volume of the sphere in mL as measured in the beaker. Convert to cm^3 knowing that 1 cm^3 = 1 mL.

- $V = V_{\text{final}} - V_{\text{initial}}$

  $V = 110\,\text{mL} - 100\,\text{mL}$

  $V = 10\,\text{mL} = 10\,\text{cm}^3$

14. Calculate the volume of the sphere in mL as measured in the graduated cylinder. Convert to cm^3 knowing that 1 cm^3 = 1 mL.

- $V = V_{final} - V_{initial}$

  $V = 182.3\,mL - 175.0\,mL$

  $V = 7.3\,mL = 7.3\,cm^3$

15. Using the density formula $D = \frac{mass}{volume}$, calculate the density of the sphere as determined by the (a) tape measure (b) beaker (c) graduated cylinder.

(a) $D = \frac{19.38\,g}{7.60\,cm^3}$

$D = 2.55 \frac{g}{cm^3}$

(c) $D = \frac{19.38\,g}{7.3\,cm^3}$

$D = 2.7 \frac{g}{cm^3}$

(b) $D = \frac{19.38\,g}{10\,cm^3}$

$D = 2 \frac{g}{cm^3}$

16. Use dimensional analysis to convert the densities into lbs/ft^3.

(a) $$\frac{2.55\,\cancel{g}}{\cancel{cm^3}} \times \frac{1\,lb}{454\,\cancel{g}} \times \left(\frac{2.54\,\cancel{cm}}{1\,\cancel{in}}\right)^3 \times \left(\frac{12\,\cancel{in}}{1\,ft}\right)^3 = 159 \frac{lbs}{ft^3}$$

(b) $$\frac{2\,\cancel{g}}{\cancel{cm^3}} \times \frac{1\,lb}{454\,\cancel{g}} \times \left(\frac{2.54\,\cancel{cm}}{1\,\cancel{in}}\right)^3 \times \left(\frac{12\,\cancel{in}}{1\,ft}\right)^3 = 100 \frac{lbs}{ft^3}$$

(c) $$\frac{2.7\,\cancel{g}}{\cancel{cm^3}} \times \frac{1\,lb}{454\,\cancel{g}} \times \left(\frac{2.54\,\cancel{cm}}{1\,\cancel{in}}\right)^3 \times \left(\frac{12\,\cancel{in}}{1\,ft}\right)^3 = 170 \frac{lbs}{ft^3}$$

CONCLUSION QUESTIONS

1. Compare the densities of the cube when the volume is measured by a ruler, beaker and graduated cylinder. Which of the instruments gave the most accurate density value? Use the concept of significant digits to explain your answer.
   - The density of the cube had 3 significant digits when measured with the ruler. After subtracting to find the difference between the initial and final water levels in the graduated cylinder and beaker there are 2 significant digits when measured with the graduated cylinder but only 1 significant digit when measured with the beaker.
   - The ruler is the more accurate measure of the volume when compared to the volume obtained by water displacement using the graduated cylinder. The tweezers used to submerge the cube will contribute a small amount to the volume recorded since they contribute to the TOTAL amount of water displaced. See if you can get your students to come up with this concept!
   - Student answers may vary in significant digits depending on equipment used.

2. A student first measures the volume of the cube by water displacement using the graduated cylinder. Next, the student measures the mass of the cube before drying it. How will this error affect the calculated density of the cube? Your answer should state clearly whether the calculated density will increase, decrease or remain the same and must be justified.
   - The calculated density of the cube would increase.
   - Measuring a wet block will make the mass appear greater. Since mass is in the numerator of the equation $D = \frac{mass}{volume}$, the density value reported will be too large.

3. A student measures the circumference of a sphere at a point slightly higher than the middle of the sphere. How will this error affect the calculated density of the sphere? Your answer should state clearly whether the calculated density will increase, decrease, or remain the same and must be justified.
   - The density of the sphere would increase.
   - If the student measured the circumference at any point other than the center, the circumference would be reported as too low.
   - If the circumference is too small then the diameter will be too small.
   - If $\frac{C_{\downarrow}}{\pi} = d \therefore d_{\downarrow}$ the diameter is reported as too small, the radius will also be reported as too small.
   - If $\frac{d_{\downarrow}}{2} = r \therefore r_{\downarrow}$ the radius is reported as too small then the volume will be reported as too small.
   - If $V = \frac{4}{3}\pi r_{\downarrow}^{3} \therefore V_{\downarrow}$ the volume is reported as too small the density will be reported as too large.

$$Density = \frac{m}{V_{\downarrow}} \therefore Density_{\uparrow}$$

Numbers in Science
Exploring Measurements, Significant Digits, and Dimensional Analysis

TAKING MEASUREMENTS

The accuracy of a measurement depends on two factors: the skill of the individual taking the measurement and the capacity of the measuring instrument. When making measurements, you should always read to the smallest mark on the instrument and then estimate another digit beyond that.

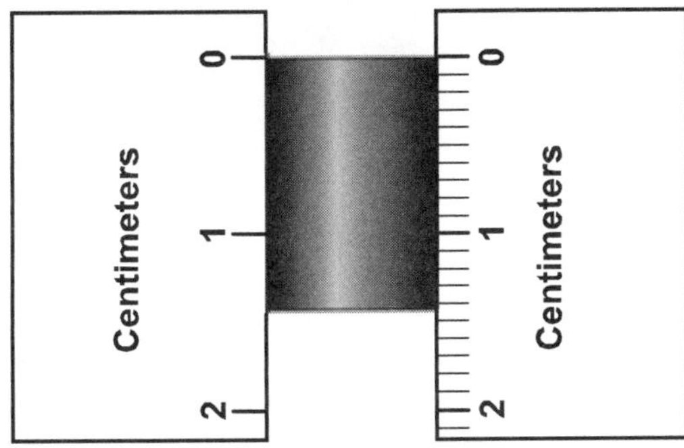

For example, if you are reading the length of the steel pellet pictured above using only the ruler shown to the left of the pellet, you can confidently say that the measurement is between 1 and 2 centimeters. However, you MUST also include one additional digit estimating the distance between the 1 and 2 centimeter marks. The correct measurement for this ruler should be reported as 1.5 centimeters. It would be incorrect to report this measurement as 1 centimeter or even 1.50 centimeters given the scale of this ruler.

What if you are using the ruler shown on the right of the pellet? What is the correct measurement of the steel pellet using this ruler? 1.4 centimeters? 1.5 centimeters? 1.40 centimeters? 1.45 centimeters? The correct answer would be 1.45 centimeters. Since the smallest markings on this ruler are in the tenths place we must carry our measurement out to the hundredths place.

If the measured value falls exactly on a scale marking, the estimated digit should be zero.

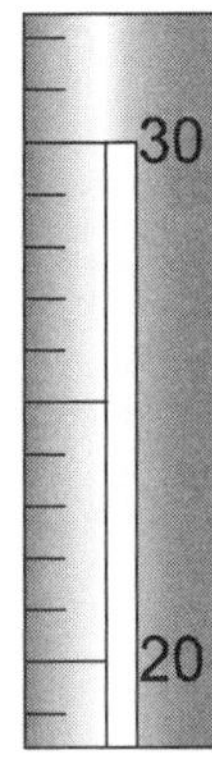

The temperature on this thermometer should read 30.0°C. A value of 30°C would imply this measurement had been taken on a thermometer with markings that were 10° apart, not 1° apart.

When using instruments with digital readouts you should record all the digits shown. The instrument has done the estimating for you.

When measuring liquids in narrow glass graduated cylinders, most liquids form a slight dip in the middle. This dip is called a *meniscus*. Your measurement should be read from the bottom of the meniscus. Plastic graduated cylinders do not usually have a meniscus. In this case you should read the cylinder from the top of the liquid surface. Practice reading the volume contained in the 3 cylinders below. Record your values in the space provided.

Left:_______________

Middle: ____________

Right:_______________

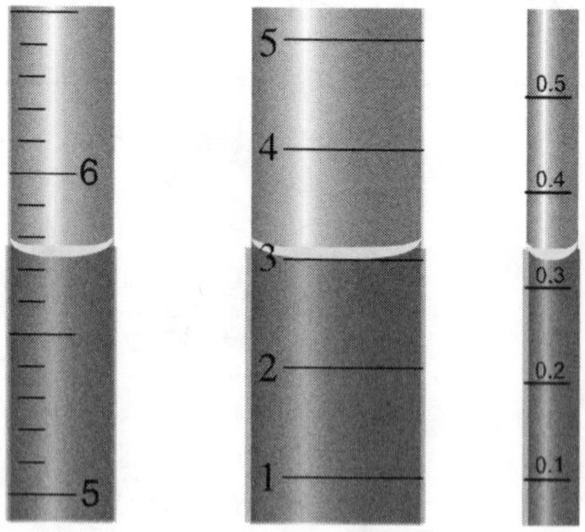

SIGNIFICANT DIGITS

There are two kinds of numbers you will encounter in science, exact numbers and measured numbers. *Exact numbers* are known to be absolutely correct and are obtained by counting or by definition. Counting a stack of 12 pennies is an exact number. Defining 1 day as 24 hours are exact numbers. Exact numbers have an infinite number of significant digits.

Measured numbers, as we've seen above, involve some estimation. Significant digits are digits believed to be correct by the person making and recording a measurement. We assume that the person is competent in his or her use of the measuring device. To count the number of significant digits represented in a measurement we follow 2 basic rules:

1. If the digit is NOT a zero, it is significant.

2. If the digit IS a zero, it is significant if
   a. It is a sandwiched zero
      OR
   b. It terminates a number containing a decimal place

Examples:

3.57 mL has 3 significant digits (Rule 1)
288 mL has 3 significant digits (Rule 1)
20.8 mL has 3 significant digits (Rule 1 and 2a)
20.80 mL has 4 significant digits (Rules 1, 2a and 2b)
0.01 mL has only 1 significant digit (Rule 1)
0.010 mL has 2 significant digits (Rule 1 and 2b)
0.0100 mL has 3 significant digits (Rule 1 and 2b)
3.20 x10^4 kg has 3 significant digits (Rule 1 and 2b)

SIGNIFICANT DIGITS IN CALCULATIONS

A calculated number can never contain more significant digits than the measurements used to calculate it.

Calculation rules fall into two categories:

1. Addition and Subtraction: answers must be rounded to match the measurement with the least number of decimal places.
   37.24 mL + 10.3 mL = 47.54 (calculator value), report as 47.5 mL

2. Multiplication and Division: answers must be rounded to match the measurement with the least number of significant digits.
   1.23 cm x 12.34 cm = 15.1782 (calculator value), report as 15.2 cm^2

DIMENSIONAL ANALYSIS

Throughout your study of science it is important that a unit accompanies all measurements. Keeping track of the units in problem can help you convert one measured quantity into its equivalent quantity of a different unit or set up a calculation without the need for a formula.

In conversion problems, equality statements such as 1 ft. = 12 inches, are made into fractions and then strung together in such a way that all units except the desired one are canceled out of the problem. Remember that defined numbers, such as the 1 and 12 above, are exact numbers and thus will not affect the number of significant digits in your answer. This method is also known as the Factor-Label method or the Unit-Label method.

To set up a conversion problem follow these steps.

1. Think about and write down all the "=" statements you know that will help you get from your current unit to the new unit.

2. Make fractions out of your "=" statements (there could be 2 fractions for each "="). They will be reciprocals of each other.

3. Begin solving the problem by writing the given amount with units on the left side of your paper and then choose the fractions that will let a numerator unit be canceled with a denominator unit and vice versa.

4. Using your calculator, read from left to right and enter the numerator and denominator numbers in order. Precede each numerator number with a multiplication sign and each denominator number with a division sign. Alternatively, you could enter all of the numerators, separated by multiplication signs, and then all of the denominators, each separated by a division sign.

5. Round your calculator's answer to the same number of significant digits that your original number had.

Example:
How many inches are in 1.25 miles?

Solution:

$$1\,\text{ft} = 12\,\text{in} \qquad \frac{1\,\text{ft}}{12\,\text{in}} \text{ OR } \frac{12\,\text{in}}{1\,\text{ft}}$$

$$5280\,\text{ft.} = 1\,\text{mile} \qquad \frac{5280\,\text{ft.}}{1\,\text{mile}} \text{ OR } \frac{1\,\text{mile}}{5280\,\text{ft.}}$$

$$1.25\,\cancel{\text{miles}} \times \frac{5280\,\cancel{\text{ft.}}}{1\,\cancel{\text{mile}}} \times \frac{12\,\text{in.}}{1\,\cancel{\text{ft.}}} = 79{,}200\,\text{in.}$$

As problems get more complex the measurements may contain fractional units or exponential units. To handle these problems treat each unit independently. Structure your conversion factors to ensure that all the given units cancel out with a numerator or denominator as appropriate and that your answer ends with the appropriate unit. Sometimes information given in the problem is an equality that will be used as a conversion factor.

Example: Suppose your automobile tank holds 23 gal and the price of gasoline is 33.5¢ per L. How many dollars will it cost you to fill your tank?

Solution: From a reference table we will find,
1 L = 1.06 qt
4 qt = 1 gal

We should recognize from the problem that the price is also an equality, 33.5¢ = 1 L
and we should know that 100¢ = 1 dollar

Setting up the factors we find,

$$23\,\cancel{\text{gal}} \times \frac{4\,\cancel{\text{qt}}}{1\,\cancel{\text{gal}}} \times \frac{1\,\cancel{\text{L}}}{1.06\,\cancel{\text{qt}}} \times \frac{33.5\cancel{¢}}{1\,\cancel{\text{L}}} \times \frac{\$1}{100\cancel{¢}} = \$29$$

In your calculator you should enter $23 \times 4 \div 1.06 \times 33.5 \div 100$ and get 29.0754717. However, since the given value of 23 gal has only 2 significant digits, your answer must be rounded to \$29.

Squared and cubed units are potentially tricky. Remember that a cm^2 is really cm x cm. So, if we need to convert cm^2 to mm^2 we need to use the conversion factor 1 cm = 10 mm twice so that both centimeter units cancel out.

Example: One liter is exactly 1000 cm^3. How many cubic inches are there in 1.0 L?

Solution:
We should know that

$$1000 \text{ cm}^3 = 1 \text{ L}$$

From a reference table we find,

$$1 \text{ in.} = 2.54 \text{ cm}$$

Setting up the factors we find,

$$1.0\,\cancel{L} \times \frac{1000\,\cancel{cm}\times\cancel{cm}\times\cancel{cm}}{1\,\cancel{L}} \times \frac{1\,\text{in}}{2.54\,\cancel{cm}} \times \frac{1\,\text{in}}{2.54\,\cancel{cm}} \times \frac{1\,\text{in}}{2.54\,\cancel{cm}} = 61\,\text{in}^3$$

(The answer has 2 significant digits since our given 1.0 L contained two significant digits.)

As you become more comfortable with the concept of unit cancellation you will find that it is a very handy tool for solving problems. By knowing the units of your given measurements, and by focusing on the units of the desired answer you can derive a formula and correctly calculate an answer. This is especially useful when you've forgotten, or never knew, the formula!

Example: Even though you may not know the exact formula for solving this problem, you should be able to match the units up in such a way that only your desired unit does not cancel out.

What is the volume in liters of 1.5 moles of gas at 293 K and 1.10 atm of pressure?

The ideal gas constant is $\frac{0.0821 \text{ L•atm}}{\text{mol•K}}$

Solution: It is not necessary to know the formula for the ideal gas law to solve this problem correctly. Working from the constant, since it sets the units, we need to cancel out every unit except L. Doing this shows us that moles and kelvins need to be in the numerator and atmospheres in the denominator.

$$\frac{0.0821\ \text{L} \bullet \cancel{atm}}{\cancel{mol} \bullet \cancel{K}} \times \frac{1.5\,\cancel{mol}}{} \times \frac{293\,\cancel{K}}{} \times \frac{}{1.10\,\cancel{atm}} = 33\,\text{L}$$

(2 significant digits since our least accurate measuement has only 2 sig.digs.)

**NOTE: NEVER consider the number of significant digits in a constant to determine the number of significant digits for reporting your calculated answer. Consider ONLY the number of significant digits in given or measured quantities.

PURPOSE

In this activity you will review some important aspects of numbers in science and then apply those number handling skills to your own measurements and calculations.

MATERIALS

small cube
metric ruler
200 mL beaker
large graduated cylinder
spherical object
tweezers
flexible tape measure
balance

PROCEDURE

*Remember when taking measurements it is your responsibility to estimate a digit between the two smallest marks on the instrument.

1. Mass the small cube on a balance and record your measurement in the data table on your student page.

2. Measure dimensions (the length, width and height) of the small cube in centimeters, being careful to use the full measuring capacity of your ruler. Record the lengths in your data table.

3. Fill the 200 mL beaker with water to the 100 mL line. Carefully place the cube in the beaker and use the tweezers to gently submerge the cube. The cube should be just barely covered with water. Record the new, final volume of water.

4. Fill the large graduated cylinder ¾ of the way full with water. Record this initial water volume. Again, use the tweezers to gently submerge the cube and record the final water volume.

5. Mass the spherical object on a balance and record your measurement in the data table.

6. Use the flexible tape measure to measure the widest circumference of the sphere in centimeters. Be careful to use the full measuring capacity of the tape measure.

7. Fill the 200 mL beaker with water to the 100 mL line. Carefully place the spherical object in the beaker and, if needed, use the tweezers to gently submerge the sphere. Record the final volume of water from the beaker.

8. Fill the large graduated cylinder ¾ of the way full with water. Record this initial water volume. If needed, use the tweezers to gently submerge the sphere and record the new water volume.

9. Dry the cube and sphere and clean up your lab area as instructed by your teacher.

Name ______________________

Period ______________________

Numbers in Science
Exploring Measurements, Significant Digits, and Dimensional Analysis

DATA AND OBSERVATIONS

Data Table				
CUBE DATA				
Mass:				
Dimensions	length:		width:	height:
Volume	Beaker initial volume: 100 mL		Beaker final volume:	
	Graduated cylinder initial volume:		Graduated cylinder final volume:	
SPHERE DATA				
Mass:				
Dimensions	Circumference:			
Volume	Beaker initial volume: 100 mL		Beaker final volume:	
	Graduated cylinder initial volume:		Graduated cylinder final volume:	
Formula for calculating the volume of a cube:				
Formula for calculating the circumference of a circle:				
Formula for calculating the diameter of a circle:				
Formula for calculating the volume of a sphere:				

ANALYSIS

- Remember to follow the rules for reporting all data and calculated answers with the correct number of significant digits.
- You may need tables of metric and English conversion factors to work some of these problems.

1. For each of the measurements you recorded above, go back and indicate the number of significant digits in parentheses after the measurement. Ex: 15.7 cm (3sd)

2. Use dimensional analysis to convert the mass of the cube to
   a. mg

   b. ounces

3. Calculate the volume of the cube in cm^3.

4. Use dimensional analysis to convert the volume of the cube from cm^3 to m^3.

5. Calculate the volume of the cube in mL as measured in the beaker. Convert the volume to cm^3 knowing that 1 cm^3 = 1 mL.

6. Calculate the volume of the cube in mL as measured in the graduated cylinder. Convert to cm^3 knowing that 1 cm^3 = 1 mL.

7. Using the density formula $D = \frac{mass}{volume}$, calculate the density of the cube as determined by the
   a. ruler

   b. beaker

   c. graduated cylinder

8. Use dimensional analysis to convert these three densities into kg/m^3.

9. Convert the mass of the sphere to
   a. kg

   b. lbs.

10. Using the measured circumference, calculate the diameter of the sphere.

11. Calculate the radius of the sphere.

12. Calculate the volume of the sphere from its radius.

13. Calculate the volume of the sphere in mL as measured in the beaker. Convert to cm^3 knowing that 1 cm^3 = 1 mL.

14. Calculate the volume of the sphere in mL as measured in the graduated cylinder. Convert to cm^3 knowing that 1 cm^3 = 1 mL.

15. Using the density formula $D = \frac{mass}{volume}$, calculate the density of the sphere as determined by the
    a. tape measure

    b. beaker

    c. graduated cylinder

16. Use dimensional analysis to convert these three densities into lbs/ft^3.

CONCLUSION QUESTIONS

1. Compare the densities of the cube when the volume is measured by a ruler, beaker and graduated cylinder. Which of the instruments gave the most accurate density value? Use the concept of significant digits to explain your answer.

2. A student first measures the volume of the cube by water displacement using the graduated cylinder. Next, the student measures the mass of the cube before drying it. How will this error affect the calculated density of the cube? Your answer should state clearly whether the calculated density will increase, decrease or remain the same and must be justified.

3. A student measures the circumference of a sphere at a point slightly higher than the middle of the sphere. How will this error affect the calculated density of the cube? Your answer should state clearly whether the calculated density will increase, decrease, or remain the same and must be justified.

Literal Equations
Manipulating Variables and Constants

OBJECTIVE
Students will review how to solve literal equations for a particular variable.

LEVEL
Middle Grades: Chemistry/Physics, Chemistry I, Physics I

NATIONAL STANDARDS
UCP.1, UCP.2, G.2

TEKS
IPC: 4(A)
Chemistry: 2(C)
Physics: 3(B)

CONNECTIONS TO AP
In AP science courses, particularly physics and chemistry, the student is often given an equation and asked to solve it for a particular variable.

TIME FRAME
45 minutes

TEACHER NOTES
Throughout chemistry and physics courses, and at times in IPC, the students will need to be able to solve an equation for a particular variable to see how that variable depends on other variables and constants. Manipulation of variables without the substitution of numbers is an important skill in helping students understand that the variables depend on each other in a certain way regardless of any particular numbers which may be substituted into the equation. For example, in the equation $F_{net} = ma$ (Newton's second law), the acceleration a is always proportional to the net force F_{net} regardless of the value of the mass. In the equation $P_1V_1 = P_2V_2$ (Boyle's law), pressure P and volume V are always inversely proportional to each other.

The following examples and exercises illustrate the manipulation of many of the literal equations that commonly appear in physics and chemistry courses. Although the students may not understand the meaning of many of the equations during this practice exercise, practicing solving the equations will sharpen their algebra skills. When they ultimately learn the meaning of the equations, they will be more likely to feel comfortable with the conceptual understanding behind the equations rather than losing the meaning of the relationships among the variables in the algebraic manipulation.

A *literal equation* is one which is expressed in terms of variable symbols (such as d, v, and a) and constants (such as R, g, and π). Often in science and mathematics the students are given an equation and asked to solve it for a particular variable symbol or letter called the *unknown*.

The symbols, which are not the particular variable we are interested in solving for, are called *literals*, and may represent variables or constants. Literal equations are solved by isolating the unknown variable on one side of the equation, and all of the remaining literal variables on the other side of the equation. Sometimes the unknown variable is part of another term. A *term* is a combination of symbols such as the products *ma* or πr^2. In this case the unknown (such as *r* in πr^2) must be factored out of the term before we can isolate it.

The following rules, examples, and exercises will help you review and practice solving literal equations from physics and chemistry.

Suggested Teaching Procedure:

1. Review the procedure section with students. Emphasize keeping their equations neat and orderly.
2. Choose several of the listed examples to work with students on the overhead or chalkboard.
3. Instruct students to complete the remaining exercises in the space provided on their student answer pages.

ANSWERS TO EXERCISES

Directions: For each of the following equations, solve for the variable in **bold** print.

1. $v = \mathbf{a}t$
   - $\frac{v}{t} = \mathbf{a}$

2. $P = \frac{F}{\mathbf{A}}$
   - $P\mathbf{A} = F$

     $\mathbf{A} = \frac{F}{P}$

3. $\lambda = \frac{\mathbf{h}}{p}$
   - $\lambda p = \mathbf{h}$

4. $F(\mathbf{\Delta t}) = m\Delta v$
   - $\mathbf{\Delta t} = \frac{m\Delta v}{F}$

5. $U = \frac{G\mathbf{m_1}m_2}{r}$

   $Ur = G\mathbf{m_1}m_2$
   - $\frac{Ur}{Gm_2} = \mathbf{m_1}$

TEACHER PAGES

6. $C = \frac{5}{9}(\mathbf{F} - 32)$

$\frac{9}{5}C = \mathbf{F} - 32$

- $\mathbf{F} = \frac{9}{5}C + 32$

7. $v^2 = v_0^{\ 2} + 2\mathbf{a}\Delta x$

$v^2 - v_0^{\ 2} = 2\mathbf{a}\Delta x$

- $\frac{v^2 - v_0^{\ 2}}{2\Delta x} = \mathbf{a}$

8. $K_{avg} = \frac{3}{2}k_B\mathbf{T}$

$\frac{2}{3}K_{avg} = k_B\mathbf{T}$

- $\frac{2K_{avg}}{3k_B} = \mathbf{T}$

9. $K = \frac{1}{2}m\mathbf{v}^2$

$2K = m\mathbf{v}^2$

- $\frac{2K}{m} = \mathbf{v}^2$

$\mathbf{v} = \sqrt{\frac{2K}{m}}$

10. $v_{rms} = \sqrt{\frac{3RT}{\mathbf{M}}}$

$v^2_{rms} = \frac{3RT}{\mathbf{M}}$

- $\mathbf{M}v^2_{rms} = 3RT$

$\mathbf{M} = \frac{3RT}{v^2_{rms}}$

TEACHER PAGES

11. $v_{rms} = \sqrt{\frac{3\mathbf{k}_B T}{\mu}}$

$$v_{rms}^{\ 2} = \frac{3\mathbf{k}_B T}{\mu}$$

- $\mu v_{rms}^{\ 2} = 3\mathbf{k}_B T$

$$\frac{\mu v_{rms}^{\ 2}}{3T} = \mathbf{k}_B$$

12. $F = \frac{1}{4\pi\varepsilon_0}\frac{Kq_1q_2}{\mathbf{r}^2}$

$$4\pi\varepsilon_o \mathbf{r}^2 F = Kq_1q_2$$

- $\mathbf{r}^2 = \frac{Kq_1q_2}{4\pi\varepsilon_o F}$

$$\mathbf{r} = \sqrt{\frac{Kq_1q_2}{4\pi\varepsilon_o F}}$$

13. $\frac{1}{s_i} + \frac{1}{s_o} = \frac{1}{\mathbf{f}}$

- $\mathbf{f} = \frac{1}{\frac{1}{s_o} + \frac{1}{s_i}}$

14. $\frac{1}{C_{EQ}} = \frac{1}{\mathbf{C}_1} + \frac{1}{C_2}$

$$\frac{1}{C_{EQ}} - \frac{1}{C_2} = \frac{1}{\mathbf{C}_1}$$

- $\mathbf{C}_1 = \frac{1}{\frac{1}{C_{EQ}} - \frac{1}{C_2}}$

15. $V = \frac{4}{3}\pi \mathbf{r}^3$

$$\frac{3}{4}V = \pi \mathbf{r}^3$$

- $\frac{3V}{4\pi} = \mathbf{r}^3$

$$\mathbf{r} = \sqrt[3]{\frac{3V}{4\pi}}$$

16. $P + \mathbf{D}gy + \frac{1}{2}\mathbf{D}v^2 = C$

$$P + \mathbf{D}\left(gy + \frac{1}{2}v^2\right) = C$$

- $C - P = \mathbf{D}\left(gy + \frac{1}{2}v^2\right)$

$$\mathbf{D} = \frac{C - P}{\left(gy + \frac{1}{2}v^2\right)}$$

17. $P + Dgy + \frac{1}{2}D\mathbf{v}^2 = C$

$$\frac{1}{2}D\mathbf{v}^2 = C - P - Dgy$$

- $D\mathbf{v}^2 = 2(C - P - Dgy)$

$$\mathbf{v}^2 = 2D(C - P - Dgy)$$

$$\mathbf{v} = \sqrt{2D(C - \text{P} - Dgy)}$$

18. $x = x_0 + v_0 t + \frac{1}{2}\mathbf{a}t^2$

$$x - v_0 t = \frac{1}{2}\mathbf{a}t^2$$

- $2(x - v_0 t) = \mathbf{a}t^2$

$$\mathbf{a} = \frac{2(x - v_0 t)}{t^2}$$

TEACHER PAGES

19. $n_1 \sin\theta_1 = n_2 \sin\theta_2$

$$\frac{n_1 sin\theta_1}{n_2} = sin\theta_2$$

- $$\theta_2 = sin^{-1}\left[\frac{n_1 sin\theta_1}{n_2}\right]$$

20. $mg \sin\theta = \mu mg \cos\theta\left(\frac{M+m}{m}\right)$

$$\frac{mg\sin\theta}{mg\cos\theta} = \mu\left(\frac{M+m}{m}\right)$$

$$\frac{\sin\theta}{\cos\theta} = \mu\left(\frac{M+m}{m}\right)$$

- $$\tan\theta = \mu\left(\frac{M+m}{m}\right)$$

$$\theta = \tan^{-1}\left[\mu\left(\frac{M+m}{m}\right)\right]$$

Literal Equations
Manipulating Variables and Constants

A *literal equation* is one which is expressed in terms of variable symbols (such as d, v, and a) and constants (such as R, g, and π). Often in science and mathematics you are given an equation and asked to solve it for a particular variable symbol or letter called the *unknown*.

The symbols which are not the particular variable we are interested in solving for are called *literals*, and may represent variables or constants. Literal equations are solved by isolating the unknown variable on one side of the equation, and all of the remaining literal variables on the other side of the equation. Sometimes the unknown variable is part of another term. A *term* is a combination of symbols such as the products ma or πr^2. In this case the unknown (such as r in πr^2) must factored out of the term before we can isolate it.

The following rules, examples, and exercises will help you review and practice solving literal equations from physics and chemistry.

PROCEDURE

In general, we solve a literal equation for a particular variable by following the basic procedure below.

1. Recall the conventional order of operations, that is, the order in which we perform the operations of multiplication, division, addition, subtraction, etc.:
   a. Parenthesis
   b. Exponents
   c. Multiplication and Division
   d. Addition and Subtraction

   This means that you should do what is possible within parentheses first, then exponents, then multiplication and division from left to right, then addition and subtraction from left to right. If some parentheses are enclosed within other parentheses, work from the inside out.

2. If the unknown is a part of a grouped expression (such as a sum inside parentheses), use the distributive property to expand the expression.

3. By adding, subtracting, multiplying, or dividing appropriately,

   (a) move all terms containing the unknown variable to one side of the equation, and

   (b) move all other variables and constants to the other side of the equation. Combine like terms when possible.

4. Factor the unknown variable out of its term by appropriately multiplying or dividing both sides of the equation by the other literals in the term.

5. If the unknown variable is raised to an exponent (such as 2, 3, or ½), perform the appropriate operation to raise the unknown variable to the first power, that is, so that it has an exponent of one.

EXAMPLES

1. $F = m\mathbf{a}$. Solve for **a**.
   $F = ma$

   Divide both sides by *m*:

   $$\frac{F}{m} = \mathbf{a}$$

   Since the unknown variable (in this case *a*) is usually placed on the left side of the equation, we can switch the two sides:

   $$\mathbf{a} = \frac{F}{m}$$

2. $P_1V_1 = P_2\mathbf{V}_2$. Solve for $\mathbf{V}_2$.
   $P_1V_1 = P_2\mathbf{V}_2$

   Divide both sides by P_2:

   $$\frac{P_1V_1}{P_2} = \mathbf{V}_2$$

   $$\mathbf{V}_2 = \frac{P_1V_1}{P_2}$$

3. $v = \frac{d}{\mathbf{t}}$. Solve for **t**.
   Multiply each side by **t**:

   $$\mathbf{t}v = d$$

   Divide both sides by *v*:

   $$\mathbf{t} = \frac{d}{v}$$

4. $PV = n\mathbf{R}T$. Solve for **R**.
   $PV = n\mathbf{R}T$

   Divide both sides by n:

   $$\frac{PV}{n} = \mathbf{R}T$$

   Divide both sides by **T**:

   $$\frac{PV}{nT} = \mathbf{R}$$

   $$\mathbf{R} = \frac{PV}{nT}$$

5. $R = \frac{\rho\mathbf{L}}{A}$. Solve for $\mathbf{L}$.

   $$R = \frac{\rho\mathbf{L}}{A}$$

   Multiply both sides by A:

   $$RA = \rho\mathbf{L}$$

   Divide both sides by ρ:

   $$\frac{RA}{\rho} = \mathbf{L}$$

   $$\mathbf{L} = \frac{RA}{\rho}$$

6. $A = h(a + \mathbf{b})$. Solve for **b**.
   Distribute the h:

   $$A = ha + h\mathbf{b}$$

   Subtract ha from both sides:

   $$A - ha = h\mathbf{b}$$

Divide both sides by h:

$$\frac{A - ha}{h} = \mathbf{b}$$

$$\mathbf{b} = \frac{A - ha}{h}$$

7. $P = P_0 + \rho \mathbf{g} h$. Solve for **g**.
   Subtract P_0 from both sides:

   $$P - P_0 = \rho \mathbf{g} h$$

   Divide both sides by ρh:

   $$\frac{P - P_0}{\rho h} = \mathbf{g}$$

   $$\mathbf{g} = \frac{P - P_0}{\rho h}$$

8. $U = \frac{1}{2}\mathbf{Q}V$. Solve for **Q**.
   Multiply both sides by 2:

   $$2U = \mathbf{Q}V$$

   Divide both sides by V:

   $$\frac{2U}{V} = \mathbf{Q}$$

   $$\mathbf{Q} = \frac{2U}{V}$$

9. $U = \frac{1}{2}k\mathbf{x}^2$. Solve for **x**.
   Multiply both sides by 2:

   $$2U = k\mathbf{x}^2$$

   Divide both sides by k:

   $$\frac{2U}{k} = \mathbf{x}^2$$

Take the square root of both sides:

$$\sqrt{\frac{2U}{k}} = \mathbf{x}$$

$$\mathbf{x} = \sqrt{\frac{2U}{k}}$$

10. $T = 2\pi\sqrt{\frac{\mathbf{L}}{g}}$. Solve for $\mathbf{L}$.

Divide both sides by 2π:

$$\frac{T}{2\pi} = \sqrt{\frac{\mathbf{L}}{g}}$$

Square both sides:

$$\frac{T^2}{4\pi^2} = \frac{\mathbf{L}}{g}$$

Multiply both sides by g:

$$\frac{gT^2}{4\pi^2} = \mathbf{L}$$

$$\mathbf{L} = \frac{gT^2}{4\pi^2}$$

11. $F = \frac{Gm_1m_2}{\mathbf{r}^2}$. Solve for $\mathbf{r}$.

Multiply both sides by $\mathbf{r}^2$:

$$F\mathbf{r}^2 = Gm_1m_2$$

Divide both sides by F:

$$\mathbf{r}^2 = \frac{Gm_1m_2}{F}$$

Take the square root of both sides:

$$\mathbf{r} = \sqrt{\frac{Gm_1m_2}{F}}$$

12. $\frac{h_i}{h_o} = -\frac{s_i}{\mathbf{s}_o}$. Solve for $\mathbf{s}_o$.
Cross-multiply:

$$h_i \mathbf{s}_o = -h_o s_i$$

Divide both sides by h_i:

$$\mathbf{s}_0 = -\frac{h_o s_i}{h_i}$$

13. $\frac{1}{R_{EQ}} = \frac{1}{R_1} + \frac{1}{R_2} + \frac{1}{\mathbf{R}_3}$. Solve for $\mathbf{R}_3$.
Subtract $\frac{1}{R_1} + \frac{1}{R_2}$ from both sides:

$$\frac{1}{R_{EQ}} - \frac{1}{R_1} - \frac{1}{R_2} = \frac{1}{\mathbf{R}_3}$$

Take the reciprocal of both sides:

$$\frac{1}{\frac{1}{R_{EQ}} - \frac{1}{R_1} - \frac{1}{R_2}} = \mathbf{R}_3$$

$$\mathbf{R}_3 = \frac{1}{\frac{1}{R_{EQ}} - \frac{1}{R_1} - \frac{1}{R_2}}$$

This equation could be solved further with several more algebraic steps.

14. $F = qvB\sin\theta$. Solve for $\boldsymbol{\theta}$.
Divide both sides by qvB:

$$\frac{F}{qvB} = \sin\theta$$

Take the inverse sine of both sides:

$$\theta = \sin^{-1}\left[\frac{F}{qvB}\right]$$

15. $\mu mg\cos\theta = mg\sin\theta$. Solve for $\boldsymbol{\mu}$.
    Divide both sides by $mg\cos\theta$:

$$\mu = \frac{mg\sin\theta}{mg\cos\theta} = \frac{\sin\theta}{\cos\theta} = \tan\theta$$

Name ______________________________

Period______________________________

Literal Equations
Manipulating Variables and Constants

EXERCISES

Directions: For each of the following equations, solve for the variable in **bold** print. Be sure to show each step you take to solve the equation for the **bold** variable.

1. $v = \mathbf{a}t$

2. $P = \frac{F}{\mathbf{A}}$

3. $\lambda = \frac{\mathbf{h}}{p}$

4. $F(\Delta\mathbf{t}) = m\Delta v$

5. $U = \frac{G\mathbf{m}_1 m_2}{r}$

6. $C = \frac{5}{9}(\mathbf{F} - 32)$

7. $v^2 = v_0^{\ 2} + 2\mathbf{a}\Delta x$

8. $K_{avg} = \frac{3}{2}k_B\mathbf{T}$

9. $K = \frac{1}{2}m\mathbf{v}^2$

10. $v_{rms} = \sqrt{\dfrac{3RT}{\mathbf{M}}}$

11. $v_{rms} = \sqrt{\dfrac{3\mathbf{k}_B T}{\mu}}$

12. $F = \dfrac{1}{4\pi\varepsilon_0}\dfrac{Kq_1q_2}{\mathbf{r}^2}$

13. $\dfrac{1}{s_i} + \dfrac{1}{s_o} = \dfrac{1}{\mathbf{f}}$

14. $\dfrac{1}{C_{EQ}} = \dfrac{1}{\mathbf{C}_1} + \dfrac{1}{C_2}$

15. $V = \dfrac{4}{3}\pi\mathbf{r}^3$

16. $P + \mathbf{D}gy + \dfrac{1}{2}\mathbf{D}v^2 = C$

17. $P + Dgy + \dfrac{1}{2}D\mathbf{v}^2 = C$

18. $x = x_0 + v_0 t + \dfrac{1}{2}\mathbf{a}t^2$

19. $n_1 \sin\theta_1 = n_2 \sin \boldsymbol{\theta_2}$

20. $mg \sin \boldsymbol{\theta} = \mu mg \cos \boldsymbol{\theta}\left(\dfrac{M+m}{m}\right)$

Graphing Skills
Reading, Constructing and Analyzing Graphs

Unit Overview

OBJECTIVE
The purpose of this lesson is to provide the teacher with basic graphing skill lessons to be used throughout the science course of study. There are many different kinds of graphs and each has a fairly specific use. By teaching graphing at all grade levels students should be able to choose the best type of graph to represent their data. Students should also become familiar with ways to analyze their graphed information realizing that there is meaning to their graph.

LEVEL
All

NATIONAL STANDARDS
UCP.1, UCP.2, G.2

TEKS
6.2(E)
7.2(E)
8.2(E)
IPC: 2(C)
Biology: 2(C)
Chemistry: 2(D)
Physics: 2(C), 2(E)

CONNECTIONS TO AP
Each of the AP Science courses requires that students are able to read, construct and analyze graphs.

TIME FRAME
45 minutes

MATERIALS

graph paper
pencil
data

TEACHER NOTES

Graphing is a skill that should be introduced at each grade level and reinforced throughout the year whenever data is available. The analysis level of the graph will vary depending on the mathematical ability of your students. The lessons presented here may be used as stand alone lessons or may be combined as a general review of graphing skills.

Graphing is an essential tool in science. Graphs enable us to visually communicate information. The lessons that follow will focus on bar graphs, pie charts and line graphs. Goals for this series of lessons on graphing include:

- Choosing an appropriate display for data (which type of graph to construct)
- Identifying data to be displayed on the x and y axes
- Scaling a graph properly
- Labeling a graph with axes labels, title, units, and legend or key if necessary
- Extrapolating and interpolating data points
- Understanding relevant relationships such as slope and area under the curve

Graphing Skills
Reading, Constructing and Analyzing Graphs

Bar Graphs and Histograms

OBJECTIVE
Students will become familiar with basic bar graphing skills to be used throughout their science course of study.

LEVEL
All

NATIONAL STANDARDS
UCP.1, UCP.2, G.2

TEKS
6.2(E)
7.2(E)
8.2(E)
IPC 2(C)
Biology 2(C)
Chemistry 2(D)
Physics 2(C), 2(E)

CONNECTIONS TO AP
Each of the AP Science courses requires that students are able to read, construct and analyze graphs.

TIME FRAME
45 minutes

MATERIALS
(For each student working individually)

4 sheets of quadrille graph paper
pencil
data

TEACHER NOTES

Graphing is a skill that should be introduced at each grade level and reinforced throughout the year whenever data is available. Before allowing students to begin this exercise, you should do the following:

- Distinguish between the four types of graphs represented in the student introduction. Key points to be made are as follows:
  - *Simple Bar Graph*: The width of bars must be the same.
  - *Grouped Bar Graph*: The width of bars must be the same. Each bar within a group needs some distinguishing mark—different colors, different markings, etc. The student must provide a legend so that the graph may easily be interpreted.
  - *Composite Bar Graph*: The width of bars must be the same. Each different component of the bar must have some distinguishing mark—different colors, different markings, etc.
  - *Histogram:* The width of bars must be the same. Clearly make the distinction here for the students that in a histogram the bar itself represents a range of independent variables rather than a single value.
- Encourage students to decide which sets of data belong on the x-axis and the y-axis. The key here is to place the independent variable on the x-axis and the dependent variable on the y-axis.
- Show the students how to properly scale a graph. The scale represents the range of frequency values shown on the graph. Visually show students how to properly accomplish this task by making an overhead transparency of a piece of the graph paper. Write down the range, count the squares on the graph paper and decide the scale by spacing appropriately. Emphasize the importance of using the entire length and width of the paper when creating the axes.
- Demonstrate proper labeling of a graph with a title, axes labels and units, and keys if necessary. Titles are usually given at the top of each graph and provide an overview of the information that is given in the graph. The axes labels should provide specific information as to what is represented. It is customary to label a graph in the format y vs x. For example if a graph is described as "Temperature vs Time" then temperature should be on the y axis and time should be on the x-axis. Depending on the level of your students you may wish to require this format.
- In analyzing a graph, show the students how to read the graph and interpret their graph by using interpolation and extrapolation. Point out that it is difficult to identify specific interpolation (between) points on bar graphs but that rough comparisons are easy. Extrapolation (beyond) points is also difficult (if not impossible) to determine on bar graphs.
- As students work on this activity monitor them closely to ensure that they have correct labels and scales on the graphs they are constructing.

SAMPLE DATA

Student graphs should look similar to the samples found below.

PART I: SIMPLE BAR GRAPH

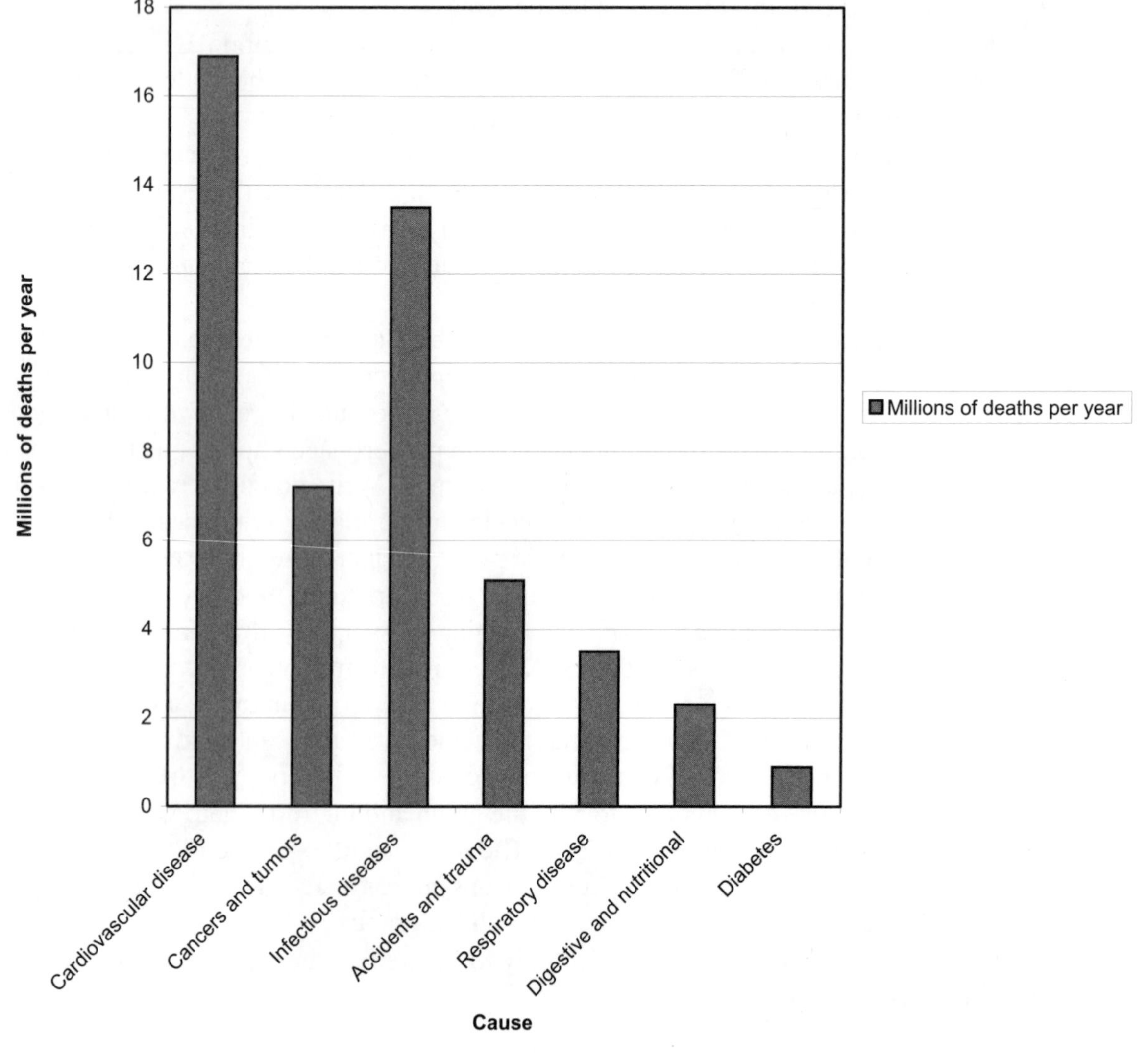

TEACHER PAGES

PART II: GROUPED BAR GRAPH

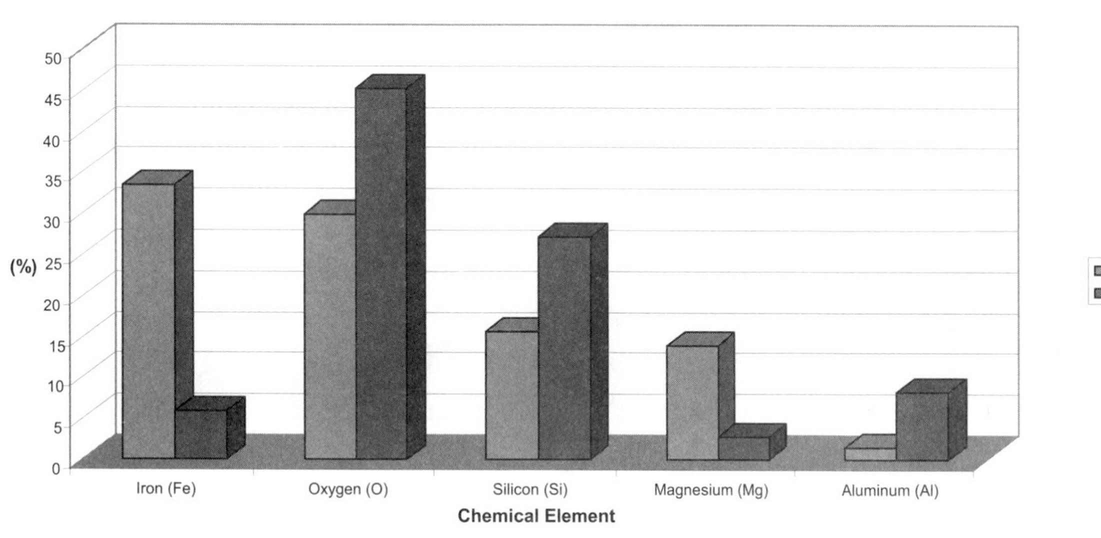

PART III: COMPOSITE BAR GRAPH

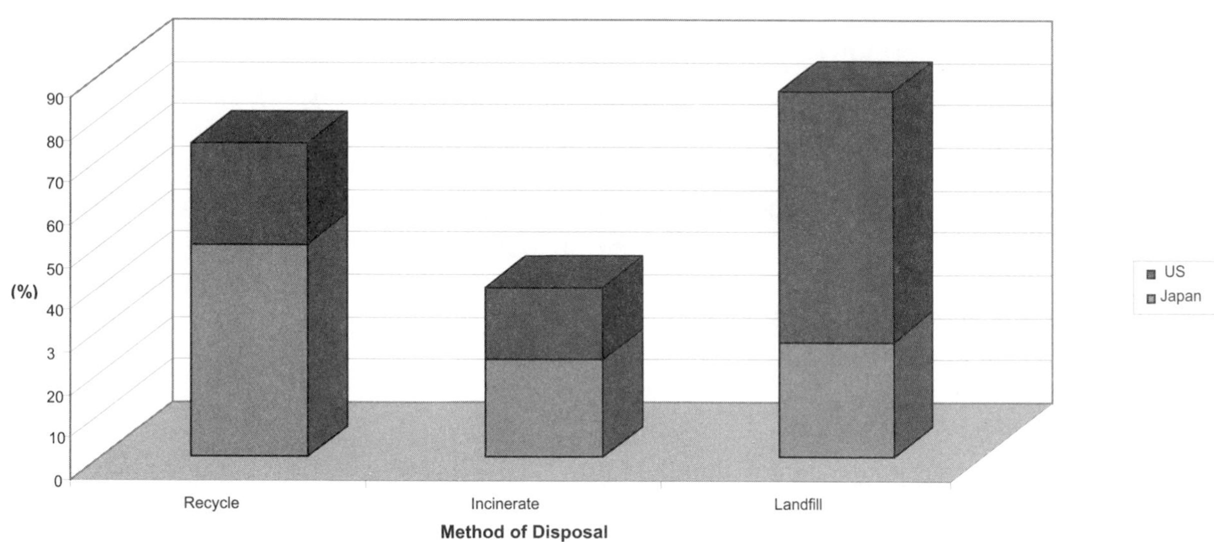

PART IV: HISTOGRAM

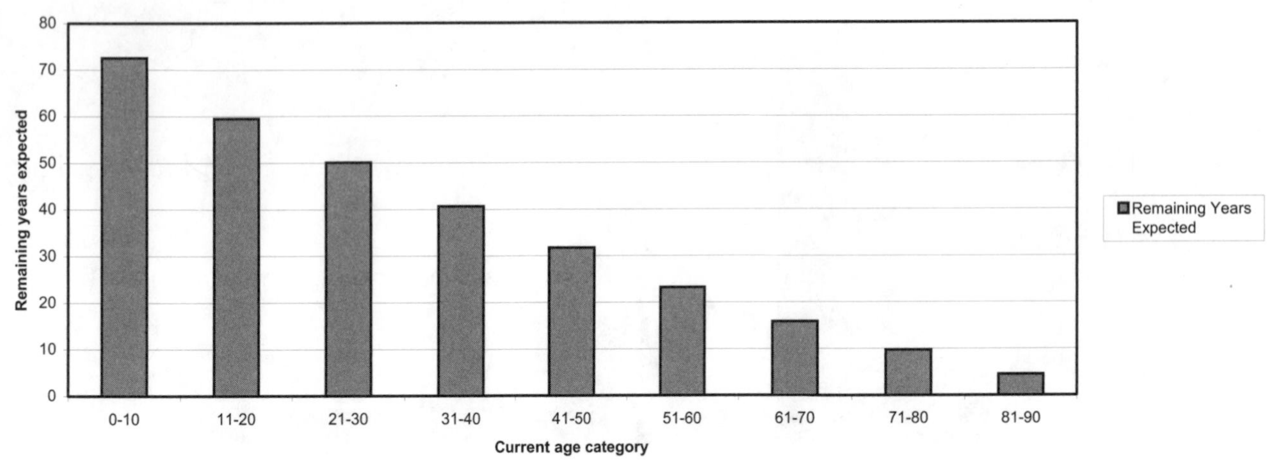

POSSIBLE ANSWERS TO THE CONCLUSION QUESTIONS

Using the graphs that you constructed, answer the following questions.

PART I: SIMPLE BAR GRAPH

1. How many deaths due to accidents and trauma occur per year?
   - 5.1 million deaths

2. Can you predict the number of deaths due to cancers and tumors for the next ten years? Explain.
   - No. This type of extrapolation is a weakness of bar graphs.

PART II: GROUPED BAR GRAPH

1. What element is the most abundant in the Earth's crust?
   - Oxygen — about 45%.

2. What element is the most abundant within the Earth?
   - Iron — about 33%.

PART III: COMPOSITE BAR GRAPH

1. What is the favored method of waste disposal for the Japanese population? Cite possible reasons for this.
    - Recycling — about 50% of their waste is disposed of this way.
    - Possible reasons might include: minimum available undeveloped land; overcrowded population.

2. What is the favored method of waste disposal for the US population? Cite possible reasons for this.
    - Landfill — about 60% of waste is disposed of this way.
    - Possible reasons might include: plenty of undeveloped land; expense associated with recycling.

PART IV: HISTOGRAM

1. Make a prediction about the remaining years of life that would be expected for someone in the current age category of 91-100.
    - Some students will attempt to find a mathematical trend in the data by looking at how the years change over each interval. Students should answer between 0 and 2 years if using this type of pattern.

2. Is the answer to question 7 an accurate number? Why or why not? Cite specific reasons.
    - No, the answer in 7 is not an accurate number.
    - This is very difficult to predict from a graph of this type.

3. What type of data is easily represented by a bar graph?
    - Data that compares amounts or frequency of occurrence.

4. Why is a legend (or key) necessary in the grouped and composite bar graphs?
    - Legends are necessary to distinguish between the bars.

5. Explain why it is difficult to make direct comparisons between recycling in Japan and the US using the composite bar graph that you drew.
    - It is difficult for comparison since the bars are merged together. In order to compare accurately, you would have to accurately measure the length of each piece separately.

6. What is the importance of scaling?
    - Scaling is important for making accurate comparisons.

7. Distinguish between the dependent and the independent variable for each of the graphs that were constructed. On which axis should the independent variable be placed?

	Dependent Variable	**Independent Variable**
Simple Bar Graph	Millions of deaths per year	Cause of death
Grouped Bar Graph	Percentages in Earth and crust	Chemical elements
Composite Bar Graph	Percentage of waste	Method of disposal
Histogram	Remaining years expected	Current age

- The *x*-axis is usually used for the independent variable.

Graphing Skills
Reading, Constructing and Analyzing Graphs

Pie Charts

OBJECTIVE
Students will become familiar with basic pie chart graphing skills to be used throughout their science course of study.

LEVEL
All

NATIONAL STANDARDS
UCP.1, UCP.2, G.2

TEKS
6.2(E)
7.2(E)
8.2(E)
IPC 2(C)
Biology 2(C)
Chemistry 2(D)
Physics 2(C), 2(E)

CONNECTIONS TO AP
Each of the AP Science courses requires that students are able to read, construct and analyze graphs.

TIME FRAME
45 minutes

MATERIALS
(For each student working individually)

2 sheets of blank paper
pencil
compass
data
protractor
colored pencils

TEACHER NOTES

Graphing is a skill that should be introduced at each grade level and reinforced throughout the year whenever data is available. Before allowing students to begin this exercise, you should do the following:

- Emphasize the usefulness of pie charts for showing percentages.
- Remind students that each pie chart should always total 100%. They will be asked to calculate the percentage for the second set of data. To find the percentage:

  $$\% = \frac{\text{specific sample of data}}{\text{total data collected}} \times 100$$

- Point out that a legend or key will be necessary for this type of display.
- Reinforce that labels for each wedge and a title are always necessary.
- Students may need to be instructed on proper use of a compass and protractor. An easy way to construct a pie chart is to have students draw a circle with the compass. Using the protractor, make four marks on the outside of the circle in 90° intervals. Next, have the students divide each quadrant into five equal sections. Each section will represent 5%. This makes estimation of points quite simple.

SAMPLE DATA

Student graphs should look similar to the samples found below.

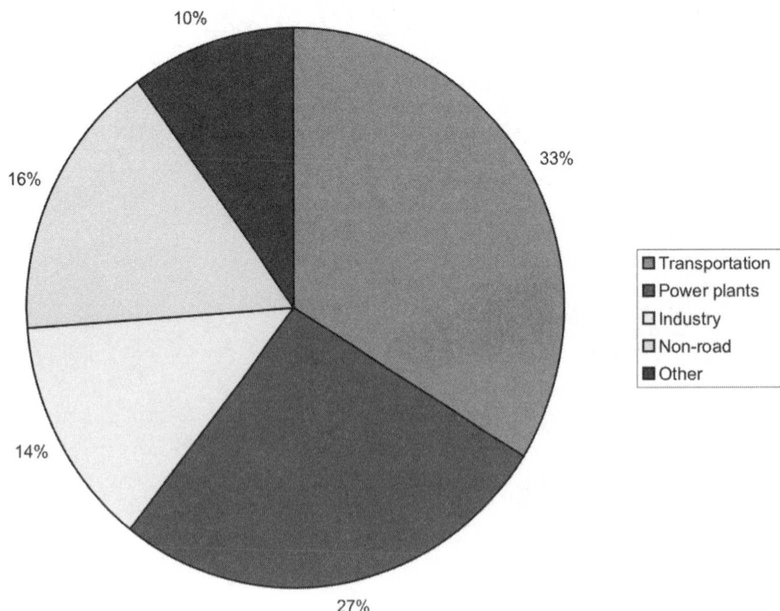

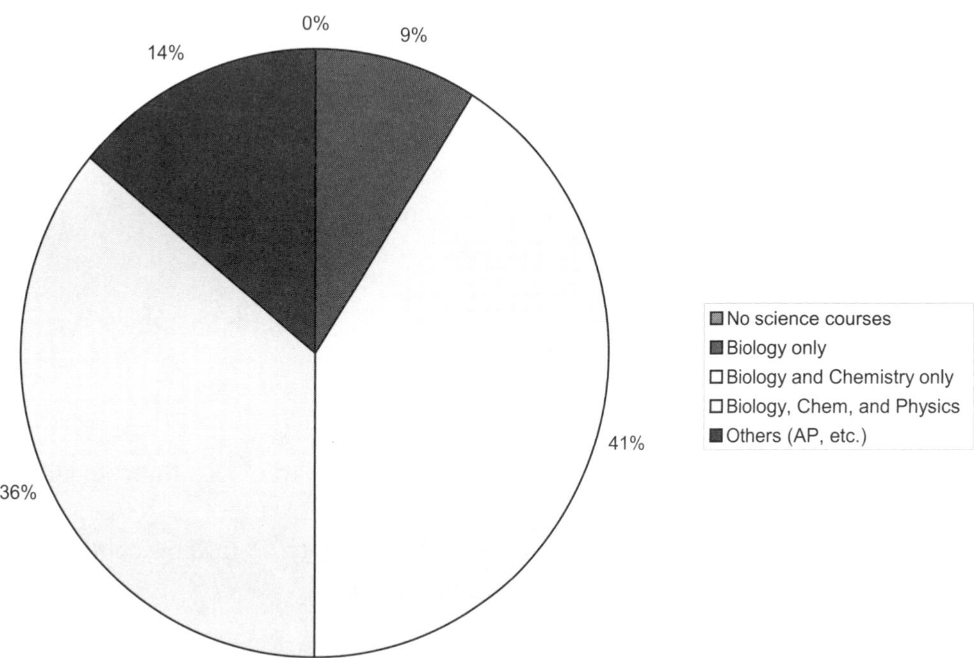

POSSIBLE ANSWERS TO THE CONCLUSION QUESTIONS

Using the graphs that you constructed, answer the following questions:

Sample Data Set 1: Sources of Nitrogen Oxide Air Pollution

1. How much nitrogen oxide air pollution is due to transportation?
   - 33%

2. Not taking into account the set of data labeled "other", what category contributes the least nitrogen oxide air pollutants into our environment?
   - Industry

3. Can you predict from a graph of this type the amount of nitrogen oxide air pollution that will be contributed by industry in the next ten years? Explain your reasoning.
   - No
   - The pie graph has no time period associated with it.

Sample Data Set 2:

1. Why must a percentage calculation be performed on the data before making the graph?
   - Pie graphs show parts of a whole, or 100%. Since there were 500 people polled, the data had to be calculated as if the sample size were 100.

2. Describe the trend displayed by this pie chart. Be specific.
   - Everyone polled had taken at least one science course. Most of those polled had taken at least two courses and many had taken three courses. The "other" category represents a small population of students who continued their science course of study or took a different science elective that was not listed.

3. Most adults polled between the ages of 25-30 years of age completed which science courses during their high school career?
   - Biology and chemistry

4. Describe the type of data that can be displayed using pie charts. List three specific places where you might see pie charts printed.
   - Pie charts visually display data that can easily be categorized into percentages.
   - Newspapers, science textbooks, and consumer labeling.

Graphing Skills
Reading, Constructing and Analyzing Graphs

Line Graphs

OBJECTIVE
Students will become familiar with basic line graphing skills to be used throughout their science course of study.

LEVEL
All

NATIONAL STANDARDS
UCP.1, UCP.2, G.2

TEKS
6.2(E)
7.2(E)
8.2(E)
IPC 2(C)
Biology 2(C)
Chemistry 2(D)
Physics 2(C), 2(E)

CONNECTIONS TO AP
Each of the AP Science courses requires that students are able to read, construct and analyze graphs.

TIME FRAME
45 minutes

MATERIALS
(For each student working individually)

4 sheets of quadrille graph paper	data
pencil	ruler

TEACHER NOTES

Graphing is a skill that should be introduced at each grade level and reinforced throughout the year whenever data is available. In this exercise students will construct line graphs using paper and pencil. Line graphs will be constructed and analyzed more than any of the other types of graphs throughout the science course of study so you should make sure that all students are comfortable with this activity.

Upon completion of the graphing exercise, analysis of the graph follows. Students should understand basic paper/pencil construction methods of graphing before proceeding to the Foundation Lessons which use Microsoft Excel and Graphical Analysis. Before allowing students to begin this exercise, you should have students make a practice graph at their desks while you make one at the overhead or chalkboard. In your example discuss the following points:

- Ask students if they can identify the *x* and *y*- axes. Label these on your sample.
- Ask students about the terms independent and dependent variable. Do they know where to place each on their graph? Below the *x*-axis write the label "independent" and beside the *y*-axis write the label "dependent". Remind the students that each of the variables should have some type of unit associated with them. Write the word "unit" in parentheses after the word "independent" and "dependent" variable on your example.
- Ask students to identify the last missing component of the graph. [Title] Write the term "title" at the top of the graph. Point out that it is common to title a graph using the dependent variable (*y*-axis vs. the independent variable (*x*-axis) format. Encourage students to give descriptive titles to their graph and not just re-name the axes. The graphs that the students construct should have "good" titles. Titles that tell exactly what information the author is trying to represent with the graph. The title should be concise, clear and complete.
- Using any set of generic data points, illustrate to students how to determine the range for each variable and how to determine the scale for each axis. Point out that graph paper must always be used to construct a graph. Each square along an axis must represent the same increment. Encourage students to use as much space as available to construct their graph. Label each axis on the graph with the proper numbers according to data given.
- Illustrate how to plot points on the graph. Emphasize that each point represents both an *x* and a *y* component. Remind students that the plotting of points in science is the same as plotting an ordered pair in the math class. (in math the points are always given as (*x*,*y*). Encourage the use of pencil to plot the data set.
- Discuss with students the importance of using a graph to understand relationships. In the science classroom graphs are not generally connect-the-dot graphs. It is common practice to draw the best smooth curve or the line of best fit that relates the data. Illustrate how this is done with the data previously plotted. If more than one set of data is to be displayed on any one graph, remind students that a legend or key will be necessary to identify each line.
- Point out to students that as their mathematical and scientific skills increase, the usefulness and meaning of their graphs will also increase.
- Illustrate the following analysis techniques:
    - Interpolation of data — find a value that lies on the smooth curve or line *between* two actual data points.
    - Extrapolation of data — find a value that lies on the smooth curve or line beyond the actual plotted points. Data can be extrapolated both on the front and back end of the line/curve.

- Linear regression of data — If the plotted relationship generates a straight line, have students write the equation for the straight line in slope-intercept form [y = mx + b]. To calculate the slope of the line use the equation:

$$slope = \frac{rise}{run} = \frac{\Delta y}{\Delta x} = \frac{y_2 - y_1}{x_2 - x_1}$$

The y-intercept can be found by extending the line of best fit backwards until it crosses the y-axis

POSSIBLE ANSWERS TO THE CONCLUSION QUESTIONS AND SAMPLE DATA

Sample Data Set 1: The following set of data was collected while experimenting with position and time of a miniature motorized car traveling on a straight track.

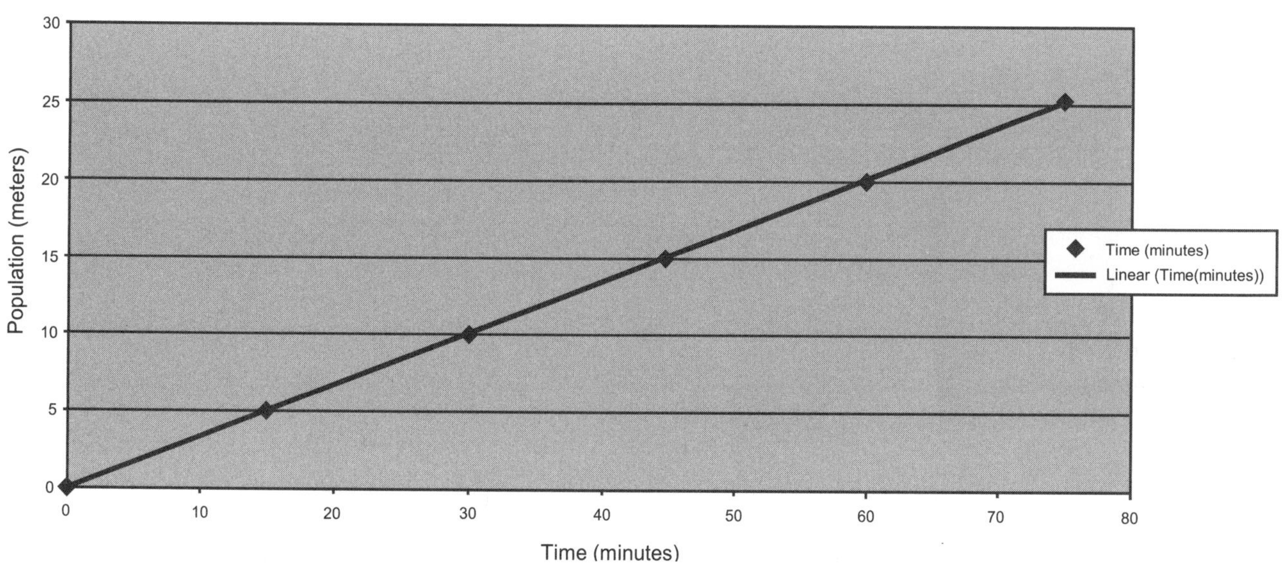

1. What is the independent variable for this graph? Explain.
   - Time is the independent variable. It is the property that is controlled by the experimenter. It is plotted on the x-axis.

2. What would be the position of the car after 25 minutes?
   - About 7.5 to 8.0 meters. Arriving at this answer requires that the student use knowledge of interpolation.

3. If the experiment were carried out for 80 minutes, what would be the position of the car?
   - About 28 meters. Arriving at this answer requires that the student use knowledge of extrapolation.

TEACHER PAGES

4. Calculate the slope of the line drawn. What does the slope of this line represent? Explain.
   - $\text{slope} = \frac{\text{rise}}{\text{run}} = \frac{\Delta y}{\Delta x} = \frac{y_2 - y_1}{x_2 - x_1}$
   - Students may choose any set of points to solve. Answers may vary slightly. Possible solution might be: $\text{slope} = \frac{\text{rise}}{\text{run}} = \frac{\Delta y}{\Delta x} = \frac{10\text{m} - 5\text{m}}{30\text{min} - 15\text{min}} = \frac{5\text{m}}{15\text{min}} = .33\,\text{m}/\text{min}$
   - The slope represents velocity — distance per time.

5. Write the equation for a straight line including the value that was determined for slope.
   - y = m x + b

     position (m) = (.33 m/min) (time) + 0

Sample Data Set 2: The following set of data was collected during an experiment to find the density for an unknown metal.

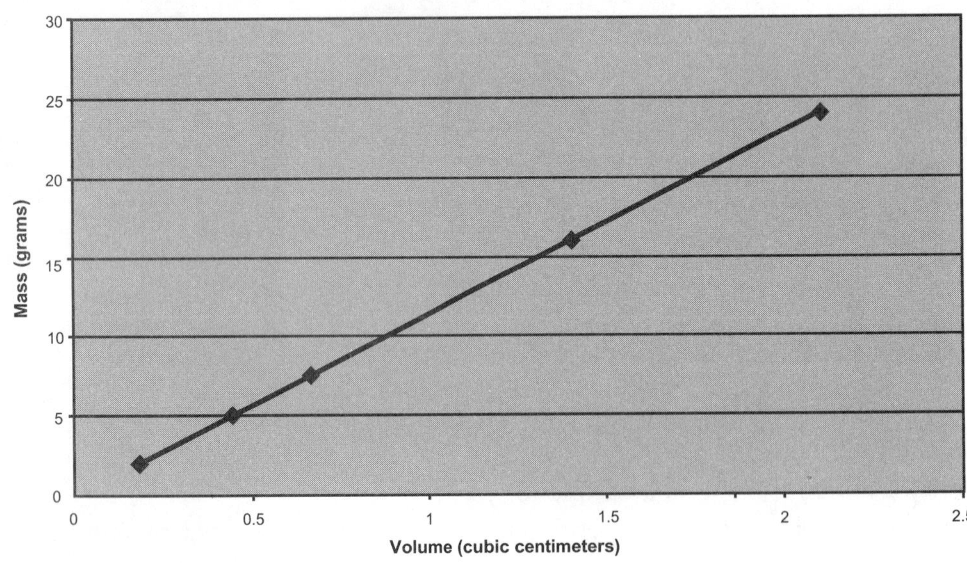

1. What values were considered when creating the scale for each axis in this experiment?
   - Mass: the range of the numbers was from 2.00 to 24.00 grams. The scale was chosen so that each line represents 5 grams. (student answers may vary as chosen scales may vary)
   - Volume: the range was from 0.18 to 2.11 cm^3. The scale was chosen so that each mark represented 0.50 cm^3.

2. What does a data point on this graph actually represent?
   - Each data point represents a mass and a volume measurement. The relationship between the two is the density which is the slope of the best-fit line.

3. What volume would a 20.00 gram sample of this substance occupy?
   - About 1.75 cm^3. Arriving at this answer requires that the student use knowledge of interpolation.

4. Calculate the density of the substance. (HINT: calculate the slope of the line.)
   - $\text{slope} = \frac{\text{rise}}{\text{run}} = \frac{\Delta y}{\Delta x} = \frac{y_2 - y_1}{x_2 - x_1}$ Students may choose any set of points to solve. Answers may vary slightly. Possible solution might be: $\text{slope} = \frac{\text{rise}}{\text{run}} = \frac{\Delta y}{\Delta x} = \frac{15\text{g} - 5\text{g}}{1.44\text{cm}^3 - .44\text{cm}^3} = \frac{10}{1.00} = 10.0\,\text{g/cm}^3$
   - The slope represents density — mass per unit volume.

5. Write the equation for a straight line including the value that was determined for slope.
y	=	m	x	+	b
mass (g)	=	(10.0 g/cm^3	(volume(cm^3))	+	0

6. Use the equation and find the mass when the volume is 5.00 cm^3.
y	=	m	x	+	b
mass (g)	=	(10.0 g/cm^3)	(volume (cm^3))	+	0
mass (g)	=	(10.0 g/cm^3)	(5.00 cm^3)	+	0
mass (g)	=	50.0 grams			

TEACHER PAGES

Sample Data Set 3: The following set of data was collected during an experiment studying the effect of light intensity on rate of photosynthesis.

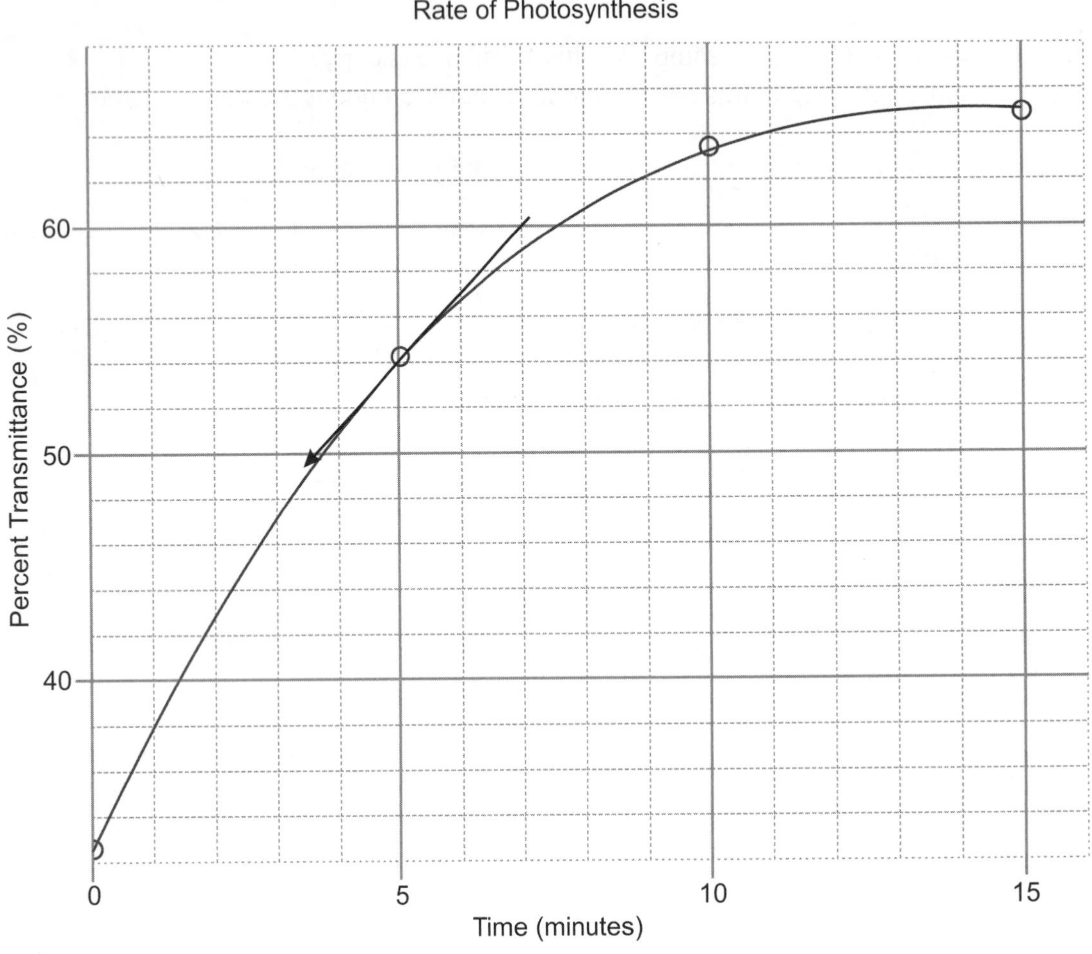

1. Does this graph represent a linear relationship? Why or why not?
   - This graph is not a linear relationship. The slope of the line changes with time.

2. What is the dependent variable in this graph? Explain.
   - The dependent variable is the percent transmittance. Time is the independent variable, the one that the person performing the experiment has control over. At each time interval, the transmittance is measured.

3. If the experiment were continued for 30 minutes, what trend in percent transmittance could be expected?
   - The graph begins to level somewhat between 10 and 15 minutes. It seems logical that the percent transmittance would soon level off or begin to fall.

Note: Middle school teachers may wish to omit the remainder of this lesson.

4. Calculate the slope of the line at 5 minutes. What does this represent?
   - A tangent line must be drawn at 5 minutes.
   - $\text{slope} = \frac{\text{rise}}{\text{run}} = \frac{\Delta y}{\Delta x} = \frac{60\% - 50\%}{7\,\text{min} - 4.5\,\text{min}} = \frac{10}{2.5} = 4.09\%/\text{min}$
   - The slope represents the instantaneous rate. Notice that the slope of the line is different at 10 minutes.

Sample Data Set 4: The following set of data was collected during a titration experiment of a diprotic acid and sodium hydroxide.

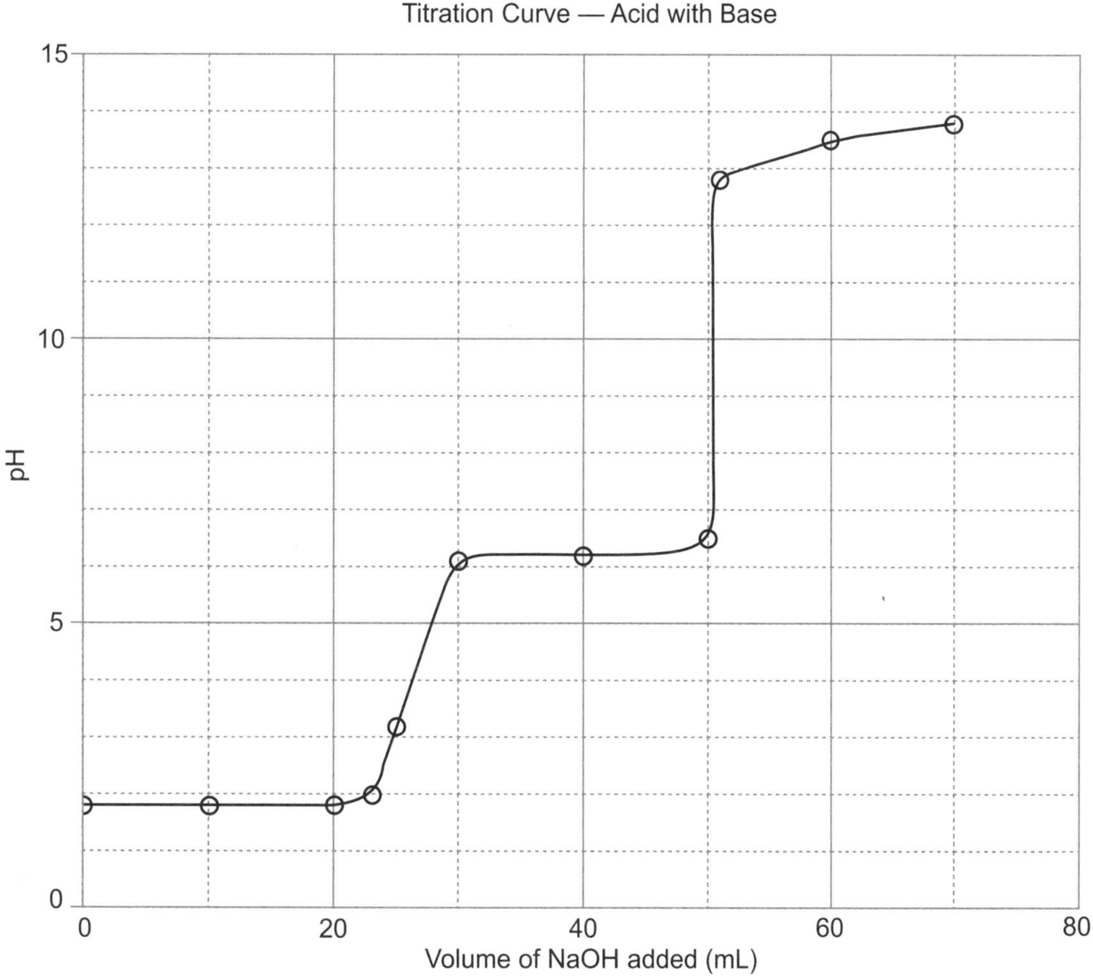

1. What is the pH of the solution after 20.0 mL of NaOH are added? After 30.0 mL are added? Would it have been easy to predict this answer?
   - The pH at 20.0 mL = 1.80; the pH at 30.0 mL = 6.10
   - The graph is not a direct relationship and thus, would not have made this easy to predict such a large jump in pH.

2. Graphs often help us to understand the progress of a chemical reaction. In the titration graph for this set of data, there are two relatively sharp, upward curves. The middle of these steep rising portions represent equivalence points (point at which the moles of acid and base are equal). Identify the volume of NaOH needed to reach each of the equivalence points.
   - The first equivalence point occurs around 28 mL. (the midpoint of the sharp, upward curve must be taken)
   - The second equivalence point occurs around 50 mL.

3. What is the pH at 65 mL. What is the pH expected to do beyond this point with greater additions of the base NaOH? Explain.
   - The pH at 65 mL is approximately 13.50.
   - Beyond 65 mL the pH will gradually rise and level off. Since NaOH is a strong base it will eventually reach close to a pH of 14.00.
   - The curve begins leveling off after the second equivalence point, therefore, the pH will not drastically change with more NaOH added. The pH after the equivalence point is only due to the amount of NaOH that is in excess of the acid.

Graphing Skills
Reading, Constructing and Analyzing Graphs
Bar Graphs and Histograms

Bar graphs are very common types of graphs. They are found in almost all science books, magazines, and newspapers. They can be useful tools in scientific study by allowing us to visually compare amounts or frequency of occurrences between different data sets. Bar graphs can be used to show how something changes over time or to compare items with one another. When reading or constructing this type of graph you should pay close attention to the title, the label on the axes, the unit or scale of the axes, and the bars.

In a simple bar graph the specific group or experimental subject is assigned the *x*-axis (horizontal) and the *y*-axis (vertical) is known as the frequency axis. In general, the *x*-axis will be divided into time periods or measurements while the *y*-axis is designated for the frequency of occurrences. When data is grouped, the *x*-axis always represents the grouped data while the y-axis shows the frequency data. A composite bar graph is often useful when displaying the sum of various dependent variables when the values are a fraction of the whole. Histograms are very similar to simple bar graphs with one exception — the bar represents a range of values rather than one single value and the intervals must all be of equal magnitude. Study the sample graphs below before completing this exercise.

Simple Bar Graph

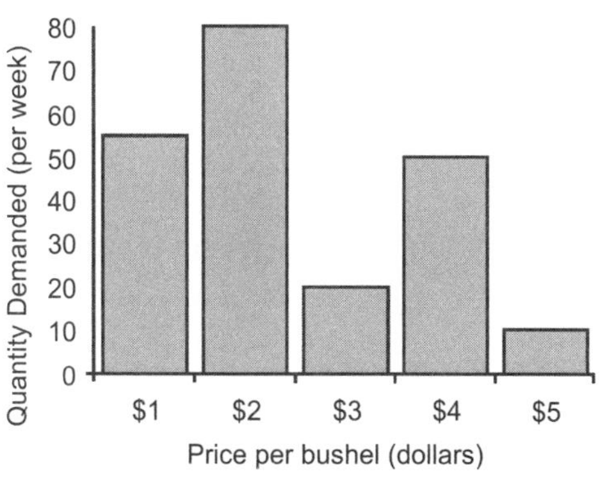

Grouped Bar Graph

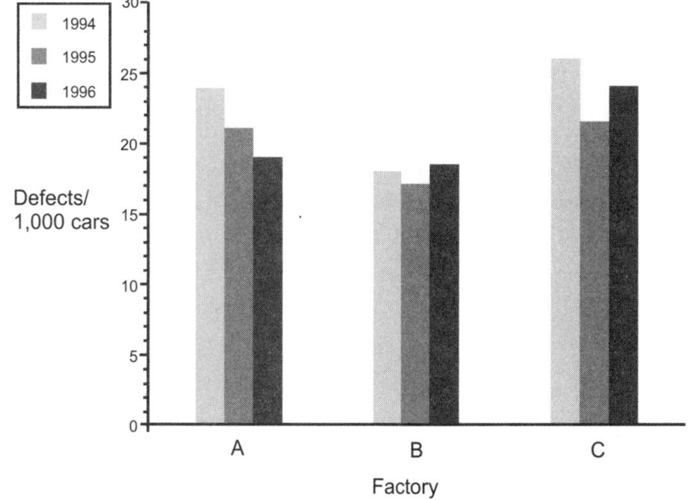

Composite Bar Graph

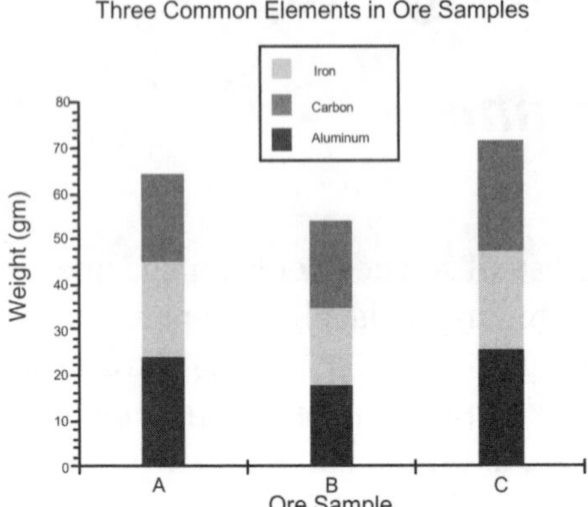

Histogram

Population Distribution

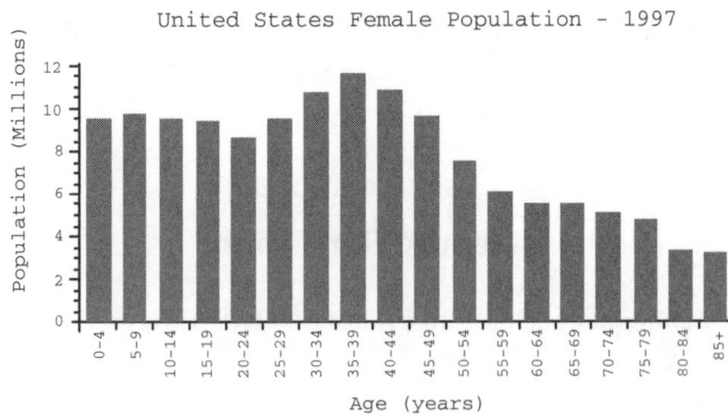

PURPOSE

In this exercise you will create simple bar graphs, grouped bar graphs, composite bar graphs and histograms. You will be expected to properly label each of your graphs and analyze each one by making statements about trends in the data.

MATERIALS

4 sheets of graph paper	data
pencils	straight edge

PROCEDURE

PART I: SIMPLE BAR GRAPH

1. Obtain one piece of graph paper and a pencil.

2. Study the data table below.

Leading Causes Of Death Worldwide	
Cause	Deaths Per Year (millions)
Cardiovascular disease	16.9
Cancers and tumors	7.2
Infectious diseases (includes AIDS, malaria, etc.)	13.5
Accidents and trauma	5.1
Respiratory disease	3.5
Digestive and nutritional	2.3
Diabetes	0.9

3. Choose the data to be graphed on the *x*-axis and the *y*-axis.

4. Survey the data and determine an appropriate scale for each axis. Be sure to utilize as much of the graph paper as possible o display your data. Use your pencil to lightly mark the scale of your *x* and *y*-axes. Have your teacher check your scale before proceeding any further. When making a bar graph, the individual bars should be constructed with the same width. You may decide the width of your bars.

5. When your teacher approves, construct your simple bar graph. Be sure to label each axis with units and give your graph a title.

PART II: GROUPED BAR GRAPH

1. Study the following data and follow the same procedure as Part I with a clean sheet of graph paper. This data should be graphed as a grouped bar graph and include a legend or key to indicate what each bar represents.

Some of the Most Common Chemical Elements of the Earth		
Chemical Element	Whole Earth (%)	Crust (%)
Iron (Fe)	33.3	5.8
Oxygen (O)	29.8	45.2
Silicon (Si)	15.6	27.2
Magnesium (Mg)	13.9	2.8
Aluminum (Al)	1.5	8.2

PART III: COMPOSITE BAR GRAPH

1. Study the following data and follow the same graphing procedure with a clean sheet of graph paper. This data should be graphed as a composite bar graph. You will need to include a legend and be sure to place the waste disposal methods in the same order for each bar drawn.

Solid Waste Recycled, Incerated, and Landfilled in US and Japan		
	Japan	US
Recycle (%)	50	24
Incinerate (%)	23	17
Landfill (%)	27	59

PART IV: HISTOGRAM

1. Study the following data and follow the same graphing procedure. This data should be graphed as a histogram. It is important that histograms have the same interval and width for each bar. For example, each bar might represent 10 years in the data table below.

Life Expectancies in the US	
Current Age	Remaining Years Expected
0-10	72.6
11-20	59.5
21-30	50.1
31-40	40.7
41-50	31.7
51-60	23.2
61-70	15.8
71-80	9.7
81-90	4.5

Graphing Skills
Reading, Constructing and Analyzing Graphs

Bar Graphs and Histograms

CONCLUSION QUESTIONS

Using the graphs that you constructed, answer the following questions.

PART I: SIMPLE BAR GRAPH

1. How many deaths due to accidents and trauma occur per year?
2. Can you predict the number of deaths due to cancers and tumors for the next ten years? Explain.

PART II: GROUPED BAR GRAPH

1. What element is the most abundant in the earth's crust?
2. What element is the most abundant within the earth?

PART III: COMPOSITE BAR GRAPH

1. What is the favored method of waste disposal for the Japanese population? Cite possible reasons for this.
2. What is the favored method of waste disposal for the US population? Cite possible reasons for this.

PART IV: HISTOGRAM

1. Make a prediction about the remaining years of life that would be expected for someone in the current age category of 91-100.

2. Is the answer to question 7 an accurate number? Why or why not? Cite specific reasons.

3. What type of data is easily represented by a bar graph?

4. Why is a legend (or key) necessary in the grouped and composite bar graphs?

5. Explain why it is difficult to make direct comparisons between recycling in Japan and the US using the composite bar graph that you drew.

6. What is the importance of scaling?

7. Distinguish between the dependent and the independent variable for each of the graphs that were constructed. On which axis should the independent variable be placed?

	Dependent Variable	Independent Variable
Simple Bar Graph		
Grouped Bar Graph		
Composite Bar Graph		
Histogram		

Graphing Skills
Reading, Constructing and Analyzing Graphs

Pie Charts

Pie charts are very commonly found in newspapers, magazines and textbooks. A pie chart is a very good way to represent percentages.

PURPOSE
In this activity you will practice constructing and analyzing basic pie charts.

MATERIALS

- blank paper
- pencil
- compass
- data
- protractor
- colored pencils

> **Safety Alert**
> 1. The sharp point on the compass should only be placed on paper.

PROCEDURE
1. After observing your teacher demonstrate the use of the compass and protractor, use Sample Data Set 1 to construct a pie chart on a piece of blank paper. Use different colors to represent different sections of your graph.

2. Be sure to label your chart with an appropriate title and be sure to provide a legend or key that distinguishes each component.

Sample Data Set 1: Sources of Nitrogen Oxide Air Pollution

Sources of Nitrogen Oxides	Percentages (%)
Power plants	53%
Transportation	68%
Industry	27%
Non-road	32%
Other	20%

3. Use Sample Data Set 2 to construct a second pie chart on another blank piece of paper. Be sure to label appropriately. *Note*: Before beginning construction of this graph, you must calculate component percentages. Show your work on the student answer page.

Sample Data Set 2: 500 adults between the ages of 25-30 were polled as to which science courses they completed in their high school years. The following data was collected.

Science Courses Completed	Number of Adults
No science courses	0
Biology only	45
Biology and Chemistry only	205
Biology, Chemistry and Physics only	180
Other classes not listed (AP, etc.)	70

Name ______________________________

Period ______________________________

Graphing Skills
Reading, Constructing and Analyzing Graphs
Pie Charts

ANALYSIS

1. Staple your two graphs behind this answer page.

2. Show your work here for Sample Data 2 - percentage calculations.

CONCLUSION QUESTIONS

Using the graphs that you constructed, answer the following questions:

Sample Data Set 1: Sources of Nitrogen Oxide Air Pollution

1. How much nitrogen oxide air pollution is due to transportation?

2. Not taking into account the set of data labeled “other”, what category contributes the least nitrogen oxide air pollutants into our environment?

3. Can you predict from a graph of this type the amount of nitrogen oxide air pollution that will be contributed by industry in the next ten years? Explain your reasoning.

Sample Data Set 2:

1. Why must a percentage calculation be performed on the data before making the graph?

2. Describe the trend displayed by this pie chart. Be specific.

3. Most adults polled between the ages of 25-30 years of age completed which science courses during their high school career?

4. Describe the type of data that can be displayed using pie charts. List three specific places where you might see pie charts printed.

Name ____________________

Period ____________________

Graphing Skills
Reading, Constructing and Analyzing Graphs

Line Graphs

There are all kinds of charts and graphs used in the science classroom. Graphs are useful tools in science. Trends in data are easy to visualize when represented graphically. A line graph is beneficial in the classroom for many different types of data. Line graphs are probably the most widely used scientific graph. They can be used to show how something changes over time, the relationship of two quantities, and can be readily used to *interpolate* (predict between measured points on the graph) and *extrapolate* (predict beyond the measured points along the same slope) data points that were not actually measured in the lab setting. The analysis of these graphs provides very valuable information.

PURPOSE
In this activity you will learn the basic procedure for constructing and analyzing line graphs.

MATERIALS

4 sheets of graph paper	data
pencil	ruler

PROCEDURE

1. Follow along with your teacher as a sample line graph is constructed. Label a blank piece of graph paper as your teacher explains the important components of a line graph.

2. Use the sample sets of data below to construct line graphs. Place only one graph on each sheet of graph paper and use as much of the graph as possible to display your points. ***Do not connect the dots!*** Draw the best smooth curve or line of best fit as your teacher demonstrated.

3. Following the steps below will help ensure that all components of the graph are correctly displayed.
   a. **Identify the variables**. Independent on the x-axis and dependent on the y-axis.
   b. **Determine the range**. Subtract the lowest value data point from the highest value data point—for each axis separately.
   c. **Select the scale units**. Divide each axis uniformly into appropriate units using the maximum amount of space available. (Remember that the axes may be divided differently but each square along the same axis must represent the same interval.)
   d. **Number and label each axis**. Be sure to include units where appropriate as part of the axis label.
   e. **Plot the data points as ordered pairs**. (x,y)

f. **Draw the best straight line or best smooth curve.** Use a straight edge to draw your line in such a way that equal numbers of points lie above and below the line.

g. **Title the graph.** The title should clearly describe the information contained in the graph. It is common to mention the dependent variable first followed by the independent variable.

4. After creating graphs for the 4 data sets below, use the graphs to answer the conclusion questions on your student answer page.

Sample Data Set 1: The following set of data was collected while experimenting with position and time of a miniature motorized car traveling on a straight track.

Position (meters)	Time (minutes)
0	0
15	5
30	10
45	15
60	20
75	25

Sample Data Set 2: The following set of data was collected during an experiment to find the density for an unknown metal.

Mass (g)	Volume (cm^3)
2.00	0.18
5.00	0.44
7.50	0.66
16.00	1.41
24.00	2.11

Sample Data Set 3: The following set of data was collected during an experiment studying the effect of light intensity on rate of photosynthesis.

Percent Transmittance (%)	Time (minutes)
32.5	0
54.3	5
63.5	10
65.0	15

Sample Data Set 4: The following set of data was collected during an acid-base titration experiment.

pH	Volume of NaOH (mL)
1.80	0.00
1.80	10.00
1.82	20.00
2.00	23.00
3.20	25.00
6.10	30.00
6.20	40.00
6.50	50.00
12.80	51.00
13.50	60.00
13.80	70.00

Name ___________________________

Period ___________________________

Graphing Skills
Reading, Constructing and Analyzing Graphs
Line Graphs

DATA AND OBSERVATIONS

Staple your completed graphs behind this answer page.

CONCLUSION QUESTIONS

Using the graphs that you constructed, answer the following questions:

Sample Data Set 1:

1. What is the independent variable for this graph? Explain.

2. What would be the position of the car after 25 minutes?

3. If the experiment were carried out for 80 minutes, what would be the position of the car?

4. Calculate the slope of the line drawn. What does the slope of this line represent? Explain.

5. Write the equation for a straight line including the value that was determined for slope.

Sample Data Set 2:

1. What values were considered when creating the scale for each axis in this experiment?

2. What does a data point on this graph actually represent?

3. What volume would a 20.00 gram sample of this substance occupy?

4. Calculate the density of the substance. (HINT: calculate the slope of the line.)

5. Write the equation for a straight line including the value that was determined for slope.

6. Use the equation and find the mass when the volume is 5.00 cm^3.

Sample Data Set 3:

1. Does this graph represent a linear relationship? Why or why not?

2. What is the dependent variable in this graph? Explain.

3. If the experiment were continued for 30 minutes, what trend in percent transmittance could be expected?

4. Calculate the slope of the line at 5 minutes. What does this represent?

Sample Data Set 4:

1. What is the pH of the solution after 20.0 mL of NaOH are added? After 30.0 mL are added? Would it have been easy to predict this answer?

2. Graphs often help us to understand the progress of a chemical reaction. In the titration graph for this set of data, there are two relatively sharp, upward curves. The middle of these steep rising portions represent equivalence points (point at which the moles of acid and base are equal). Identify the volume of NaOH needed to reach each of the equivalence points. .

3. What is the pH at 65 mL. What is the pH expected to do beyond this point with greater additions of the base NaOH? Explain.

Microsoft Excel
Using Excel in the Science Classroom

OBJECTIVE
Students will take data and use an Excel spreadsheet to manipulate the information. This will include creating graphs, manipulating data, finding averages and calculating standard deviation.

LEVEL
All

NATIONAL STANDARDS
UCP.1, UCP.2, A.1, A.2, E.1, E.2, G.2

TEKS
6.2 (E), 6.4(A)
7.2(E), 7.4(A)
8.2 (E), 8.4(A), 8.4(B)
IPC: 2(C)
Biology: 2(C)
Chemistry: 2(D)
Physics: 2(C), 2(E)

CONNECTIONS TO AP
Graphing skills, data management, using technology

TIME FRAME
30 minutes (for each lesson)

MATERIALS
Computers with Microsoft Excel software

TEACHER NOTES
This foundation lesson contains four sub-lessons: bar graphs, line graphs, scatter plots with linear regressions, and data management. You may want to teach each lesson as a stand alone, or as they are relevant to a current lab. The graphing and data lessons can be completely independent of one another.

Sample data has been provided for you to use if you would like to teach these as a stand-alone lesson. It is probably best used as a follow up to a data collection lab so that students can use real data.

Microsoft Excel
Using Excel in the Science Classroom

Part I: How to Make a Bar Graph

PURPOSE

To use the software program Microsoft Excel to generate a bar graph.

MATERIALS

data from this handout
computer
Microsoft Excel software

PROCEDURE

In science class you have collected data to see how much the density of water changes as you add grams of salt. Your teacher wants you to take the data and produce and a bar graph using Excel. The data is as follows:

Grams of Salt	Density
0	1.00
5	1.03
10	1.07
15	1.11
20	1.14

1. Open the Excel program on your computer. A blank workbook will appear. Notice that the columns are identified with letters and the rows are identified by numbers.

2. In the box "A1", type Grams of Salt.

3. In the box "B1", type Density. If you need to make a box larger, take your cursor to the top of the column and place it between two boxes. A double arrow should appear and you can stretch the column to the size you need.

4. Enter the data in the boxes below each section. Be careful to enter the coordinating data in the correct row.

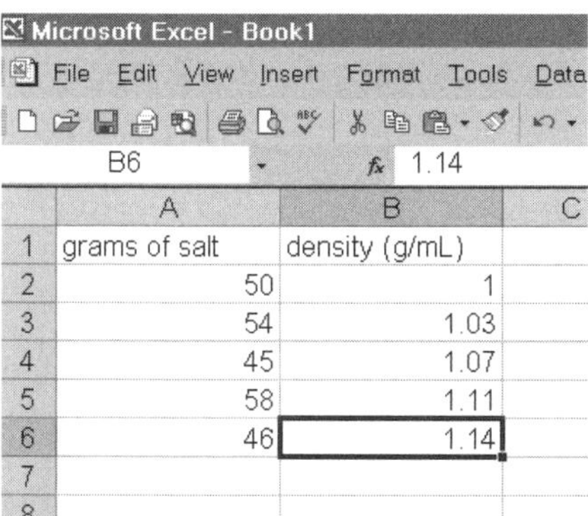

5. On your toolbar there is a very small, colorful bar graph icon. This is called the Chart Wizard. Click on the Chart Wizard icon.

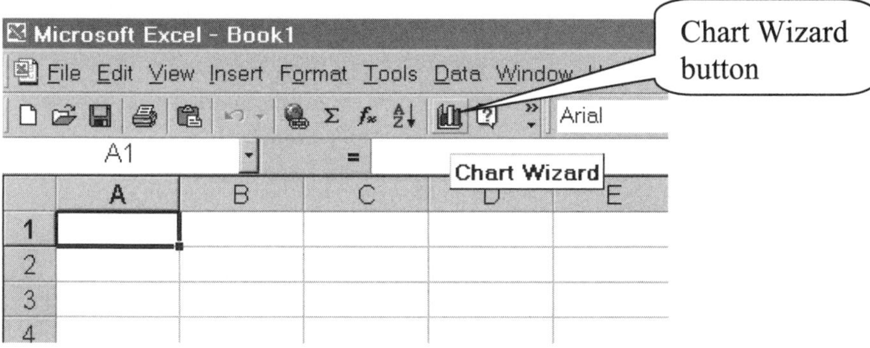

6. After clicking the Chart Wizard button, the first window that opens identifies chart type. Choose "Column" on the left- hand side, and under the chart sub-type on the right side click on the first choice available.

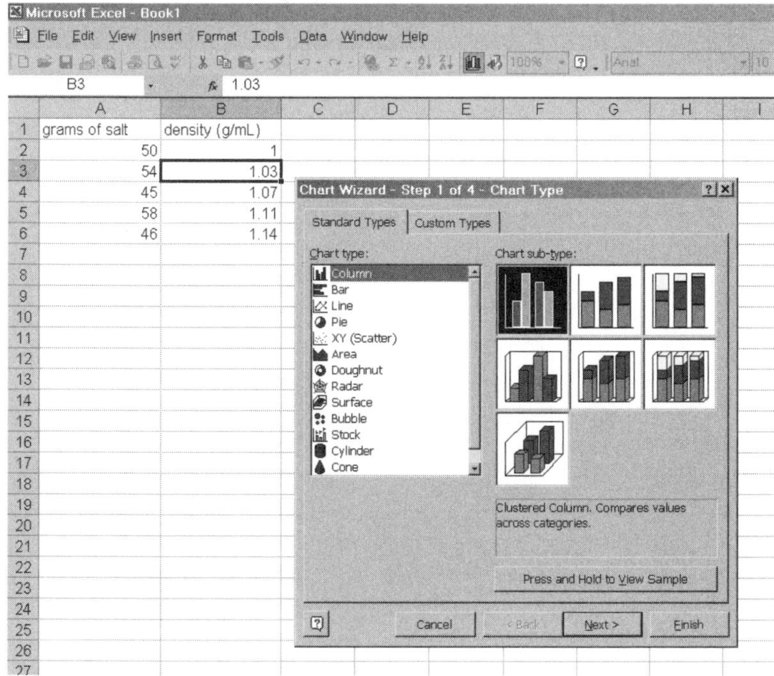

7. Click Next.

8. The next window that appears has two tabs: Data Range and Series. Click on Series and **remove all existing data sets from the series box**.

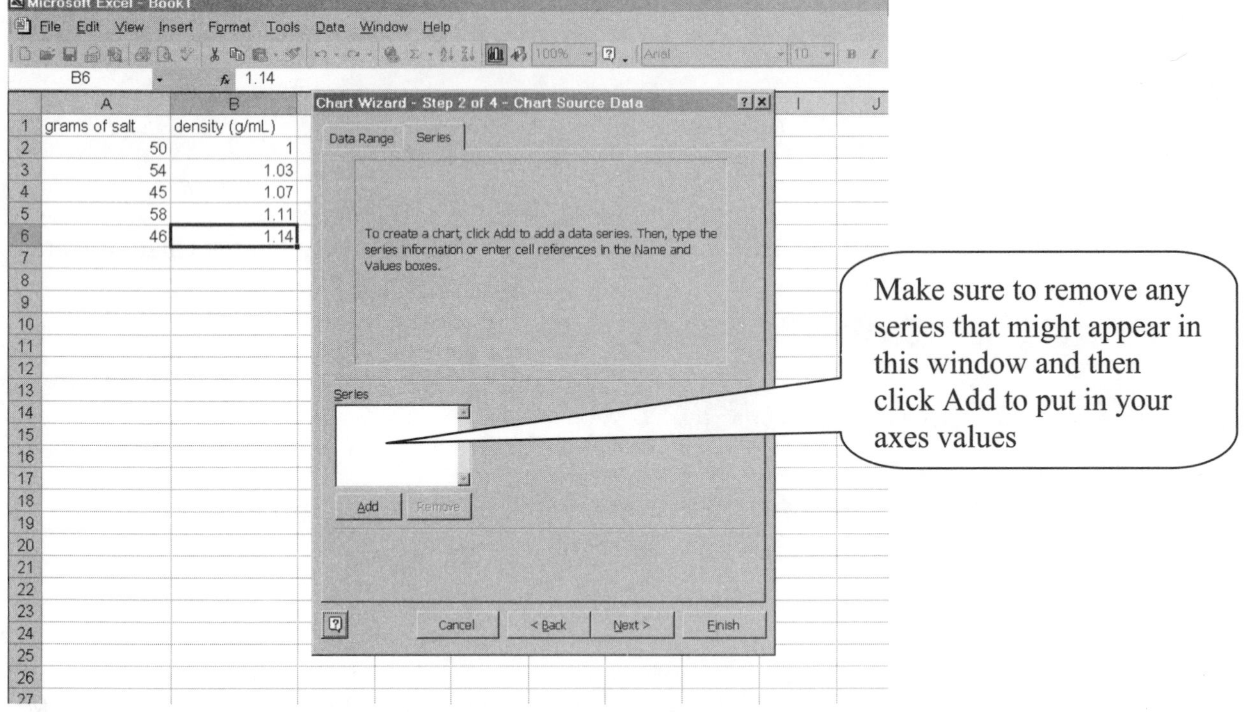

9. Now click **Add** to add your data series. On the bottom of the window is "Category (X) Axis Labels". In the right corner of the Category (X) axis labels is a small button with a tiny graph containing a red arrow. Click on this button.

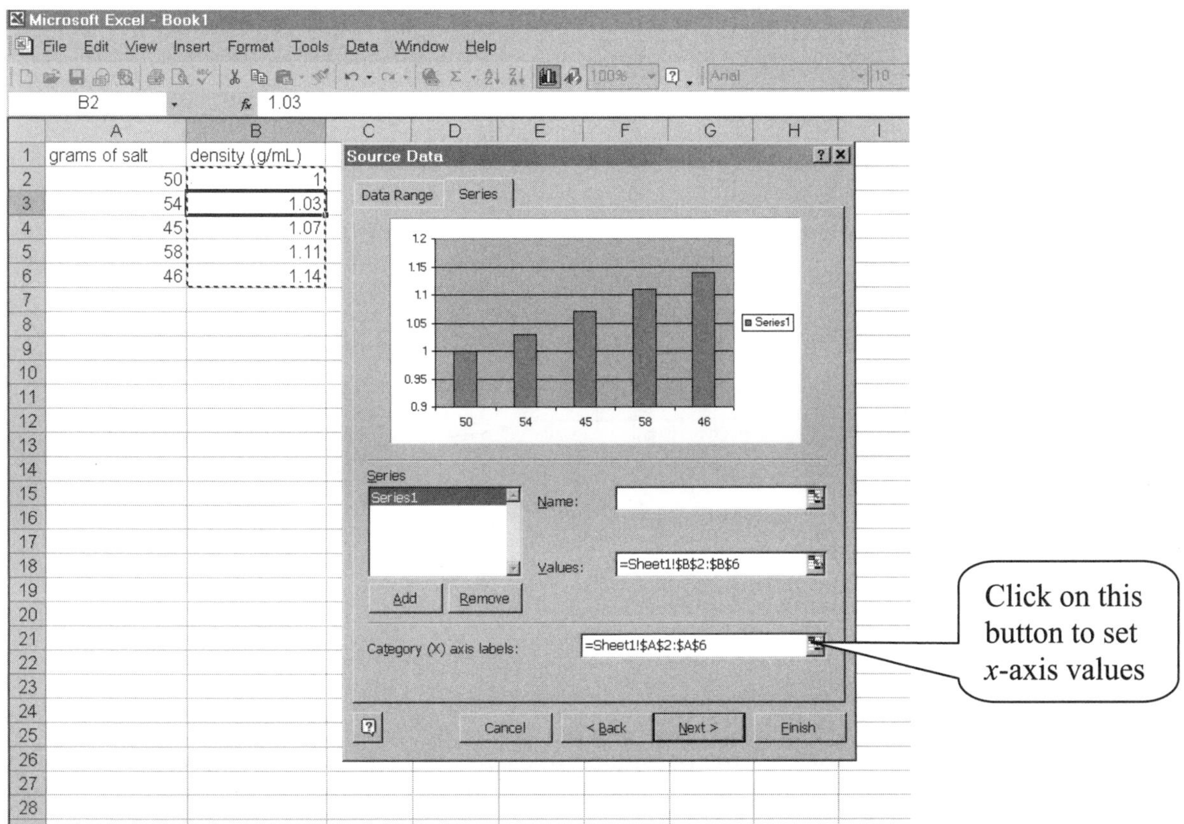

10. Clicking on the button takes you back to your spreadsheet of data. With your mouse, highlight the data you want on the *x*-axis, in this case, the grams of salt, or boxes B1-F1. Press Enter after highlighting.

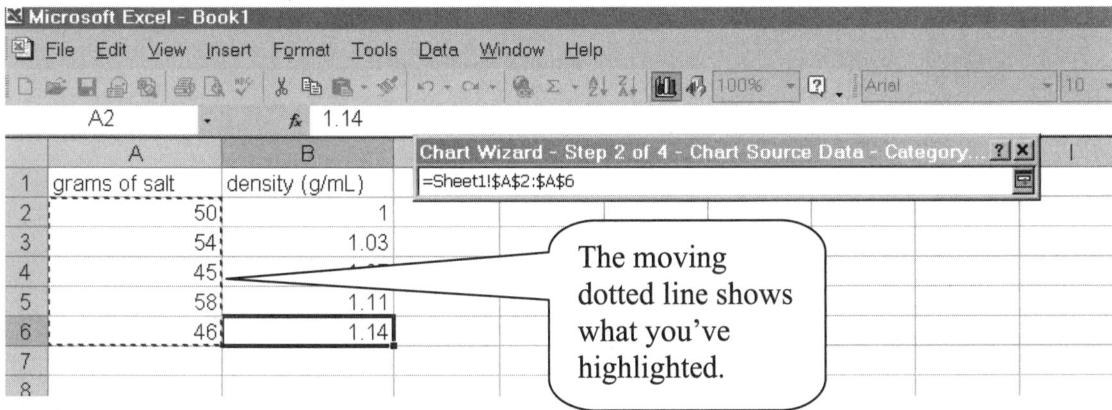

11. The chart wizard screen should now reappear. Click on the small graph button next to the spot labeled Values. This is your *y*-axis label.

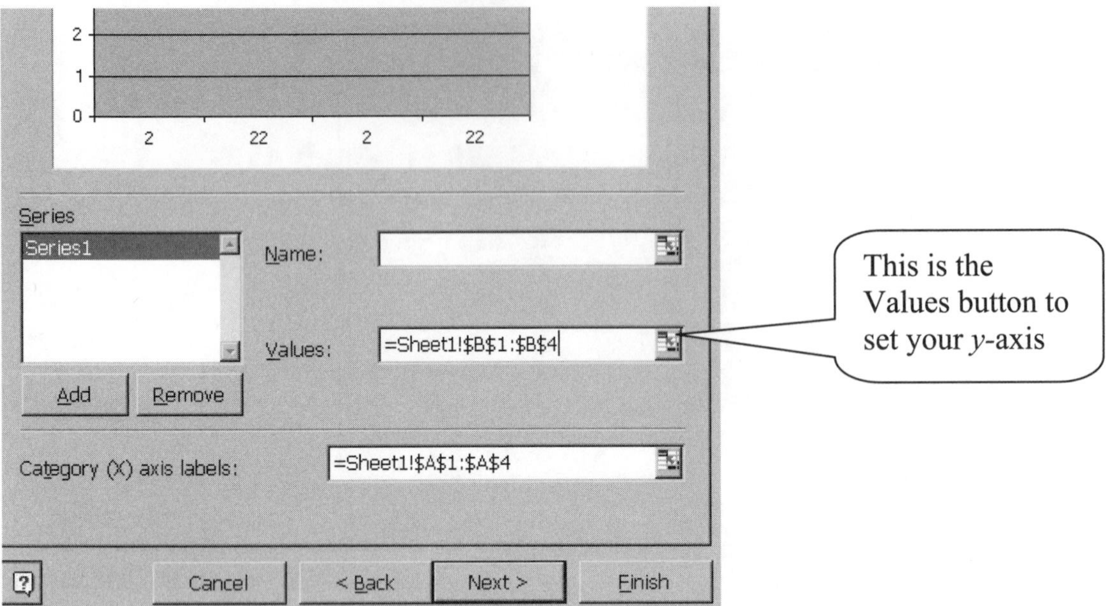

This is the Values button to set your *y*-axis

12. After clicking on the Values button, the computer takes you back to your spreadsheet and now you want to highlight your *y*-axis values, in this case density, B2-F2. Press Enter after highlighting.

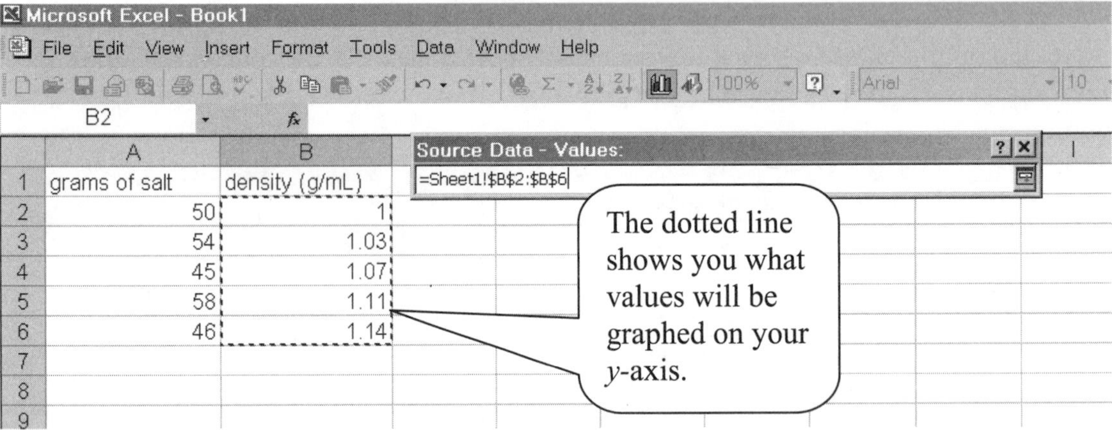

The dotted line shows you what values will be graphed on your *y*-axis.

13. The Chart Wizard screen will reappear. Click next on the bottom of the screen.

14. The new screen allows you to name your graph and label your axis. Fill in the blanks with the appropriate information and click Finish.

15. You now have finished your bar graph and Excel will ask you if you want the graph to appear on your spreadsheet, or on a separate page. Choose whichever you need. Below is a copy of the graph inserted into the spreadsheet page.

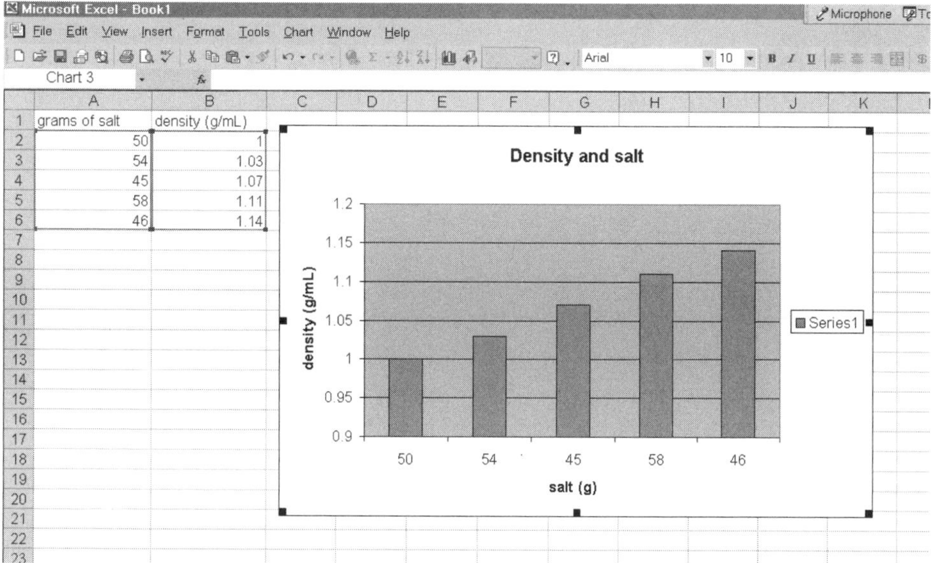

16. You may now print your completed graph by selecting print from the file menu on the task bar.

Microsoft Excel
Using Excel in the Science Classroom
Part II: How to Make a Line Graph

PURPOSE

To use the software program Microsoft Excel to create a line graph.

MATERIALS

data from this handout
computer
Microsoft Excel software

PROCEDURE

In science class you have collected data to see how much the density of water changes as you add grams of salt. Your teacher wants you to take the data and produce and a line graph using Excel. The data is as follows:

Grams of Salt	Density
0	1.00
5	1.03
10	1.07
15	1.11
20	1.14

1. Open an Excel Workbook. Notice that the columns are identified with letters and the rows are identified by numbers.

2. In the box "A1", type Grams of Salt.

3. In the box "B1", type Density. If you need to make a box larger, take your cursor to the top of the column and place it between two boxes until a double arrow appears. Now stretch the column to the size you need.

4. Enter the data in the boxes below each section. Be careful to enter the coordinating data in the correct row.

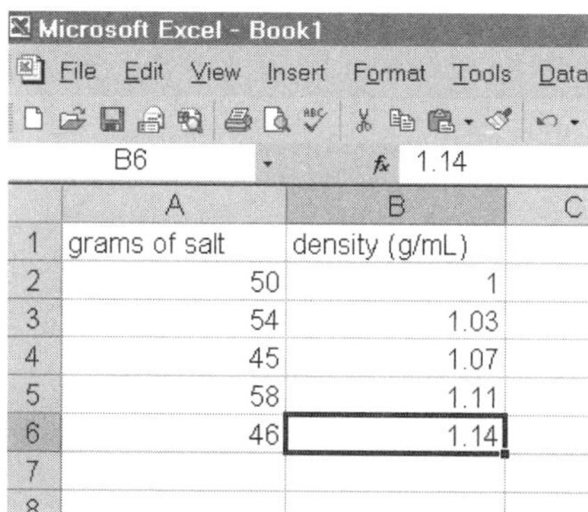

5. On your toolbar there is a very small, colorful bar graph icon. This is called the Chart Wizard. Click on the Chart Wizard icon.

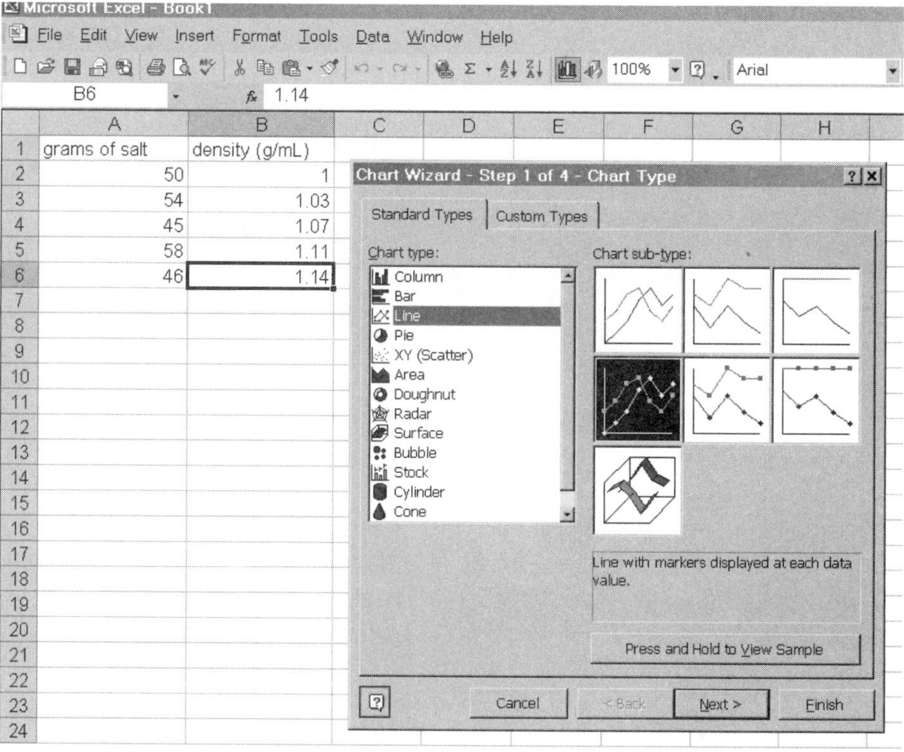

6. The first window to open is to identify chart type. Choose "Line" on the left hand side, and under the chart sub-type on the right side click on the first choice on the second line. Click Next.

7. The next window that appears has two tabs: Data Range and Series. Click on Series and **remove all existing data sets from the series box**.

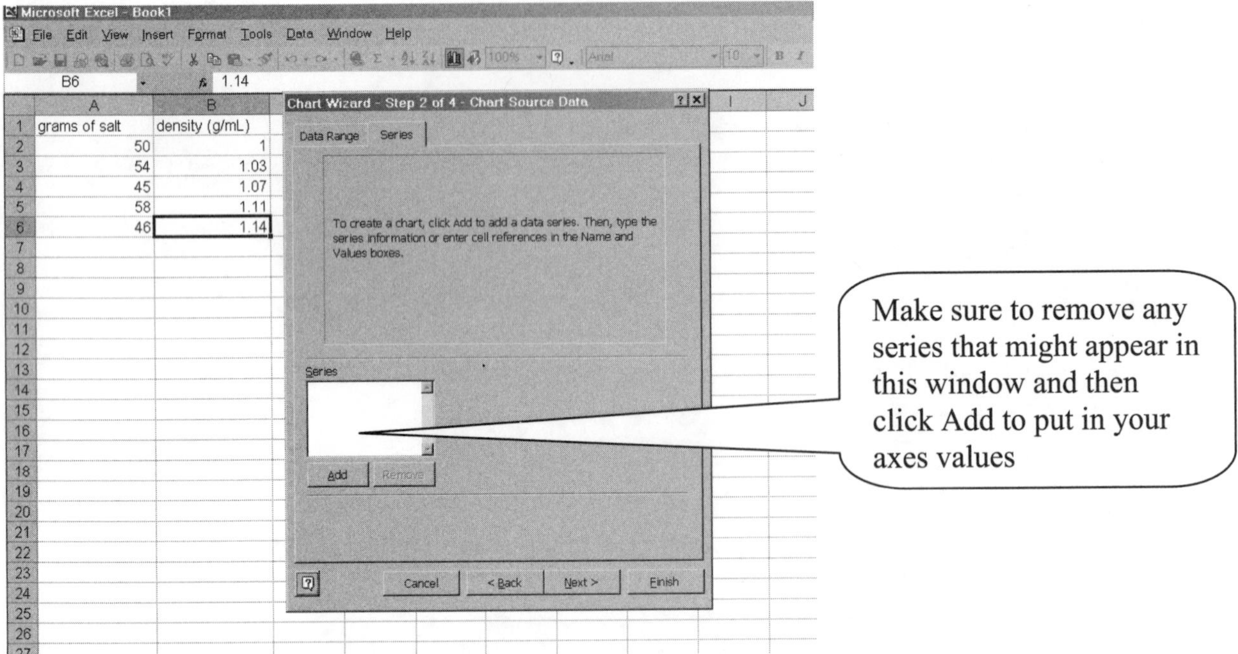

8. Now click **Add** to add your data series. On the bottom of the window is "Category (X) Axis Labels". In the right corner of the Category (X) axis labels is a small button with a tiny graph containing a red arrow. Click on this button.

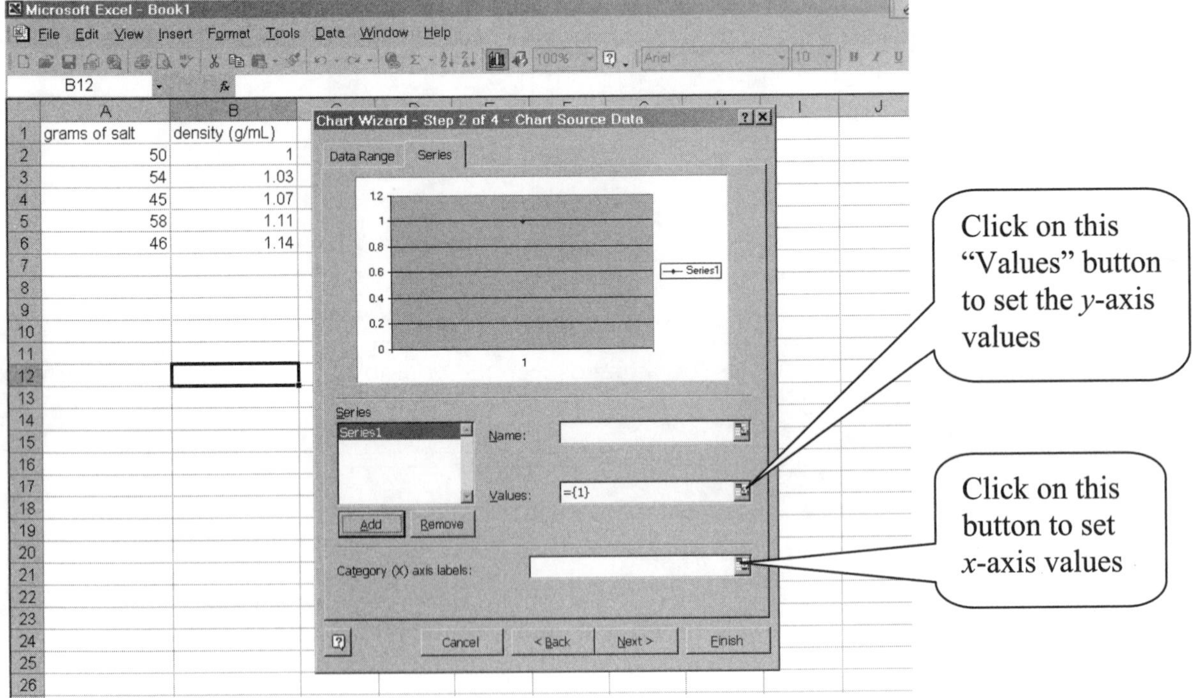

9. Clicking on the button takes you back to your spreadsheet of data. With your mouse, highlight the data you want on the *x*-axis, in this case the grams of salt, or boxes B1-F1. Press Enter after highlighting.

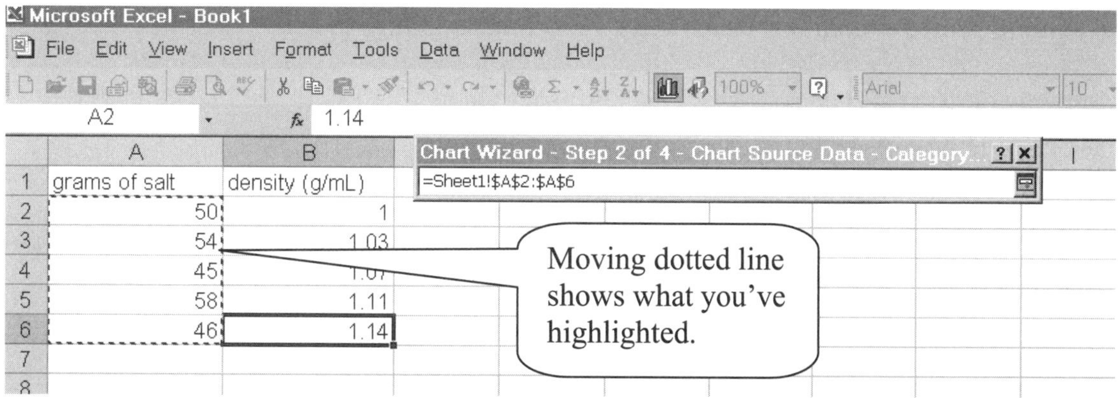

10. The Chart Wizard screen should now reappear. Click on the small graph button next to the spot labeled Values. This is how you add data to your *y*-axis.

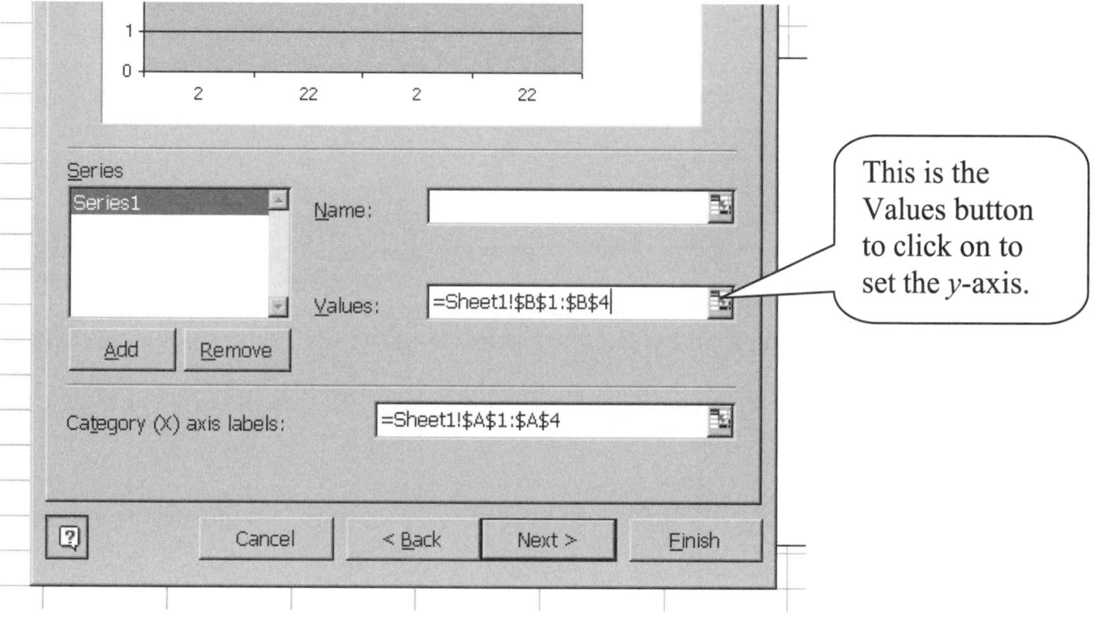

11. Clicking on the button takes you back to your spreadsheet and you now want to highlight your *y*-axis values, in this case density, B2-F2. Press Enter after highlighting.

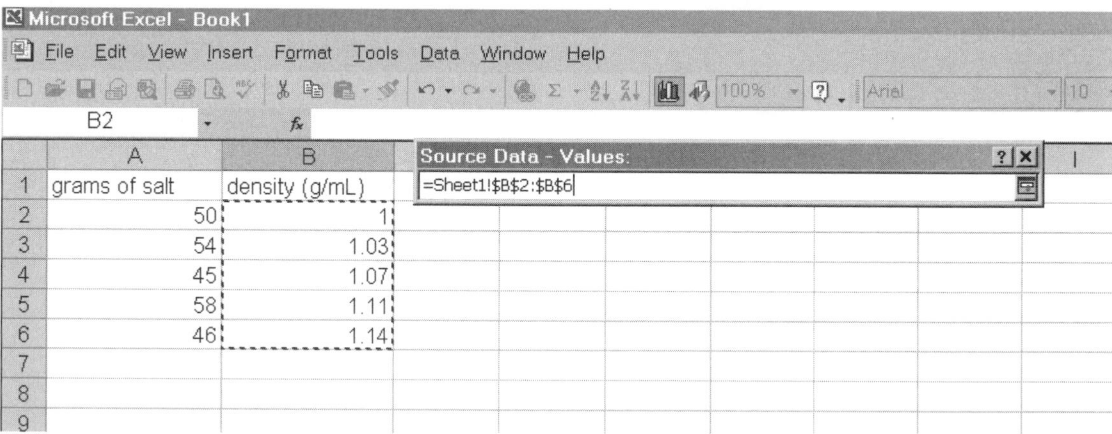

12. The Chart Wizard screen should reappear. Click Next on the bottom of the screen.

13. The new screen allows you to name your graph and label your axis. Fill in the blanks with the appropriate information and click Finish.

14. You now have finished your graph and Excel will ask you if you want the graph to appear on your spreadsheet, or on a separate page. Choose the one you need. Below is a copy of the graph inserted into the spreadsheet page.

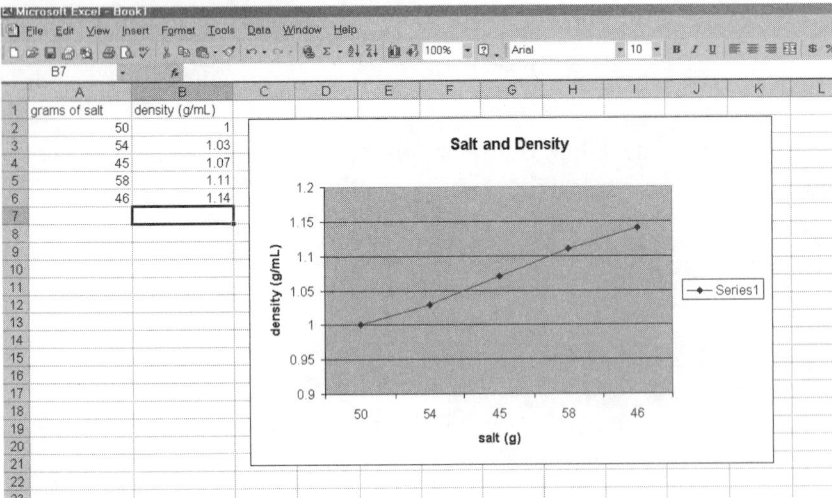

15. You may now print your completed graph by selecting print from the file menu on the task bar.

Microsoft Excel
Using Excel in the Science Classroom

Part III: How to Create a Scatter Plot and Linear Regression Equation

PURPOSE

To use the software program Microsoft Excel to create a line graph.

MATERIALS

data from this handout
computer
Microsoft Excel software

PROCEDURE

In science class you have collected data to see how much the density of water changes as you add grams of salt. Your teacher wants you to take the data and produce and a line graph using Excel. The data is as follows:

Grams of Salt	Density
0	1.00
5	1.03
10	1.07
15	1.11
20	1.14

1. Open an Excel Workbook. Notice that the columns are identified with letters and the rows are identified by numbers.

2. In the box "A1", type Grams of Salt.

3. In the box "B1", type Density. If you need to make a box larger, take your cursor to the top of the column and place it between two boxes until a double arrow appears. Now stretch the column to the size you need.

4. Enter the data in the boxes below each section. Be careful to enter the coordinating data in the correct row.

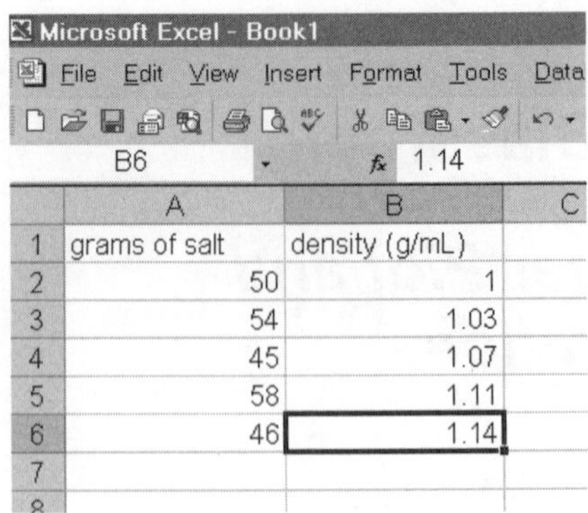

	A	B
1	grams of salt	density (g/mL)
2	50	1
3	54	1.03
4	45	1.07
5	58	1.11
6	46	1.14

5. To create a scatter plot graph, click on the small, colorful bar graph icon. This is called the Chart Wizard.

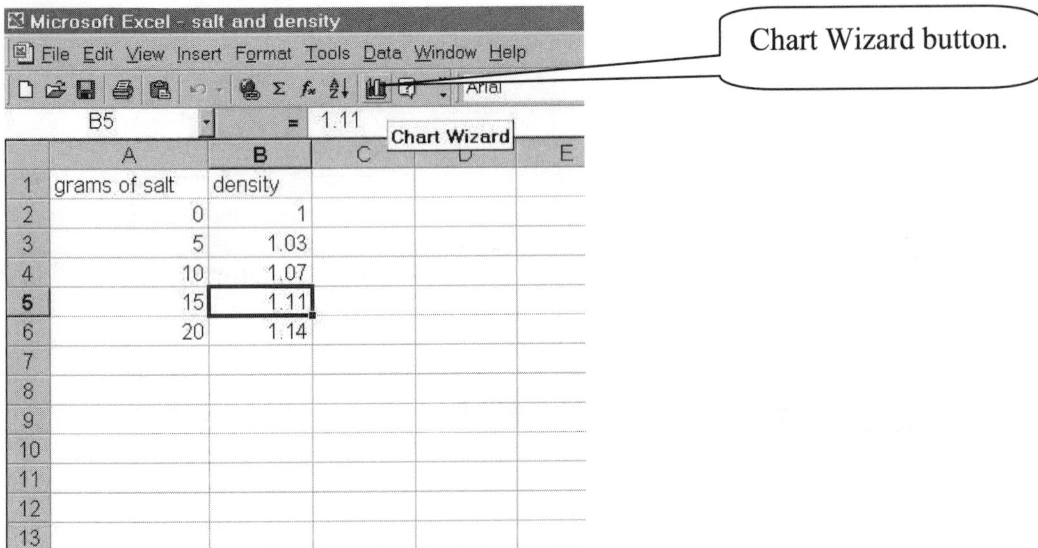

	A	B
1	grams of salt	density
2	0	1
3	5	1.03
4	10	1.07
5	15	1.11
6	20	1.14

6. After clicking on the chart wizard button a dialogue screen will appear that allows you to choose Chart type. Choose XY SCATTER as the type of chart. *Do not choose a subtype with any lines connecting the dots*. Click Next.

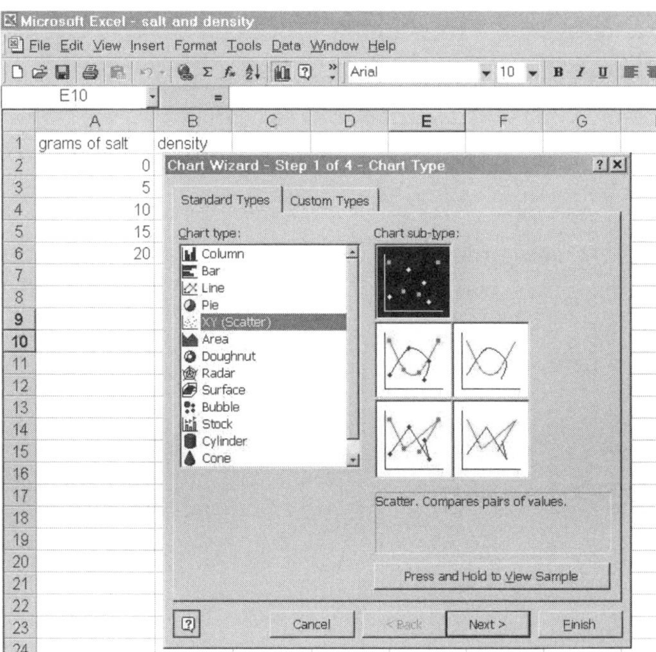

7. At the next dialogue box you will see a preview of your graph. Click the Series tab at the top of the box.

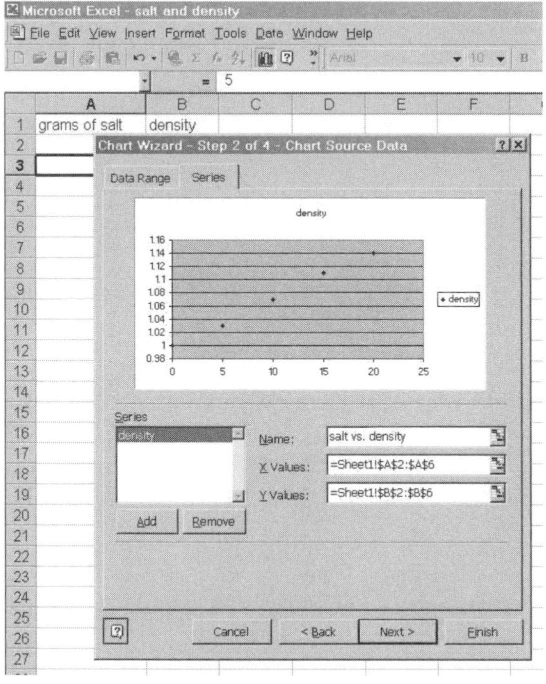

8. On the bottom left of this box it lists the series of data being plotted. To the right there is a blank cell where you can name this series. Name the series in terms of what variables are being graphed in the *y* vs. *x* format (i.e. density vs. salt).

9. Under the Name cell there are two cells that are labeled X values and Y values. The letters in these boxes correspond to the columns in the worksheet. Make sure the data is plotted on the correct axis. If they are not where you want them, click on the small button next to the X values button and it will take you back to your data table. Highlight the column you want to be plotted on your *x*-axis. Do the same for the *y*-axis.

10. When you are satisfied that the correct columns are being plotted and you have named your series, click Next. The next dialogue box, Chart Options, gives you the opportunity to label your axes (include units!). Click Next when you are finished.

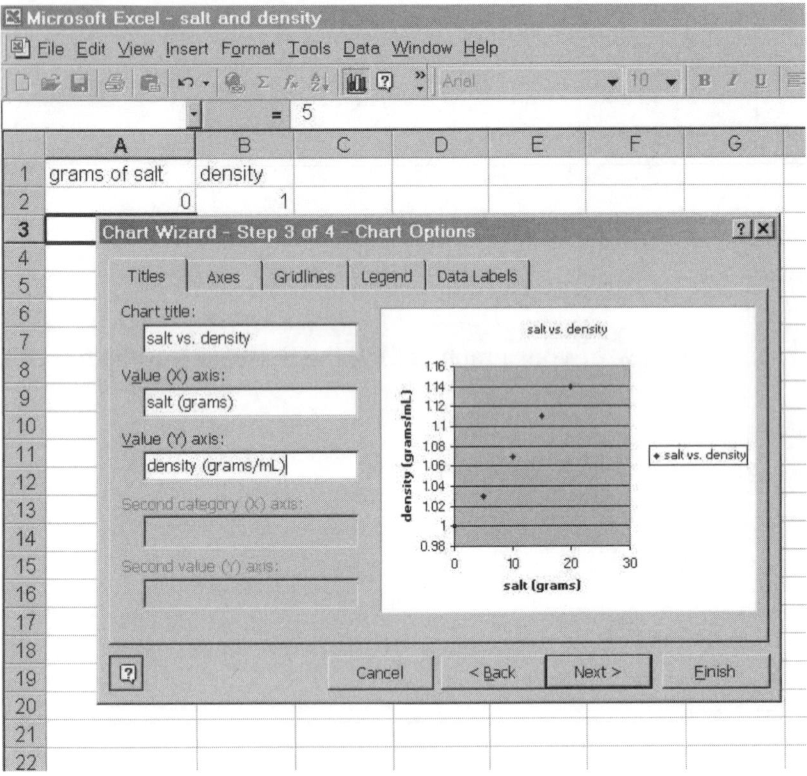

11. The final dialogue box will ask you if you want the graph to appear on your spreadsheet, or on a separate page. Click Finish when you are done.

12. To add a mathematically calculated regression line or best fit curve, choose Add Trendline from the Chart pull-down menu on your toolbar.

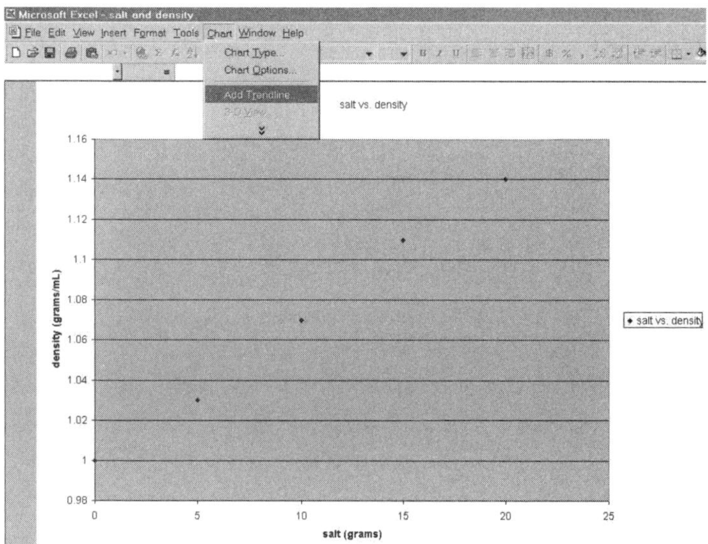

13. The next dialogue box allows you to choose the type of regression you desire.

14. The Options tab allows you to see the mathematical equation and correlation constant (R^2) if the boxes are checked for these options.

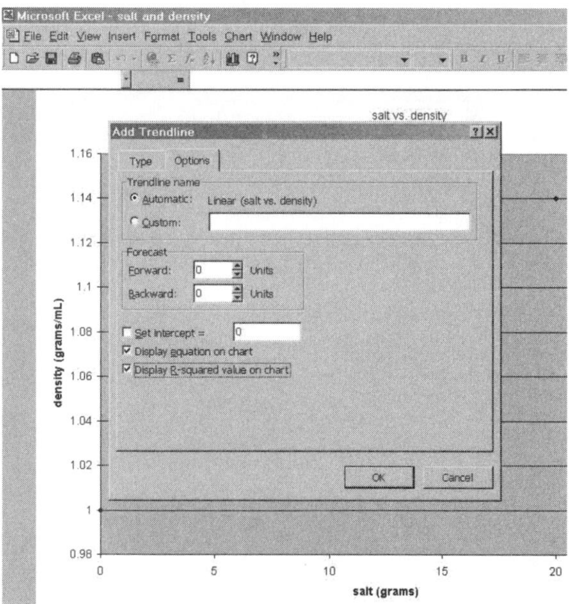

15. If you need to extrapolate data beyond the range of data you have calculated, increase the numbers in the forecast box.

16. If the preset y-intercept of 0 causes your graph axis and area to shift too much, set your y-intercept more within your data range.

17. You can also title this regression line something that tells about its origin (i.e. linear regression, power regression, etc.)

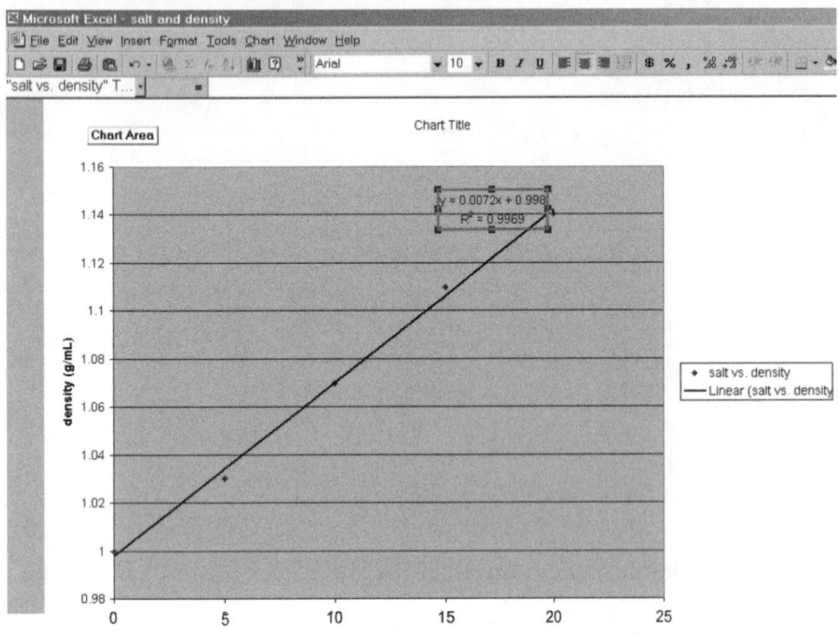

Microsoft Excel
Using Excel in the Science Classroom

Part IV: How Excel Can Manage Data

PURPOSE

To use the software program Microsoft Excel for manipulating data and determining statistical information.

MATERIALS

data from this handout
computer
Microsoft Excel software

PROCEDURE

The table below contains data collected to see how the circumference of the human head relates to the length of the face. For 5 students the data is as follows:

Circumference of Head (cm)	Length of face (cm)
50	11
54	13
45	10
58	14
46	9

1. Open an Excel Workbook. Notice that the columns are identified with letters and the rows are identified by numbers.

2. In the box “A1”, type Circumference of Head (cm).

3. In the box “B1”, type Length of Face (cm). If you need to make a box larger, take your cursor to the top of the column and place it between two boxes until the double arrows appear. Click and stretch the column to the size you need.

4. Enter the data in the boxes below each section. Be careful to enter the coordinating data in the same row.

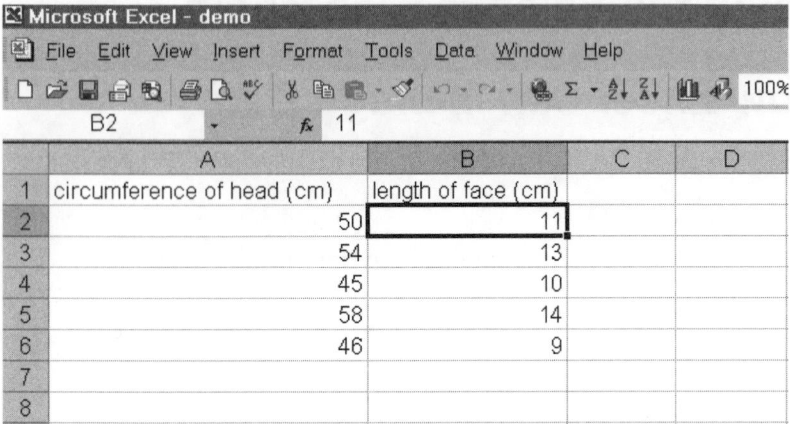

Microsoft Excel - demo

File Edit View Insert Format Tools Data Window Help

B2 | fx 11

	A	B	C	D
1	circumference of head (cm)	length of face (cm)		
2	50	11		
3	54	13		
4	45	10		
5	58	14		
6	46	9		
7				
8				

5. You are now going to have the computer calculate an index value for each person by dividing the length of the face by the circumference of the head. Label the new column in C1, skull index.

6. Click in box C2. Notice on the lower tool bar there is an empty box next to a small *fx*. Put your cursor in the box and type an equal sign (=).

7. Following the equal sign enter B2/A2. Press Enter.

8. Your spreadsheet will now reappear and you will see an index number in box C2. Right click your mouse on C2 and choose copy and then drag your mouse down column C for as far as there is data. This will apply the same formula to all of these cells.

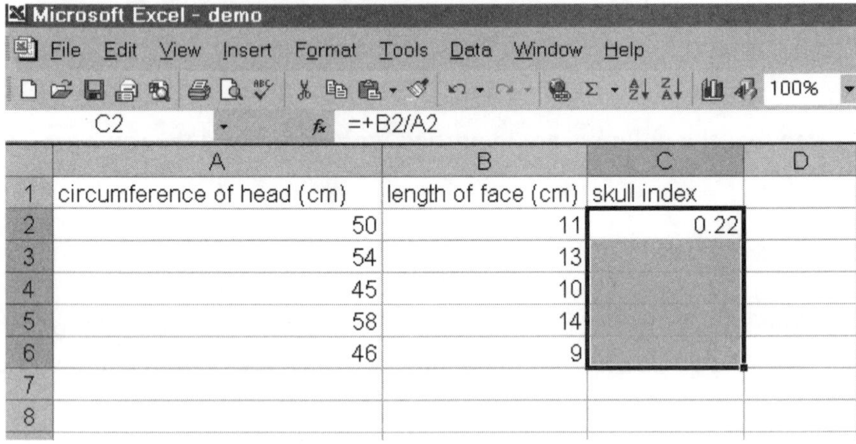

Microsoft Excel - demo

File Edit View Insert Format Tools Data Window Help

C2 | fx =+B2/A2

	A	B	C	D
1	circumference of head (cm)	length of face (cm)	skull index	
2	50	11	0.22	
3	54	13		
4	45	10		
5	58	14		
6	46	9		
7				
8				

9. Press enter. Excel will calculate and fill in all the indices.

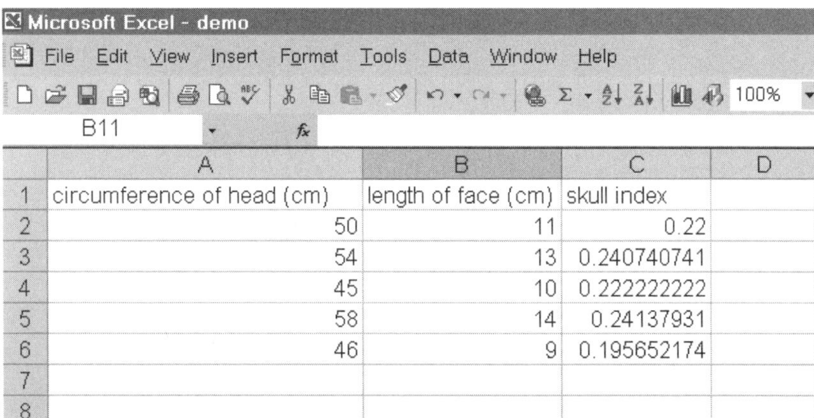

	A	B	C	D
1	circumference of head (cm)	length of face (cm)	skull index	
2	50	11	0.22	
3	54	13	0.240740741	
4	45	10	0.222222222	
5	58	14	0.24137931	
6	46	9	0.195652174	
7				
8				

10. To reduce the numbers to two significant figures, right click on the number in cell C3 and select format cell. Click in number and then choose 2 decimal places.

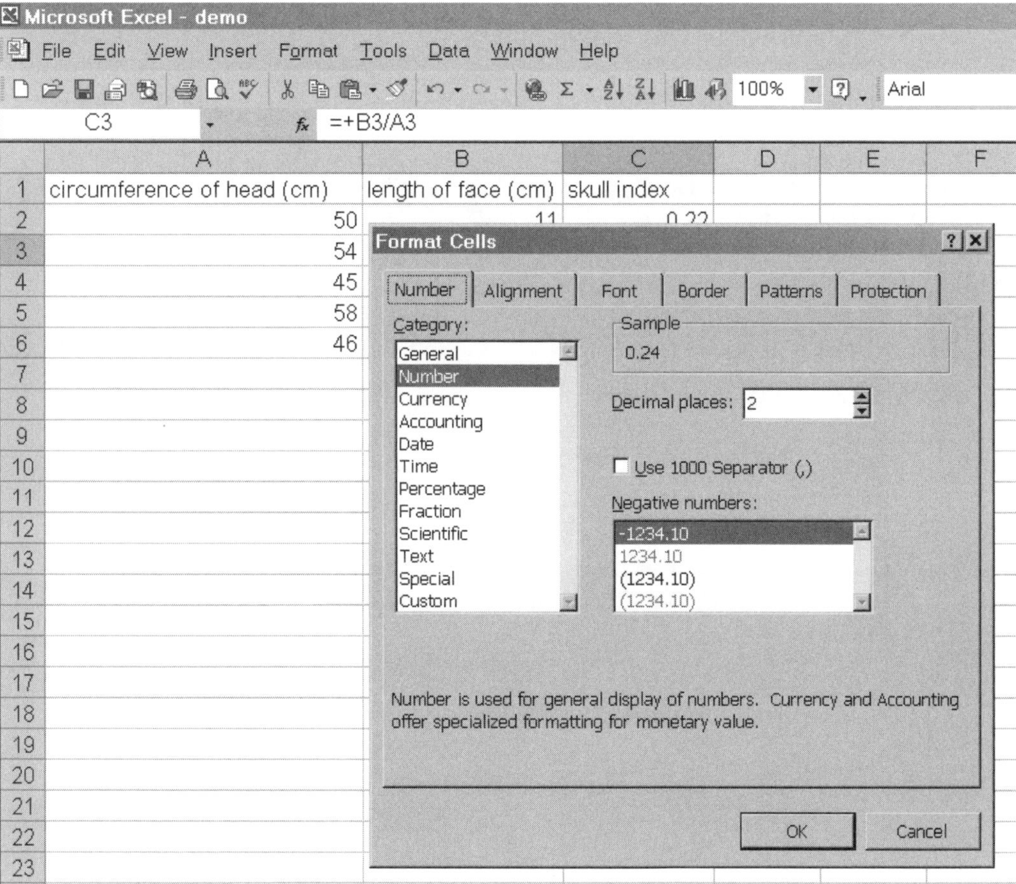

11. Click OK to exit this dialogue box and notice that one cell has changed to two decimal points. Right click on cell C3, select copy, and drag down the rest of your column. Press Enter and all numbers should change to two decimals.

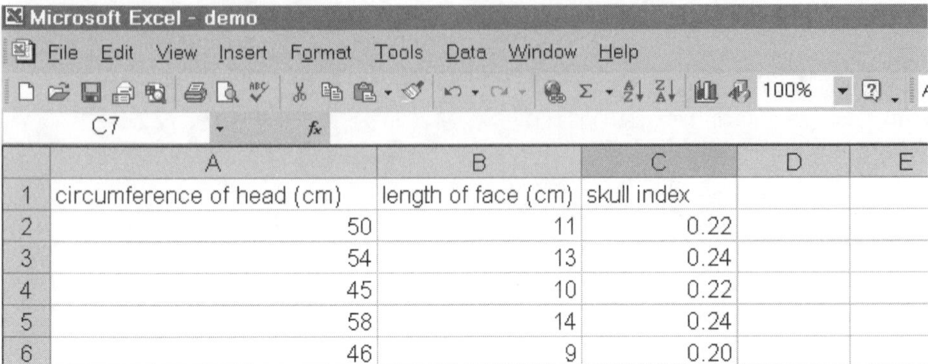

12. To calculate the average of the skull index, click in box C7, below your last index value.

13. Click on *fx* and choose average from the select a function box.

14. The next dialogue box asks you to identify what you want averaged. Highlight the five index values and then press Enter.

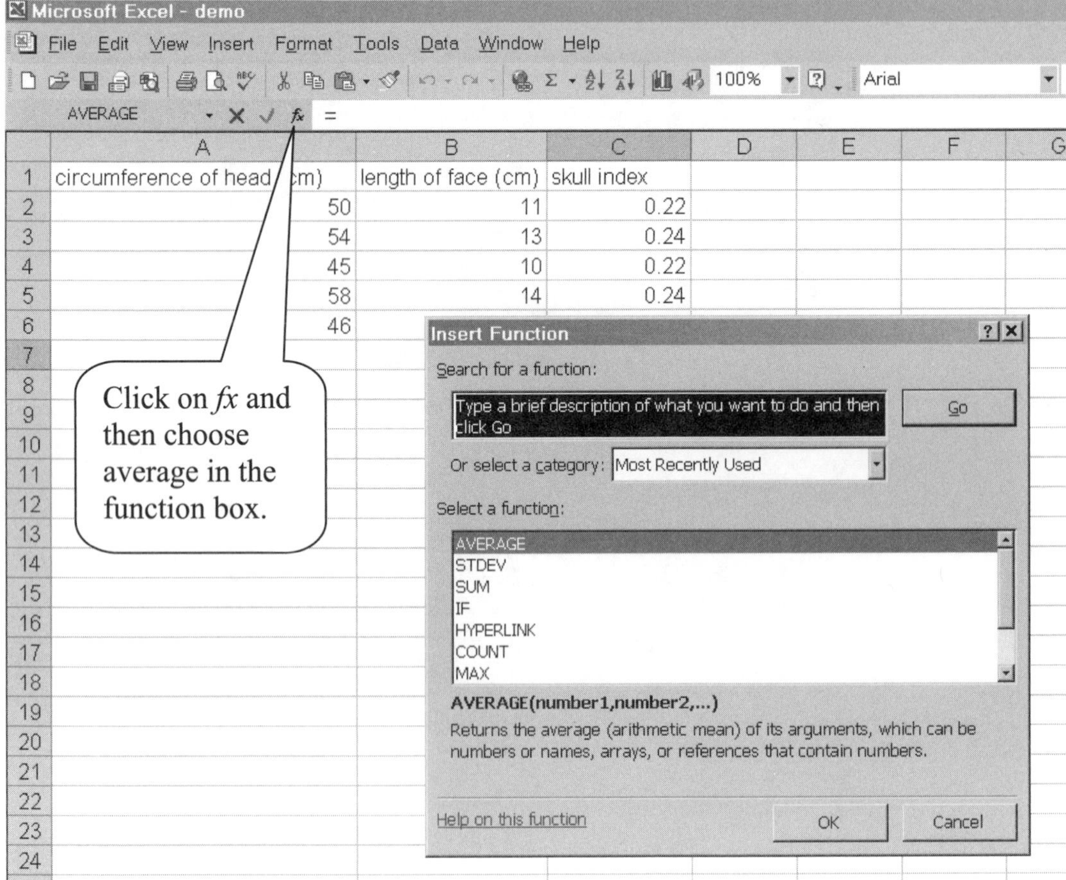

15. The next dialogue box asks you to identify what you want averaged. Highlight the five index values and then press enter. The average value will appear in cell C7.

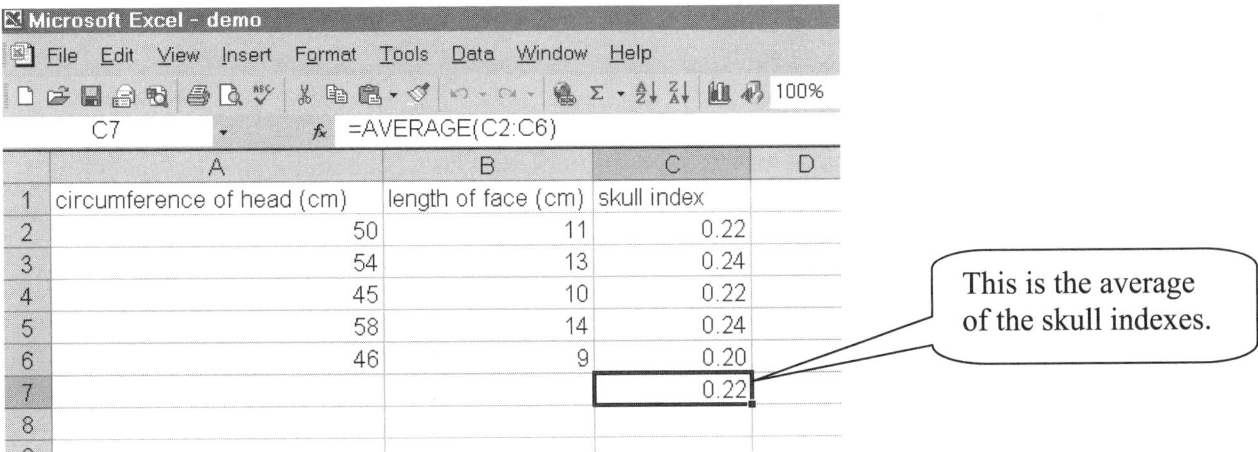
Microsoft Excel - demo

C7 | =AVERAGE(C2:C6)

	A	B	C	D
1	circumference of head (cm)	length of face (cm)	skull index	
2	50	11	0.22	
3	54	13	0.24	
4	45	10	0.22	
5	58	14	0.24	
6	46	9	0.20	
7			0.22	
8				

This is the average of the skull indexes.

16. To calculate the sum, standard deviation, maximum or minimum you would follow the same procedure except in step #13 choose the appropriate function.

17. To graph your data follow the procedure outlined in Microsoft Excel Part I or II.

Graphing Calculator
Using the TI-83+ in the Science Classroom

OBJECTIVE
Students will follow the teacher's oral instructions through a series of calculator menus and settings. Students will then enter sets of data to generate graphs, regression equations, and interpolations.

LEVEL
All

NATIONAL STANDARDS
UCP.1, UCP.2, A.1, A.2, E.1, E.2, G.2

TEKS
6.2 (E), 6.4(A)
7.2(E), 7.4(A)
8.2 (E), 8.4(A), 8.4(B)
IPC: 2(C)
Biology: 2(C)
Chemistry: 2(D)
Physics: 2(C), 2(E)

CONNECTIONS TO AP
All AP science courses use graphing skills to analyze data. The calculator is a tool to assist in manipulating data, seeing relationships, and drawing conclusions.

TIME FRAME
90 minutes or two class periods

MATERIALS

graphing calculator
teaching calculator
link cords
view screen and overhead projector
OR TI Presenter

TEACHER NOTES

During the past decade, the graphing calculator, along with its companion data collection devices and probes, have swept the educational field in both mathematics and science. More than any other technology, it has changed the way science is taught. Because we are able to obtain excellent data very rapidly, we may now spend our time in analysis and synthesis of the data. This tool has been found to be extremely effective helping students at all levels understand complex scientific systems.

Unfortunately, many teachers were in school in a time BC (before calculator) and the graphing calculator may seem intimidating. These notes are intended to be a quick guide to navigation of the graphing calculator. The notes are based on a TI-83+, however, other calculators have similar functions.

This document is meant to be a guide to start students on the graphing calculator. It is also designed for you to use as a reference. You should take the students through the basic steps of using the calculator. If a teaching calculator and view screen is available, it facilitates the presentation.

Suggested Teaching Procedure:

TIP #1: You cannot hurt your calculator.

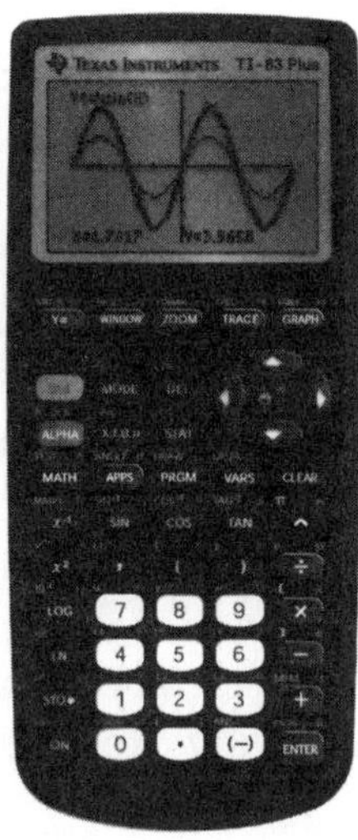

1. ***Layout and Important buttons:***

There are several important keys. Use the diagram to locate each of them.

[ENTER] Used to enter data and execute functions.

[2nd] Accesses the yellow function above each of the keys

[ALPHA] Accesses the green letters above the keys and allows for typing in text.

[◄][▲][►][▼] Operate like a mouse or computer arrows.

APPS Store applications which drive data collection devices or other study aids.

[Y=][WINDOW][ZOOM][TRACE] Graphing keys located across top that allow for graphing. They also serve as function keys for some applications.

2. ***Adjusting the brightness of the screen***

   Turn your calculator on. Use [2nd] [▲] or [2nd] [▼] arrow to increase or decrease the darkness of the printing on the screen. A number at the top right indicates your battery setting. If you are using rechargeable batteries, recharge the batteries when the setting level is at 6. You will get a warning if your batteries are running low.

3. ***Setting mode***

   Select [MODE] to see a selection menu, which looks like the one below. Use [◄][▲][►][▼] to move around on the screen. We will move through each line of this menu to see which of these functions you will most likely be using. Because many of the programs that drive the probes set the decimal at 2 or 3 decimal places, it is often necessary to re-set this function back to Float.

4. ***Using the CATALOG***

   The CATALOG has all of the calculator's functions listed in it. You will find the CATALOG by pressing [2nd][0]. We will use the catalog to turn on statistical diagnostics. When you turn on diagnostics, you will enable your calculator to provide you with a correlation of regression when you attempt to curve fit. The closer the value of the "r" is to 1.000 or –1.000, the better the data fit the function which is analyzed. You will notice when you open the catalog it is locked into [ALPHA] mode. You can tell this by the [A] in the middle of the curser. You can go to any letter in the alphabet by hitting that key. Press "D" which is above the [x^{-1}] button. Arrow down, [▼], to **Diagnostics On**. Select it by pressing [ENTER]. Execute it by pressing [ENTER] again. It will say, "DONE".

   Tip #1: If you are selecting a function from a menu of functions, pressing [ENTER] once selects the function. Pressing [ENTER] a second time actually executes the function.

   Tip #2: If you are having difficulty in navigation, read the entire screen!

5. ***Numbers in Scientific Notation***

   The EE function must be used. This is the [2nd] [,]. The [,] is located above the 7 key. It is very important that you not use the x 10[^] method of putting numbers in scientific notation. Operations that are commutative will work regardless of how the number is entered. Non-commutative operations will not be calculated properly.

- **Exercise:** Note how entering the number incorrectly affects the value of the answer: The calculator interprets 2.5E-2 as a single number and divides the numerator by that number. In the second, and incorrect example, the calculator interprets 2.5 as one factor and 10^{-2} as another factor, so the numerator is divided by 2.5 and multiplied by 10^{-2}.

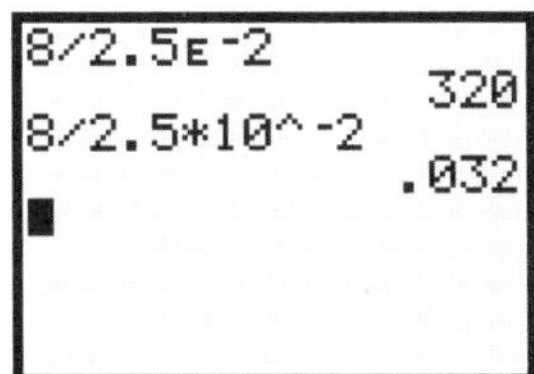

6. ***Managing memory in TI-83+***

Enter [2nd][+] to get the following screen. This menu allows you to do several important operations. The operations you will be using most include the following:

- **1: About** will tell you about your operating system. Because the 83+ has a flash memory, it is possible to constantly update your operating system as new advances come out. To do this, you will need a GraphLink cable and a program called TI Connect. You can download this program *free* from the Internet.
- **2: Mem Mgmt/Del** allows you to delete programs or applications you may not be using.
- 4: **ClrAllLists** is the easiest way to remove data from multiple lists.
- **7: Reset** will reset all of your memory. At this point you will have the choice of resetting your RAM or just your defaults.

One of the advantages to the TI-83+ is that it allows you to place programs into an archived file to free up memory that is needed to do other tasks. Programs that are in archived files have an * in front of them. To take them out of archives, arrow to 2:Mem Mgmt/Del. Arrow to 7:Prgm. Scroll to the program you wish to take out of archives and press [ENTER]. This feature toggles on and off.

7. ***Linking calculators and transferring programs***

Firmly press the link cord into both calculators. Press [2nd] [X,T,Θ,n] for the calculator receiving information.

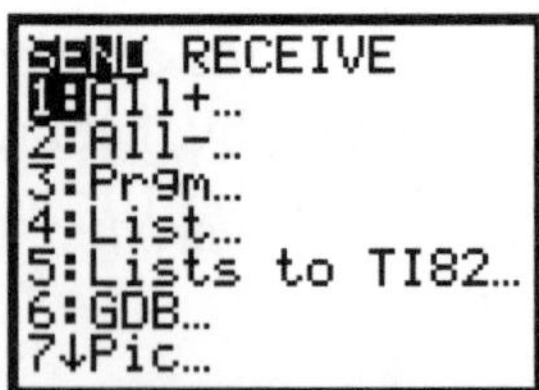

Arrow [▶] to receive and press [ENTER]. The screen should look like the one below.

Press [ENTER]. The receiving calculator should now display "Waiting".

Now set up the transmitting calculator by pressing [2nd] [X,T,Θ,n]. This window displays the various information or items available for transfer. Use the down arrow, [▼], to select the desired information or item to be transferred. Press [ENTER]. A new window appears displaying more specific items. Use the down arrow, [▼], to select the item to be transferred and press [ENTER]. Additional items may be selected for transfer using this same method.

When you have finished selecting your items, arrow, [▶], to TRANSMIT and press [ENTER]. If a selected item is already present on the receiving calculator, such as a List, a dialog box will appear allowing the user to overwrite that particular item.

8. ***Entering numbers in a list***

Numbers to be analyzed or graphed are stored in the calculator's lists. The lists are handled by the statistical function. Press the [STAT] key.

The operations you can perform from this menu are:

1: Edit: This is where you will go to enter or change numbers in the list

2: Sort A(: This will sort the numbers from smallest to largest

3: Sort D(: This will sort the numbers from largest to smallest

4: ClrList: This will allow you to clear a specific list, however you must enter an argument specifying which lists to clear.

5: SetUpEditor: Run this option if you need to reestablish lists that have been deleted or altered

9. ***Managing Lists***

Press [STAT] then select EDIT, press [ENTER]. You have 6 lists and may enter up to 999 data points in each list. You may also create additional lists with the LIST function. However, that is rarely needed for ordinary classroom work.

Clearing lists: There are three major ways to clear lists.

(a) Use the arrow key to move to the top of the list where it says L1. Press clear, press [ENTER]. That specific list will be cleared.

(b) Go to [2nd][+] to get to (mem)ory. Go to 4:ClearAllLists. Press [ENTER][ENTER].

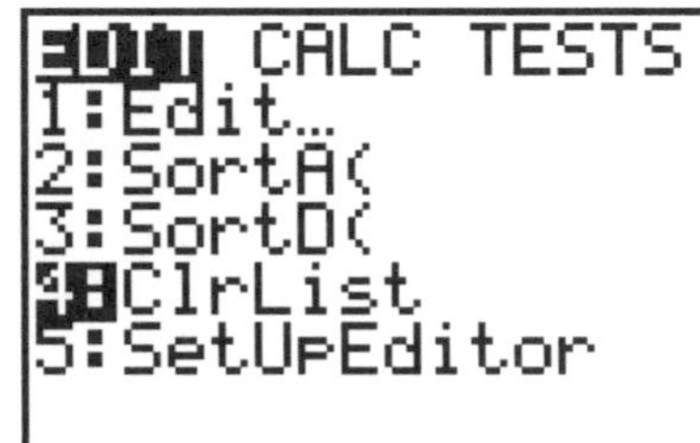

(c) Go to [STAT]. Arrow to 4:ClrList. Press [ENTER]. Clear Lists 1 and 2 by pressing [2nd][1][,][2nd][2]). This method will only clear the list(s) that you tell it to clear. If you want to clear multiple lists, separate them by commas.

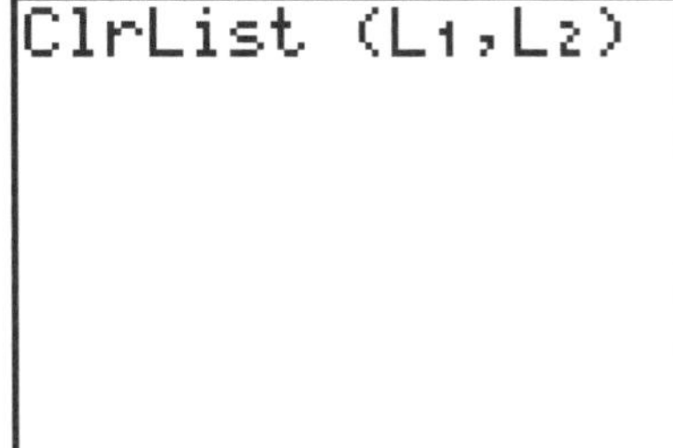

10. ***Working with sample data:***

This data is similar to the Middle Grades Chemistry lesson titled "*What's That Liquid?*". It involves a simple density problem.

A Physical Science class took the following data. Students poured a liquid into a graduated cylinder, and took the mass of several pre-determined volumes.

Enter the volume in L_1. Enter the mass in L_2.

Volume (mL)	Mass (g)
2	52.4
5	56.0
8	59.6
15	68.0
20	74.0

11. ***Clearing* [Y=] *functions***

Make sure that all equations from any previous user are removed from [Y=]. To do this, press [Y=] and position your cursor on the = sign and press [CLEAR].

12. ***Setting up STAT PLOT***

Go to [2nd] [Y=] to get to STAT PLOT.

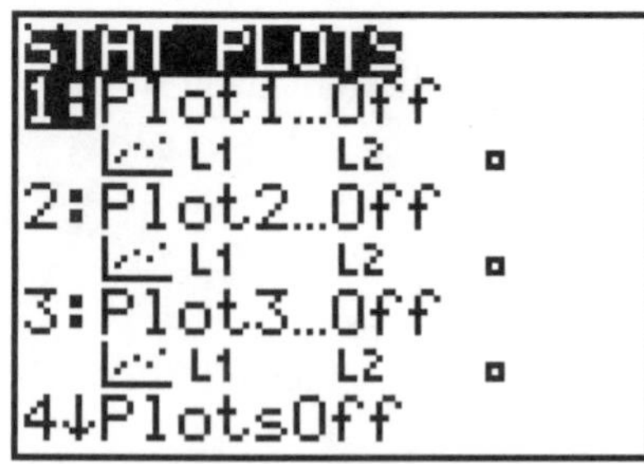

Press [ENTER] to get to Plot 1. Use the down arrow, [▼], and [ENTER] to turn on Plot 1. Move down a row. Select the first choice, a scatterplot. Be sure that XList is L_1 and YList is L_2. Arrow to the next row and choose a point protector style.

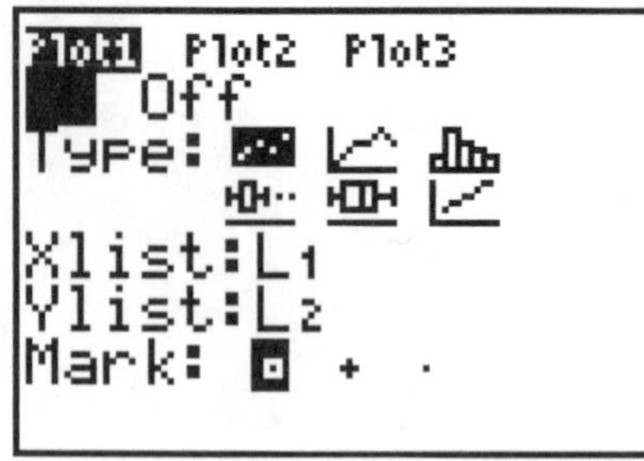

13. ***Graphing Statistical Data***

Statistical data are most easily graphed by using the ZOOMSTAT. Press [ZOOM] and arrow down to ZOOMSTAT. Since this is also the 9th choice, it can be accessed by [ZOOM] [9] as well. Your graph should now be shown on the screen.

```
ZOOM MEMORY
3↑Zoom Out
4:ZDecimal
5:ZSquare
6:ZStandard
7:ZTrig
8:ZInteger
9↓ZoomStat
```

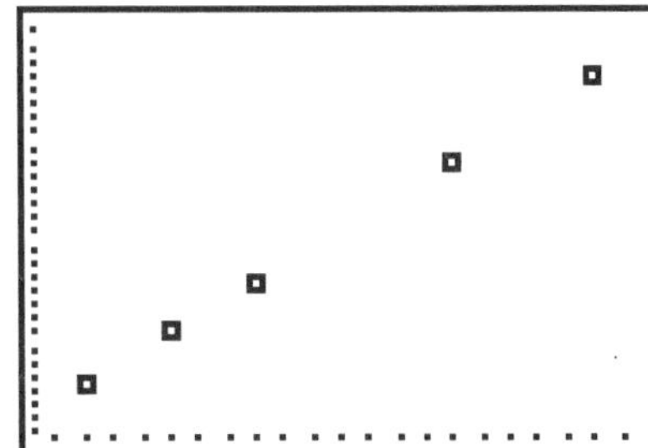

Tip #3: If you THINK you should be seeing a graph but you are not, try using [ZOOM] [9] to re-set your window to the range that includes your data.

14. ***Regressions***

If the data in your graph looks as though it might be linear, you should run a linear regression to find out the function. If students have done a considerable amount of graphing, they should understand the meaning of "line of best fit".A linear regression is simply a mathematical "line of best fit". Press [STAT] and side arrow [▶] over to CALC. Arrow down to 4:LinReg (ax + b). You should see the following screen.

```
EDIT CALC TESTS
1:1-Var Stats
2:2-Var Stats
3:Med-Med
4:LinReg(ax+b)
5:QuadReg
6:CubicReg
7↓QuartReg
```

Press [ENTER] [ENTER] to get to the screen shown below.

```
LinReg
 y=ax+b
 a=1.2
 b=50
 r²=1
 r=1
```

This will give a linear equation in the form of $\mathbf{y = ax + b}$. In this case, the function is $y = 1.2x + 50$. The correlation coefficient or correlation of regression is given by "r" and in this case is 1. That would indicate that this is a very nice linear function. In a real-life laboratory situation, the correlation coefficient would not usually be 1.00, but rather more like 0.999 or 0.998. Again, the closer the correlation coefficient is to 1.000 or -1.000, the more likely the data fit the function chosen.

15. ***Pasting the function into*** [Y=]

This is one of the more difficult sets of keystrokes to make. Open [Y=] Press [VARS]. Since we are dealing with statistical data, arrow down [▼] to Statistics. [ENTER]. Arrow over [▶] to EQ and [ENTER]. The equation for the line in the form of $y = ax + b$ will be pasted into your [Y=] menu. Now press [ZOOM] [9] to see both the scatterplot and the regression line.

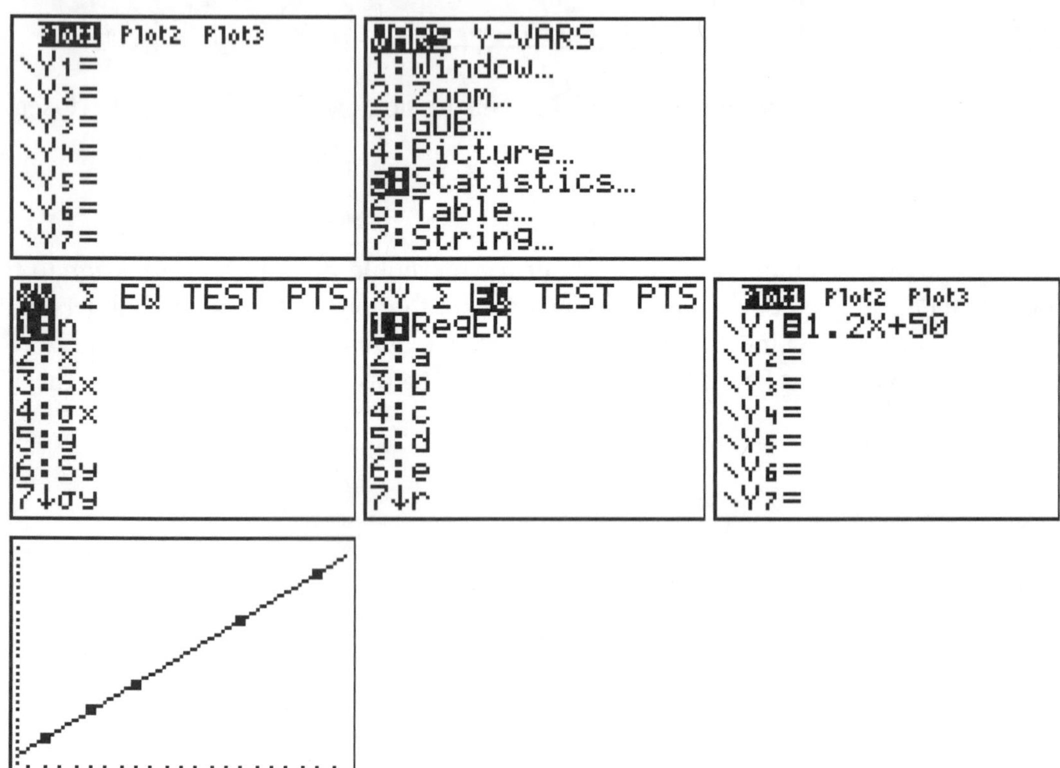

16. ***A second method to paste a function into*** [Y=]

If you are reasonably certain of the function that the data expresses, it is possible to run the regression and paste it into [Y=] in one step. Follow the screens to perform this set of operations. Start with [STAT] Calc 4:LinReg [ENTER]. Then go to [VARS] and side arrow [▶] to Y-VARS. Press [ENTER][ENTER][ENTER]. You can see the regression equation and it will be pasted into [Y=] at the same time. View your graph by pressing [ZOOM][9].

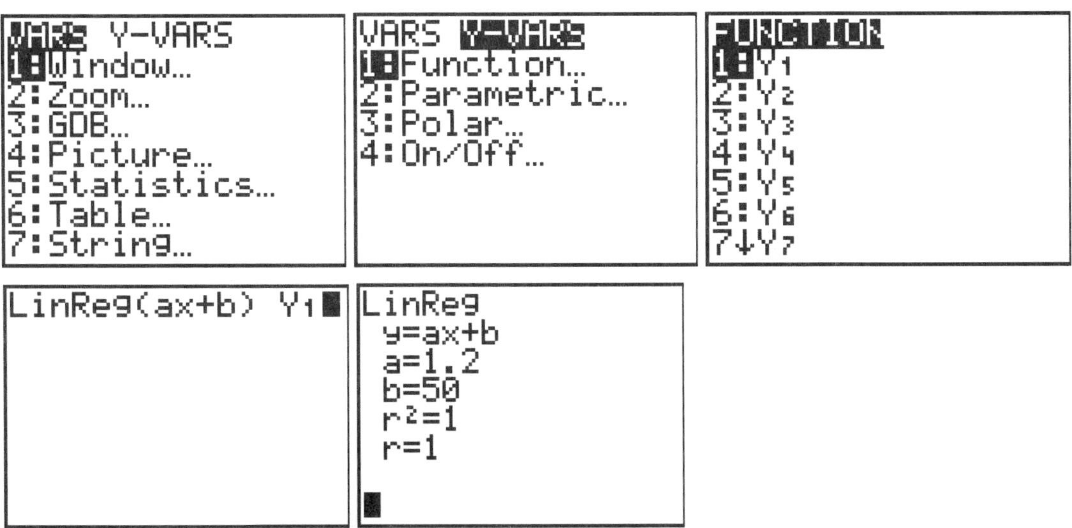

17. ***Tracing on the graph***

 Go to [TRACE]. In the upper left corner you should see a P1:L_1,L_2. This means that you are in a statistical plot of your data. Use the sideways arrows to move from data point to data point. The X and Y values are shown at the bottom of the screen. Now press the up arrow, [▲]. Notice that the designation in the upper right hand corner has changed, and you should have your regression equation on the screen. Your cursor is now on the regression line so that you may interpolate values. Again the X and Y values are shown at the bottom of the screen.

18. ***Helping students interpret the graph***

 This is a very good time to help students realize that a graph is simply a mathematical picture of a real world situation. You can talk about independent and dependent variables, rewrite the equation in terms of words, and discuss the meaning of the value for b. For the example that we were using, Y is the mass of the liquid and the graduated cylinder; X is the volume of the liquid. The slope of the line, rise over run, is mass/volume and thus is the density. The y-intercept is the mass of the empty graduated cylinder. The equation can then be expressed in words: Total Mass = Density x Volume + Mass of graduated cylinder.

19. ***Calculating a value***

 We would like to be able to use this equation that has been developed. Students can be asked to apply their algebraic knowledge to solve certain problems about the situation. They can also use the graph itself to interpret information and make predictions. Let us say that we would like to know the total mass when there is 17-mL of liquid in the graduated cylinder. Press [2nd][TRACE] to get to CALC. 1: VALUE. Press [ENTER] You will see a prompt at the bottom of your graph that says X=. Enter 17 and press [ENTER]. The mass of the cylinder and liquid will be displayed at the bottom.

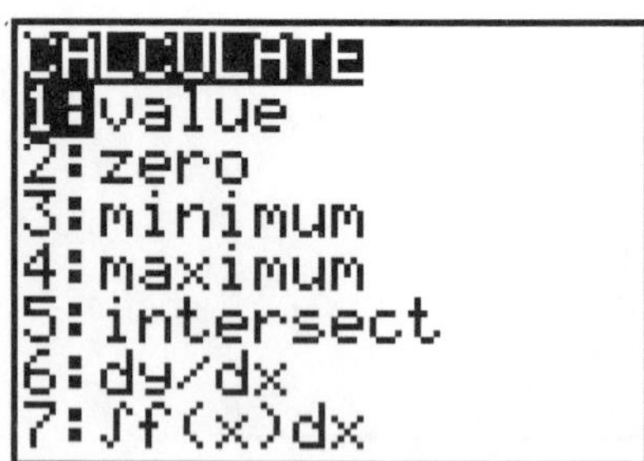

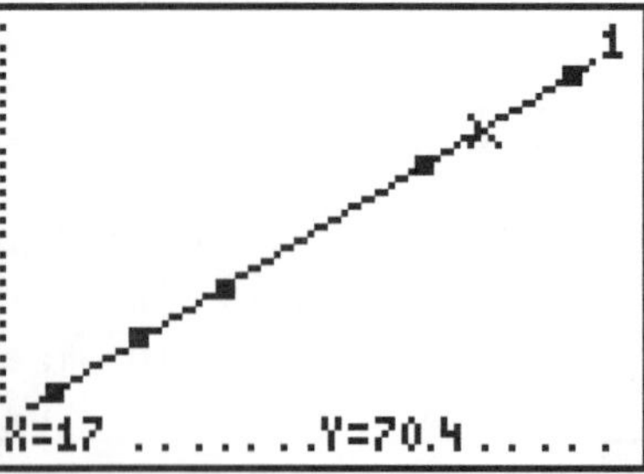

POSSIBLE ANSWERS TO THE CONCLUSION QUESTIONS

1. Enter the following data in your calculator and answer the questions.

   Pressure of a gas at various temperatures

L_1 Temperature (Kelvins)	L_2 Pressure (torr)
200	600
250	750
300	900
350	1050
400	1200

   a. What is the equation for this function?
   - $y=3x$

   b. What is the pressure when the temperature is 0 Kelvin?
   - 0 torr

2. Enter this as Pressure vs. Distance below the surface of water. Remember that the title of a graph is always the dependent variable (*y*-axis) vs. independent variable (*x*-axis). It is easiest if the *x* value is placed in L_1 and the y value is placed in L_2.

   Water pressure is measured at various depths in the ocean.

Distance below surface of water (feet)	Pressure (lb/in^2)
5	16.93
20	23.61
33	29.40
50	36.97

   a. What is the pressure at the surface of the water?
   - 14.7 lb/in^2

   b. What does this represent?
   - The atmospheric pressure at the surface.

3. On a distant planet, far, far away, the atmosphere is different from that of Earth. The speed of sound is not the same. The following data were collected:

Independent variable Temperature (Degrees Celsius)	Dependent variable Speed of sound (m/s)
0	276
10	289
20	302
30	315
50	341

   a. What is the slope of this line?
      - 1.3 m/s °C

   b. What is the temperature when the speed of sound is 295?
      - 14.6 °C

4. A small toy car is given a push to start it rolling down an inclined plane. The distance verses time is plotted as follows.

Time (seconds)	Distance (meters)
1	15.00
2	50.00
3	105.0
4	180.0
5	275.0
10	1050

   a. Does this look like a linear function?
      - No, it is curved.

   b. Can you describe the motion of the car in words?
      - The car is going faster and faster.

Challenge: What is the mathematical function that describes this data?

- $y = 10x^2 + 5x + 0$

What does the "b" in this particular equation represent?

- The initial speed before the car started down the inclined plane.

Graphing Calculator
Using the TI-83+ in the Science Classroom

The graphing calculator is an extremely valuable and powerful tool in both math and science classes. You will be using it in many of your classes during your educational experience. The document provided is intended to be a quick reference for many of the skills you will be using in science. Your teacher will walk you through the basic maneuvers and skills you are expected to know.

PURPOSE
In this activity you will practice using the graphing calculator to analyze data.

graphing calculator
pencil

PROCEDURE
Your teacher will take you through the basic functions found on your graphing calculator. You should follow along and do each of the steps on your own calculator. When you get home, go through the steps again on your own, using this guide.

1. ***Layout and important buttons***:

   There are several important keys. Use the diagram to locate each of them.

   [ENTER] Used to enter data and execute functions.

   [2nd] Accesses the yellow function above each of the keys

   [ALPHA] Accesses the green letters above the keys and allows for typing in text.

   [◄][▲][►][▼] Operate like a mouse or computer arrows.

   APPS Store applications which drive data collection devices or other study aids.

   [Y=][WINDOW][ZOOM][TRACE] Graphing keys located across top that allow for graphing. They also serve as function keys for some applications.

2. ***Adjusting the brightness of the screen***

   Turn your calculator on. Use [2nd] [▲] or [2nd] [▼] arrow to increase or decrease the darkness of the printing on the screen. A number at the top right indicates your battery setting. If you are using rechargeable batteries, recharge the batteries when the setting level is at 6. You will get a warning if your batteries are running low.

3. ***Setting mode***

Select [MODE] to see a selection menu, which looks like the one below. Use the [◄][▲][▼][►] arrows to move around on the screen. We will move through each line of this menu to see which of these functions you will most likely be using. Because many of the programs that drive the probes set the decimal at 2 or 3 decimal places, it is often necessary to re-set this function back to Float.

4. ***Using the CATALOG***

The CATALOG has all of the calculator's functions listed it. You will find the CATALOG by pressing [2nd][0]. We will use the catalog to turn on statistical diagnostics. When you turn on diagnostics, you will enable your calculator to provide you with a correlation of regression when you attempt to curve fit. The closer the value of the "r" is to 1.000 or –1.000, the better the data fit the function which is being analyzed. You will notice when you open the catalog it is locked into [ALPHA] mode. You can tell this by the Ⓐ in the middle of the curser. You can go to any letter in the alphabet by hitting that key. Press "D" which is above the [x^{-1}] button. Arrow down, [▼], to Diagnostics On. Select it by pressing [ENTER]. Execute it by pressing [ENTER] again. It will say, "DONE".

Tip #1: If you are selecting a function from a menu of functions, pressing [ENTER] once selects the function. Pressing [ENTER] a second time actually executes the function.

Tip #2: If you are having difficulty in navigation, read the entire screen!

5. ***Numbers in Scientific Notation***

The EE function must be used. This is the [2nd] [,]. The [,] is located above the 7. It is very important that you not use the x 10[^] method of putting numbers in scientific notation. Operations that are commutative will work regardless of how the number is entered. Non-commutative operations will not be calculated properly.

- **Exercise:** Note how entering the number incorrectly affects the value of the answer: The calculator interprets 2.5E-2 as a single number and divides the numerator by that number. In the second, and incorrect example, the calculator interprets 2.5 as one factor and 10^{-2} as another factor, so the numerator is divided by 2.5 and multiplied by 10^{-2}.

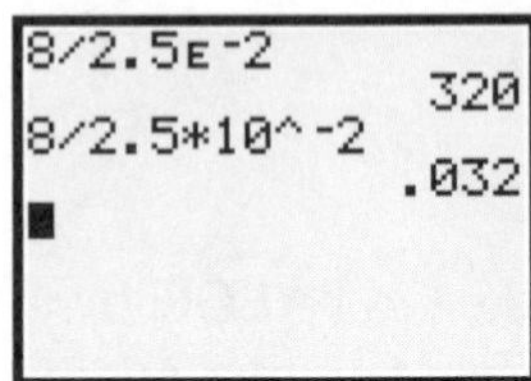

6. ***Managing memory in TI-83+***

Enter [2nd][+] to get the following screen. This menu allows you to do several important operations. The operations you will be using most include the following:

- **1: About** will tell you about your operating system. Because the 83+ has a flash memory, it is possible to constantly update your operating system as new advances come out. To do this, you will need a GraphLink cable and a program called TI Connect. You can download this free program from the Internet.
- **2: Mem Mgmt/Del** allows you to delete programs or applications you may not be using.
- 4: **ClrAllLists** is the easiest way to remove data from multiple lists.
- **7: Reset** will reset all of your memory or your defaults.

One of the advantages to the TI-83+ is that it allows you to place programs into an archived file to free up memory that is needed to do other tasks. Programs that are in archived files have an * in front of them. To take them out of archives, arrow to 2:Mem Mgmt/Del. Arrow to 7:Prgm. Scroll to the program you wish to take out of archives and press [ENTER]. This feature toggles on and off.

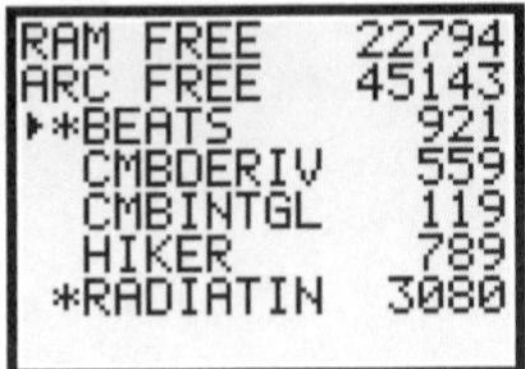

7. ***Linking calculators and transferring programs***

Firmly press in the link cord into both calculators. Press [2nd] [X,T,Θ,n] for the calculator receiving information.

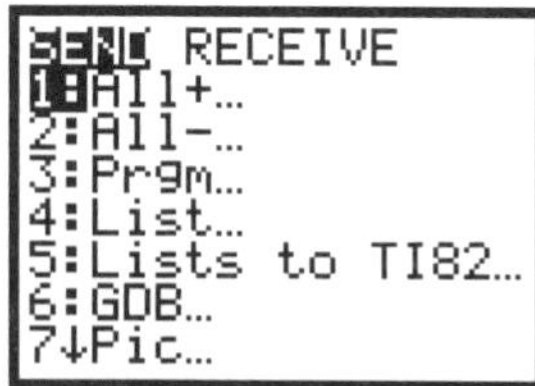

Arrow [▸] to receive and press [ENTER]. The screen should look like the one below.

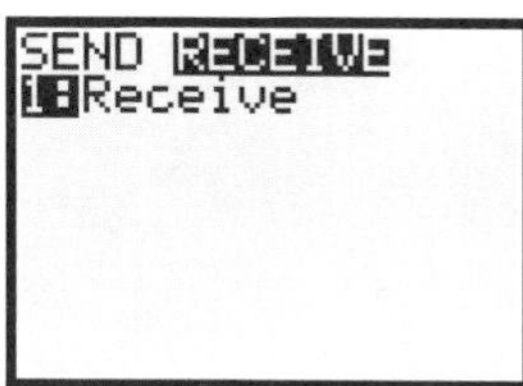

Press [ENTER]. The receiving calculator should now display "Waiting".

Now set up the transmitting calculator by pressing [2nd] [X,T,Θ,n]. This window displays the various information or items available for transfer. Use the down arrow, [▾], to select the desired information or item to be transferred. Press [ENTER]. A new window appears displaying more specific items. Use the down arrow, [▾], to select the item to be transferred and press [ENTER]. Additional items may be selected for transfer using this same method.

When you have finished selecting your items, arrow, [▸], to TRANSMIT and press [ENTER]. If a selected item is already present on the receiving calculator, such as a List, a dialog box will appear allowing the user to overwrite that particular item.

8. ***Entering numbers in a list***

Numbers to be analyzed or graphed are stored in the calculator's lists. The lists are handled by the statistical function. Press the [STAT] key.

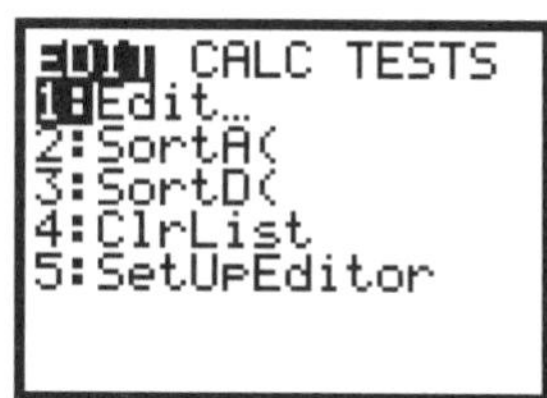

The operations you can perform from this menu are:

1: Edit: This is where you will go to enter or change numbers in the list

2: Sort A(: This will sort the numbers from smallest to largest

3: Sort D(: This will sort the numbers from largest to smallest

4: ClrList: This will allow you to clear a specific list, however you must enter an argument specifying which list(s) to clear. If you want to clear multiple lists, separate them by commas.

5: SetUpEditor: Run this option if you need to reestablish lists that have been deleted or altered

9. ***Managing Lists***

From the [STAT] EDIT screen, press [ENTER]. You have 6 lists and may enter up to 999 data points in each list. You may also create additional lists with the LIST function. However, that is rarely needed for ordinary classroom work.

Clearing lists: There are three major ways to clear lists.

(a) Use the arrow key to move to the top of the list where it says L1. Press clear, press [ENTER]. That specific list will be cleared.

L1	L2	L3 1
2	3	------
4	9	
6	15	
8	21	
10	28	
------	------	

L1 =

(b) Go to [2nd][+] to get to (mem)ory. Go to 4:ClearAllLists. Press [ENTER][ENTER].

(c) Go to [STAT]. Arrow to 4:ClrList. Press [ENTER]. Clear List 1 and 2 by pressing [2nd][1][,][2nd][2] and pressing [ENTER]. This method will only clear the lists that you tell it to clear.

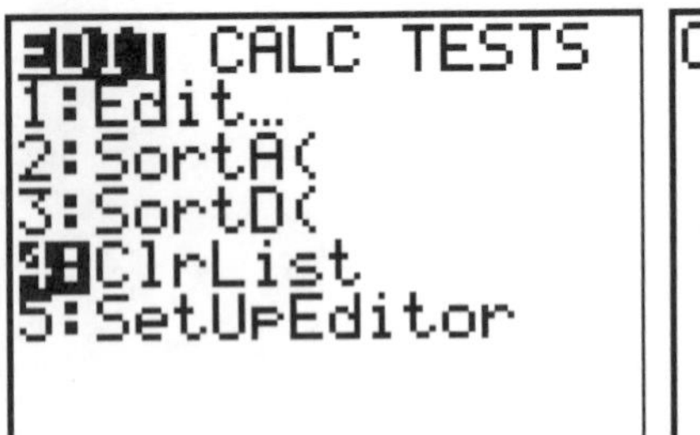

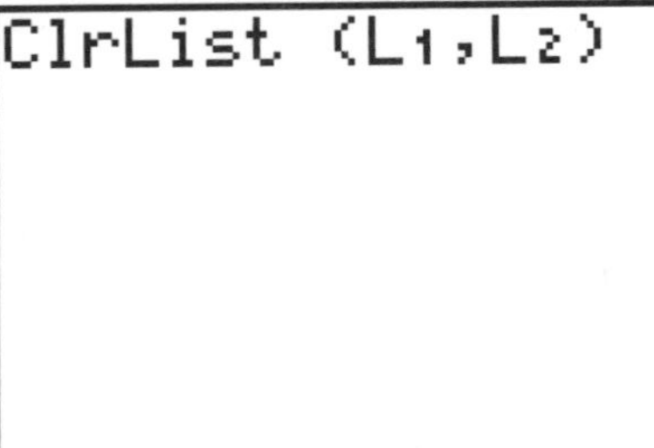

10. ***Working with sample data:***

Sample Data: Physical Science students poured liquid into a graduated cylinder and measured the mass of several pre-determined volumes.

Enter the volume in L_1. Enter the mass in L_2.

Volume (mL)	Mass (g)
2	52.4
5	56.0
8	59.6
15	68.0
20	74.0

11. ***Clearing [Y=] functions***

Make sure that all equations from any previous user are removed from [Y=]. To do this, press [Y=] and position your cursor on the = sign and press [CLEAR].

12. ***Setting up STAT PLOT***

Go to [2nd] [Y=] to get to STAT PLOT.

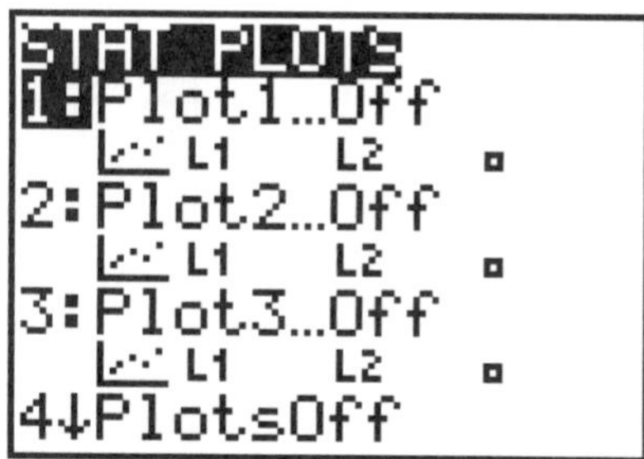

Press [ENTER] to get to Plot 1. Use the down arrow, [▼], and [ENTER] to turn on Plot 1. Move down a row. Select the first choice, a scatterplot. Be sure that XList is L_1 and YList is L_2. Arrow to the next row and choose a point protector style.

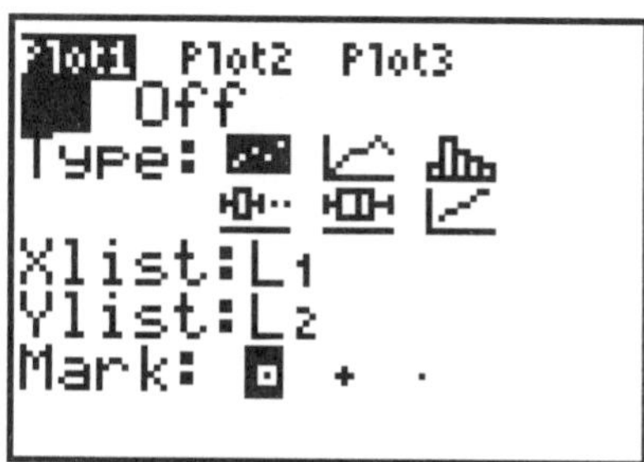

13. ***Graphing Statistical Data***

Statistical data are most easily graphed by using the ZOOMSTAT. Press [ZOOM] and arrow down to ZOOMSTAT. Since this is also the 9th choice, it can be accessed by [ZOOM] [9] as well. Your graph should now be shown on the screen.

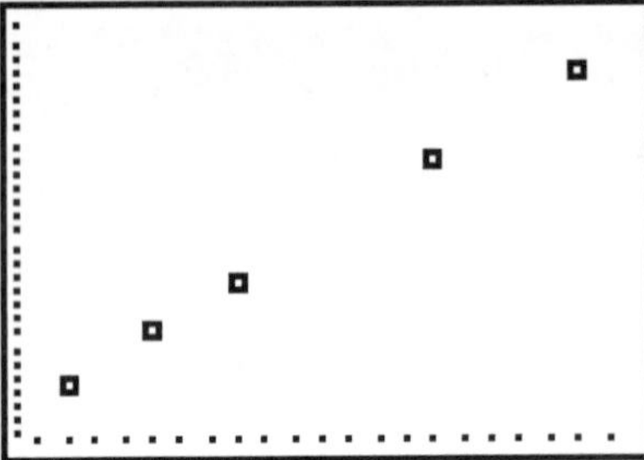

Tip #3: If you think you should be seeing a graph but you are not, try using [ZOOM] [9] to re-set your window to the range that includes your data.

14. ***Regressions***

If the data in your graph looks as though it might be linear, you should run a linear regression to find out the function. If students have done a considerable amount of graphing, they should understand the meaning of "line of best fit".A linear regression is simply a mathematical "line of best fit". Press [STAT] and side arrow [▶] over to CALC. Arrow down to 4:LinReg (ax + b). You should see the following screen.

```
EDIT CALC TESTS
1:1-Var Stats
2:2-Var Stats
3:Med-Med
4:LinReg(ax+b)
5:QuadReg
6:CubicReg
7↓QuartReg
```

Press [ENTER] [ENTER] to get to the screen shown below.

```
LinReg
 y=ax+b
 a=1.2
 b=50
 r²=1
 r=1
```

This will give a linear equation in the form of $\mathbf{y = ax + b}$. In this case, the function is $y = 1.2x + 50$. The correlation coefficient or correlation of regression is given by "r" and in this case is 1. That would indicate that this is a very nice linear function. In a real-life laboratory situation, the correlation coefficient would not usually be 1.00, but rather more like 0.999 or 0.998. Again, the closer the correlation coefficient is to 1.000 or –1.000, the more likely the data fit the function chosen.

15. ***Pasting the function into*** [Y=]

This is one of the more difficult sets of keystrokes to make. Open [Y=] Press [VARS]. Since we are dealing with statistical data, arrow down [▼] to Statistics. Press [ENTER]. Arrow over [▶] to EQ and press [ENTER]. The equation for the line in the form of $y = ax + b$ will be pasted into your [Y=] menu. Now press [ZOOM] [9] to see both the scatterplot and the regression line.

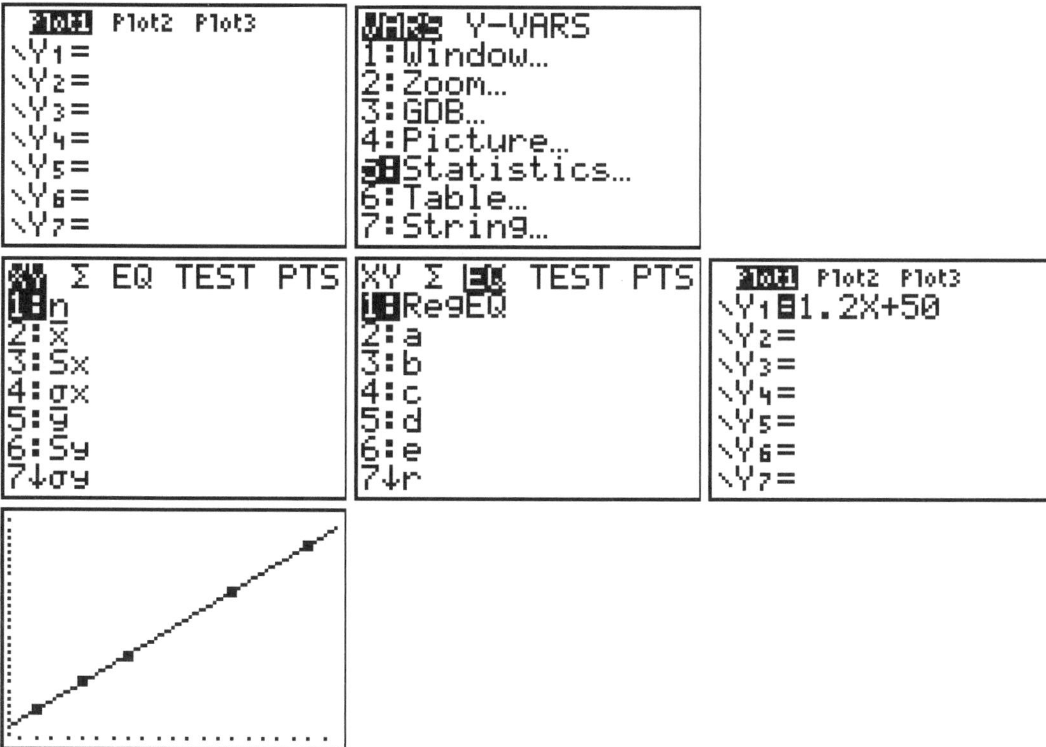

16. ***A second method to paste a function into*** [Y=]

If you are reasonably certain of the function that the data expresses, it is possible to run the regression and paste it into [Y=] in one step. Follow the screens to perform this set of operations. Start with [STAT] Calc 4:LinReg [ENTER]. Then go to [VARS] and side arrow [▶] to Y-VARS. Press [ENTER][ENTER][ENTER]. You can see the regression equation and it will be pasted into [Y=] at the same time. View your graph by pressing [ZOOM][9].

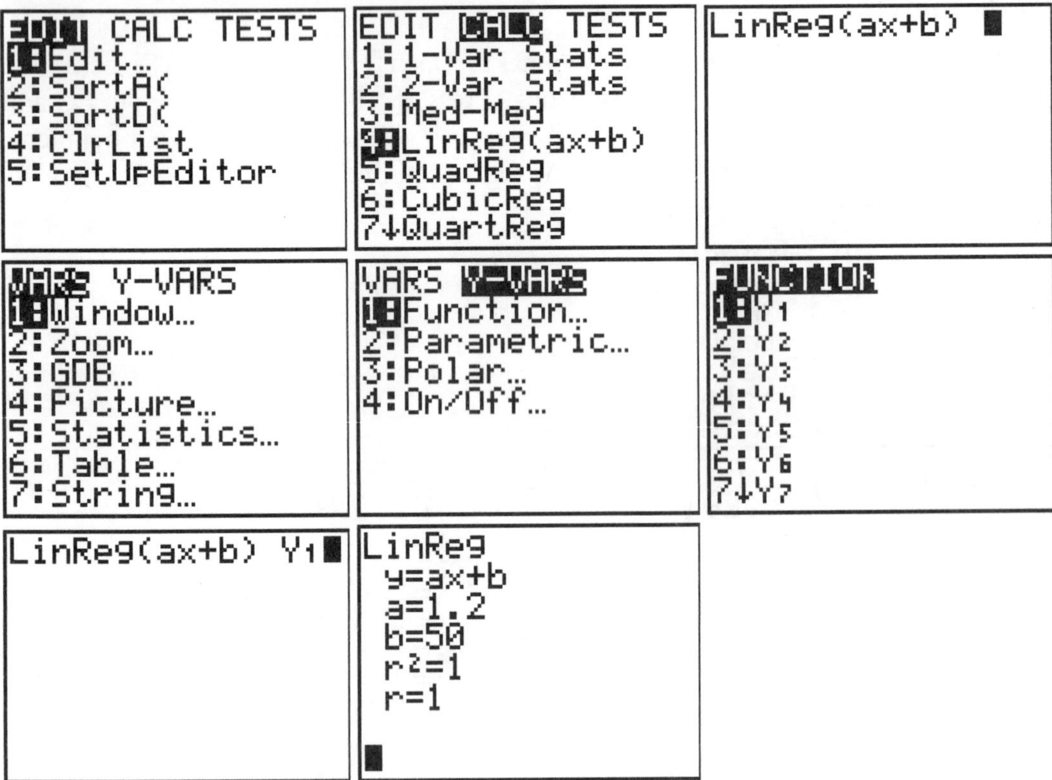

17. ***Tracing on the graph***

Press [TRACE]. In the upper left corner you should see a P1:L_1,L_2. This means that you are in a statistical plot of your data. Use the sideways arrows to move from data point to data point. The X and Y values are shown at the bottom of the screen. Now press the up arrow, [▲]. Notice that the designation in the upper right hand corner has changed, and you should have your regression equation on the screen. Your cursor is now on the regression line so that you may interpolate values. Again the X and Y values are shown at the bottom of the screen.

18. ***Calculating a value***

We would like to be able to use this equation that has been developed. Let us say that we would like to know the total mass when there is 17 mL of liquid in the graduated cylinder. Press [2nd][TRACE] to get to CALC. 1: VALUE. Press [ENTER]. You will see a prompt at the bottom of your graph that says X=. Enter 17 [ENTER]. The mass of the cylinder and liquid will be displayed at the bottom.

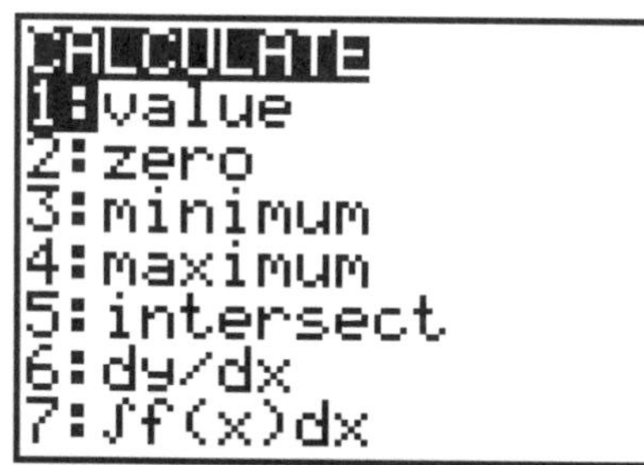

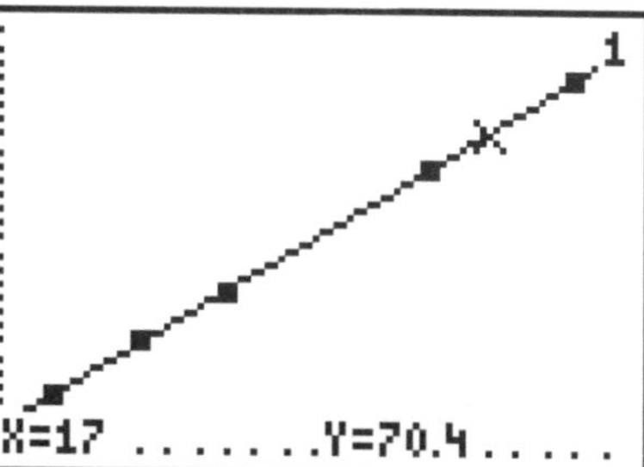

Name ______________________________

Period______________________________

Using the Graphing Calculator
Analysis of Data Sets

EXERCISES

1. Enter the following data in your calculator and answer the questions.

   Pressure of a gas at various temperatures

L_1 Temperature (Kelvins)	L_2 Pressure (torr)
200	600
250	750
300	900
350	1050
400	1200

   a. What is the equation for this function?

   b. What is the pressure when the temperature is 0 Kelvin?

2. Enter this as Pressure vs. Distance below the surface of water. Remember that the title of a graph is always the dependent variable (y-axis) vs. independent variable (x-axis). Analysis is easiest if the x value is placed in L_1 and the y value is placed in L_2.

   Water pressure is measured at various depths in the ocean.

Distance below surface of water (feet)	Pressure (lb/in^2)
5	16.93
20	23.61
33	29.40
50	36.97

a. What is the pressure at the surface of the water?

b. What does this represent?

3. On a distant planet, far, far away, the atmosphere is different from that of Earth. The speed of sound is not the same. The following data were collected:

Independent variable Temperature (Degrees Celsius)	Dependent variable Speed of sound (m/s)
0	276
10	289
20	302
30	315
50	341

a. What is the slope of this line?

b. What is the temperature when the speed of sound is 295?

4. A small toy car is given a push to start it rolling down an inclined plane. The distance verses time is collected as follows.

Time (seconds)	Distance (meters)
1	15.00
2	50.00
3	105.0
4	180.0
5	275.0
10	1050

a. Does this look like a linear function?

b. Can you describe the motion of the car in words?

Challenge: What is the mathematical function that describes this data?

What does the "b" in this particular equation represent?

Data Collection Devices
Determining the Amount of Energy Found in Food

OBJECTIVE
Students will determine the amount of energy in a sample of peanut and walnut. The students will calculate the percent yield and percent error in the experiment and evaluate the sources of error.

LEVEL
All

NATIONAL STANDARDS
UCP.2, UCP.3, A.1, B.5, C.5, E.1, E.2, G.2

TEKS
6.1(A), 6.2(A), 6.2(B), 6.2(C), 6.2(D), 6.2(E), 6.4(A), 6.9(A)
7.1(A), 7.2(A), 7.2(B), 7.2(C), 7.2(D), 7.2(E), 7.4(A)
8.1(A), 8.2(A), 8.2(B), 8.2(C), 8.2(D), 8.2(E), 8.4(A), 8.4(B), 8.10(A), 8.10(C)
IPC: 1(A), 2(A), 2(B), 2(C), 2(D), 8(A), 8(B)
Biology: 1(A), 2(A), 2(B), 2(C), 2(D), 9(A)
Chemistry: 1(A), 2(A), 2(B), 2(C), 2(D), 2(E), 5(A), 5(B), 5(C)
Physics: 1(A), 2(A), 2(B), 2(C), 2(D), 2(E), 2(F), 7(A), 7(B)

CONNECTIONS TO AP
Use of probeware enhances the AP student to accurately and quickly obtain data for a variety of experiments. Energy is a common theme studied in all AP science courses.

TIME FRAME
50 minutes

MATERIALS
(For a class of 28 working in pairs)

14 TI-83 or TI-83 + graphing calculators
(used for graphing calculator lab)
14 computers
(used for computer lab)
14 10 cc syringes
(used for graphing calculator lab)
14 sheets heavy aluminum foil
14 temperature probes
14 30 mL test tubes
1 package of peanuts
28 goggles
28 aprons

14 Lab Pro's or CBL's
(used for graphing calculator lab)
14 Lab Pro's or Serial Interface Device
(used for computer lab)
14 10 mL graduated cylinder
(used for computer lab)
14 packages of matches
14 calorimeters
1 balance
1 package of walnuts
14 test tube clamps
14 corks with inserted needle

TEACHER PAGES

TEACHER NOTES

The calorimeter can be made by using a tin vegetable can and drilling a center hole large enough to fit a 30 mL test tube and many small holes to vent. See diagram in step 11 of student procedures.

1. Calculator Information

Students will need a graphing calculator and either the CBL 2 (Calculator-Based Laboratory System) or LabPro® interface. TI 83, 83+, 85, 86, 89 or 92 calculators may be used. The temperature probe that is needed for this lab comes from Vernier. The calculators and interfaces can also be purchased from Vernier. The address is:

Vernier Software Company
13979 SW Millikan Way
Beaverton, OR 97005-2886
(503)-277-2299
www.vernier.com

2. Calculator Software Information

This activity uses DATAMATE as the data collection program. This program must be updated periodically and can be downloaded free from Vernier. A TI-GraphLink cable is necessary for connecting the CBL 2 or LabPro to a computer for download or upload processes. Once updated, it can be installed on the graphing calculators directly from the CBL 2 or LabPro.

3. Computer Hardware Information

Macintosh System Requirements
Power Macintosh or newer computer
At least 32 MB of RAM
Operating System 7.5 or newer

Windows System Requirements
Windows 98/NT/ME/2000/XP
At least 32 MB of RAM
Pentium processor-based or compatible PC

4. Computer Software Information

The software that is used in conjunction with the temperature probe is **Logger Pro 3® Software**. It can be purchased for the PC or Mac. Start the program. Under file there will be a number of folders, open "Probes & Sensors", then open "Temperature Probes", then open, "Stainless Steel Temp Probe.MBL" or "Direct Connect Temp Probe.MBL" for the Direct Connect Temperature probe.

One nice feature of Logger Pro Software is that there are templates for the probes already installed. They can be modified to fit your own experiment and then saved under your own title for the students. The following steps work nicely for this experiment:

- It is important that you try this lab and software settings before working with students so that you can modify the templates or instructions to meet the particular needs of your own experiment.
- Be sure you have the experimental apparatus set up for this experiment by connecting the interface to the computer through the modem port and the temperature probe to Port 1 or Ch 1on the interface.
- Pull down the **Set Up Menu** and highlight **Data Collection**. Then click on **Mode**. Make sure that **Real Time Collect** is selected. Next, click on **Sampling** and select **minutes** and key in **5**. Below that, move the slide bar so that 10 pts/minute is selected. Press **OK**.
- The axes of the graph are modified by first highlighting the last number on the *x*-axis, Time (minutes). Now type in the amount of time that you wish to run the experiment. Type in 5. This means that the experiment will run for five minutes. The *y*-axis should have a range of 15-105. If it does not have this range, highlight the top number, type in 105 and then highlight the lower number and type in 15. The temperature of the water should increase 20-30 degrees Celsius.
- Once you have accomplished this, you can save your experiment so that you do not have to set up the software again. Pull down the **File Menu** and highlight **Save Experiment As**. A dialog box will appear. Type in the name you would like to use for your lab. Decide where you want to save this on the hard drive or a disk. Highlight **Save**. Another dialog box will appear and ask you if you would like to save the calibration for this experiment. Click **Yes**. Now the experiment can be used by your students without having to set up the software. As long as you use that same probe with the same computer, the calibration should be good for a long while.

TEACHER PAGES

ANSWERS TO PRE-LAB QUESTIONS

1. After reading the background information, define the terms autotroph and heterotroph.
   - An autotroph can make its own energy rich organic compounds from inorganic compounds. Heterotrophs can not make their own energy rich organic compounds and must obtain them from the environment.

2. What are two purposes of food?
   - Food is providing energy to the organism and comprises the building blocks for synthesizing their own polymers.

3. What is free energy?
   - Free energy is the amount of energy available to do work.

4. What is entropy?
   - Entropy is a measurement of disorder in the system.

5. What is a calorie, a Calorie and a kilocalorie?
   - A calorie is the amount energy it takes to raise the temperature of one gram of water, one degree Celsius. One thousand calories is equal to one Calorie or one kilocalorie.

6. Write the equations to be used to determine the number of calories, percent yield, and percent error.

$$\text{calories} = (\text{Final Temperature} - \text{Beginning Temperature}) * 10\text{ g}$$

$$\text{Kilocalories or Calories} = \frac{\text{calories}}{1000}$$

$$\text{calories} = 10\text{ g } H_2O \times (\text{final temperature} - \text{initial temperature}) \times 1\frac{\text{calorie}}{\text{g}\bullet{}^{\circ}\text{C}}$$

$$\text{Kilocalories or Calories} = \frac{\text{calories}}{1000}$$

$$\frac{\text{kcal}}{\text{g of food}} = \frac{\text{kcal}}{\text{mass of sample}}$$

$$\text{Percent Error} = \frac{(\text{Experimental Value} - \text{Actual Value})}{\text{Actual Value}} \times 100$$

$$\text{Percent Yield} = \frac{\text{Experimental Value}}{\text{Actual Value}} \times 100$$

$$\text{Percent Error} = \frac{(\text{Experimental Value} - \text{Actual Value}) * 100}{\text{Actual Value}}$$

POSSIBLE ANSWERS TO THE CONCLUSION QUESTIONS AND SAMPLE DATA

Data Table						
Experiment	**Mass of Sample**	**Temperature Before Burning**	**Temperature After Burning**	**# of calories**	**# of kilocalories**	**# of kilocalories/gram**
Peanut # 1	0.23	22	62	400	0.4	1.74
Peanut # 2	0.2	21.5	65	435	0.435	2.18
Peanut # 3	0.24	22	61	390	0.39	1.63
Average						1.85
Walnut # 1	0.2	22	67	450	0.45	2.25
Walnut # 2	0.18	22	62	400	0.4	2.22
Walnut # 3	0.21	21.5	39	475	0.475	2.26
Average						2.24

1. Which nut contained the greatest number of kilocalories per gram?
   - The walnut has the greatest number of kilocalories per gram 2.24 kc/g

2. What was the shape of the graph displayed on your screen? What relationship did it establish?
   - The relationship is not linear. At first it increases and then slows down.

3. The nutritional labels show that peanuts are 6.00 kcal/gram and walnuts are 7.02 kcal/gram. What was your percent yield and was it greater than or less than the actual value?
   - Walnut = (2.24 / 7.02) * 100 = 31.9%
   - Peanut = (1.85 / 6.00) * 100 = 30.1%

4. Give two reasons why your answer varied from the actual values.
   a. One reason the percent yield is less is that some of the nut was not burned.
   b. A second is a large percent of the heat escaped into the environment and did not go into the test tube.

5. What is your percent error? Do you think that it is acceptable? Why or why not?
   - The percent error is 68% and 69% respectively

6. Nuts are high in lipids. What foods might you investigate to determine their calorie content for carbohydrates? Proteins?
   - Answers will vary.

TEACHER PAGES

7. A student fails to replace the 10 grams of water in the test tube between the second and third trials for the walnut. How will this error affect the calculated energy result? Your answer should clearly state that the calculated value will increase, decrease or remain the same. Mathematically justify your answer.
   - The calculated energy value will decrease. The water was extremely hot as a result of trial 2. There is not sufficient time between trials for the very hot water to cool back down to room temperature. This will cause the change in temperature (ΔT) to be reported as too low.

   Since $\text{Energy} = \text{mass} \times \Delta T \times 1 \frac{\text{calorie}}{\text{g} \bullet °\text{C}}$ the quantity of energy will be reported as too low.

REFERENCE

Milani, Jean P., Revision Coordinator. *Biological Science, A Molecular Approach*. Dubuque: Kendall Hunt Publishing Company, 1990. pp. 628-630

Data Collection Devices
Determining the Amount of Energy Found in Food Using a Graphing Calculator

All living systems require energy. In the case of autotrophs such as plants and related organisms, they have the ability to take inorganic compounds from the environment and make high energy compounds required for their survival. Heterotrophs, however, are unable to synthesize high energy, organic nutrients from inorganic compounds and therefore must obtain these high-energy nutrients from the environment. From a human point of view, their nutrition translates into our food. All food contains energy. The amount it contains depends on the type of food it is and the organic compounds it contains.

Food is a source of both energy and the basic building blocks needed for the synthesis of macromolecules. Living systems follow the 1st and 2nd Laws of Thermodynamics. The first law states that energy cannot be created or destroyed but only converted from one form to another. This energy conversion is never 100%. Energy is always lost in the form of heat. For living systems, this is especially true. The energy content in food is converted from chemical energy to mechanical energy as muscles contract. In fireflies, the chemical energy found in food is converted to electromagnetic energy as they light up the summer skies with their bioluminescence. It is also possible to convert the chemical energy in a candy bar into another form of chemical energy. The sugar in the candy converts to fat. The fat will be later stored in our adipose tissue. As stated earlier, heat energy always accompanies any energy transfer. This type of energy is never found by itself but is always associated with one of the other forms of energy. In each of the previous examples, as energy converts from one form to another a certain amount of heat energy was released.

Free energy is the amount of energy available to do work. Heat energy that is released during an energy conversion is considered to be wasted energy and is not available to do work. This explains why energy conversions are not 100% efficient. Suppose that a candy bar had 180 kilocalories of chemical energy. Suppose you ate the candy bar in order to have mechanical energy available to play a volleyball game. At best, your body would only use 72 kilocalories of the 180 available and the rest would be released as heat energy. That's over 108 kilocalories lost!

180 kcal Total Energy				180 kcal Total Energy
Candy Bar	—— ENERGY CONVERSION →	Muscle Movement	+	Heat Energy
180 kcal	————————→	72 kcal	+	108 kcal
Free Energy	————————→	Free Energy	+	Wasted Energy

This brings us to the Second Law of Thermodynamics. Suppose there is a closed system which means energy can not enter or leave the system. This would mean that its *total* energy content could not increase or decease, it must therefore remain constant. As time passes, energy conversions occur, and more and more of the free energy available to do work converts to unusable heat energy. The unusable heat energy is unavailable to do work. If this process continued indefinitely, then eventually there would be no free energy and the system would decease in its order, becoming more chaotic. The Second

Law of Thermodynamics states that in a closed system, one in which energy can not enter or leave, there will be an increase in the system's disorder. Entropy is a measurement of the disorder of a system.

In biology, energy is often measured in calories. A calorie is the amount of heat energy needed to raise the temperature of one gram of water one degree Celsius. The amount of energy found in food is measured in kilocalories (symbolized by C or called Calories). So if a candy bar says it has 180 Calories, it really means that it has 180,000 calories. A calorimeter is used to determine the amount of calories found in food.

In this investigation you will burn a sample of food with known mass. Above the burning food sample is a test tube of water that contains 10 mL of water or 10 g of water. The temperature of the water is recorded before and after the sample is burned. The change in temperature, ΔT is calculated.

By using the equation $\text{Energy} = \text{mass} \times \Delta T \times 1 \frac{\text{calorie}}{\text{g} \bullet {}^\circ\text{C}}$ the change in temperature, ΔT, is multiplied by the number of grams of water used (10 g) and the specific heat of the water. This allows you to calculate the amount of heat energy absorbed by the water. Since the energy absorbed by the water was the result of the burning the food, it also represents the amount of energy contained in the food sample. Since the amount of energy you calculated is in calories, it needs to be converted to kilocalories using the relationship, 1000 calories equals one kilocalories or Calorie. To make the energy relative to the particular sample you used, the energy value should be divided by the mass of your sample. This will allow the energy per gram of your sample to be compared to the energy per gram of other samples.

$$\text{calories} = 10\ \text{g}\ H_2O \times (\text{final temperature} - \text{initial temperature}) \times 1 \frac{\text{calorie}}{\text{g} \bullet {}^\circ\text{C}}$$

$$\text{Kilocalories or Calories} = \frac{\text{calories}}{1000}$$

$$\frac{\text{kcal}}{\text{g of food}} = \frac{\text{kcal}}{\text{mass of sample}}$$

This lab will be repeated three times to obtain an average energy value and increase the validity of your experiment. Your teacher will give you the actual number of the Calories found in the food sample used. You are to determine the percent yield.

$$\text{Percent Yield} = \frac{\text{Experimental Value}}{\text{Actual Value}} \times 100$$

You can also determine the percent error by using the formula below:

$$\text{Percent Error} = \frac{(\text{Experimental Value} - \text{Actual Value})}{\text{Actual Value}} \times 100$$

TEACHER PAGES

PURPOSE

In this activity you will determine the amount of energy found in a walnut and a peanut by using a calorimeter and compare it to the actual value.

MATERIALS

- temperature probe
- interface
- matches
- test tube clamps
- calorimeter
- balance
- 10 cc syringe
- graphing calculator
- aprons
- test tube
- heavy aluminum foil
- goggles
- samples of walnut and peanut

> **Safety Alert**
> 1. CAUTION: Needles are sharp. Exercise care.
> 2. CAUTION: Be sure to wear goggles anytime a flame is present in the room.
> 3. CAUTION: If you burn yourself, immediately place the burned area under cold running water and notify your teacher.

PROCEDURE

1. Answer the pre-lab questions on your student answer page.

2. In the space marked HYPOTHESIS on your student answer page, identify whether the peanut or walnut contains the most energy.

3. Measure out three pieces of peanut and three individual pieces of walnut, approximately 0.2 g each. Determine the exact mass of each piece and record this information on your data table. Do not get the pieces mixed. Be able to identify which piece has what mass.

4. Slide the calculator and CBL2 or LabPro Interface in the bottom part of the cradle and it will click into place. Snap the calculator into the top portion of the cradle.

5. Plug the short black link cable into the link port on the bottom of the TI Graphing Calculator and the interface. Follow the instructions below to activate the **DATAMATE** program for data collection.
   a. TI-83/TI-73
      - Press PRGM, then press the number key that precedes the **DATAMATE** program. Press ENTER, then press CLEAR when you reach the Main screen.

   b. TI-83+
      - Press APPS, and then press the calculator key for the number that precedes the **DATAMATE** program. Press ENTER, then press CLEAR when you reach the Main screen.

   c. TI-86
      - Press PRGM, then F1 to select **<NAMES>**, and press a menu key to select **<DATAM>** (usually F1). Press ENTER and then press CLEAR when you reach the Main screen.

   d. TI-89/TI-92
      - Press 2nd, – [VAR LINK]. Use ↓ or cursor pad to scroll down to "Datamate", then press ENTER. Press) to complete the open parenthesis that follows "Datamate" on the entry line and press ENTER. When you reach the Main screen, press CLEAR.

6. Plug the temperature probe into channel 1 of the interface. At this time the interface should have automatically identified your temperature probe and the correct temperature should be displayed in the upper right hand corner. If the correct temperature is not displayed, do the following:
   - Select **SETUP** from the MENU by pressing 1
   - Select "CH1" from the MENU and press ENTER.
   - Select TEMPERATURE from the SELECT SENSOR MENU and press ENTER.
   - Select the type of temperature probe that is connected to the interface.
   - Press 1 to indicate o.k.

7. Select **SET UP** from the MENU by pressing 1.
   - Select MODE by pressing the ↑ key and then ENTER.
   - Select TIME GRAPH by pressing 2 and then 2 again to change the time settings.

8. Set up the calculator and the interface for data collection.
   - Enter "5" as the time between samples, in seconds. Press ENTER.
   - Enter "60" as the number of samples (the interfaced will collect data for 5 minutes), press ENTER.

9. Another window will appear with the summary of the probes and the length of the experiment. Press [1] to indicate OK. Press [1] again to return to the main menu.

10. A new window will appear, and the calculator is now ready to start the experiment. DO NOT press [2] until you are ready to run the experiment.

11. Obtain a calorimeter. Place one piece of the walnut on the needle anchored in the cork.
    - CAUTION: Needles are sharp. Exercise care when doing this step.
    - CAUTION: Be sure to wear goggles anytime a flame is lit in the room.

12. Place the nut, needle, and cork setup on a folded piece of heavy-duty aluminum foil and set the calorimeter over the setup. Put a rolled piece of masking tape around the test tube to prevent it from sliding through the hole. Slide the test tube into the hole in the top of the calorimeter. Adjust the test tube so that it is about 2 cm above the nut. See the diagram below:

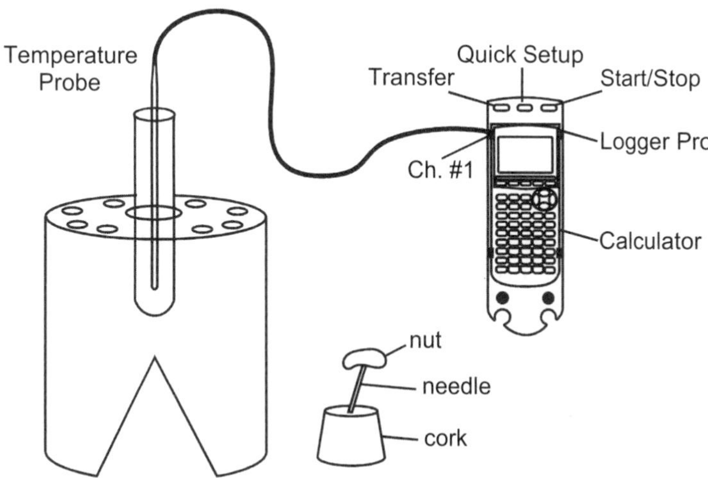

Calorimeter set-up with probe

13. Remove the calorimeter with the test tube in it from over the nut, being careful not to change the position of the test tube. Measure 10 cc of water and pour it in the test tube.

14. Put the temperature probe into the test tube. After about 15 seconds, the temperature should stabilize. Press [2] to begin data collection. The experiment will run for 5 minutes. There should be 4 short beeps and the quick setup light will flash. You should notice that the temperature is being graphed as the data is being collected.

15. When the experiment is complete, four short beeps will sound and the quick set up light will flash. Now a labeled, fitted graph will be displayed.

16. Using a match, set fire to the nut. Quickly and carefully, position the calorimeter over the burning nut.
    - CAUTION: If you burn yourself, immediately, place the burned area under cold running water. Notify your teacher.

17. You should notice that the temperature is being graphed as the data is being collected. It will continue taking data for five minutes. When the experiment is complete, 4 short beeps will sound and the quick setup light will flash. Upon completion of the data collection a labeled, fitted graph will be displayed.

18. Burn the nut completely. If your nut burns out before it is completely burned, quickly relight it.

    Use the ◄ and ► keys to move the cursor. View the data points displayed at the bottom of the graph. Use these keys to determine the minimum and maximum temperature values of the water and record these in your data table on your student answer page.

19. Press ENTER on the calculator and you will return to the main menu. The parameters that you set for this experiment are still in the calculator. Another run of the experiment can be done without resetting the calculator.

20. Repeat this experiment two more times with the other pieces of walnut and three more times with the pieces of peanut. It is important not to mix the pieces of nuts so that correct energy per gram values will be obtained.
    - Caution: Be sure to get 10 cc of new water and take care in the handling of the test tube, as it is extremely hot.

21. Clean up your area and return your equipment to its original condition.

Data Collection Devices
Determining the Amount of Energy Found in Food Using a Computer

All living systems require energy. In the case of autotrophs such as plants and related organisms, they have the ability to take inorganic compounds from the environment and make high energy compounds required for their survival. Heterotrophs, however, are unable to synthesize high energy, organic nutrients from inorganic compounds and therefore must obtain these high-energy nutrients from the environment. From a human point of view, their nutrition translates into our food. All food contains energy. The amount it contains depends on the type of food it is and the organic compounds it contains.

Food is a source of both energy and the basic building blocks needed for the synthesis of macromolecules. Living systems follow the 1st and 2nd Laws of Thermodynamics. The first law states that energy cannot be created or destroyed but only converted from one form to another. This energy conversion is never 100%. Energy is always lost in the form of heat. For living systems, this is especially true. The energy content in food is converted from chemical energy to mechanical energy as muscles contract. In fireflies, the chemical energy found in food is converted to electromagnetic energy as they light up the summer skies with their bioluminescence. It is also possible to convert the chemical energy in a candy bar into another form of chemical energy. The sugar in the candy converts to fat. The fat will be later stored in our adipose tissue. As stated earlier, heat energy always accompanies any energy transfer. This type of energy is never found by itself but is always associated with one of the other forms of energy. In each of the previous examples, as energy converts from one form to another a certain amount of heat energy was released.

Free energy is the amount of energy available to do work. Heat energy that is released during an energy conversion is considered to be wasted energy and is not available to do work. This explains why energy conversions are not 100% efficient. Suppose that a candy bar had 180 kilocalories of chemical energy. Suppose you ate the candy bar in order to have mechanical energy available to play a volleyball game. At best, your body would only use 72 kilocalories of the 180 available and the rest would be released as heat energy. That's over 108 kilocalories lost!

180 kcal Total Energy				180 kcal Total Energy
Candy Bar	—— ENERGY CONVERSION →	Muscle Movement	+	Heat Energy
180 kcal	————————————→	72 kcal	+	108 kcal
Free Energy	————————————→	Free Energy	+	Wasted Energy

This brings us to the Second Law of Thermodynamics. Suppose there is a closed system which means energy can not enter or leave the system. This would mean that its *total* energy content could not increase or decease, it must therefore remain constant. As time passes, energy conversions occur, and more and more of the free energy available to do work converts to unusable heat energy. The unusable heat energy is unavailable to do work. If this process continued indefinitely, then eventually there would be no free energy and the system would decease in its order, becoming more chaotic. The Second

Law of Thermodynamics states that in a closed system, one in which energy can not enter or leave, there will be an increase in the system's disorder. Entropy is a measurement of the disorder of a system.

In biology, energy is often measured in calories. A calorie is the amount of heat energy needed to raise the temperature of one gram of water one degree Celsius. The amount of energy found in food is measured in kilocalories (symbolized by C or called Calories). So if a candy bar says it has 180 Calories, it really means that it has 180,000 calories. A calorimeter is used to determine the amount of calories found in food.

In this investigation you will burn a sample of food with known mass. Above the burning food sample is a test tube of water that contains 10 mL of water or 10 g of water. The temperature of the water is recorded before and after the sample is burned. The change in temperature, ΔT is calculated.

By using the equation $\text{Energy} = \text{mass} \times \Delta T \times 1 \dfrac{\text{calorie}}{\text{g} \bullet {}^\circ\text{C}}$ the change in temperature, ΔT, is multiplied by the number of grams of water used (10 g) and the specific heat of the water. This allows you to calculate the amount of heat energy absorbed by the water. Since the energy absorbed by the water was the result of the burning the food, it also represents the amount of energy contained in the food sample. Since the amount of energy you calculated is in calories, it needs to be converted to kilocalories using the relationship, 1000 calories equals one kilocalories or Calorie. To make the energy relative to the particular sample you used, the energy value should be divided by the mass of your sample. This will allow the energy per gram of your sample to be compared to the energy per gram of other samples.

$$\text{calories} = 10 \text{ g } H_2O \times (\text{final temperature} - \text{initial temperature}) \times 1 \frac{\text{calorie}}{\text{g} \bullet {}^\circ\text{C}}$$

$$\text{Kilocalories or Calories} = \frac{\text{calories}}{1000}$$

$$\frac{\text{kcal}}{\text{g of food}} = \frac{\text{kcal}}{\text{mass of sample}}$$

This lab will be repeated three times to obtain an average energy value and increase the validity of your experiment. Your teacher will give you the actual number of the Calories found in the food sample used. You are to determine the percent yield.

$$\text{Percent Yield} = \frac{\text{Experimental Value}}{\text{Actual Value}} \times 100$$

You can also determine the percent error by using the formula below:

$$\text{Percent Error} = \frac{(\text{Experimental Value} - \text{Actual Value})}{\text{Actual Value}} \times 100$$

PURPOSE

In this activity you will determine the amount of energy found in a walnut and a peanut by using a calorimeter and compare it to the actual value.

MATERIALS

- temperature probe
- matches
- test tube clamps
- calorimeter
- balance
- 10 mL graduated cylinder
- computer with Logger Pro® installed
- aprons
- test tube
- heavy aluminum foil
- goggles
- samples of walnut and peanut
- Lab Pro® interface box

Safety Alert

1. CAUTION: Needles are sharp. Exercise care.
2. CAUTION: Be sure to wear goggles anytime a flame is present in the room.
3. CAUTION: Matches are flammable. If you burn yourself, immediately place the burned area under cold running water. Notify your teacher.

PROCEDURE

1. Answer the pre-lab questions on your student answer page.
2. In the space marked HYPOTHESIS on your student answer page, identify whether the peanut or walnut contains the most energy.
3. Plug the temperature probe into Port 1 or CH 1 of the interface box.
4. Mass three individual pieces of peanut and three individual pieces of walnut, approximately 0.2 g each. Record the exact mass of each piece in your data table. Store each nut piece on a small square of paper labeled with its mass. It is very important not to mix up the pieces.
5. Turn on the computer. Click on the folder called **Experiment Templates**, and open **Calorimeterss** (for stainless steel probe) or **Calorimeterdc** (for direct connect temperature probe). Logger Pro® should open.
    - CAUTION: Electricity is being used. Take care not to spill any liquids on any of the computer equipment or electrical outlets.
6. Obtain a calorimeter.
7. Place one of the walnuts on the needle anchored in the cork.
    - CAUTION: Needles are sharp. Exercise care.

8. Place nut, needle, and cork setup on a folded piece of heavy-duty aluminum foil and set the colorimeter over the setup. Put a rolled piece of masking tape around the test tube to prevent it from sliding through the hole. Slide the test tube into the hole in the top of the calorimeter. Adjust the test tube so that it is about 2 cm above the nut. See the diagram below:

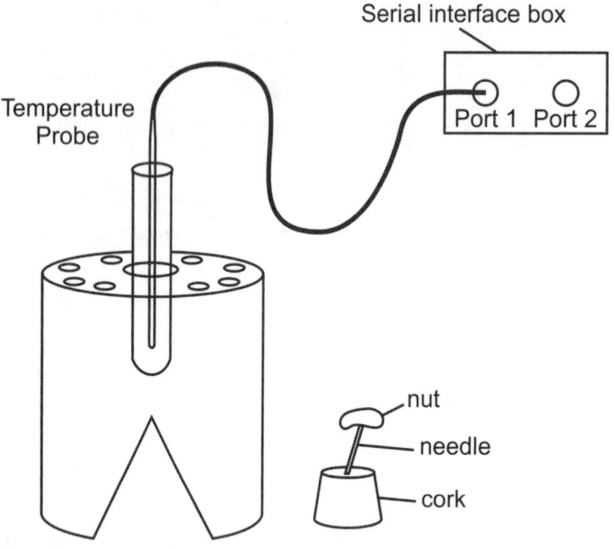

Calorimeter set-up with probe

9. Remove the calorimeter with the test tube in it from over the nut, being careful not to change the adjust position of the test tube. Measure 10 mL of water and pour it in the test tube.

10. Put the temperature probe into the test tube.

11. Using a match, set fire to the nut. Quickly and carefully position the calorimeter over the burning nut.
    - CAUTION: If you burn yourself, immediately, place the burned area under cold running water. Notify your teacher.

12. Click **Collect** and the temperature probe should start taking temperature readings immediately. Record the starting temperature.

13. Burn the nut completely. If your nut burns out before it is completely burned out, quickly relight it. When it burns out, look at the computer screen and record the final temperature. Note the shape of the graph and its axes.

14. Pull down the **Analyze Menu** and highlight **Statistics**. A statistics box will appear. It will list the maximum and minimum temperature. Record this information in your data table on the student answer page. Click the very small, gray square in the corner of the statistics window to close it.

15. Repeat this experiment two more times with the other pieces of walnut and three more times with the pieces of peanut. If you would like to keep the data that is being collected so that you can compare the various runs of the experiment, pull down the **Data Menu** and click **Store Latest Run**. This will cause the line on the graph to become a lighter red. If you do not wish to save your data you can **Delete the Latest Run** when you pull down the **Data Menu**. If you do neither of these, the Logger Pro® software will ask you if you would like to erase the previous data, you must click **Yes** to continue. It is important not to mix the pieces of nuts so that correct energy per gram values will be obtained.

16. If your teacher would like you to print a graph for this lab, pull down the **File Menu** and highlight **Print**. A dialog box will appear. Type in the number of desired copies and click **OK** or press Enter on the keyboard.

17. After you have finished close all windows on the computer. Clean up your area and return your equipment to its original condition.

Name ______________________________

Period ______________________________

Data Collection Devices
Determining the Amount of Energy Found in Food

HYPOTHESIS

DATA AND OBSERVATIONS

Data Table						
Experiment	**Mass of Sample**	**Temperature Before Burning**	**Temperature After Burning**	**# of calories**	**# of kilocalories**	**# of kilocalories/gram**
Peanut # 1						
Peanut # 2						
Peanut # 3						
Average						
Walnut # 1						
Walnut # 2						
Walnut # 3						
Average						

PRE-LAB QUESTIONS

1. After reading the background information, define the terms autotroph and heterotroph.

2. What are two purposes of food?

3. What is free energy?

4. What is entropy?

5. What is a calorie, a Calorie and a kilocalorie?

6. Write the equations to be used to determine the number of calories, percent yield, and percent error.

CONCLUSION QUESTIONS

1. Which nut contained the greatest number of kilocalories per gram?

2. What was the shape of the graph that screen displayed for you (if using a graphing calculator) or that Logger Pro® displayed for you (if using a computer) and what relationship did it establish?

3. The nutritional labels show that peanuts are 6.00 kcal/gram and walnuts are 7.02 kcal/gram. What was your percent yield and was it greater than or less than the actual value?

4. Give two reasons why your answer varied from the actual values.

5. What is your percent error? Do you think that it is acceptable? Why or why not?

6. Nuts are high in lipids. What foods might you investigate to determine their calorie content for carbohydrates? Proteins?

7. A student fails to replace the 10 grams of water in the test tube between the second and third trials for the walnut. How will this error affect the calculated energy result? You answer should clearly state that the calculated value will increase, decrease or remain the same. Mathematically justify your answer.

Computer Graphing Software
Using Graphical Analysis® 3 or Logger Pro® 3

OBJECTIVE
Students will learn to use Graphical Analysis® 3 or Logger Pro® 3 computer graphing software to graph and analyze data as well as generate a lab report by importing their data and graphs into a word processing document.

LEVEL
All

NATIONAL STANDARDS
UCP.1, UCP.2, A.1, A.2, E.1, E.2, G.2

TEKS
6.2 (E), 6.4(A)
7.2(E), 7.4(A)
8.2 (E), 8.4(A), 8.4(B)
IPC: 2(C)
Biology: 2(C)
Chemistry: 2(D)
Physics: 2(C), 2(E)

CONNECTIONS TO AP
All AP science exams ask students to read and interpret graphs.

TIME FRAME
90+ minutes

MATERIALS
either Graphical Analysis® 3 software or Logger Pro® 3 software
computer

TEACHER NOTES

Ideally, this lesson would follow a lesson on graphing calculators and the use of data collection devices. The data from the calculator can be imported into either of these pieces of software for further analysis. It is important to load the TI Connect software *first*, followed by the graphing software you have chosen. *Foundation Lesson VII: Data Collection Devices*, addresses the collection of data using Logger Pro. It is the intent of this lesson to simply use these computer graphing programs to analyze a set of sample data to learn the features of the program and then to generate a lab report by cutting and pasting the data and graphs into a word processing document. The students are directed to skip two of the more mathematically advanced tutorials and told they may do them count for extra credit.

Both of these graphing software programs are available for purchase from Vernier Software & Technology, 13979 SW Millikan Way, Beaverton, Oregon 97005-2886. You can also purchase on-line at www.vernier.com. At the time of this printing, Graphical Analysis® 3 can be purchased at a cost of $80 and Logger Pro® 3 at a cost of $100. This gives your campus a site license that allows you to load the program on any and every computer on campus and give a copy of the program to each of your students.

What is the difference between these two programs? Graphical Analysis® 3, GA3, is simply a user friendly graphing software program that can be used alone or with TI graphing calculator, CBL 2, or LabPro compatibility. Data can be imported from a TI graphing calculator, CBL 2 or LabPro into GA3 in a matter of seconds with the use of a TI-Graph Link cable. Logger Pro® 3, LP3, has GA3 embedded within it, but is also capable of communicating directly with a LabPro and probes to collect data bypassing the need for a calculator. Logger Pro® 3 houses all of the experiment files found in the TI and Vernier Lab Manuals and has more capability than GA3. Logger Pro also contains some sample movies that graph data as they play so that the data can be analyzed. You may also add your own movies and synchronize them with data collection for further analysis. Logger Pro® 3 is the software to purchase if you have access to several computers for student use in your laboratory.

The complete user's manual to either piece of software is available at www.vernier.com.

****IF you are using a USB TI Graph-Link, you need to first load TI Connect from the TI website**, http://education.ti.com/us/product/accessory/connectivity/down/download.html.

****THEN load the graphing software**. TI Connect contains the driver for the USB Graph-Link. Neither Graphical Analysis nor Logger Pro contains this driver. **You will not be able to import data from the calculator if you load the graphing software first.** If you are using the older gray or black Graph-links, you do not need TI Connect software at all.

TEACHER PAGES

Graphical Analysis® 3 Computer Requirements

Windows requirements:

- Windows 95, Windows 98, Windows 2000, Windows NT 4.x, Windows ME, and Windows XP.
- 133 MHz Pentium processor or better.
- 16 MB physical RAM plus free hard disk space (for virtual memory).
- Color monitor (>=256 colors)

Macintosh requirements:

- Mac OS 8.x, MacOS 9.x, MacOS X.
- 66 MHz PowerPC processor or better.
- 16 MB machine RAM, 8MB for the application partition.

Logger Pro® 3 Computer Requirements

- Windows 98®, 2000, ME, NT, or XP on a Pentium Processor or equivalent, 133 MHz, 32 MB RAM, 25 MB of hard disk space, for a minimum installation.
- Mac OS® 9.2, or Mac OS X (10.1 or newer), with 25 MB of hard disk space for a minimum installation.
- Using the movie feature of Logger Pro will require a faster processor and an additional 100 MB of hard disk space.

Note: Logger Pro cannot be used with the ULI or Serial Box interface.

Loading Graphical Analysis or Logger Pro onto Your Hard Drive

(Remember to load the TI Connect software first, before the graphing software)

To install Logger Pro or Graphical Analysis on a computer running Windows 98/2000/ME/NT/XP, follow these steps: [note that GA3 will run on Windows 95, but LP3 will NOT]

1. Place the software CD in the CD-ROM drive of your computer.

2. If you have Autorun enabled, the installation will launch automatically; otherwise choose Settings→Control Panel from the Start menu. Double click on Add/Remove Programs. Click on the Install button in the resulting dialog box.

3. The software installer will launch, and a series of dialog boxes will step you through the installation. You will be given the opportunity to either accept the default directory [recommended] or enter a different directory.

To install Graphical Analysis or Logger Pro on a computer running MacOS 8.x, MacOS 9.x, MacOS X, follow these steps:

1. Place the Graphical Analysis CD in the CD-ROM drive of your computer.

2. Double-click on the Install Graphical Analysis icon and follow the directions.

Setting Preferences Within the Software

There is one aspect of both programs that needs to be changed. The setting in the start-up file for both programs has the "Connect Lines" or "Connected Points" feature as the default. One of your primary goals is to have Pre-AP students mathematically model data rather than draw a dot-to-dot picture of the data. You will spend a great deal of time encouraging students to break this habit. You want students to mathematically model their data using curve-fitting so that they can use the equation of the curve to interpolate and extrapolate. This setting is easy to change, but must be done on each computer or on the master *copy* of the software that you issue to students. Follow these steps:

1. Start the program and double click on the blank graph. This dialogue box appears:

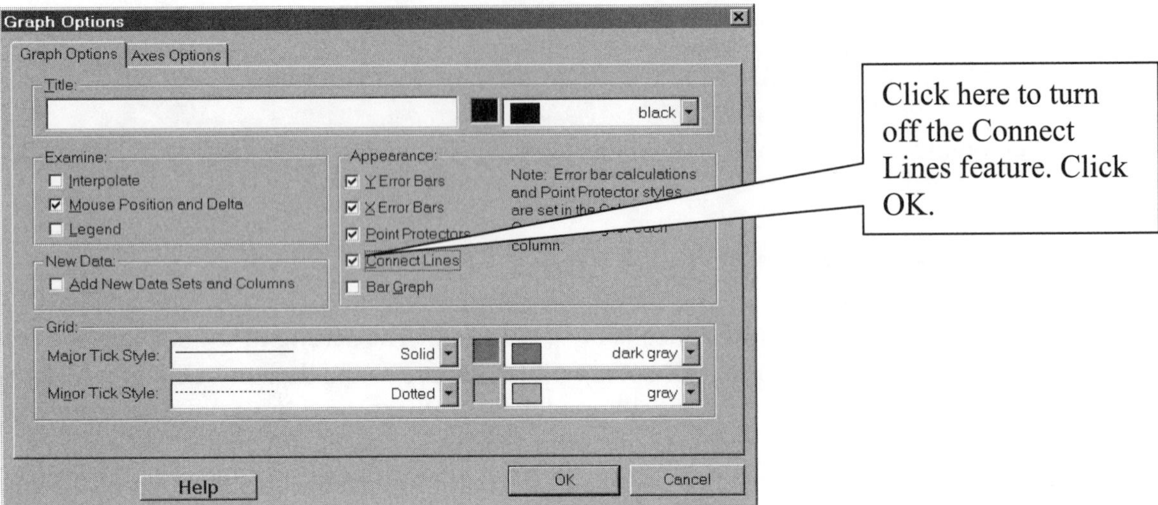

2. Go to File and select preferences and make sure the Start up file box is checked. You can also change other features such as removing the automatic curve fitting option for students if you wish.

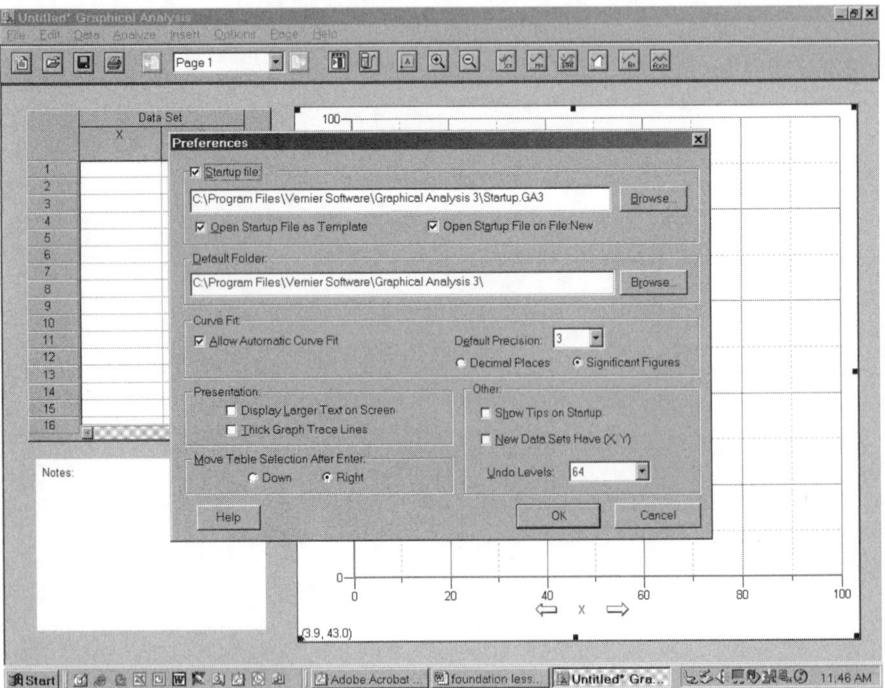

3. Go to File and select Save As. If using GA3, select the file titled startup.ga3. If using LP3, select the file titled startup.xmbl.

4. Right click on the file and scroll to the bottom of the pop up box and select Properties. The Properties dialogue box will appear. Click to remove the Read Only status of the startup file. Click OK. Click SAVE. The program will inform you that the file already exists and ask you if you wish to replace it, click YES.

5. Failure to disable the read only status will result in this error message:

Click OK and simply repeat step 4.

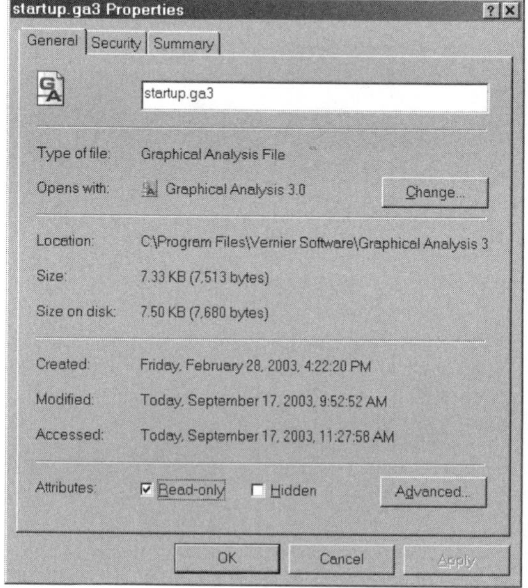

6. If you did not get the error message, you were successful. However, you must restore your new and improved startup file to Read Only status to protect it from corruption. Go to File, Save As and select the startup file again. Right click and select properties at the bottom of the pop up box. Click to replace the Read Only checkmark. Click OK. Click Cancel.

7. Repeat these steps on each of your student computers.

8. Since you may make copies of the CD for distribution to students you may wish to do these steps **once** on your own computer. When you are setting up the files to burn your master *copy* for distribution, simply delete the factory startup file before you burn the disk and replace it with the one from the hard drive on the computer you are working from once you have completed steps 1-7. The startup file is found in C:\Program Files\Vernier Software\Graphical Analysis 3 if using GA3. The startup file is found in C:\Program Files\Vernier Software\Logger Pro 3 if using LP3. Performing this step *before* burning your master *copy* CD for student distribution will save you a great deal of time and make the student's home computer begin the program just as it does at school.

NOTE: Since the tutorials in this lesson do NOT use the startup file, do not be surprised if this change is not apparent. It will take effect anytime a new file is created.

STUDENT SAMPLE

This sample can serve as your grading key. Since all students are following the same set of tutorials, their reports should be nearly identical and thus easy to grade.

Learning to Use Graphical Analysis [or Logger Pro]

Ima Student

8th Grade Science, Period 4

Basic Operations Tutorial Results

How much garbage was generated per person in 1994?

- 2511 lb/person/yr

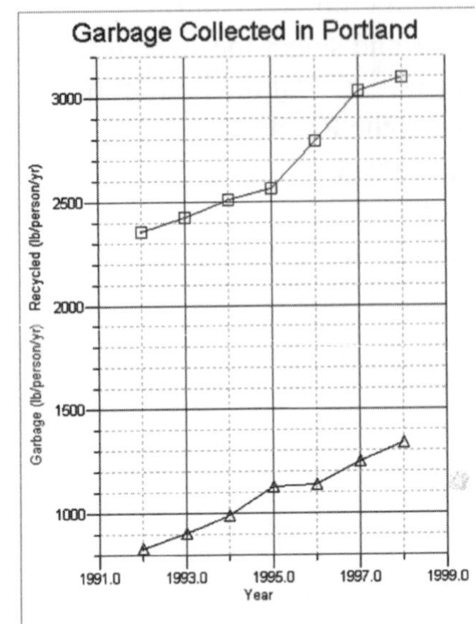

Customization Tutorial Results

	Data Set	
	X	Y
1	1.00	2.00
2	2.00	4.00
3	3.00	5.80
4	4.00	6.70
5	5.00	8.20
6	6.00	10.0
7	7.00	12.0
8	8.00	14.3
9	9.00	15.6
10	10.0	17.0
11		
12		
13		
14		
15		
16		
17		
18		

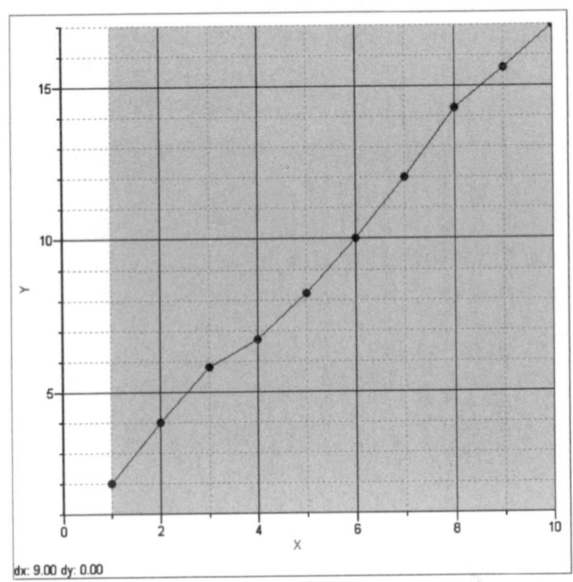

Viewing Graphs Tutorial Results

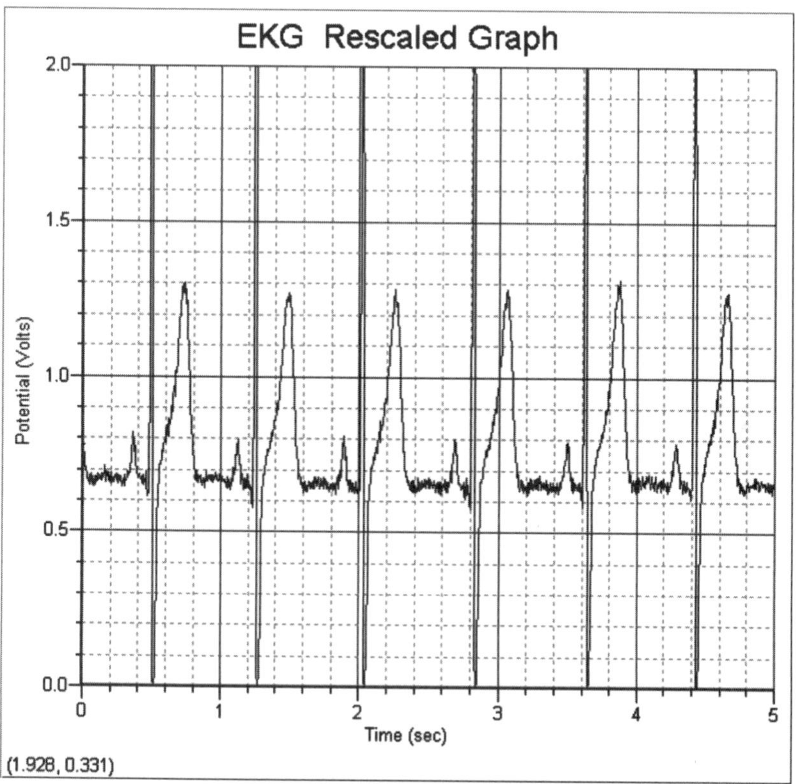

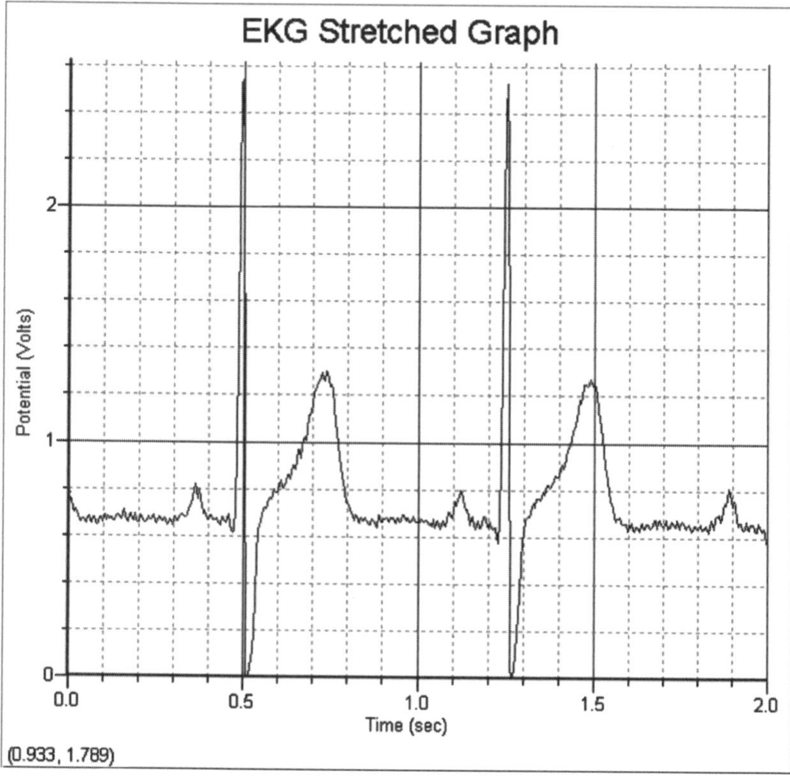

TEACHER PAGES

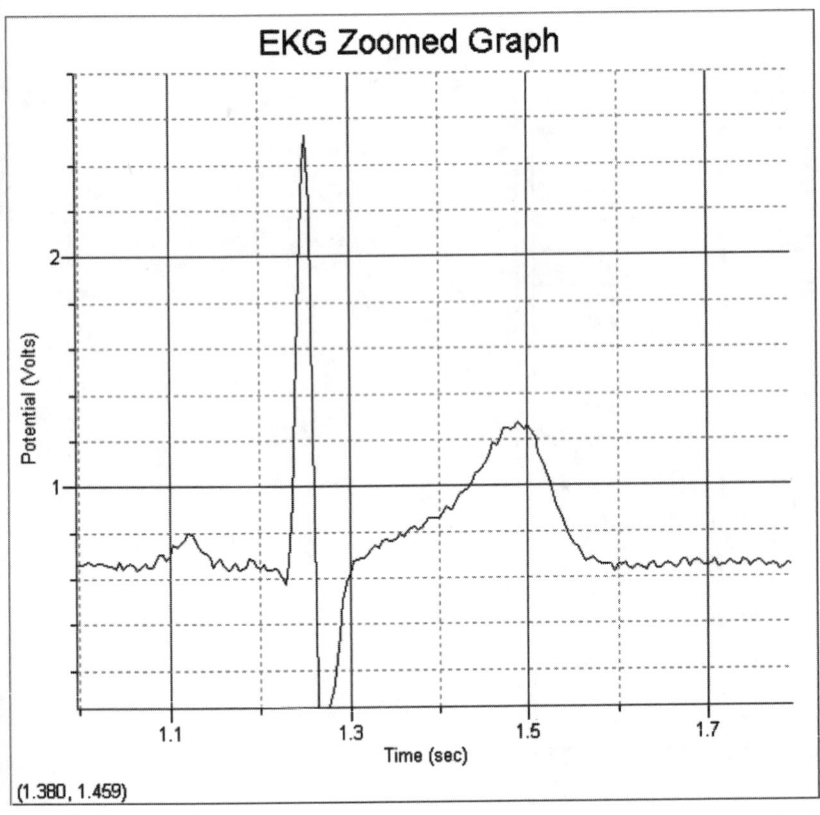
EKG Zoomed Graph
Potential (Volts)
2
1
1.1
1.3
1.5
1.7
Time (sec)
(1.380, 1.459)

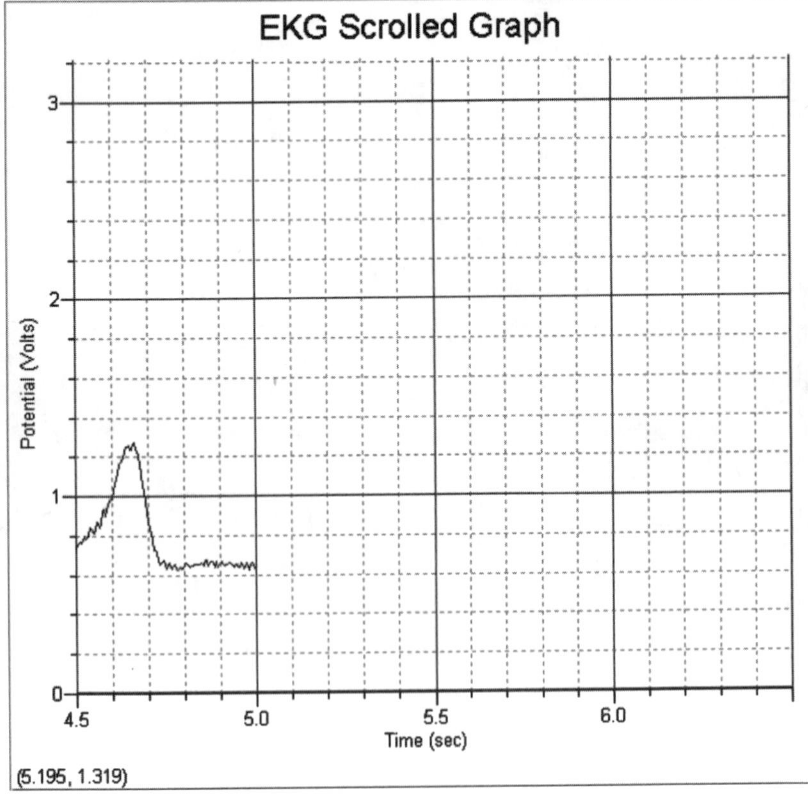
EKG Scrolled Graph
Potential (Volts)
3
2
1
0
4.5
5.0
5.5
6.0
Time (sec)
(5.195, 1.319)

Linearization Part 1 Tutorial Results

Is Population proportional to Time Interval ^2?

- Yes since the graph of Population vs. Time Interval squared is linear.

The top graph on the right shows a different kind of relationship. What is it?

- It is an inverse relationship since y decreases as x increases.

Linearization Part 2 Tutorial Results

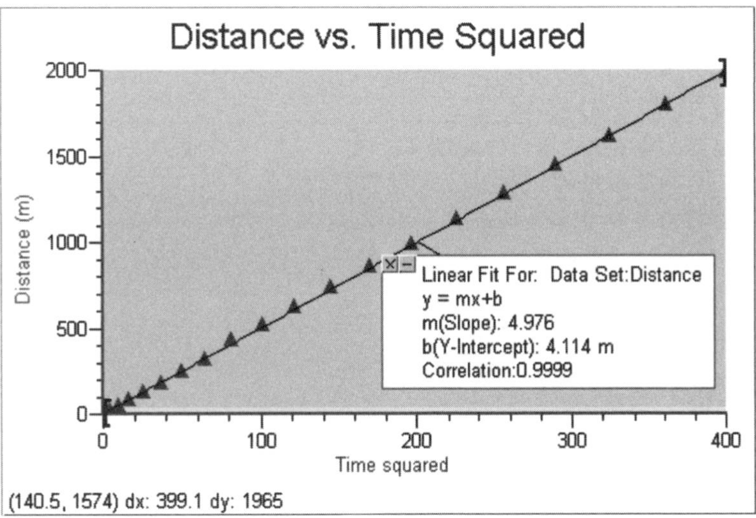

Is the graph now a straight line? If so, then you've found the relationship.

- Yes it is. The equation for the straght line is $y = 4.976x + 4.11$ with a correlation of 0.999. This means that Distance = 4.976 (time^2) + 4.11 m.

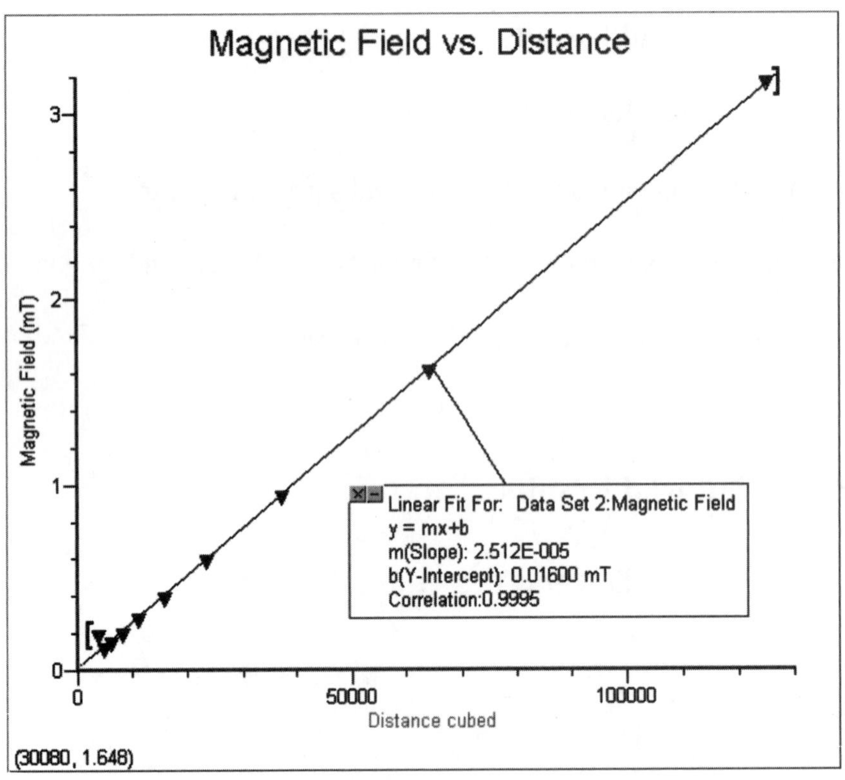
Magnetic Field vs. Distance
Magnetic Field (mT)
3
2
1
0
0
50000
100000
Distance cubed
Linear Fit For: Data Set 2:Magnetic Field
y = mx+b
m(Slope): 2.512E-005
b(Y-Intercept): 0.01600 mT
Correlation:0.9995
(30080, 1.648)

Computer Graphing Software
Using Graphical Analysis® 3

You will be asked to graph and analyze a vast amount of data in this course as well as future science courses. In the past, this was a daunting and time consuming task. Your school has purchased either Graphical Analysis® 3 (GA3) to greatly simplify analyzing and communicating the data you have collected during your laboratory exercises. The program also allows you to cut and paste your data tables and graphs into a word processing program such as Microsoft Word. This will be very helpful in generating lab reports. The site license your school has purchased allows you to load a copy of the software on any computer in your school or at home.

PURPOSE

In this activity you will learn the basic features of Graphical Analysis or Logger Pro computer graphing software so that you may use this valuable tool throughout this course and future science courses.

MATERIALS

Computer graphing software, Graphical Analysis® 3

PROCEDURE FOR GRAPHICAL ANALYSIS® 3 SOFTWARE

1. Start the program by double clicking either the Graphical Analysis  icon.
2. The program may greet you with a Tip of the Day. Read the tip, close it and go to File and select Open or simply click on the second icon from the right to open files. Open the Tutorials folder and this dialogue box will appear:

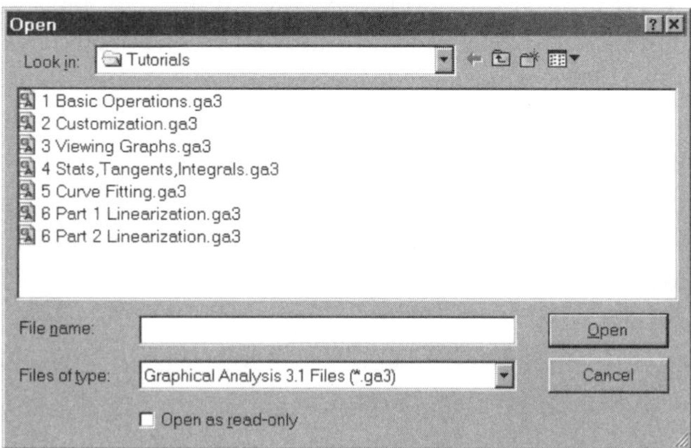

3. Double click on "1 Basic Operations.ga3" to open the file.

4. Without closing GA3, open a word processing program such as Microsoft Word®. Start a new file and title this document "Learning to Use Graphical Analysis". Your title should be centered with 18 point bold font. Type your name under your title making it centered with 16 point bold font. Type your course name and class period together under your name making it centered with 14 point bold font. Press the Enter key three times and type "Basic Operations Tutorial Results". Subtitles such as this one should be left justified, bold 14 point font. Press Enter twice, change the font to 12 point, and remove the bold. This will be the formatting for all of the body text in today's lab report. SAVE this document. Do not close the program; just minimize it since you will be going back and forth between GA3 and your document.

5. Go back to GA3 by clicking on it at the bottom of your screen. Read and follow all instructions contained within the tutorial. As you proceed through this tutorial, the pop up dialogue boxes may obscure the directions. You can move the dialogue boxes by clicking on the blue title bar of the box and dragging them to another part of the screen, out of your way. Don't forget that you will get tool tips if you let your mouse pointer hover over a button, these are very useful.
   a. When you reach page 5, you will be instructed to title your graph "Garbage vs. Year". This is not a title, but rather a restatement of the axes. Title your graph "Garbage Collected in Portland" instead.
   b. You will be asked questions throughout these tutorials about the data presented. In all cases, cut and paste the questions from GA3 by clicking on the box containing the question, highlighting the question, and pressing Ctrl+C to copy the question to the clipboard. Go to your word processing document and place your cursor under the appropriate subtitle heading and press Ctrl+V to paste the question into your document. Type your answer to the question. Pay special attention to the units of the answer. No naked numbers!

6. Continue through the tutorial until you reach the "Congratulations" page. Make sure you have cut and pasted (as well as answered) all questions throughout the tutorial. Once you are finished, go back 2 pages to your graph. Check to make sure it has a correct title, then click on the graph to select it and copy it onto the clipboard using Ctrl+C. Return to your document and press Enter twice to separate the graph from the questions asked. Use Ctrl+V to paste your completed graph from the first tutorial into this document. Resize the graph in your document so it takes up less space. Reduce it by a factor of *about* one half. Resize all of your graphs by a factor of *about* one half throughout the rest of your document.

7. Go back to GA3 and go to File, Open and select "2 Customization". **Do NOT save your changes to the first tutorial.** Proceed through this second tutorial.

8. Continue until you reach the "Congratulations" page. Once you are finished, go back 2 pages to your graph. Click on the graph to select it and copy it onto the clipboard using Ctrl+C.

9. Go back to your minimized word processing document. Press Enter twice and type the subtitle "Customization Tutorial Results". Press Enter once followed by Ctrl+V to paste your customized graph into this document. Resize the graph in your document. SAVE. Do not close the program, just minimize it.

10. Go back to GA3 and page back to page 3. Cut and paste the improved data table into your word processing document. Resize the data table in your document.

11. Go back to Graphical Analysis and go to File, Open and select "3 Viewing Graphs". **Do NOT save your changes to the second tutorial.** Proceed through this third tutorial.

12. Once you have rescaled the graph at the end of the first page, change its title to "EKG Rescaled Graph" and copy it to the clipboard.

13. Go back to your minimized word processing document. Press Enter once followed by Ctrl+V to paste your rescaled graph into this document. Resize the graph in your document. SAVE. Do not close the program, just minimize it.

14. Go back to Graphical Analysis and continue the tutorial. Once you have stretched the graph on page 2 of the tutorial, change its title to "EKG Stretched Graph" and copy it to the clipboard.

15. Go back to your minimized word processing document. Press Enter twice and type the subtitle "Viewing Graphs Tutorial Results". Press Enter once followed by Ctrl+V to paste your zoomed graph into this document. Resize the graph in your document. SAVE. Do not close the program, just minimize it.

16. Go back to Graphical Analysis and continue the tutorial. Once you have zoomed in on the graph on page 3 of the tutorial, change its title to "EKG Zoomed Graph" and copy it to the clipboard.

17. Go back to your minimized word processing document. Press Enter twice and type the subtitle "Viewing Graphs Tutorial Results". Press Enter once followed by Ctrl+V to paste your zoomed graph into this document. Resize the graph in your document. SAVE. Do not close the program, just minimize it.

18. Go back to Graphical Analysis and continue the tutorial. Continue until you reach the "Congratulations" page. Once you are finished, go back 1 page to your graph. Click on the graph to select it, change its title to "EKG Scrolled Graph" and copy it onto the clipboard using Ctrl+C.

19. Go back to your minimized word processing document. Press Enter once followed by Ctrl+V to paste your scrolled graph into this document. Resize the graph in your document. Resize the graph in your document. SAVE. Do not close the program, just minimize it.

20. Go back to Graphical Analysis and go to File, Open and select "6 Linearization Part 1" [Yes, we are skipping tutorials 4 & 5, they will be extra credit!]. **Do not save your changes to the third tutorial**. Proceed through this next tutorial. Be sure to cut and paste the two questions into your report under the subtitle "Linearization Part 1 Tutorial Results". There are no graphs to paste into your report, but you will need to use the skills presented in this tutorial to be successful in Part 2. You may want to print the last page of this tutorial for future reference.

21. Go to File, Open and select "6 Linearization Part 2". Follow all of the directions on page one and paste your data tables and your graphs into your report under the subtitle "Linearization Part 2 Tutorial Results". Be sure and run the linear regression on your data so that your graph shows the statistics box. Do this by highlighting the data on your graph and pressing the R= button.

22. SAVE. Continue to the end of the tutorial and paste your second graph into your report. [Hint: The shape of the second graph tells you it is an inverse function.] When you calculate your column you will need to use the reciprocal of one of the variables. Be sure and include the algebraic equation for your line of best fit once you have pasted the graphs into your document.

23. You may add the appropriate graphs from tutorials 4 & 5 to your report for extra credit. Be sure and include the proper subtitle headings and continue the proper format for the report.

Computer Graphing Software
Using Graphical Logger Pro® 3

You will be asked to graph and analyze a vast amount of data in this course as well as future science courses. In the past, this was a daunting and time consuming task. Your school has purchased either Logger Pro® 3 (LP3) to greatly simplify analyzing and communicating the data you have collected during your laboratory exercises. The program also allows you to cut and paste your data tables and graphs into a word processing program such as Microsoft Word. This will be very helpful in generating lab reports. The site license your school has purchased allows you to load a copy of the software on any computer in your school or at home.

PURPOSE

In this activity you will learn the basic features of Graphical Analysis or Logger Pro computer graphing software so that you may use this valuable tool throughout this course and future science courses.

MATERIALS

Computer graphing software, Logger Pro® 3

PROCEDURE FOR LOGGER PRO® 3 SOFTWARE

1. Start the program by double clicking the Logger Pro icon. 

2. The program may greet you with a Tip of the Day. Read the tip then close it. You may also be asked about continuing without an interface attached. Choose to continue without an interface and click OK. Go to File and select Open or simply click on the second icon from the right to open files. Open the Tutorials folder and this dialogue box will appear:

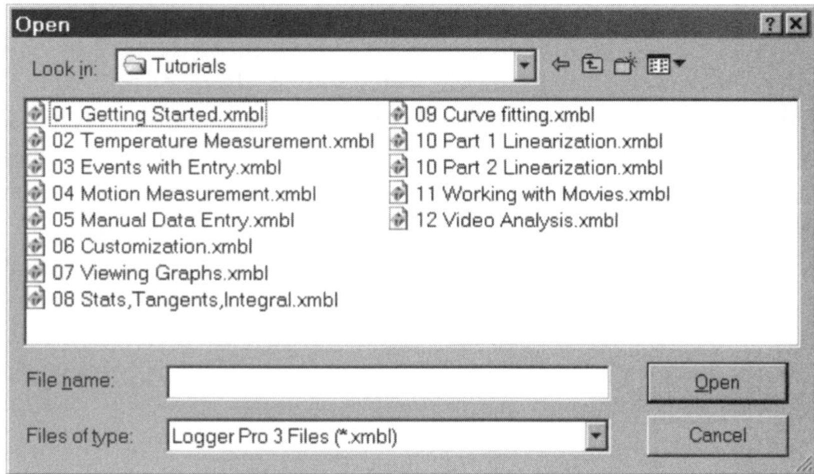

3. Double click "01 Getting Started.xmbl" to open the file.

4. Without closing LP3, open a word processing program such as Microsoft Word®. Start a new file and title this document "Learning to Use Logger Pro". Your title should be centered with 18 point bold font. Type your name under your title making it centered with 16 point bold font. Type your course name and class period together under your name making it centered with 14 point bold font. Press the Enter key three times and type "Manual Data Entry Tutorial Results". Subtitles such as this one should be left justified, bold 14 point font. Press Enter twice, change the font to 12 point, and remove the bold. This will be the formatting for all of the body text in today's lab report. SAVE this document. Do not close the program; just minimize it since you will be going back and forth between LP3 and your document.

5. Go back to LP3 by clicking on it at the bottom of your screen. Read and follow all instructions contained within the tutorial. Continue through this tutorial until you reach the "Congratulations" page.

6. Go to File, Open and select "05 Manual Data Entry". **Do NOT save your changes to the first tutorial.** As you proceed through this tutorial, the pop up dialogue boxes may obscure the directions. You can move the dialogue boxes by clicking on the blue title bar of the box and dragging them to another part of the screen, out of your way. Don't forget that you will get tool tips if you let your mouse pointer hover over a button, these are very useful.
   a. When you reach page 5, you will be instructed to title your graph "Garbage vs. Year". This is not a title, but rather a restatement of the axes. Title your graph "Garbage Collected in Portland" instead.
   b. You will be asked questions throughout these tutorials about the data presented. In all cases, cut and paste the questions from LP3 by clicking on the box containing the question, highlighting the question, and pressing Ctrl+C to copy the question to the clipboard. Go to your word processing document and place your cursor under the appropriate subtitle heading and press Ctrl+V to paste the question into your document. Type your answer to the question. Pay special attention to the units of the answer. NO naked numbers!

7. Continue until you reach the "Congratulations" page. Make sure you have cut and pasted (as well as answered) all questions throughout the tutorial. Once you are finished, go back 2 pages to your graph. Check to make sure it has a correct title, then click on the graph to select it and copy it onto the clipboard using Ctrl+C. Return to your document and press Enter twice to separate the graph from the questions asked. Press Ctrl+V to paste your completed graph from the first tutorial into this document. Resize the graph in your document so it takes up less space. Reduce it by a factor of *about* one half. Resize all of your graphs by a factor of *about* one half throughout the rest of the document.

8. Go back to LP3 and go to File, Open and select "6 Customization". **Do NOT save your changes to the first tutorial.** Proceed through the customization tutorial.

9. Continue until you reach the "Congratulations" page. Once you are finished, go back 2 pages to your graph. Click on the graph to select it and copy it onto the clipboard using Ctrl+C.

10. Go back to your minimized word processing document. Press Enter twice and type the subtitle "Customization Tutorial Results". Press Enter once followed by Ctrl+V to paste your customized graph into this document. Resize the graph in your document. SAVE. Do not close the program, just minimize it.

11. Go back to LP3 and page back to page 3. Cut and paste the improved data table into your word processing document. Resize the data table in you document.

12. Go back to Logger Pro and go to File, Open and select "07 Viewing Graphs". **Do NOT save your changes to the customization tutorial.** Proceed through the viewing graphs tutorial.

13. Once you have rescaled the graph at the end of the first page, change its title to "EKG Rescaled Graph" and copy it to the clipboard.

14. Go back to your minimized word processing document. Press Enter once followed by Ctrl +V to paste your rescaled graph into this document. Resize the graph in your document. SAVE. Do not close the program, just minimize it.

15. Go back to LP3 and continue the tutorial. Once you have stretched the graph on page 2 of the tutorial, change its title to "EKG Stretched Graph" and copy it to the clipboard.

16. Go back to your minimized word processing document. Press Enter twice and type the subtitle "Viewing Graphs Tutorial Results". Press Enter once followed by Ctrl+V to paste your zoomed graph into this document. Resize the graph in your document. SAVE. Do not close the program, just minimize it.

17. Go back to LP3 and continue the tutorial. Once you have zoomed in on the graph on page 3 of the tutorial, change its title to "EKG Zoomed Graph" and copy it to the clipboard.

18. Go back to your minimized word processing document. Press Enter twice and type the subtitle "Viewing Graphs Tutorial Results". Press Enter once followed by Ctrl+V to paste your zoomed graph into this document. Resize the graph in your document. SAVE. Do not close the program, just minimize it.

19. Go back to LP3 and continue the tutorial. Continue until you reach the "Congratulations" page. Once you are finished, go back 1 page to your graph. Click on the graph to select it, change its title to "EKG Scrolled Graph" and copy it onto the clipboard using Ctrl+C.

20. Go back to your minimized word processing document. Press Enter once followed by Ctrl+V to paste your scrolled graph into this document. Resize the graph in your document. Resize the graph in your document. SAVE. Do not close the program, just minimize it.

21. Go back to LP3 and go to File, Open and select "10 Linearization Part 1" [Yes, we are skipping tutorials 08 and 09, they will be extra credit!]. Do not save your changes to the tutorial. Proceed through this next tutorial. Be sure to cut and paste the two questions into your report under the subtitle "Linearization Part 1 Tutorial Results". There are no graphs to paste into your report, but you will need to use the skills presented in this tutorial to be successful in Part 2. You may want to print the last page of this tutorial for future reference.

22. Go to File, Open and select "10 Linearization Part 2". Follow all of the directions on page one and paste your data tables and your graphs into your report with the subtitle "Linearization Part 2 Tutorial Results". Be sure and run the linear regression on your data so that your graph shows the statistics box. Do this by highlighting the data on your graph and pressing the R= button.

23. SAVE. Continue to the end of the tutorial and paste your second graph into your report. [Hint: The shape of the second graph tells you it is an inverse function.] When you calculate your column you will need to use the reciprocal of one of the variables. Be sure and include the algebraic equation for your line of best fit once you have pasted the graphs into your document.

24. You may add the appropriate graphs from tutorials 4 & 5 to your report for extra credit. Be sure and include the proper subtitle headings and continue the proper format for the report.

Essay Writing Skills
Developing a Free Response

OBJECTIVE
This lesson is designed to introduce the students to the skill of planning appropriate free response essays.

LEVEL
All

NATIONAL STANDARDS
UCP.1, UCP.2, G.1, G.2

TEKS
6.2(C), 6.2(D)
7.2(D)
8.2(D)
IPC: 2(D)
Biology: 2(D)
Chemistry: 2(E)
Physics: 2(D)

CONNECTIONS TO AP
Writing appropriate free response answers is a fundamental skill needed in both AP Biology and AP Environmental Science.

TIME FRAME
45 minutes

MATERIALS
transparencies of Practice Essay #1-4
student copies of the practice pages
transparency of *Writing a Free Response* strategies page

TEACHER NOTES
An appropriately written Free Response essay for an AP Biology or AP Environmental Science exam is markedly different from the type of essay that students are typically asked to write in English courses. For this reason, the skill of writing an essay in AP Biology and AP Environmental Science must be explicitly addressed. This activity is designed to help students understand how to set up a mechanical outline or plan to use when writing free response essays in AP science courses. It emphasizes the need for planning a response prior to writing. This planning and pre-thinking approach gives the students a tool to use and enables them to dissect complex prompts into manageable units. This practice activity focuses on the mechanics of dissecting the prompt rather than on writing the specific content. Once

students have mastered the skill of planning or outlining a free response prompt, they need to practice writing essays using specific content throughout the school year.

SUGGESTING TEACHING PROCEDURE:

1. Explain the need for knowing how to write appropriate essays in a science class and describe strategies for writing essays using the handout: Tips for Writing Free Response Essays as your guide.

2. Show the transparency of Practice Essay #1 and explain how to use the strategies covered in step 1 with the sample essay. Explain to students how a mechanical outline of a response to this prompt might look (see answer key to student pages). Note, at this point, students may not be able to provide the correct content for the response, so focus on the mechanics of what should be included.

3. Distribute copies of the Essay Writing Outline Practice pages and show the transparency of Practice Essay # 2 as you model how to outline an appropriate response for the students (see answer key for Practice Essay #2). Elaborate on tip 5 by showing the students a possible outline for the question.

4. Focus student attention on Practice Essay #3 and allow students time to work alone to outline the major items that should be included in an appropriate free response. After 2-3 minutes of individual planning, have students compare their outline to that of their partners. Call on two or three volunteer pairs to write their outlines on the board for all students to see.

5. Have students read the prompt for Practice Essay #4 and prepare an outline of the items that should be included in a well designed free response. Restate tip 5 from the strategies list.

6. Show the students the sample student answer to essay # 3. Ask them to look at the response and identify 4 things that this student could do to make this essay better. Use the annotated and revised student response to show the students how the incorrect answer could be written more appropriately.

7. Follow up this activity in future lessons by including the outlining and writing of free response type questions in your daily warm-ups, daily quizzes, homework assignments, and major tests. The following list of grading hints taken from Advanced Placement and TEKS: A Lighthouse Initiative for Texas Science Classrooms may assist you as you approach the inclusion of free response questions in your assessment strategies:
   a. Start early in the year writing a free response (over a simple topic) in class and going over the rubric for it. Sharing the rubric with the students helps them gain insight into what types of information should and could be included.
   b. Create a rubric with positive points when you write the question. Students are more willing to take a chance when writing an essay in which points are collected rather than lost.
   c. Highlight or check off correct parts of free response answers as you grade them to make it easier for you to add up the points.
   d. Grade all free response answers at one sitting to develop a flow/pattern and encourage consistency in your grading.

TEACHER PAGES

e. On math problems, a correct answer with correct unit and work shown clearly earns full credit. Give partial credit for
   i. Set up of problem
   ii. Correct labels
   iii. Hint-look for final answer; if correct, just scan that work is present.

f. Encourage students to separate and label each section as this will help them organize their response and allow for easier grading.
g. Go over the rubric with the entire class to eliminate the need for making individual remarks. Alternately, you can use colored highlighter to mark the papers using a code such as blue — this statement scores a point, yellow — this statement included unnecessary or off topic information, and pink — this sentence contains incorrect information.
h. Use the College Board prompts and rubrics whenever possible

Tips for Writing Free Response Essays
AP Biology and AP Environmental Science*

1. Read the question twice.
2. Dissect the question to determine exactly what is being asked. (Highlight or underline)
3. Prepare a skeleton outline of the main components of your response.
4. Begin answering the question in the order it is written and DO NOT restate the question or write an introductory paragraph.
5. If the question says to 'discuss' or 'describe'
   a. Define the topic.
   b. Describe or elaborate on the topic.
   c. State an example of that topic.
6. If the question says to 'compare and contrast'
   a. Clearly state what the items have in common.
   b. Clearly state how items are different.
7. If the question asks for a graph to be made
   a. Label each axis with a name and units.
   b. Title the graph.
   c. Scale and number the axes correctly.
   d. Use the correct type of graphs (line or bar).
8. If the question asks a mathematical problem
   a. Show every single step of all work.
   b. Set up problems so that units cancel out (dimensional analysis).
   c. Write answers with units.
   d. If numbers are very large or very small, use scientific notation.
9. If the question asks for lab design
   a. State a hypothesis in the "if, then" format.
   b. Describe each step of a planned experiment in detail including what will be measured and how often the readings will be taken.
   c. Clearly identify the control(s).
   d. State that the experiment will have multiple trials for validity.
   e. Describe the expected results.
10. For ALL questions
   a. Answer in complete sentences, DO NOT use lists, charts, outlines in your final response.
   b. Label each section of your response as it is labeled in the question.
   c. Diagrams can support your statements but will not be scored.
   d. For every statement you write, ask yourself "why". If there is an answer to that why, keep on writing!
   e. Do not answer more than what is asked for. For example, if the question says to choose 3 out of 5 topics, ONLY answer 3 of the 5; If the question asked about RNA specifically, do not discuss DNA replication.
   f. Remember — this writing is timed. Use your time wisely.

*Edited from strategies list provided on page 85 of *A Lighthouse Initiative for Texas Science Classrooms.*

TEACHER PAGES

POSSIBLE ANSWERS TO THE CONCLUSION QUESTION AND SAMPLE DATA

1) Practice Essay#1-#4 could be dissected/outlined as follows:

Practice Essay #1

Main Topic: Carbon & Organic Compounds

A) Characteristics of carbon atom
   * characteristic #1
   * characteristic #2
   * characteristic #3

B) Structure and function of
   a. Lipids
      i. Structure
      ii. Function
   b. Proteins
      i. Structure
      ii. Function
   c. Nucleic Acids
      i. Structure
      ii. Function

Practice Essay #2

Main Topic: Usefulness of the Scientific Method

Components

Name & describe

Name & describe

Name & describe

Name & describe

1. How used in biological discovery # 1

2. How used in biological discovery # 2

TEACHER PAGES

Practice Essay #3

Main Topic: Changes in rate of Photosynthesis

A. Descriptions
   How low levels of light affect the rate of photosynthesis.

   How high temperature will affect the rate.

   How low levels of water will affect the rate.

B. An adaptation to low levels of light
   a. Describe adaptation
   b. Give an example

Practice Essay #4

Main Topic: Growth curve fluctuations

A. Explain what is happening in phase A

B. Three factors that might cause changes in phase B
   a. Factor one
   b. Factor two
   c. Factor three

C. Strategies
   a. Explain (r) strategy
   b. How (r) strategies effect population size
   c. Explain (K) strategies
   d. How (K) strategies effect population size

Annotated and Revised Student Response to Practice Essay #3

Sections labeled to match prompt

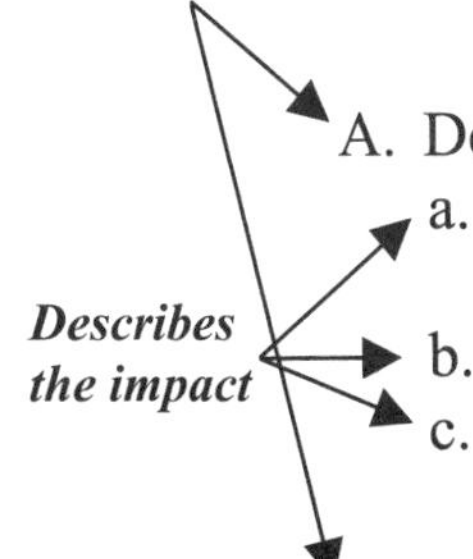

A. Descriptions
   a. Low light levels make it hard for plants to have enough solar energy to go through photosynthesis (so the rate of photosynthesis will go down in low light).
   b. Low amounts of water will (also reduce the rate of photosynthesis).
   c. When temperatures get really high plants lose too much water when they open their stoma (causing photosynthesis rate to decline) so some plants are adapted to opening their stoma at night in order to take in carbon dioxide to use in photosynthesis.

B. Some plants have special adaptations that allow them to survive in extreme environments (such as low levels of light).
   a. Some plants have broad leaf surfaces to catch any available sun rays and can live in low light levels while some have thin leaves.

Gives an example

Revised Student Answer

A. Low light levels make it hard for plants to have enough solar energy to go through photosynthesis so the rate of photosynthesis will go down in low light. Low amounts of water will also reduce the rate of photosynthesis. hen temperatures get really high plants lose too much water when they open their stoma causing photosynthesis rate to decline so some plants are adapted to opening their stoma at night in order to take in carbon dioxide to use in photosynthesis.

B. Some plants have special adaptations that allow them to survive in extreme environments such as low levels of light. Some plants have broad leaf surfaces to catch any available sun rays and can live in low light levels while some have thin leaves.

REFERENCE

Jones, Kristen, Project Editor. *Advanced Placement and TEKS: A Lighthouse Initiative for Texas Science Classrooms*. Austin: Texas Education Agency, 2003. pg. 87

Essay Writing Skills
Developing a Free Response

An appropriately written free response essay for an AP Biology or AP Environmental Science exam is markedly different from the type of essays that are typically written in English courses. For this reason, you can improve your free response writing skills through the practice of dissecting a prompt and preparing a brief outline of the components that should be included in a quality answer. The free response portion of an AP Exam is a timed exercise and as such requires efficient use of the allotted time. By making an outline prior to actually writing the essay, you will be much more likely to include the important parts of a good response. With practice you will become able to dissect even the most complex prompts into manageable pieces.

PURPOSE

In this activity you will practice the skill of dissecting a free response prompt and preparing a mechanical outline of an appropriate response.

MATERIALS

copy of *Tips for Writing Free Response Essays*
copy of Practice Essay Prompts #1-4

PROCEDURE

1. Read through Tips for Writing Free Response Essays as you teacher explains specific tips mentioned in the document.

2. Read the prompt for Practice Essay #1. Observe and record the sample mechanical outline shown by your teacher of an appropriate response for this prompt.

3. Read the prompt for Practice Essay #2, record the outline of an appropriate response as your teacher goes through this essay with the class.

4. Read the prompt for Practice Essay #3. For 2-3 minutes, work alone to use the tips discussed in Tips for Writing Free Response Essays to prepare a mechanical outline for this prompt. When the individual planning time expires, compare the outline you have designed with that of your partner's. You may be asked to share you outline with the class.

5. Read the prompt for Practice Essay #4 and prepare an outline of the items that should be included in a well designed free response. You will be working alone to prepare your outline. Refer to Tips for Writing Free Response Essays if needed.

6. Read through the sample student response to Practice Essay #4. This response is written incorrectly. In the space below the prompt identify 4 things that this student could have done to make this essay more appropriate.

Name ____________________

Period ____________________

Free Response:
Planning for Success

PRACTICE ESSAY # 1

Prompt:
Structure and function are closely related in living systems. For example, the structure of the carbon atom allows it to be the building block of a variety organic compounds.

A. Explain the characteristics of carbon that allow its atoms to provide molecular diversity.
B. Chose three of the following categories of organic compounds and describe each in terms of the compound's structure and function in living organisms.
   1. Carbohydrates
   2. Lipids
   3. Proteins
   4. Nucleic Acids

Main Topic: ____________________

A. ____________________
- * ____________________
- * ____________________
- * ____________________

B. ____________________

____
____
____

____
____
____

____
____
____

PRACTICE ESSAY # 2

Directions: Read the prompt and prepare an outline of the major components that should be included in a response using the lines and bullets as your guide.

Prompt:
The scientific method of problem solving is a useful tool for scientific investigation. Describe the components of the scientific method and cite two examples of how the scientific method has been used to make biological discoveries.

Main Topic: ______________________________

____

- ______________________
- ______________________
- ______________________
- ______________________
- ______________________

1. ______________________________
2. ______________________________

PRACTICE ESSAY #3

Directions: Read the prompt and prepare a mechanical outline of the major components that should be included in a response

Prompt:
The rate of photosynthetic activity may change in various environmental conditions.

a. Describe how each of the following environmental conditions could impact the rate of photosynthesis in a terrestrial plant.
   *low levels of light
   *high temperature
   *low availability of water
b. Select one of the conditions listed above and describe an adaptation that would allow a plant species to photosynthesize effectively in that specific environmental condition.

Main Topic: ______________________

A______________________

____

____

____

B______________________

* ______________________

* ______________________

Essay 4: Ecology question from 2003 exam

Directions: Read the prompt and prepare an outline of the major components that should be included in a response

Many populations exhibit the following growth curve:

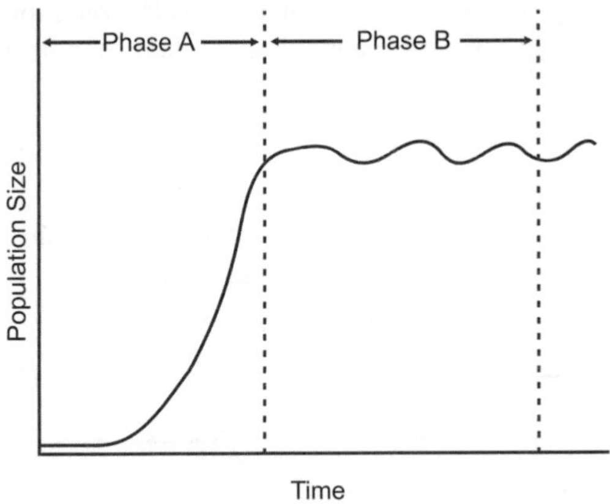

a. Describe what is occurring in the population during phase A.
b. Discuss THREE factors that might cause the fluctuations shown in phase B.
c. Organisms demonstrate exponential (r) or logistic (K) reproductive strategies. Explain these two strategies and discuss how they affect population size over time.

Main Topic: ______________________________

A. ______________________________

B. ______________________________

a. ____________________

b. ____________________

c. ____________________

C. ____________________

* ______________________________

* ______________________________

* ______________________________

* ______________________________

Read the following student's response to Essay #3. Identify 4 things that this student could do to make this essay better.

Prompt:
The rate of photosynthetic activity may change in various environmental conditions.

a. Describe how each of the following environmental conditions could impact the rate of photosynthesis in a terrestrial plant.
   *low levels of light
   *high temperature
   *low availability of water
b. Select one of the conditions listed above and describe an adaptation that would allow a plant species to photosynthesize effectively in that specific environmental condition.

Student's Answer

The rate of photosynthetic activity may change in various environmental conditions. Some plants have special adaptations that allow them to survive in extreme environments. Some plants have broad leaf surface to catch any available sun rays and can live in low light levels while some have thin leaves. Low light levels make it hard for plants to have enough solar energy to go through photosynthesis. Low amounts of water will harm plants. When temperatures get really high plants lose too much water when they open their stoma so some plants are adapted to opening their stoma at night in order to take in carbon dioxide to use in photosynthesis.

List 4 things this student could have done differently to improve the quality of this free response:

1.

2.

3.

4.

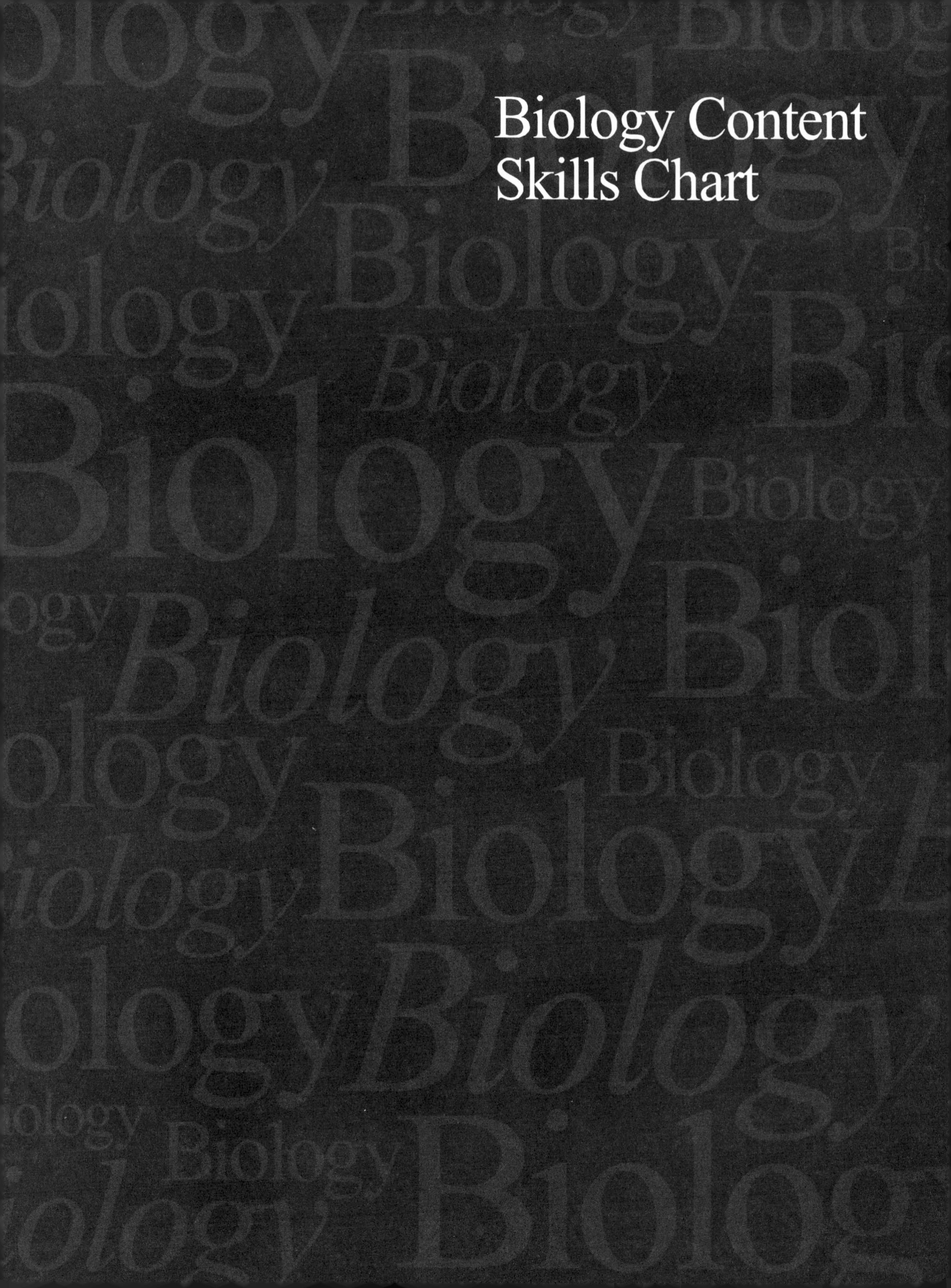

Biology Content Skills Chart

BIOLOGY CONTENT SKILLS CHART

AP Connections	Scope	Activities
	Nature of Science Safety Equipment use and identification Scientific Measurement Scientific method	 **Green Beans the Wonderful Fruit** **Vitruvian Man Meets the Scientific Method** Have students practice making careful scientific observations.
	Experimental design Analyzing Data Communicating scientific information	**Seed Germination** **Foundation Lesson: Essay Writing** **Preparing Formal Lab Reports**
I. Molecules and Cells A. Chemistry of Life 1. Water	**Water** Universal solvent Bonding properties	 Demonstrations such as how many drops of water fit on a penny. Labs dealing with pH
2. Organic Molecules in Organisms	**Biological Molecules** Atomic structure and bonding, carbon emphasis Hydrolysis and dehydration synthesis Structure and properties of carbohydrates Structure and properties of lipids Structure and properties of proteins Structure and properties of nucleic acids	 Review subatomic particles. Use chemical models to demonstrate structure. **McMush Lab**
3. Free Energy Changes	**Energy** Forms of energy ATP structure and function	 **Foundation Lesson: Determining the Amount of Energy in Food**
4. Enzymes	**Enzyme structure and function** Properties of an enzyme Factors affecting enzyme reaction rates	**Enzyme Activity** **The Hydrogen Peroxide Breakdown**

AP Connections	Scope	Activities
B. Cells 1. Prokaryotic and Eukaryotic Cells	**Cells** Microscope use Microscopic measurement Cell Theory Prokaryotic cells Eukaryotic cells	Microscope lab **Microscopic Measurement Lab** General comparison of these two types of cells.
2. Membranes	**Cell Membranes** Surface to volume ratio Fluid Mosaic Model of membrane structure Selective permeability and transport **Osmosis and Diffusion** Cellular homeostasis Diffusion and factors affecting its rate Osmosis Endocytosis Exocytosis, phagocytosis, pinocytosis	**Larger is Not Always Better** **The Fluid Mosaic Membrane** **Plasmolysis** **The Gate Keepers**
3. Subcellular Organization	**Cell Organelle** Structure and function of cell organelles Compare plant and animal cell	Observe and compare plant and animal cells. Microscopically compare structural similarities and differences of typical plant and animal cell.
4. Cell Cycle and its Regulation	**Cell Cycle** Events of Cell Cycle Purpose of Mitosis Events of Mitosis Cytokinesis	**Chromosome Manipulative** **Stages of Mitosis**
C. Cellular Energetics 1. Coupled reactions	**Cell Energy**	
2. Fermentation and cellular respiration	Respiration Fermentation Chlorophyll	Stress the universal nature of respiration. **Yeast and Molasses** **Picking Out the Pigments**
3. Photosynthesis	Light Reactions of Photosynthesis Dark Reactions of Photosynthesis	**Light, Dark, Does it Really Matter?** **Observing Starch Production**

AP Connections	Scope	Activities
II. Heredity and Evolution A. Heredity 1. Meiosis and gametogenesis	**Meiosis** Purpose of meiosis Events of meiosis Compare mitosis and meiosis	Beads or pipe cleaners can be used to model the chromosomal events of meiosis.
2. Eukaryotic chromosomes	Karyotyping	Any of a variety of karyotyping activities can address the diagnostic value of this procedure.
3. Inheritance patterns	Mendel Mendelian Laws Monohybrid Crosses Dihybrid Crosses Inheritance patterns, Mendelian traits-vs-linkage	**Numbers Do Indeed Make a Difference** **Mendel and His Peas** **The Amazing Maize**
B. Molecular Genetics 1. RNA and DNA structure and function	**DNA to Proteins** DNA structure Replication RNA structure Types of RNA and purpose Transcription Translation	Perform a DNA extraction. Paper and pencil activity modeling DNA structure and replication. **Proteins, the Essence of Life**
2. Gene Regulation	Operon theory	**The *trp* Operon**
3. Mutation	Types of mutations	Indicate that not all mutations are harmful.
4. Viral Structure and Replication		
5. Nucleic acid technology and applications	**Biotechnology** Fundamentals of electrophoresis Recombinant DNA Plasmids Restriction enzymes	An electrophoresis lab separating various food colors can be used to introduce electrophoresis techniques. **Protein Properties** **Bacterial Transformation** Any of a variety of kits can be used for wet lab activities dealing with plasmids, recombinant DNA and the process of transformation.

AP Connections	Scope	Activities
C. Evolutionary Biology 1. Early evolution patterns	**Evolution** Microevolution-Changing the Allelic Frequency of the Gene Pool	Include a discussion Hardy-Weinberg Equilibrium.
2. Evidence for evolution	Charles Darwin	
3. Mechanisms of evolution	Darwinian Theory of Evolution	**Quackers** Include concepts supporting Darwin's theory of evolution.
	Natural Selection Macroevolution-Speciation	**Life in the Cold** Concepts should include phylogeny, speciation, diversity, adaptation and extinction.
III. Organisms and Population A. Diversity of Organisms	**Taxonomy**	The evolutionary relationships and phylogenetic classification among the various kingdoms should be examined as they are surveyed.
	Examining the taxonomic hierarchy	**Classification Webquest**
1. Evolutionary patterns	Viruses	Using a dichotomous key activity.
2. Survey of the Diversity of Life	Monereans (archae bacteria and eubacteria)	**"Killer Defects"**
3. Phylogenetic classification	Fungi Protista Plantae Animalia	
B. Structure and Function of Plants and Animals	**Plants**	
1. Reproduction, growth and development	Plant structures and functions	Include material on adaptations of leaves, roots and stems with emphasis on structure and function.
2. Structural, physiological and behavioral adaptations		**Monocots and Dicots, Two Plants with Differences**
	Transport	**"Hole-y" Moley** **Transpiration**
	Hormones Reproduction	**Those "Foolish" Plant Hormones** Any flower lab comparing Monocots versus Dicots. **Plant Wars**

AP Connections	Scope	Activities
	Animals	This should include emphasis on the structure and function of the various organs and structures found in each system. Include material in the inter-relationship among the various systems. For example, relate function blood circulation to gas exchange or excretion. Information about the process of homeostasis should be included when possible.
	Evolutionary Trends	This should include major developments in evolution of a particular system.
	Digestive system	**Yeast Cells and Digestion of Nutrients**
	Circulatory system	**Circulatory System**
	Excretory system	**Urinalysis**
	Muscular/skeletal system	**Chicken Leg Dissection**
	Respiratory system	**Kermit Versus Mickey Mouse**
	Immune system	**Specific Immune Response**
	Endocrine system	
3. Response to the environment	Nervous system	**Making Sense of It All** **Planarian Behaviors**
C. Ecology 1. Population dynamics	**Populations and the environment**	
	Population Growth	Make use of interactive Internet sites that simulate population growth.
	Biomes	Pencil and paper activity of data that graphs and analyzes predator/prey relationships Compare and contrast characteristics of r-strategists with K-strategists. Web quest on biomes
2. Communities and ecosystems	**Communities, energy flow and nutrient cycles**	**Wonderful Pond Water** **Ecotones**
3. Global issue	Energy pyramids	
	Food webs/chains	Opportunity to connect systems to the ecosystem. For example, the effect of gas exchange on the carbon cycle.
	Nutrient cycles	

National
Standards

National Standards

The National Standard codes used in the lessons throughout the Laying the Foundation series are based on the following coding system. We encourage you to read the National Standards for your content area found at http://www.nap.edu/readingroom/books/nses/html.

Unifying Concepts and Processes

UCP.1 Systems, order, and organization
UCP.2 Evidence, models, and explanation
UCP.3 Change, consistency, and measurement
UCP.4 Evolution and equilibrium
UCP.5 Form and function

Science as Inquiry

A.1 Abilities necessary to do scientific inquiry
A.2 Understandings about scientific inquiry

Physical Science

B.1 Structure of atoms
B.2 Structure and properties of matter
B.3 Chemical reactions
B.4 Motions and forces
B.5 Conservation of energy and increase in disorder
B.6 Interactions of energy and matter

Life Science

C.1 The cell
C.2 Molecular basis of heredity
C.3 Biological evolution
C.4 Interdependence of organisms
C.5 Matter, energy, and organization in living systems
C.6 Behavior of organisms

Earth and Space Science

D.1 Energy in the earth system
D.2 Geochemical cycles
D.3 Origin and evolution of the earth system
D.4 Origin and evolution of the universe

Science and Technology

E.1 Abilities of technological design
E.2 Understanding about science and technology

Science in Personal and Social Perspectives

F.1 Personal and community health
F.2 Population growth
F.3 Natural resources
F.4 Environmental quality
F.5 Natural and human-induced hazards
F.6 Science and technology in local, national, and global challenges

History and Nature of Science

G.1 Science as a human endeavor
G.2 Nature of scientific knowledge
G.3 Historical perspective

Syllabi

Developing a Course Syllabus

There are many reasons to develop a course syllabus. The most important reason is to communicate to your students that you have carefully planned your course. It is often thought of as a contract between an instructor and a student. It conveys the message that each of you is committed to meeting the objectives of the course. Research has shown that students who are told what they are supposed to learn and how they are to be evaluated perform better than those who are not so instructed. The syllabus should specify the duties and responsibilities of the student while communicating a commitment from the instructor to respect a timeline. Once the syllabus has been published and distributed, it is important to do your very best not to change it. Students will feel that the rules have been changed in the middle of the game.

Other reasons to develop a course syllabus include:

- Clearly communicating course expectations to administrators and parents.
- Creating an organizational tool for yourself if you teach more than one kind of course.
- Organizing your laboratory time and resources for maximum efficiency.
- Enhancing cooperation and communication with your colleagues so that multiple teachers teaching the same course deliver the same quality of instruction to each student.
- Reducing the amount of time spent deciding what to do each class period; the plan has already been formulated making execution of the plan easier.
- Documenting what has been taught.
- Empowering students to take more responsibility for their education.
- Helping students better manage their time and set priorities while improving their study habits.

Constructing a syllabus is actually quite easy. A suggested procedure follows:

1. Realize that a school year usually consists of 36 weeks and that you are fortunate if you are able to instruct for 32 of those weeks. Factors such as semester exam weeks, TAKS testing, benchmark testing for TAKS, pep-rallies, assemblies and other unscheduled interruptions will consume up to 4 weeks of your instructional time.
2. Examine the course scope found in the front of this guide. Without regard for the fact that you only have 32 weeks, estimate how much time it would take for you to cover each major topic, including laboratory time and testing time.
3. Determine the mid-point of the course, which is the point you wish to reach by the end of the first semester. Tally the ideal number of weeks required for each semester.
4. Obtain an accurate district calendar and count the number of weeks you have for each semester. (The first semester is usually shorter if your district ends the semester before January.)

1. Compare. Do not be alarmed if your tally exceeds 32 weeks. Decide if you can shift the mid-point a bit. If not, it is time to adjust the ideal number of weeks so that they fit into your actual time frame. This may mean radically changing the structure of your course. You may have to change the number of activities that you do in a given unit, change the type of notes students are expected to take, or other instructional methods to free up time to cover the entire scope of the content.
2. Now that you have determined the number of weeks, break each unit down by day and choose logical starting and stopping points for each class period. Allow a two day cushion at the end of each grading period for unforeseen obstacles such as personal illness, re-teaching, fire drills, etc…

3. If you find it daunting to publish the whole semester on a syllabus, consider publishing it in 3 week intervals. That way the plan stays more current as those unforeseen interruptions occur.
4. Now that you have a plan for student success, stick to the plan. Realize that you will have to teach bell-to-bell in order to successfully complete your plan.

The syllabi that follow were contributed by some of the best and most experienced Pre-AP teachers in the region, representing classes at both public and private schools. Each of these teachers has played an integral part in developing a successful Pre-AP and AP program at their school. Each of them would tell you there is no one right way to teach a Pre-AP science course. It is our hope that you will survey the collection of syllabi presented and formulate your own syllabus to share with your students and colleagues. Understand that your first attempt will require monitoring and adjusting. Keep careful notes about your timeline expectations and what worked and did not work on your initial syllabus. Do not be alarmed if it takes a couple of tries to create a syllabus that works consistently in your classroom year after year.

TEACHER

Lynn Cook
Putnam City West High School
Oklahoma City, Oklahoma

SCHOOL PROFILE

School Location and Environment: Putnam City West High School is located on the far west side of Oklahoma City in Oklahoma County. It is considered a suburban school, but has become much more "urbanized" as the number of apartment dwellers that feed into the school has grown tremendously over the past several years. The majority of students come from single-parent homes and fall into the low to middle income socioeconomic categories. Our Hispanic students make up about 14% of our minority percentage; many of these students have begun speaking English in the last two years. Presently, about 40% of our students are eligible for the Free/Reduced Lunch Program.

Our school is on the accelerated or 4x4 block schedule. Students enroll in 8 courses during the school year; 4 are completed in the fall and 4 are completed in the spring. Classes meet for 18 weeks; during those 18 weeks, each class meets for 90 minutes each day.

Grades the school contains: 9-12

Type of school: (public or private) Public; total enrollment is approximately 1690

Percentage of minorities: 40.4%

College Record:
% of graduating seniors attending post-secondary institutions: 66.4%
% of graduating seniors attending 4-year institutions: n/a

Do you teach the AP course at your school? Yes

If not, is it offered at your school?

Number of students taking the PAP science course in your discipline: 80

Number taking the AP course in your discipline: 24

Course sequence of the PAP courses in your school: Pre-AP Bio as freshman or sophomore, Pre-AP Chemistry as sophomore or junior, Pre-AP Physics as sophomore or junior

In what year is the AP course in your discipline taken? Generally junior or senior; occasionally sophomore year

SYLLABUS

Unit 1 Timeline Approx. 8 days

Topics: Nature or Science, Tools of Science, Characteristics of Life

Labs/Activities: Check Lab, Collecting Biological Data on Life Characteristics of Pill Bugs, Microscope Mystery

Unit 2 Timeline Approx. 8 days

Topics: Basic Chemistry and Macromolecules

Labs/Activities: Testing Cohesiveness of Water, pH Lab—Household Acids and Bases, Identifying Biomolecules in Foods, Starch Hydrolysis, Reaction Rates in Enzymes—Toothpickase Lab, Electrophoresis of Proteins

Unit 3 Timeline Approx. 9 days

Topics: Ecology, Cooperation and Competition of Organisms, Nutrient Cycling, Biomes

Labs/Activities: Soil Investigation Lab—pH, Particle Size and Density, Carbon Cycle Roundhouse Diagrams, Building Energy Pyramids, Predator/Prey Lab, Human Environmental Impact Essays, Biodiversity Activities

Unit 4 Timeline Approx. 9 days

Topics: Cells, Membranes, Transport Across Membranes

Labs/Activities: Cell Theory Writing Project, Viewing Cells, Travel Brochure for a Cell, Using Bubbles to Explore Membranes, Design A Cell—Diffusion and Surface Area to Volume Ratios, Osmosis with Potatoes, Endocytosis "Jelly Bean Problem", Homeostatic Response of Cells and Tissues in Solutions

Unit 5 Timeline Approx. 5 days

Topics: Cell Cycle and Mitosis, Cancer, Meiosis

Labs/Activities: Online Mitosis Activity, Mitosis with Pipe Cleaners, The Meiosis Game, Faces of Cancer (NIH activity), Understanding Cancer Tutorial

Unit 6 Timeline Approx. 10 days

Topics: DNA Structure, Replication, Protein Synthesis, Mendelian Inheritance, Genetic Disorders, Gene Technology

Labs/Activities: Berry Full of DNA—Extraction Lab, Building A Fruit Loop Model of DNA, Protein Synthesis—From DNA to RNA Transcription with Stickers, Modeling Mutations, Rebops—Marshmallow Meiosis, Pedigree Analysis, Karyotyping/Chromosomal Abnormalities, Restriction Enzymes & DNA Goes to the Races, DNA Gel Electrophoresis, Gene Therapy Posters, Genes & Environment—Human Variation in Height (NIH Activity)

Unit 7 Timeline Approx. 8 days

Topics: History of Life, Natural Selection, Adaptation, Cladograms

Labs/Activities: Radiometric Dating to Determine a Fossil's Age, String Timelines, Evolution of Barbellus, Natural Selection with Teddy Grahams, Adaptations of Birds, Not Just a Bag of Beans—Population Genetics, Bear Branch on the Tree of Life—DNA Comparison

1st Nine Weeks Projects: Winogradsky Column, Selection of Soil Bacteria, Geneticist For A Day

Unit 8 Timeline Approx. 5 days
Topics: Matter and Energy in Living Systems, Photosynthesis, Fermentation, Cell Respiration
Labs/Activities: Plant Pigment Chromatography, What Factors Influence Photosynthesis?, Microbial Brew—Making Root Beer, Yeast Fermentation Lab, Snail/Elodea Lab

Unit 9 Timeline Approx. 5 days
Topics: Phylogenetic Classification, Microbes and Microbiology, Aseptic Technique, Viruses
Labs/Activities: Dichotomous Keys/Salamander, Microbe Hunt, Antibiotic Sensitivity, Viral Disease Research

Unit 10 Timeline Approx. 5 days
Topics: Plant Structure and Function, Transpiration
Labs/Activities: Are Corn Seeds Alive?, Transpiration in Monocots vs. Dicots, What Affects Seed Germination?—Design A Lab, Plant Response to the Environment

Unit 11 Timeline Approx. 8 days
Topics: Invertebrate Diversity, Digestion, Respiration and Circulation, Nervous System
Labs/Activities: Termite Trail Lab, Invertebrate Investigation Lab, Homeostasis and Circulation in Goldfish Tail
2nd Nine Weeks Projects: Fetal Pig Dissection, Biological Concepts "Choose A Project", Owl Pellet Dissection, Vertebrate Field Project or Vertebrate Books

Of the remaining 10 days, a minimum of 3 are spent in EOI testing and semester testing. The other 7 are spent in lab doing dissections or projects, as well as building in time in the schedule for shortened class time for school activities, assemblies, etc.

TEACHER

Patti O'Connor/Carol Leibl
James Madison High School
San Antonio, Texas

SCHOOL PROFILE

School Location and Environment: James Madison High School is located in the far northeast corner of San Antonio. The school boasts the Agriscience magnet program for students interested in agriculture. Not only does it sponsor programs in animal husbandry but also diverse courses such as floral design, and meat processing. This program has received many national awards. While this school was once in an area of farmland, the suburbs of San Antonio now surround the campus. James Madison High School is a member of the North East Independent School District.

Grades the school contains: 9-12

Type of school: (public or private): Public

Percentage of minorities: 41% Hispanic, 9.4% African-American, 2.9% Other

College Record:
% of graduating seniors attending post-secondary institutions: 76%
% of graduating seniors attending 4-year institutions: 43%

Do you teach the AP course at your school? Yes

Number of students taking the PAP science course in your discipline: 141

Number taking the AP course in your discipline: 24 in AP Biololgy

Course sequence of the PAP courses in your school: Pre AP Biology - 9th grade,
Pre AP Chemistry - 10th grade, Pre AP Physics - 11th grade, OR IPC - 9th grade, Pre AP Biology
Pre AP Biology - 10th grade, Pre AP Chemistry - 11th grade, Pre AP Physics - 12th grade

In what year is the AP course in your discipline taken? 11th or 12th grade. It maybe taken concurrently with another science course.

SYLLABUS

Tuesday, August 19
Pass Out Books
Safety Contracts
Book Condition Forms
Rules
Grading
Notes Atoms
HmWk - Reading Ch. 1 & 2 pg. 21-34, pg. 1-36

Lab - Tuesday, August 19
Yeast Cells and Molasses (due Tuesday August 21)

August 21
Notes - Water/Carbon
Functional Groups
HmWk - Reading
Read pg. 34-52

Lab - Thursday, August 21
Yeast Cells and Sucrose (due August 26)

August 25
Notes - Carbohydrates, Lipids
HmWk - Read pg. 47-58

Lab - Tuesday, August 26
Ozazone Lab (due August 28)

August 27
Notes - Proteins Nucleic Acids
Read pg. 58-70

Lab - Thursday, August 28
Enzyme Lab (due September 2)

August 29
Notes - Enzymes
TEST - September 3

Lab - Tuesday, September 2
Review Session for Test

September 3
Test 55 minutes - Organic Chemistry
Notes - Cell Structure
Read pg. 121-130

Lab - Thursday, September 4
Protein Electrophoresis (due September 9)

September 5
Notes - Cell Organelles
Read pg. 131-150

September 9
Notes - Cell Membranes
Read pg. 85-102

Lab - Tuesday, September 9
Osmosis Lab (due September 11)

September 11
Notes - Cell Transport
Read pg. 102-118
TEST - September 15

Lab - Thursday, September 11
Review Session for Cell Test

September 15
Test 55 minutes
Notes - Light
Read pg. 153-159

Lab - Tuesday, September 16
Lab - Length of DNA (due September 18)

September 17
Notes - Light Reaction
Read pg. 179-186

Lab - Thursday, September 18
Lab - Hill Reaction Lab

September 19
Notes - Calvin Cycle, C4 photosynthesis
Read pg. 190-202

Lab - Monday, September 22
Review for Photosynthesis Test

September 23
Test 55 minutes - Photosynthesis
Notes - Respiration
Read pg. 159-161

September 25
Notes - Glycolysis
Read pg. 162-167

Lab - Thursday, September 25
Pea Lab (due September 30)

September 29
Notes - Calvin Cycle
Read pg. 167-177
TEST - Respiration October 1

Lab - Tuesday, September 30
Review for Respiration Test

October 1
Test 55 minutes - Respiration
Notes - Cellular Reproduction
Read pg. 309-315

Lab – Thursday, October 2
Lab - Fruit Flies

October 3
Notes - Mitosis
Read pg. 315-321

October 7
Notes - Life Cycles
Read pg. 330-335

Lab - Tuesday, October 7
Lab - Mitosis (due October 9)

October 9
Notes - Meiosis
Read pg. 321-330

Lab - Thursday, October 9
Review for Test

October 14
Test 55 minutes - Meiosis
Practical Fruit Flies

Lab - Tuesday, October 14
Lab - Meiosis

October 16
Notes - DNA Replication
Read pg. 205-212

Lab - Thursday, October 16
Transformation Lab

October 21/22
Turn in - C.C. pg. 85
Review Sheet
***Test - Cells and Membranes Ch. 3 and Ch. 6
Notes - Cell Energy
HmWk - Read pg. 62-66
C.C. pg. 66

TEKS 4B

October 23/24
Turn in - C.C. pg. 66
Notes - Ch. 5 Glycolysis
Lab - Computer Yeast Cell Lab
Analysis Questions
HmWk - Read pg. 134-143
C.C. pg. 144

TEKS 4B

October 27/28
***Benchmark Test
Turn in - C.C. pg. 144
Notes - Kreb's Cycle
HmWk - Read pg. 135-140, 144-148
C.C. pg. 148
Review Sheet due October 31
TEST - October 31

TEKS 4B, 9B

October 29/30
Turn in - C.C. pg. 148
Notes - Chemiosmosis
Lab - Effects of Temperature on Respiration
Analysis
TEST - October 31

TEKS 4B, 9B

October 31/November 3
Turn in - Review Sheet
***Test - Respiration and Cell Energy
Notes - Light Reaction Photosynthesis Ch. 4
HmWk - Coloring Sheet Mitochondria and
Chloroplasts
C.C. pg. 113
Read pg. 101-113

TEKS 4B, 9B

November 4/5
Turn in - Coloring sheets
C.C. pg. 113
Notes - Ch 4. Photosynthesis
Lab - Plant Pigments
HmWk - C.C. pg. 122
Read pg. 113-122

TEKS 9B

November 6/7
Turn in - C.C. pg. 122
Notes - Calvin Cycle
Lab - Hill Reaction
HmWk - Review Sheet
C.C. pg. 125
Read pg. 122-125
TEST - November 10, 12

TEKS 9B

November 10/12
Turn in - C.C. pg. 125
Review Sheet
***Test - Ch. 4 Photosynthesis
Notes - Cell Cycle
HmWk - C.C. pg. 216
Read pg. 213-216

TEKS 6E

November 13/14
Turn in - C.C. pg. 216
Notes - Cell Cycle and Mitosis
Lab - Cell Cycle Computer
HmWk - C.C. pg. 225
Read pg. 222-225

TEKS 6E

November 17/18
Turn in - C.C. pg. 225
Notes - DNA replication Ch. 8
Lab - DNA with Bananas
HmWk - C.C. pg. 222
Read pg. 216-222

TEKS 6B

November 19/20
Turn in - C.C. pg. 222
Video - Mitosis and DNA
Lab 8A - DNA Replication
HmWk - Review Sheet
C.C. pg. 229
Read pg. 222-229
TEST - November 21/24

TEKS 6B, 6E

November 21/24
Turn in - C.C. pg. 229
Review Sheet
***Test - DNA and Mitosis Ch. 8

TEKS 6B, 6E

November 25/December 1
Notes - Protein Synthesis Transcription Ch. 9
Lab - Separation of Proteins by Electrophoresis
HmWk - C.C. pg. 247
Read pg. 240-247

TEKS 6B

December 2/3
Turn in - C.C. pg. 247
Notes - Protein Synthesis Translation Ch. 9
Lab - Building Proteins
HmWk - C.C. pg. 254
Read pg. 247-254

TEKS 6A

December 4/5
Turn in - C.C. pg. 254
Notes - Protein Synthesis Continued
Video - Protein Synthesis
HmWk - C.C. pg. 240
Read pg. 233-240

TEKS 6A, 6B

December 8/9
Turn in - C.C. pg. 240
Lab - Epidemiology
Notes - Viruses
HmWk - Review Sheet
TEST - December 10/11

TEKS 4C

December 12/15
Semester Review Day

December 16
Final Exam P. 1, 3

December 17
Final Exam P. 5, 7

December 18
Final Exam 2, 4

December 19
Final Exam 6, 8

January 6/7
45 min. - Alumni Day Library
Article on Genetic Therapy
Notes on Classification Ch. 18
HmWk - Read pg. 461-474
C.C. pg. 474

TEKS 8B, 8C

January 8/9
Turn in - C.C. pg. 474
Notes - Ch. 18 Classification
Lab - Species and the Dichotomous Key
Analysis Questions
HmWk - Read pg. 474-481
C.C. pg. 481

TEKS 8A, 8B, 8C

January 12/13
Turn in - C.C. pg. 481
Notes - Classification
Animal WebQuest
HmWk - Review Sheet

January 14/15

TEKS 8A, 8B, 8C

January 14/15
Turn in - WebQuest
Review Sheet
***Test - Classification
Notes on Life Cycles
Read pg. 317-324
C.C. pg. 324

TEKS 6E

January 16/20
Turn in - C.C. 324
Notes - Meiosis
Lab - Modeling Meiosis pg. 741-742
HmWk - Analysis Question pg. 741-742

TEKS 6E

January 21/22 (Extended Advisory for Registration) (22/23 English 10th blocked for field testing
Turn in - Analysis Questions
Notes - Monhybrid Crosses
Lab - Effect of Sample Size and Monohybrid Crosses
Read pg. 343-351
HmWk - Analysis Question to Labs
Problems Monohybrid crosses

TEKS 6D

January 23/26 (22/23 English 10th blocked for field testing
Turn in - Lab
Problems
Notes - Dihybrid Crosses
Lab - Kangasaurus Dihybrid Crosses
HmWk - Problem Dihybrid Crosses
C.C. pg. 351, 358
Read pg. 351-358

TEKS 6D

January 27/28
Turn in - Lab
Problems - C.C. pg. 351, 358
Notes - Incomplete Dominance
Lab - Amazing Maize
HmWk - Problems Incomplete Dominance
C.C. pg. 365
Read pg. 358-365
Review Sheet Due February 4/5

TEKS 6D

January 29/30 (Course Fair P2 - 10th attend for 30 mins)
Turn in - Lab
Problems - C.C. pg. 365
Notes - Linked Genes, Sex Linked Gene
Karyotyping
Lab - Kangasaurus
HmWk - Problems Sex Linked Genes
TEST - February 4/5

TEKS 6D

February 2/3
Turn in - Problems
Lab
Notes - Pedigrees and Karyotyping
NIH Lab Karyotyping
TEST - February 4/5

TEKS 6D

February 4/5
Turn in - Review Sheet
***Test - Genetics/Benchmark Test
HmWk - Read pg. 369-381
C.C. pg. 381

TEKS 6B, 6E

February 6/9
Turn in - C.C. pg. 381
Notes - Biotechnology
Lab - Determining the Length of an Unknown Piece of DNA
HmWk - Read pg. 382-387
C.C. pg. 387

TEKS 2B, 2C, 6C

February 10/11
Turn in - C.C. pg. 387
DNA Lab
Notes - Biotechnology
Lab - NIH Imaging Harris Hawks Lab
HmWk - Read pg. 391-413
C.C. pg. 406, 413

TEKS 2B, 2C, 6C

February 12/17
Turn in - C.C. pg. 406
Notes - Biotechnology
Lab - Transformation Lab
HmWk - Review Sheet
Read pg. 406-413
TEST - February 18/19

TEKS 2B, 2C, 6C

February 18/19
Turn in - Review Sheet
***Test - Biotechnology
Notes - Evolution
HmWk - C.C. pg. 422
Read pg. 417-422

TEKS 7A, 7B

February 20/23
Turn in - C.C. pg. 422
Notes - Hardy-Weinberg
Lab - Natural Selection and Quackers
HmWk - C.C. pg. 433
Read pg. 422-433

TEKS 7A, 7B

February 24 (TAKS 9-11th No Classes meet)
Move to a B/A schedule
School Wide Testing

February 25/26
Turn in - C.C. pg. 433
Notes - Evolution
Lab - NIH Imaging Analogous and Homologous Structures
HmWk - C.C. pg. 507
Read pg. 499-507
Review Sheet Due March 2/3

TEKS 7A, 7B

February 27/March 1
Turn in - C.C. pg. 507
Notes - Evolution
Lab - How Long is a Long Time
HmWk - C.C. pg. 515
Read pg. 507-515
TEST - March 8/9

TEKS 7A, 7B

March 2/3
Turn in - C.C. pg. 515
Notes - Evolution
Lab - NIH Imaging-Evolutionary Bottlenecking
HmWk - Review Sheet
TEST

TEKS 7A, 7B

March 4/5
Turn in - Lab
Notes - Evolution
Set up Plants for Gravitropism
HmWk - Review Sheet

TEKS 10C

March 8/9
Turn in - Review Sheet
***Test Evolution
Notes - Plant Structure
Stem Lab
HmWk - C.C. pg. 190
Coloring Sheet on Plant Stucture

TEKS 10C

March 10/11
Turn in - C.C. pg. 190
Turn in Coloring Sheet
Stomate Lab
Final Data for Gravitropism
Notes - Secondary Growth
HmWk - C.C. pg. 300
Read pg. 291-300

TEKS 10C

March 12/22
Turn in - Coloring Sheet on Plant Structure
Notes - Plant Structure and Secondary Growth
Stem Lab
Coloring Sheet Xylem and Phloem

TEKS 10C

March 23/24
Turn in - Coloring Sheet
Notes - Transpiration
Lab - Set up Transpiration Lab
HmWk - Read pg. 301-311
C.C. pg. 308, 311

TEKS 10B, 10C

March 25/26
Turn in - C.C. pg. 308, 311
Notes - Plant Hormone
Take data on Transpiration Lab
HmWk - C.C. pg. 148
Review Sheet
***TEST - March 29, 30

TEKS 10B, 10C

March 29/30
***Test Botany
Notes - Development
HmWk - Read pg. 261-269
C.C. pg. 269

TEK 5B, 5C

March 31/April 1
Turn in - C.C. pg. 269
Notes - Fertilization, Gastrulation, and Neurulation
HmWk - Read pg. 269-277
C.C. pg. 277
Coloring Sheet Development

TEKS 5B, 5C

April 2/5
Turn in - C.C. pg. 277
Coloring Sheet
Notes - Development
Lab - Chicken Egg
HmWk - C.C. pg. 277
Read pg. 277-287

TEKS 5B, 5C

April 6/7
Turn in - C.C. pg. 27
Notes - Mechanisms of Development
Lab - Comparing Development Chick, Frog, and Human
HmWk - Review Sheet
***TEST - April 8,12

TEKS 5A, 5B, 5C

April 8/12
Turn in - Review Sheet
***Test - Ch. 10 Development
Notes - Digestion Survey
HmWk - C.C. pg. 73
Read pg. 67-73

TEKS 5A, 5B, 5C

April 13/14
Turn in - C.C. pg. 73
Notes - Digestion Anatomy
Lab - NIH Imaging Value of Villi
HmWk - Coloring Sheet Anatomy of Digestive System

TEKS 10A, 10B

April 15/16
Turn in - Coloring Sheet
Notes - Digestion Physiology
Lab - Enzyme Specificity Lab Computer
HmWk - Review Sheet

TEKS 10A, 10B

April 19/20
Turn in - Review Sheet
***Test - Ch. 2 Digestion
Notes - Survey of Circulation
HmWk - Read pg. 191-198
C.C. pg. 198

TEKS 10A, 10B

April 21/22
Turn in - C.C. pg. 198
Notes - Anatomy of the Circulatory System
Dissection of a Beef Heart

TEKS 10A, 10B

April 26/27 (TAKS 10th SS and 11th Math "crunch schedule")
Turn in - C.C. pg. 198
Notes - Physiology of the Circulatory System
Lab - NIH Imaging, Enlarged Heart
HmWk - C.C. pg. 209
Read pg. 200-209

TEKS 10A, 10B

April 28/29 *(TAKS- 28th, 10th Math, 11th Science/29th, 10th Science, 11th SS "crunch schedule")*
Turn in - C.C. pg. 209
Notes - Clottting Blood
Lab - Body Works
HmWk - Review Sheet
***Test - April 30, May 3

TEKS 10A, 10B

April 30/May 3
Turn in - Review Sheet
***Test
Notes - Non-specific Immune Response
HmWk - C.C. pg. 609
Read pg. 603-609

TEKS 10A, 10B, 4C, 11D

May 4/5
Turn - C.C. pg. 609
Lab - Modeling the Immune System
Notes - Cell Mediated Response
HmWk - C.C. pg. 617
Read pg. 609-617

TEKS 10A, 10B, 4C, 11D

May 6/7
Turn in - C.C. pg. 617
Lab - Simulating the Immune Response
Notes - Cell Mediated Response
HmWk - C.C. pg. 627
Read pg. 617-627

TEKS 10A, 10B, 4C, 11D

May 10/11
Turn in - C.C. pg. 627
Lab - Simulating the Immune Response
Notes - Respiratory System and Urinary System
HmWk - C.C. pg. 97
Read pg. 87-97
Review Sheet Homeostasis-Immune,
Respiratory and Urinary Systems
***Test - May 12, 13

TEKS 10A, 10B, 4C, 11A, 11B, 11D

May 12/13
Turn in - C.C. pg. 627
Review Sheet
***Test
HmWk - Review for Final Exam

May 14/17
Rat Dissection
HmWk - Review for Final Exam
Study Sessions

May 18/19
Rat Dissection
HmWk - Review for Final Exam
Study Sessions

May 20/21
Turn in - Rat Lab
Rat Practical
Review for Final Exam
Study Sessions

May 24/25
Final Exam

May 26/27
Final Exam

TEACHER

Nancy Ramos
Northside Health Careers High School
San Antonio, Texas

SCHOOL PROFILE

School Location and Environment: Northside Health Careers High School, a magnet school, is designed for students whose interests lie in the allied health/medical areas. It is located on 13 acres donated by the San Antonio Medical Foundation. It is in the shadows of the South Texas Medical Center in Northwest San Antonio. Health Careers High School was dedicated in 1984 and is operated under the auspices of the Northside Independent School District.

Grades the school contains: 9-12

Type of school: (public or private): Public

Percentage of minorities: 46% Hispanic, 5% African-American, 14% Asian

College Record:
% of graduating seniors attending post-secondary institutions: 98%
% of graduating seniors attending 4-year institutions: 81%

Do you teach the AP course at your school? Yes

Number of students taking the PAP science course in your discipline: 96

Number taking the AP course in your discipline: 65 in AP Biololgy

Course sequence of the PAP courses in your school: Pre AP Biology - 9th grade, Pre AP Chemistry - 10th grade

In what year is the AP course in your discipline taken: 11th or 12th grade

SYLLABUS

Aug. 18-19	Introduction, books, safety
20-21	Safety cont., **Pre Assessment and Safety Quiz**
22-25	Scientific method, identification of variables
26-27	Pre lab Corn Seed Lab, begin characteristics of life, data collection
28-29	Lab analysis, graphing, cont.' characteristics of life
Sept. 2-3	**Scientific method Quiz**, characteristics of life
4-5	Set up experimental design, writing a lab report
8-9	Data collection on exp. design, adaptations
10-11	Data collection, lab analysis, begin ecology
12-15	**Unit 1 Test**
16-17	Populations, population growth
18-19	Pop. Lab set up, relationships in a community, succession in a biome
22-23	Lab observations, trophic organisms and levels, food chains/webs, energy flow
24-25	Lab observations, nutrient recycling- nitrogen
26-28	**Ecology Unit Test**
Sept. 30-Oct. 1	Matter, atomic structure, chemical bonding especially in water
Oct. 2-3	Chemical and biological significance of water, pH, buffers
6-7	pH Lab
8-9	Lab analysis, **Chemistry Quiz**
10-14	Structure and function of carbohydrates, lipids, proteins, nucleic acids
15-16	Dehydration synthesis and hydrolysis in organic compounds
17-20	Organic Chemistry Lab and Identification of an Unknown Organic Cpd.
21-22	**Organic Chemistry Quiz**
23-24	Cell classification, begin organelle discussion
27-28	Cont. organelles, Animal Cell Lab and analysis
29-30	Cont. organelles, District Benchmark Assessment, Plant Cell Lab
Oct. 31-Nov. 3	Plant Cell Lab Cont. and analysis, cell membrane structure and function
Nov. 4-5	Diffusion/Osmosis Lab
6-7	Lab analysis, osmosis cont., active transport, phagocytosis
10-11	**Cell Unit Test**
12-13	Cell cycle, mitosis
14-17	Cell Surface to Volume Lab, mitosis home lab
18-19	Lab Analysis, Intro. to Genetics, Monohybrid crosses
20-21	**Cell cycle/Mitosis Quiz**
Dec. 1-2	Cont. monohybrid crosses, begin dihybrid crosses
3-4	Meiosis
5-8	Applications of meiosis to dihybrid crosses
9-10	Gene linkage, mutations
11-12	**Genetics Quiz**
15-16	Semester Review
17-19	**Semester Exams**

Jan. 6	Cell Cycle
8	Mitosis Cont. Importance of Cell Size Lab
12	Lab Discussion/Wrap up on Cell cycle
14	**Cell Cycle Test**; Introduction to Genetics
16	Monohybrid Inheritance; Introduction to Meiosis
21	Meiosis Continued; Dihybrid Inheritance
23	Dihybrid Cont.
27	Sex-linked inheritance, Intro. to DNA
30	**Genetics Test**
Feb. 2	DNA Construction and Replication
4	RNA, Intro. to Protein Synthesis
6	Protein Synthesis
10	Angiotensin Study and Mutations
12	**DNA/Protein Synthesis Test**
17	**District Benchmark Assessment**
19	Biotechnology
23	Biotechnology Lab
25	Begin Evolution, Mechanisms of evolution
27	Moths and Natural Selection Lab
Mar. 2	Post Lab, Evidence for Evolution
4	Evidence for Evolution Lab Study
8	Post lab, Review
10	**Evolution Test**
12	Classification, Taxonomy
23	Classification Lab
25	Classification Lab
29	Enzyme Study
31	Enzyme Study
April 2	ATP, Begin Cell Respiration
6	Aerobic Cell Respiration
8	Anaerobic Cell Respiration
13	Fermentation Lab
15	Lab Discussion/Wrap up Cell Respiration
19	**Cell Respiration Quiz**, Introduction to Photosynthesis
21	Chromatography and Leaf Stomate Lab
26	Rate of Photosynthesis Lab
28	Lab Analysis/Wrap up Photosynthesis
30	**Test on Cell Respiration and Photosynthesis**

May 4	Body Systems
6	Body Systems
10	Body Systems
12	Body Systems
14	**District Benchmark Assessment**
18	**Body System Unit Test**
20	Semester Review
24-27	**Semester Exams**

TEACHER

Debbie Richards
Bryan High School
Bryan, Texas

SCHOOL PROFILE

School Location and Environment: Bryan High School is located in Brazos County which is in the south, central region of Texas. Our community is neighbored on the south by College Station and Texas A&M University. Our school operates under a seven period per day bell schedule and with 43% of the population identified as low socio-economic.

Grades the school contains: approximately 3,700 students in grades 9-12

Type of school: (public or private) Public

Percentage of minorities: 43%

College Record:
% of graduating seniors attending post-secondary institutions: 70%
% of graduating seniors attending 4-year institutions: 32%

Do you teach the AP course at your school? Yes

If not, is it offered at your school?

Number of students taking the PAP science course in your discipline: Pre-AP Biology has an enrollment of approximately 200 students.

Number taking the AP course in your discipline: Two sections that average 20 students per section.

Course sequence of the PAP courses in your school: The majority of the Pre-AP Biology students are freshman. After Pre-AP Biology, the students typically take Pre-AP Chemistry followed by Pre-AP Physics.

In what year is the AP course in your discipline taken? The vast majority of the AP Biology students are seniors.

SYLLABUS

Biology I
Scope and Sequence

First Six Weeks

The Study of Biology (10 days)
- Laboratory Safety
- Laboratory Equipment
- Using SI system in Biology
- Designing Experiments
- Conducting Experiments
- Reporting Experimental Results
- Themes of Biology
- Traits of Life

The Chemistry of Biology (10 days)
- Atoms and Bonding
- Traits of Water
- The Structure and Function of Macromolecules
  - Carbohydrates
  - Lipids
  - Proteins
  - Nucleic Acids

The Interdependence of Biology Part I (9 days)
- Major Biomes
- Interdependence in Food Webs and Food Chains
- Interdependence in Biogeochemical Cycles
  - Water
  - Carbon
  - Nitrogen
  - Oxygen

Benchmark
*Project – Effect of Acid Rain on Germination

Second Six Weeks

The Interdependence of Biology Part II (10 days)
- Interdependence in Populations and Communities
- Population Growth
- Human Impact and Intervention

Cell Structure and Function (8 days)
- Use of Microscope
- Microscopic Measurement
- Cell Theory
- Structure and Function of Cell Organelles

Membrane Structure and Function (10 days)
- Fluid Mosaic Membrane
- Passive Transport
- Active Transport
- Enzymes

Benchmark

Project: Phase 3 Level Inquiry Experiment. Designer French Fries
- Design Stage

Third Six Weeks

Project: Phase 3 Level Inquiry Experiment. Designer French Fries
- Data Collection, Reporting

Cellular Energy Part I (8 days)
- Enzyme Functions
- Light Reactions of Photsynthesis
- Dark Reactions of Photosynthesis

Energy Transformations (8 days)
- ATP structure and function
- Respiration

Genes and Gene Expression (8 days)
- Central Dogma, Hierarchy
- DNA structure and Replication
- RNA structure and types
- Transcription
- Translation
- Operon Theory

Semester Review and Finals (5 days)

Second Semester

Fourth Six Weeks

Mitosis and Meiosis (10 days)
- Events of the Cell Cycle
- Events and Purpose of Mitosis
- Events and Purpose of Meiosis
- Contrasting Mitosis and Meiosis
- Mutations and Karyotyping

Genetics (11 days)
- Mendelian Laws
- Monohybrid Crosses
- Dihybrid Crosses
- Inheritance Patterns
- Human Genetics and Pedigrees

Biotechnology (5 days)
- Human Genome
- Electrophoresis
- Restriction Enzymes
- Recombinant DNA

Benchmark

Genetics of Populations (beginning) (9 days)
- Mechanisms of Natural Selection

Fifth Six Weeks

Genetics of Populations Continued
- Natural Selection Continued
- Mechanisms of Speciation
- History of Life

Taxonomy and Viruses (6 days)
- Classification Systems
- Kingdom Overview
- Viral Structure and Cycles

Bacteria, Protists, and Fungi (6 days)
- Diversity of Bacteria
- Characteristics of Protists
- Types and Role of Fungi

Kingdom Plantae Part I (12 days)
- Phylogeny of Plantae
- Plant Life cycles
- Plant Anatomy
- Plant Reproduction

Benchmark

Sixth Six Weeks

Kingdom Animalia and Introduction to Systems (6 days)
- Animalia Phylogeny Overview
- Animal Organizational Hierarchy
- Integumentary and Muscle System

Animal Systems Part I (10 days)
- Digestive System
- Circulatory System
- Respiratory System
- Excretory System

Animal Systems Part II (8 days)
- Nervous System
- Endocrine System
- Reproductive System

TAKS

Review and Final Exams (5 days)

TEACHER

Jackie Snow
Troy High School
Troy, Texas

SCHOOL PROFILE

School Location and Environment: Population 1,500. Located along I-35 about 30 miles south of Waco and 65 miles north of Austin. Very small 3A school with 389 students in the high school. We offer 5 different AP Courses in our school with pre-AP offered in English, biology and chemistry. All of the students are active in band, athletics or both during the year they are enrolled in pre-AP biology. My school has a very active AG Science program and about 40% of our students stay active for all four years of high school. This group of students includes our best and brightest.

Grades the school contains: 9-12

Type of school: (public or private) Public; total enrollment is approximately 389

Percentage of minorities: 20%

College Record:
% of graduating seniors attending post-secondary institutions: 77%
% of graduating seniors attending 4-year institutions: 26%

Do you teach the AP course at your school? Yes

If not, is it offered at your school?

Number of students taking the PAP science course in your discipline: 33

Number taking the AP course in your discipline: 10

Course sequence of the PAP courses in your school: (These are the students on the accelerated math track)

- 9th Pre-AP Biology
- 10th Pre-AP Chemistry
- 11th Physics and A&P
- 12th AP Biology

Some students may choose to take the PAP science courses at any point, we are not exclusive. However, non-math accelerated students typically take IPC during their freshman year.
In what year is the AP course in your discipline taken? Students usually take the AP Biology course during their senior year, but juniors have taken the course and have been successful.

SYLLABUS

First Semester

Week 1

Introduction to the Course: issue textbooks, hand out a six weeks calendar, and explain the expectations of the course.
Unifying themes of Biology
Characteristics of Living Things
Overview of Scientific Processes
Design Your Own Experiment: Pill Bug Investigation

Week 2

Chemistry of Life: Atoms and Chemical Bonding
Water Chemistry: Polarity, aqueous solutions, pH, "polar" bear activity, sample pH of various common substances
Carbon Compounds: Macromolecules and their functions, functional groups

Week 3

Enzymes: Lecture accompanied with starch agar plate/ amylase demo.
Review for Test
First Major Test
Organic Compounds Lab: six stations for each lab team to work through in two days. These stations are for making observations, collecting data, and making predictions, there is no formal lab write up for these days in lab.

Week 4

Cell Structure: Different kinds of microscopes and their micrographs
Why is it important that cells be small? Cell Size Activity
Cell Theory; Compare Prokaryotic and Eukaryotic cells; Cell Membrane Structure
Cell Organelles: Class notes with detailed diagrams and micrographs, stress differences between plant and animal cells
Cell Lab: Use microscopes to view plant/animal cells and produce drawings

Week 5

Review the cell for Test
Second Major Test
Membrane Transport; Fluidity of the Cell Membrane (soap bubble demonstration)
Active transport and Passive Transport
"Egg" Osmosis Activity (Takes place over four days and on the last day we collect and record final data. Students will submit their analysis in terms of this week's lessons.)
Part A of AP Lab #1 is done as a demonstration and the students fill in data tables and answer questions.

Week 6

Cell Respiration: Cellular Energy, ATP, and Formula for Respiration
ATP Demonstration: Dart Gun as ATP
Glycolysis, Kreb's Cycle, Electron Transport Chain
Respiration as a Redox Reaction
Fermentation
Evaluate the Importance of O_2 in Respiration

Week 7

Photosynthesis: Structure of a Chloroplast; Absorption of Light Energy, Products of the Light Reactions
Calvin Cycle (Light Independent Reactions); Reactants and Products of the Calvin Cycle
Light Reactions and Calvin Cycle as Coupled Reactions
Model of a Chloroplast with all Reactants, Products, and Intermediate Compounds
Review for Respiration and Photosynthesis Test
Third Major Test

Week 8

Chromosomes and Cell Reproduction: Differentiation between a Gene, DNA, Chromosome, and a Chromatid; Cell Cycle
Cell Division in Eukaryotes and Prokaryotes
Introduce *haploid* and *diploid*
Mitosis and Cytokinesis
Lab Activity: Observing the Stages of Mitosis in Onion Root Tip Cells and in Whitefish Blastula Cells
Review for Test
Fourth Major Test

Week 9

Meiosis and Sexual Reproduction: Formation of Haploid Cells, Genetic Variation, Gamete Formation
Sexual and Asexual Reproduction
Sexual Life Cycles in Eukaryotes
Chromosome Activity with Pop Beads
Mendel and Heredity
The Laws of Heredity
Punnett Squares; Monohybrid and Dihybrid

Week 10

Outcomes of Crosses
Genetic Disorders
Review of Meiosis and Mendelian Genetics
Fifth Major Test
DNA: The Genetic Material: Structure of DNA, Replication of DNA
Role of Enzymes in Replication of DNA
DNA Extraction from Strawberries and Kiwi

Week 11

Transcription of DNA
Translation into Proteins
Gene Regulation and Structure
Lab Activity: Modeling Protein Synthesis
Review Meiosis, DNA Structure, Protein Synthesis
Sixth Major Test

Week 12

Gene Technology, Genetic Engineering, DNA Fingerprinting
Risks and Ethical Questions
Review for Test
Seventh Major Test

Week 13

Principles of Evolution: Evolution of Prokaryotes and Eukaryotes
Multicellularity, Mass Extinctions
Theory of Evolution, Natural Selection, Evolution of Populations
Plants and Fungi on Land, Arthropods and Vertebrates
Activity: Modeling Radioactive Decay
Comparative Anatomy Activity

Week 14

Review Evolution
Eighth Major Test
Classification of Organisms: Taxonomy(binomial nomenclature)
Identifying a Species, Evolutionary History

Week 15 (usually the week of Thanksgiving)

Activity: Making a Dichotomous Key

Week 16

Revisit Topics in Classification
Review for Test
Ninth Major Test
Exam Review

Week 17

Exam Review
First Semester Exam

Second Semester

Week 1

Introduction to the Kingdoms of Biology
The Three Domains of Biology: Bacteria, Archaea, and Eukarya
Kingdom Protista
Kingdom Fungi

Week 2

Kingdom Plantae
Kingdom Animalia
Review of the Kingdoms
First Major Test
Lab Activity: Six stations with activities designed to reinforce characteristics and appreciate the diversity of the kingdoms

Week 3

Lab Activity Continued
Viruses and Bacteria: Viral Structure, Reproduction, HIV, Viral Diseases
Bacterial Structure and Reproduction, Eu- and Archae-bacteria
Pathogenic Bacteria, Antibiotics, Importance of Bacteria
Preventive Practices to Avoid Serious Infections

Week 4

Lab Activity: Staining and Observing Bacteria
Guest Speaker: Microbiologist
Review Viruses and Bacteria
Second Major Test
Protists: Diversity and Reproduction

Week 5

Amoeba, Algae, Diatoms, Flagellates, Protistan Molds Sporozoans
Human Diseases Caused by Protists
Lab Activity: Pond Water
Review Protists
Third Major Test

Week 6

Kingdom Fungi: Structures, Nutrition, Reproduction
Ascomycetes, Zygomycetes, and Basidiomycetes
Symbiotic Relationships
Lab Activity: Observing Various Common Molds
Lab Activity: Culturing Molds from the Places We Live

Week 7

Review of Kingdom Fungi
Fourth Major Test
Lab Activity: Yeast Fermentation
Introduction to Plants: Plants on Land
Vascular Tissue, Seeds, and Flowers

Week 8

Nonvascular Plants, Seedless Vascular Plants
Gymnosperms, Angiosperms
Lab Activity: Six stations allowing observation of various types of plants and their structures.
Plant Review

Week 9

Fifth Major Test
Plant Reproduction: Alternation of Generations
Reproduction in Seedless Plants and in Seed Plants, Role of Animals In Plant Reproduction
Lab Activity: Effects of Nutrition on Plant Reproduction

Week 10

Review Plant Reproduction
Sixth Major Test
Plant Structure and Function: Roots Stems and Leaves
Transport in Plants: Transpiration
Transpiration Lab

Week 11

Plant Growth and Development: Nutrients, Hormonal Control
Lab Activity: Seed Germination
Review for Test
Seventh Major Test

Week 12

Introduction to Animals: Body Symmetry, Body Cavity,
Segmentation, Tissues and Organs, Reproductive Strategies
Invertebrates: Sponges, Cnidarians, Flatworms, and Roundworms
Mollusks and Annelids
Arthropods: Arachnids, Insects, Crustaceans, Echinoderms,
Invertebrate Chordates

Week 13

Review of Invertebrates
Eighth Major Test
Introduction to Vertebrates: Fish, Amphibians, Reptiles, Birds, and Mammals

Week 14

Lab Activity: Comparing the Vertebrate Morphology
Review of Vertebrates
Ninth Major Test

Week 15

Human Body Systems: Circulatory, Respiratory
Digestive, Excretory, Immune, Nervous, Endocrine and
Reproductive Systems

Week 16

Review of Body Systems
Tenth Major Test
Ecology and the Environment: Populations,
Ecosystems, Biological Communities
The Environment and Conservation Biology

Week 17

Review for Final Exam
Final Exam

Personal notes about my syllabus:
This syllabus is not comprehensive. Over the years it has become my goal to allow the students an experience for each topic covered. These may be something from the day's headlines or an opportunity to explain a topic to their neighbor which may only take a couple of minutes. I try to have as many "hands-on" activities as possible; this may mean more than one in a day's class period. These activities come from workshops, textbooks, word of mouth, Internet, and some are just "ideas" or modifications of something we've done in AP Biology. These keep me very busy and on my feet, but they provide "anchors" for the next topic and for review.

I build in a review day for every major test and this allows me a little extra time for covering content material. Because students can become overwhelmed with note taking, I usually hand out "skeletal" notes that they "flesh out' during lectures.

I love to get the students in the lab as often as possible even if it is only for a fifteen minutes. The more they "do", the more they remember and understand.

We have adopted Prentice Hall's *Biology: The Living Science* for our Biology I classes and we do not have a different text for PAP Biology, so I supplement a great deal from other texts. I especially love the baby Campbell, *Concepts and Connections*, and BSCS *Biology: The Molecular Approach.*

TEACHER

Sharon A. Hamilton
Fort Worth Country Day School
Fort Worth, Texas

SCHOOL PROFILE

Fort Worth Country Day School is an independent, coeducational K-12 college preparatory school providing a rigorous and balanced curriculum emphasizing academics, athletics and the arts. Located in southwest Fort Worth, the school enrolls 1100 students and employs a full-time faculty of 120. In 1998, the U. S. Department of Education honored the Upper School (grades 9-12) as a Blue Ribbon School, with a special emphasis award in Arts Education. FWCDS is accredited by the Independent Schools Association of the Southwest, an organization recognized, but not regulated by the Texas Education Agency.

Of the 375 students in the Upper School, 14% are considered minority. One hundred percent attend four-year colleges and universities after graduation from FWCDS.

Most students entering the ninth grade attended FWCDS Middle School. The traditional life science course emphasizing the unity and diversity of living things is taught to seventh graders. Each year, about 21% of the ninth grade class is new to FWCDS.

Three years of laboratory science are required for graduation. Ninth graders take biology, tenth graders take chemistry and eleventh graders take physics. A few students take an AP science as well as physics as juniors. Each year, approximately 40% of the ninth grade class (95 students) enter pre-AP (Honors) biology. Students may move into or out of the honors track each year with departmental approval. Most students taking AP sciences are seniors. Classes in AP Biology, Chemistry, Environmental Science and Physics are taught every year. The number of seniors taking AP Biology varies, from 34 (37% of the senior class) in 2003 to 22 (24%) in 2004.

SYLLABUS

Honors (pre-AP) Biology 2003-2004

Fall Semester

Week 1 Safety in the Laboratory
"Safety Tour" Lab

Week 2 Measurements and Instruments
Metric conversions, Instruments and Measurements Lab, Use of the Microscope Lab

Week 4 Nature of Science: What is "Science?" What is "Pseudoscience?"
Research paper on pseudoscience, Scientific Observations Lab, Experimental Design Lab

Week 5 Biological Chemistry
Review of chemistry concepts, organic compounds, carbohydrates, lipids, proteins, nutrition
Molecular Models Lab, Qualitative Identification of Carbohydrates, Lipids, Proteins Labs

Week 8 Cells
Types of cells (prokaryotic, eukaryotic, plant, animal), structure and function of cell components, cell size
Cells and Sizes Lab

Week 9 Cell Membranes
Structure, movement across the membrane, surface area/vol ratios
Diffusion and Osmosis Labs: egg, dialysis tubing, Elodea

Week 11 Enzymes
Structure, function, lock and key model, denaturing
Rate of Reaction: Paperase Lab (Graphing Skills), Catalase Lab

Week 12 Energy
Potential/kinetic energy, endergonic/exergonic reactions, ATP, ecosystems, trophic levels/ pyramids of energy
Energy in Food Lab (Calorimetry)

Week 14 Plants and Photosynthesis
Nature of light and color, leaf pigments, reactions of photosynthesis
Chromatography of plant pigments lab, leaf structure and function lab

Week 15 Review for Semester Exams

Week 16 Semester Exam Week

Spring Semester

Week 1 Cell Respiration and the Human Respiratory system
Reactions of cell respiration, aerobic vs. anaerobic, human respiratory system structure & function
CO^2 Production in Humans Lab, Fermentation in Yeast Lab

Week 3 Cell Cycle
Stages of cycle, cell cycle and cancer
Cell Cycle in Onion Root Tips and Fish Embryos Lab
Staining Onion Cells to Observe Mitosis Lab

Week 5 DNA to Proteins and Biotechnology
DNA structure, function and replication, DNA → mRNA → proteins, DNA electrophoresis
Paper DNA Model Lab, Isolating DNA from Fruits Lab, Protein Synthesis Sentences Lab, DNA Electrophoresis Lab

Week 8 Genetics and Reproduction
Mendelian genetics, genes "beyond Mendel," genes are on chromosomes, meiosis, human reproductive system structure and function
Probability Lab, Genetics of Corn Lab, Human Genetics Lab, Meiosis in Reebops Lab

Week 11 Evolution and Natural Selection
Origin of life, geological time scale, review of plant and animal phyla
Geological Time Line, Simulated Natural Selection Lab

Week 13 Infectious Disease and the Human Immune System
Causes of infectious disease, immune system structure & function, immune disorders
Handshake Lab

Week 14 Organs and Systems in Mammals
Digestive, circulatory, excretory, nervous, muscular, endocrine systems structures &functions
Dissection of the fetal pig with Lab Practical Exam, Pulse rate and Exercise Lab, Effects of Drugs on Daphnia's Heart Rate Lab, Urinalysis Lab, Reflexes Lab, Dissection of Sheep Eye Lab

Week 18 Review for Semester Exam

Week 19 Semester Exams

Lessons

Green Beans the Wonderful Fruit
Using Scientific Measurement

OBJECTIVE
The students will work in pairs to select appropriate tools, make metric measurements, and confirm variation within a sample of plant seed pods. Students will design their own data table to record data and generate appropriate graphs. Students will use 2 different pod samples to determine averages for pod length, pod mass, and pod volume and compare their sample averages to class averages.

LEVEL
Biology I

NATIONAL STANDARDS
UCP.2, UCP.3, A.1, A.2, C.2, E.1, E.2, F.3, F.6, G.1, G.2

TEKS
6(D), 2(A), 2(B)

CONNECTIONS TO AP
Process skills such as measurement, graphing and data presentation are needed in all AP science courses.
AP Biology: Variation among organisms.

TIME FRAME
45 minutes

MATERIALS
(For a class of 28 working in pairs)

- 84 green bean pods
- 84 snow pea pods
- beakers of various sizes
- graduated cylinders, several sizes
- meter sticks
- metric rulers, small
- balances

TEACHER NOTES
Students are expected to make many independent choices as they collect the data for this activity. To begin with, they must select the appropriate measurement tools. You should put out a variety of linear measurement tools and liquid measurement tools from which they will choose.

Encourage students to share data with other groups to increase their sample size and validity. Some students may have difficulty coming up with the volume displacement method. Ask leading questions rather than tell them the correct procedure. Hopefully after determining the volume for a couple of pods using this laboratory skill, they will work together to find a faster way. At this point they may ask for a larger beaker so they can measure the entire sample for displacement and then divide by the number of pods. Have several beakers of varying sizes ready and be sure to remind them of the low level of accuracy achieved by measuring volume using the graduations on the outside of the beaker. They will probably apply the "whole sample" procedure when determining the average mass.

You will have to continually press to get them to write down the steps used in their procedure, but this is excellent practice for writing free response essays where they will be expected to detail procedures.

This activity requires students to prepare four data tables. Most often they have been given a pre-labeled data table and may struggle with how to arrange their data into a useful format. You will want to discuss the attributes of a quality data table prior to this activity. Avoid the temptation of setting up the data table for them. Have scratch paper handy for them to use in planning the format of their table. This will be particularly necessary as they modify their procedures to reflect "whole sample" data collection. Emphasize that if using the "whole sample" method their data table will still need to include their initial and final measurements and not just the averages. Additionally, emphasize the importance of differentiating between what is measured and what is calculated. For instance, initial and final volumes are measurements whereas net volume is NOT measured, but rather calculated.

Students must think through the design of the graph(s) in this activity. A review of independent and dependent variables may be in order. They are asked to take data from two of their tables and create graphs.

Snow peas make a good choice for a second type of seed pod. The produce and frozen foods sections of the grocery store should provide sources of whole seed pods.

Make a transparency of the following chart for groups to record their averages.

Group Number	Average Green Bean Pod Length	Average Snow Pea Pod Length	Average Green Bean Pod Volume	Average Snow Pea Pod Volume	Average Green Bean Pod Mass	Average Snow Pea Pod Mass

POSSIBLE ANSWERS TO THE CONCLUSION QUESTIONS AND SAMPLE DATA

Data Table 1: Length of Green Bean Pods	
Bean pod #1	13.2 cm (measurements will vary)
Bean pod #2	14.1 cm
Bean pod #3	13.7 cm
Bean pod #4	15.8 cm
Bean pod #5	13.6 cm
Bean pod #6	16.5 cm
Average Bean Pod Length	13.5 cm
Class Average Bean Pod Length	14.2 cm

Data Table 2: Length of Snow Pea Pods	
Snow Pea pod #1	8.0 cm (measurements will vary)
Snow Pea pod #2	7.5 cm
Snow Pea pod #3	9.1 cm
Snow Pea pod #4	8.8 cm
Snow Pea pod #5	7.9 cm
Snow Pea pod #6	9.3 cm
Average Snow Pea Pod Length	8.4 cm
Class Ave. Snow Pea Pod Length	8.2 cm

Data Table 3: Average Green Bean and Snow Pea Pods Volume		
Pod Comparison	Green Beans	Snow Peas
Amount of water displaced by all pods	33.2 mL	28.6 mL
Average pod volume (Water displaced divided by the number of pods.)	5.5 mL	4.8 mL
Class Average pod volume	5.8 mL	4.6 mL

Data Table 4: Average Green Bean and Snow Pea Pod Mass		
Pod Comparison	Green Beans	Snow Peas
Mass of all pods	15.6 g	14.3 g
Average mass of one pod (mass divided by the number of pods.)	2.6 g	2.3 g
Class Average pod mass	2.7 g	2.1 g

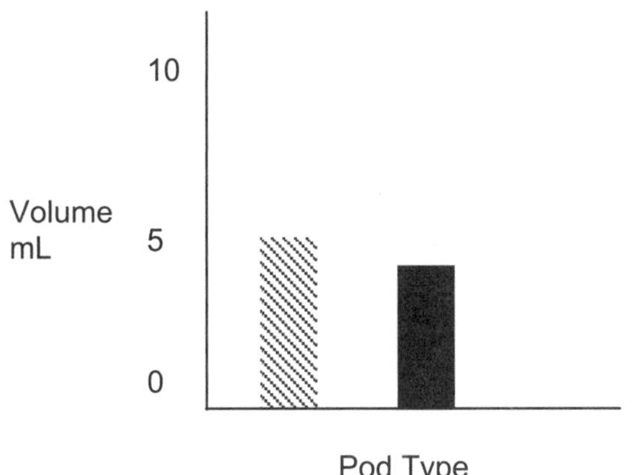

- Graphs 1 & 2 will vary with bean and pea samples but will be comparative bar graphs.
- Graphs should contain title, axis labels, legends and units.

TEACHER PAGES

ANALYSIS

1. What is the range of length variation for the bean pods in your sample?
   - Students should report the range of shortest to longest pods.

2. What is the range of length variation for the snow peas in your sample?
   - Students should report the range of shortest to longest pod.

3. Is your green bean pod length average the same as the class average? Explain the reason for your answer.
   - Answers will vary but most groups will not exactly match the class average because their sample size is small.

4. How much variation is there when you compare the average pod volumes in your green bean and snow pea samples to that of the class?
   - Students should use numbers to show how their sample compares to the class average.

5. How much variation is there when you compare the average pod masses in your green bean and snow pea samples to that of the class?
   - Students should use numbers to show how their sample compares to the class average.

CONCLUSION QUESTIONS

1. Does your green bean sample show variation in mass, length, and volume? Support your answer with data.
   - Answers will vary. Student should include specific data when answering.

2. Describe the procedure used for measuring the volume of the pods.
   - Students will describe their version of measuring volume by displacement.

3. If you were told that an unidentified bean was 115 mm long, would you predict that this bean is most likely a green bean or a snow pea? Explain.
   - Green bean
   - 11.5 cm is closer to the class average for green bean pods than for snow pea pods.

4. If you were randomly given a green bean of the same variety used in this activity, what would you expect its mass to be? Explain.
   - Answer should be equal to the class average
   - The class average is more representative of the typical green bean pod length.

REFERENCES

Miller, Kenneth and Levine, Joseph. *Biology*. Pearson Education, Inc. pg. 372, pg. 25

Green Beans the Wonderful Fruit
Using Scientific Measurement

Darwin's theory of natural selection included the observation that individuals in a population of any species vary in many inheritable traits. Darwin realized that this variation is what makes natural selection possible. Offspring will resemble, but not be identical to, each other and their parents. The variation found among species members may provide some members with a slight advantage. This advantage can lead to an increase in that variant within the population. Some of the variation within a species is measurable. For example, one tree may be slightly taller at maturity than its sibling. One dog may be milliseconds faster than its litter mate. This small speed advantage may make the dog able to catch the rabbit first, avoid starvation and thereby live long enough to reproduce. Variation is essential to the survival of a species in an ever-changing ecosystem.

PURPOSE

In this activity you will work with a partner to select the appropriate tools to make metric measurements. You will collect the data needed to determine the averages for pod length, pod mass, and pod volume of two different species of plant pods. You will then design your own data table, record the data, and generate appropriate graphs for communicating the data.

MATERIALS

- 5-6 green bean pods
- 5-6 snow pea pods
- beakers of various sizes
- graduated cylinders, several sizes
- meter stick
- metric ruler, small
- balance

Safety Alert
Do not eat or drink in the laboratory.

PROCEDURE

PART 1: VARIATIONS IN POD LENGTH

1. Design a data table in the space labeled Data Table 1 on the student answer page. Your table should include places to record the length of 6 green bean pods, the average length of green bean pods in your sample, and the class' average green bean pod length.
2. Obtain 6 green bean pods and select the tools that you will use to measure the pods' length.
3. Measure the length of the pods and record the data in Data Table 1.
4. Determine the average pod length for your sample and record it in Data Table 1.

5. Share your average with the other groups in the class as your teacher instructs.

6. Design a data table in the space labeled Data Table 2 on the student answer page. Your table should include places to record the length of 6 snow pea pods, the average length of snow pea pods in your sample, and the class' average snow pea pod length.

7. Obtain 5-6 snow pea pods and select the tools that you will use to measure the pods' length.

8. Measure the length of the pods and record the data Data Table 2.

9. Determine the average pod length for your sample and record the average in Data Table 2.

10. Share your average with the other groups in the class as your teacher instructs.

PART II: POD VOLUME

1. Devise a method for determining the volume of each of your green bean pods and record the steps you will follow on question 7 of the student answer sheet.

2. Design a data table in the space labeled Data Table 3 on the student answer page. Your table should include places to record the volume of 6 snow pea pods and 6 green ban pods, the average volume of snow pea pods in your sample and the average volume of green bean pods in your sample, and the class' average snow pea pod volume and green bean pod volume.

3. Collect the volume data and record it in Data Table 3.

4. Share your average green bean and snow pea pod volumes with the class as your teacher instructs.

5. In the space marked Graph 1 on the student answer page, construct a graph of the data found in Data Table 3. Be sure to include all of the appropriate parts of a graph.

PART III: POD MASS

1. Design a data table in which you will record the average pod mass based on your green bean sample, the average pod mass based on your snow pea sample, and the class pod average for both types. Your data table should contain any measurements taken as you determine the average pod mass for each type of pods. This table will be Data Table 4.

2. Collect the mass data and record it in Data Table 4.

3. Share your average green bean and snow pea pod masses with the class as your teacher instructs.

Name ____________________

Period ____________________

Green Beans the Wonderful Fruit
Using Scientific Measurement

DATA AND OBSERVATIONS

Data Table 1: Length of Green Bean Pods

Data Table 2: Length of Snow Pea Pods

Data Table 3: Average Green Bean and Snow Pea Pods Volume

Data Table 4: Average Green Bean and Snow Pea Pod Mass

ANALYSIS

1. What is the range of length variation for the bean pods in your sample?

2. What is the range of length variation for the snow peas in your sample?

3. Is your green bean pod length average the same as the class average?

4. How much variation is there between your average pod volume for green beans and snow peas and that of the class?

5. How much variation is there when you compare the average pod masses in your green bean and snow pea samples to that of the class?

Graph 1 Title: ____________________

Graph 2 Title: ____________________

CONCLUSION QUESTIONS

1. Does your green bean sample show variation in mass, length, and volume? Support your answer with data.

2. Describe the procedure used for measuring the volume of the pods.

3. If you were told that an unidentified bean was 115 mm long, would you predict that this bean is most likely a green bean or a snow pea? Explain.

4. If you were given the value for the mass of a green bean of the same variety used in this activity, what would you expect its mass to be? Explain.

Write Your Notes and Ideas Here!

Vitruvian Man Meets the Scientific Method
Writing and Testing Appropriate Hypotheses

OBJECTIVE
Students will devise and test a hypothesis regarding Vitruvius' human proportions theory. Additionally, students will devise and test a hypothesis regarding the relationship between foot and arm span lengths.

LEVEL
Biology I

NATIONAL STANDARDS
UCP.2, E.1, E.2, G.1, G.2, G.3

TEKS
2(A), 2(B), 2(C), 2(D)

CONNECTIONS TO AP
Experimental design and hypothesis writing are skills that are assessed on the AP Biology exam. Additionally, these skills are used in all AP science courses.

TIME FRAME
45 minutes

MATERIALS
14 metric measuring tapes

TEACHER NOTES
Students find hypothesis writing to be impersonal at times. This activity has the student design hypotheses that can be accepted or rejected based on data from their own body.

It will help speed the measurement process to mark the metric measurements for height on one of the door frames in your room.

POSSIBLE ANSWERS TO THE CONCLUSION QUESTIONS AND SAMPLE DATA

Data Table 1: Lab Partner Data			
Measured in cm	Arm Span	Height	Difference
Your measurements	165.1	167.6	2.5
Your Partners measurements	167.5	157.4	10.1

Data Table 2: Class Data in cm			
Person M/F	Arm Span	Height	Difference
Tanica (F)	163.4	164.4	1.0
Jackie (F)	158.6	160.6	2.0
Ryan (M)	170.5	168.7	1.8
Marilyn (F)	165.0	154.9	11.1
Labrisa (F)	167.1	159.0	8.0
Derk (M)	170.3	173.4	3.1
Sandy (M)	164.2	165.8	1.6
Jamie (F)	159.4	159.3	0.1
Hector (M)	166.6	170.1	3.5
Paige (F)	152.4	150.6	1.8

Data Table #3: Foot Size/Arm Length Comparison			
Person M/F	Length of foot	Length of forearm	Difference
Carolyn (F)	22.0	26.6	4.6
Denise (F)	25.4	27.9	2.5
Fred (M)	25.5	2.51	0.4
Kirbo (F)	24.8	28.4	3.6
Shonda (F)	20.5	24.2	3.7

The data for Data Table 1, Data Table 2 and Data Table 3 will vary from class to class. The data typically do not support Vitruvius' theory.

1. Does your individual data for height and arm span support Vitruvius' hypothesis? Why or why not?
   - Answers will vary based on student's measurements.
   - Yes, my data varies. There was a difference of 2.5 in my measurements and a difference of 10.1 in my partner's data.

2. How do your height and arm span results compare to other groups in the class? Explain.
   - Answers will vary based on student's measurements.
   - My lab group data varies and so does the rest of the groups' data.

3. Does the class height and arm span data support Vitruvius' hypothesis? Why or why not?
   - Answers will vary based on student's measurements but typically do not support Vitruvius's theory.
   - No, our data does not support Vitruvius' hypotheses because every person's data shows variation.

4. When comparing males and females, does one group fit Vitruvius' hypothesis more closely than the other? Explain your answer.
   - Answers will vary based on student's measurements.
   - Males in this class have less variation in the measurements than do females.

5. Write a conclusion statement based on the data that you have collected.
   - The data collected in this investigation does not support Vitruvius' hypothesis.
   - Students should indicate whether or not the hypothesis is supported or not supported by the data collected.
   - Answers will vary based on student's measurements

6. Based on the data that you have collected is there a correlation between the length of the forearm and the length of the foot? Explain your answer.
   - Answers will vary based on student's measurements.
   - There was a 2.5 cm and 4.6 cm difference in the measurements when we compared our foot measurements to our forearm lengths.

7. Why was it necessary to collect data from other students in the class?
   - Sample size is important to add validity to the conclusions drawn from the data.

8. Write a conclusion statement based on the data that you have collected for Hypothesis #2.
   - There is not a direct correlation between the length of the forearm and foot length.
   - Students should indicate whether or not the hypothesis is supported or not supported by the data collected.

REFERENCES

Miller, Kenneth and Levine, Joseph. *Biology*. Pearson Education, Inc. pp. 8-10

Greenberg, John, Revision editor. *BSCS Biology, A Molecular Approach*. Chicago: Everyday Learning, 2001. pp. 8-9

Vitruvian Man Meets the Scientific Method
Writing and Testing Appropriate Hypotheses

Leonardo da Vinici's drawing *Vitruvian Man* shows how the proportions of the human body fit perfectly into a circle or a square. This diagram by Leonardo da Vinci is an illustration of Vitruvius' theory. According to Vitruvius's theory the distance from fingertip to fingertip (arm span) should be equal to the distance from head to heel (height). In this activity you will explore the legitimacy of Vitruvius' theory by developing a hypothesis regarding the Vitruvian Man.

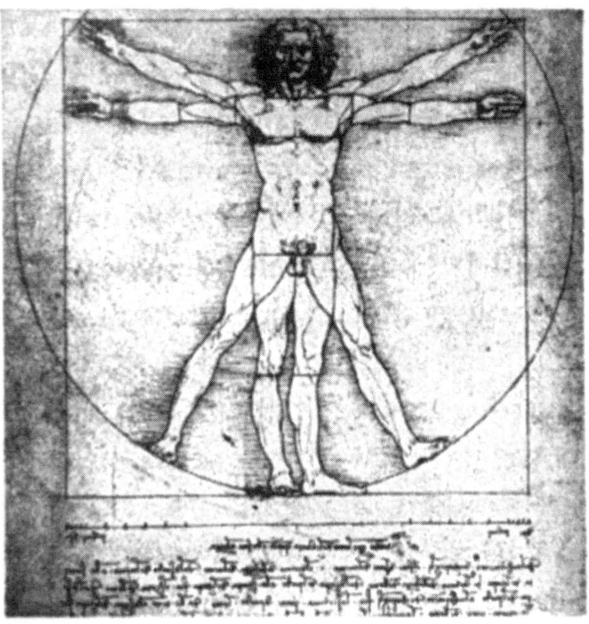

A hypothesis is a possible explanation for a set of observations or an answer to a scientific question. A hypothesis is useful only if it can be tested. Testable hypothesis are generally written in a formalized format using an *if/then* statement.

- If my car does not start because the battery is dead, then when I replace the old battery with a new one it will start.
- If increasing physical activity causes a person to burn calories and lose weight, then I should lose weight if I run 2 miles a day.

Formalized hypotheses contain both a dependent and an independent variable. The independent variable is the one that you change and the dependent variable is the one you observe and measure to collect data. Using the *if-then* format, if I change temperature, then what will happen to movement. Temperature is the independent variable because I change it and movement is the dependent variable because it is the one that is observed to look for change. Using the *if-then* format forces the scientist to think about what results are expected.

PURPOSE

In this activity you will devise and test a hypothesis regarding Vitruvius' theory on human proportions. In Part II, you will devise and test a hypothesis concerning the relationship between foot and arm span lengths.

MATERIALS

14 metric measuring tapes

PROCEDURE

PART I

1. Write an *if-then* hypothesis based on Vitruvius' theory relating arm span and height. Record your hypothesis on the student answer page.

2. Working with a partner, measure your arm span by standing against a flat surface and spreading your arms out as far as possible. Have your partner measure the distance from the longest finger on one hand to the tip of the longest finger on the other hand. Record your measurements in Data Table 1.

3. Repeat step two on your partner.

4. Remove your shoes and have your partner measure your height as you stand against a flat surface. Measure the distance from the top of your head to the floor. Record your measurements in Data Table 1.

5. Repeat step 4 on your partner.

6. Calculate the difference between your arm span and your height (arm span-height). Record your calculations in Data Table 1.

7. Gather data from 10 additional students in the classroom. Record the student's name, sex and data in Data Table 2.

PART II

1. Some people have observed that the length of their foot is the same as the length of their forearm. Others disagree saying there is no relationship between the two. You have been assigned to investigate this phenomenon. As a good scientist, you know that first thing you need to do is write a hypothesis. Is there a direct relationship between the length of a person's foot and the length of their forearm? Write an *if-then* hypothesis for this relationship on the student answer page in the space labeled Hypothesis #2.

2. Collect foot-forearm data from five people and record the measurements in Data Table 3.

Name ____________________

Period ____________________

Vitruvian Man Meets the Scientific Method
Writing and Testing Appropriate Hypotheses

HYPOTHESIS #1

HYPOTHESIS #2

DATA AND OBSERVATIONS

Data Table 1: Lab Partner Data			
Measured in cm	Arm Span	Height	Difference
Your measurements			
Your Partners measurements			

Data Table 2: Class Data in cm			
Person M/F	Arm Span	Height	Difference

Data Table #3: Foot Size/Arm Length Comparison			
Person M/F	Length of foot	Length of forearm	Difference

CONCLUSION QUESTIONS

1. Does your individual data for height and arm span lead you to accept or reject Vitruvius' hypothesis? Why or why not?

2. How do your height and arm span results compare to other groups in the class? Explain.

3. Does the class height and arm span data support Vitruvius' hypothesis? Why or why not?

4. When comparing males and females, does one group fit Vitruvius' hypothesis more closely than the other? Explain your answer.

5. Write a conclusion statement based on the data that you have collected.

6. Based on the data that you have collected is there a correlation between the length of the forearm and the length of the foot? Explain your answer.

7. Why was it necessary to collect data from other students in the class?

8. Write a conclusion statement based on the data that you have collected for Hypothesis #2.

Seed Germination
Examining the Effects of Acid Rain

OBJECTIVE
Students will investigate the effects of acid rain on seed germination. They will design their own laboratory experiment using a set of designated materials. The student will generate appropriate data tables and graphs and analyze their results. They will evaluate their experimental design and results.

LEVEL
Biology I

NATIONAL STANDARDS
UCP.2, UCP.3, A.1, A.2, C.4, C.5, E.1, F.1, F.3, F.4, F.5, F.6

TEKS
1(A), 2(A), 2(B), 2(C), 2(D), 3(C), 12(C)

CONNECTIONS TO AP
AP Biology:

III. Organisms and Populations, B. Structure and Function of Plants and Animals
1. Reproduction, growth and development of plants, C. Structure and Function of Plants and Animals 3. Global Issues

AP Environmental Science:

Environmental quality, types of major pollutants and effects of pollutants on vegetation. Global changes and their consequences.

TIME FRAME
Day 1, 50 minutes
Days 2-7, 10 minutes

MATERIALS
(for a class of 28 working in teams of 4)

400 - 500 pea seeds
7 rulers
7 syringes (10 cc)
7 scissors
28 goggles
28 lab aprons
paper towels
70 Petri dishes
7 graduated cylinders (10 mL)
7 permanent markers
7 tweezers
graph paper
28 pairs latex gloves
access to balance
1 liter of the following buffered solutions at the following pHs 3.0, 4.0, 5.0, 6.0, 7.0, 8.0

Safety Alert

1. Goggles, aprons and gloves must be worn.
2. Work with concentrated acids ONLY under a fume hood.
3. Clearly label all solutions used in this laboratory exercise with CAUTION: *Irritant*
4. Also alert students to the following: CAUTION: These solutions contain acids. These solutions are irritants and can damage clothing. Avoid skin/eye contact; do not ingest. Immediately run water over any skin that the liquid comes in contact with. Continue to flush the affected area for 10 minutes. Notify your teacher immediately.
5. CAUTION: Scissors are sharp; handle with care.

TEACHER NOTES

This exercise can be used to supplement environmental curriculum or reinforce experimental design. This is an inquiry lab experiment.

A buffer resists a change in pH. A germinating seed may slightly alter the pH of its environment. Using buffered acids ensures the pH of the environment is held to a constant pH. This lab works well without buffered acids. Hydrochloric acid is readily available in most high school chemistry labs and can be used. Sulfuric acid may be used if it is available as one of the acids found in acid rain. Distilled water exposed to air will not have pH of 7 because carbon dioxide from the air will go into the distilled water. This will lower the pH of the distilled water as it forms carbonic acid. To obtain a pH of 7 distilled water should be boiled and then put into a bottle without any air.

To make 1000 mL of each buffered solution mix the following:
Use the following table to mix your own set of buffered solutions. The stock solutions involved are:

- 0.2 M HCl (hydrochloric acid)
- 0.2 M NaOH (sodium hydroxide)
- 0.2 M $KHC_8 H_4O$ (potassium acid pthalate)
- 0.2 M KH_2PO_4 (potassium dihydrogen phosphate)
- 0.2 M $H_3 BO_3$-KCl (boric acid-potassium chloride)

pH	add	to	dilute to
2.0	500 mL	-	1000 mL
3.0	51 mL HC1	125 mL KHC_8H_4O	1000 mL
4.0	1. 0 mL NaOH	125 mL KHC_8H_4O	1000 mL
5.0	59.63 mL NaOH	125 mL KHC_8H_4O	1000 mL
6.0	113.5 mL NaOH	125 mL KHC_8H_4O	1000 mL
7.0	73.88 mL NaOH	125 mL KH_2PO_4	1000 mL
8.0	10.00 mL NaOH	125 mL H_3BO_3-KCl	1000 mL

You may just use acids at a particular pH instead of buffered solutions. First make a 0.1 M of HCl by slowly adding 8.3 mL of concentrated HCL to 500 mL of distilled water Bring up to a volume of 1000 mL using a volumetric flask. This solution will have a pH of 1.0. To make HCl with solutions with a pH of 2-6, do the following:

pH	Add	To	New Molarity
2.0	100 mL 0.1 M HCl	900 mL distilled water	0.01 M
3.0	100 mL 0.01 M HCl	900 mL distilled water	0.001 M
4.0	100 mL 0.001 M HCl	900 mL distilled water	0.0001 M
5.0	100 mL 0.0001 M HCl	900 mL distilled water	0.00001 M
6.0	100 mL 0.00001 M HCl	900 mL distilled water	0.000001 M
7.0	Boil distilled water to remove carbon dioxide		

If you would like to use sulfuric acid, follow the steps above for making the hydrochloric acid solutions using a 0.1 M solution of sulfuric acid instead of 0.1 M solution hydrochloric acid. Make a 0.1 M of H_2SO_4 by slowly adding 55.5 mL of concentrated H_2SO_4 to 500 mL of distilled water. Bring up to a volume of 1000 mL using a volumetric flask. This solution will have a pH of 1.0. Dilute as instructed for the hydrochloric acid above for the desired pH.

The peas can be purchased at your local garden supply store when in season. Alternatively, you can use peas, such as black-eyed peas, purchased at the grocery store. These peas will have a lower germination rate than the garden quality seeds but will supply sufficient germination for this activity. It is strongly recommended that you briefly rinse the grocery store peas in a 10% bleach solution to reduce fungal contaminants prior to using them.

Before allowing the students to begin, discuss the following questions with them:

A. How many acids of varying pH will you use in your experimental design?
Let students know that you have prepared acids having a pH of 2, 3, 4, 5, 6, and 7. Students may not want to utilize all of the various acids in their experimental design. Students should use at least three of the varying pH solutions, one of which is distilled water.

B. How many seeds will you use per container? Point out to the students that they have 50 total seeds with which to work and that the more experimental subjects used, the more reliable the data collected.

C. Which variables will serve as controls for your experimental design? Students should understand the importance of controlling all variables so that each set-up should be watered with the same amount of acid, and each dish should have the same amount of paper towels to control the amount of moisture and so forth.

D. What volume of acid will you use to promote germination? Remind the students that the germination environment needs to be wet enough so that the seeds can absorb the liquid but not so wet that the seeds suffocate. Usually 5-10 mL is sufficient.

E. At what time intervals will you check the seeds for their progress? Students can check the progress every day or every other day to obtain good results.

F. What sort of data will you collect at each time interval? This may vary. Guide the students to include the radicle if they choose to measure the length of the seeds. Make sure students understand the embryonic structures within the seed and which structures emerge during the germination process. Some students may want to use changes in mass as their measurements.

G. How will you design your data table? How will you graph your data? What is your independent variable? What is your dependent variable? Guide the students toward averaging their data for the number of peas in each dish. When constructing their graphs, be sure they graph the pH as the independent variable and the change pea size as the dependent variable.

POSSIBLE ANSWERS TO THE CONCLUSION QUESTIONS & SAMPLE DATA

The following data was collected using 5 seeds per dish utilizing solutions with a pH of 2-7. The measurements were taken every other day. [What were the measurements? No units?]

Data Table						
Day 1						
Pea Measurements (cm)	pH 2	pH 3	pH 4	pH 5	pH 6	pH 7
pea # 1	0.9	1.0	1.0	1.0	1.0	0.9
pea # 2	1.0	0.9	0.9	1.0	0.9	0.9
pea # 3	1.1	0.9	1.0	0.8	1.0	1.0
pea # 4	0.9	1.1	0.8	1.0	0.8	1.0
pea # 5	1.0	1.0	1.0	1.0	0.9	1.0
Averages	0.98	0.98	0.94	0.96	0.92	0.96
Day 3						
Pea Measurements (cm)	pH 2	pH 3	pH 4	pH 5	pH 6	pH 7
pea # 1	1.1	1.2	1.1	1.3	1.1	1.1
pea # 2	1.1	1.0	1.1	1.2	1.1	1.1
pea # 3	1.2	1.0	1.1	1.1	1.1	1.2
pea # 4	1.3	1.2	1.2	1.2	1.2	1.1
pea # 5	1.2	1.1	1.0	1.1	1.1	1.2
Averages	1.18	1.1	1.1	1.18	1.12	1.14
Day 5						
Pea Measurements (cm)	pH 2	pH 3	pH 4	pH 5	pH 6	pH 7
pea # 1	1.1	1.2	1.2	1.4	2.7	2.6
pea # 2	1.2	1.8	2.7	2.4	2.4	2.7
pea # 3	1.1	1.6	2.2	2.9	2.1	2.5

pea # 4	1.3	1.3	1.1	1.2	3.5	2.7
pea # 5	1.2	1.4	1.3	1.2	2.6	2.9
Averages	1.18	1.46	1.7	1.82	2.66	2.68
			Day 7			
Pea Measurements (cm)	pH 2	pH 3	pH 4	pH 5	pH 6	pH 7
pea # 1	1.1	1.3	1.2	1.5	3.0	3.6
pea # 2	1.2	1.5	3.0	3.7	3.3	3.3
pea # 3	1.2	1.3	2.9	3.6	3.0	3.7
pea # 4	1.3	1.2	1.1	1.2	4.2	3.3
pea # 5	1.2	1.2	1.4	1.2	4.2	3.5
Averages	1.2	1.3	1.92	2.24	3.54	3.48

1. What is the optimal pH for the germination of pea seeds based on the data you collected? Their data should reflect an optimum pH between 6 and 7.

2. What is the relationship between the pH of the solution used and seed germination? Their data should show that a decrease in pH results in a decrease in the length of the radicle of the pea and thus the germination.

3. Why does altering the pH of a seed's environment during germination have an effect on the germination of seeds and their metabolism and growth? Enzymes control the metabolism of all living things. Enzymes which are proteins are denatured when the pH of their surrounding environment shifts from the optimal value.

4. How might acid rain have an impact on crops and the economy? Because acid rain can affect seed germination, crops will not produce the expected yield. This will affect the economy by increasing the price of food and decreasing availability to the human population.

5. What action should be taken to end acid rain pollution? What governmental intervention is necessary to implement your action? What impact will your action have on industry? What impact will your action have on agriculture? This may vary depending on the student's conception of governmental regulations and their general understanding of economics as it relates to agriculture.

6. Evaluate your experiment. Include in your evaluation sources of errors, and recommend improvements for your experiment should you be asked to repeat it. This will vary with the design and outcome of the student's experiment.

REFERENCES

Alexander, Joseph, Paul Brandwein, and Evelyn Morhort. *A Sourcebook for the Biological Sciences*. New York: Harcourt, Brace & World, Inc., 1958. pg. 172.

Brown, Theodore, and H. Eugene LeMay. *Chemistry, the Central Science*. Englewood Cliffs: Prentice-Hall, 1977. pp. 492-498, 291-298

Milani, Jean P., Revision Coordinator. *Biological Science, An Ecological Approach*. Dubuque: Kendall Hunt Publishing Company, 1987. pp. 76-77

Seed Germination
Examining the Effects of Acid Rain

One of the major concerns in environmental science is acid precipitation resulting from pollutants in the atmosphere. This pollution can harm plants, kill fish and other animals, and cause damage to buildings and statues. The majority of this pollution comes from the burning of fossil fuels from both automobiles and industry. The burning of fossil fuels results in emission of sulfur dioxide and nitrogen oxides. We refer to these oxides as SO_x and NO_x [pronounced "socks and knocks"]. These oxides combine with water to form nitric acid and sulfuric acid that is contained in the precipitation that falls to earth.

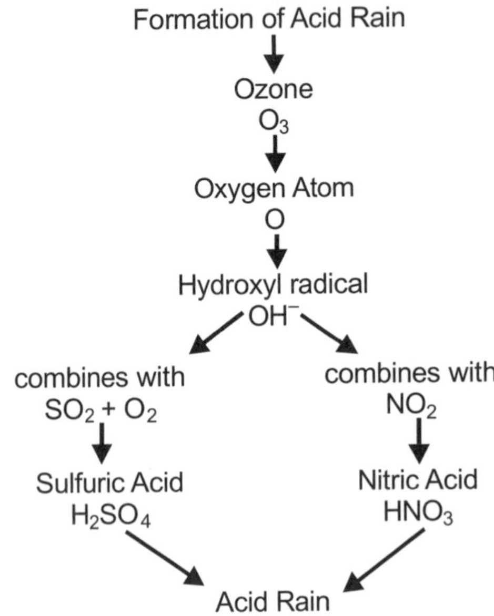

Normal rain has a pH of 5.6. Acid rain has a pH that ranges from 5.5 to 2.4. When acid rain accumulates in lakes and rivers it lowers the pH of the run-off water. This affects forests by killing trees and many other plants. It also kills fish and aquatic life as the acid accumulates in the lakes and ponds.

You will be working in a group of 3-4 students. Your group will design an experiment to investigate the effects of acids with varying pH on the germination of pea seeds. If seeds cannot germinate, then of course the plants will not grow. The investigation is limited to the materials provided by the teacher unless the teacher agrees to the use of different materials. The design of your experiment must be reasonable, and **the procedure must have the approval of your teacher.** There is a two-week time limitation on the experiment.

As your team begins to design this experiment, keep the following questions in mind.

A. How many acids of varying pH will you use in your experimental design?

B. How many seeds will you use per container?

C. Which variables serve as controls for your experimental design?

D. What volume of acid you will use to promote germination?

E. At what time intervals will you check the seeds for their progress?

F. What sort of data will you collect at each time interval?

G. How will you design your data table? How will you graph your data? What is your independent variable? What is your dependent variable?

PURPOSE

The purpose this investigation to examine the effects of acid rain on seed germination.

MATERIALS

Petri dishes, 10 ea
ruler
syringes 10 cc
goggles
latex gloves
permanent maker
tweezers
paper towels
graduated cylinders 10 mL
access to balance
lab aprons
graph paper
scissors
package of pea seeds
acids and a base at the following pH: 2.0 3.0, 4.0, 5.0, 6.0, 7.0, 8.0

Safety Alert

1. Goggles, aprons and gloves must be worn.
2. **These solutions contain acids. These solutions are irritants and can damage clothing. Avoid skin/eye contact; do not ingest. Immediately run water over any skin that the liquid comes in contact with. Continue to flush the affected area for 10 minutes. Notify your teacher immediately.**
3. Scissors are sharp; handle with care.

PROCEDURE

1. Write a paragraph concerning the impact of acid rain on the environment on your student answer page.

2. Formulate a hypothesis for your experimental design and record it on your student answer page. Use and "if, then" format and address the effect varying pH has on seed germination.

3. Outline a procedure to test your hypothesis and write it down on the student answer sheet.

4. Design a data table to record the measurements that will be taken as you execute your experimental design. Put this on the student answer sheet.

5. Obtain your teacher's approval before proceeding with your experiment.

6. For the next seven class days, record your measurements in your data table.

7. At the end of this investigation graph your data and analyze any trends that you find. Make sure your graph is properly constructed, paying special attention to your independent and dependent variables.

8. Write a conclusion for this experiment. Remember, a well written conclusion explains why the results occurred as opposed to restating those results.

9. Answer the conclusion questions on the student answer page.

Name ______________________

Period ______________________

Seed Germination
Examining the Effects of Acid Rain

IMPACT PARAGRAPH

HYPOTHESIS

PROCEDURE

ANALYSIS

This space is provided for your data tables and graphs.

CONCLUSION

This area is provided for your conclusion.

CONCLUSION QUESTIONS

1. What is the optimal pH for the germination of pea seeds based on the data you collected?

2. What is the relationship between the pH of the solution used and seed germination?

3. Why does altering the pH of a seed's environment during germination have an effect on the germination of seeds and their metabolism and thus growth rate?

4. How might acid rain have an impact on crops and the economy?

5. What action should be taken to end acid rain pollution? What governmental intervention is necessary to implement your action? What impact will your action have on industry? What impact will your action have on agriculture?

6. Evaluate your experiment. Include in your evaluation sources of errors, and recommend improvements for your experiment should you be asked to repeat it.

Write It Up
Preparing Formal Lab Reports

OBJECTIVE
Students will become familiar with the process of writing up a formal lab report.

LEVEL
Biology I

NATIONAL STANDARDS
UCP.2, G.2

TEKS
2(A), 2(C), 2(D)

CONNECTIONS TO AP
A formal evaluation of the laboratory notebook is often required by the university before AP credit is granted.

TIME FRAME
20 minutes

MATERIALS
transparency of grading rubric
copies of a sample formal lab report
copies of instructions on writing up report
transparency of formal lab report (optional)

TEACHER NOTES
Occasionally, first year biology students in a course that is preparing them for success in AP Biology should be expected to prepare a formal report. Formal lab reports provide an opportunity for students to organize their thoughts and communicate them to others. Additionally, through the formal report the student is required to present data in tables and graphs as well as demonstrate the ability to formulate and test a hypothesis. These skills will be useful to the students in *all* future AP courses.

The lab report format presented here is offered as a suggestion or guide. It is highly recommended that you discuss this topic with the AP Biology teacher as well as other AP science teacher(s) to develop a coordinated format for use in your classroom.

A lab that generates quantifiable data would be a suitable choice for the first formal lab write-up of the school year. For example, experiment #3 of this manual is an activity that readily lends itself to being used in conjunction with a formal lab report.

You will need to decide whether you want the report handwritten or word processed. The advantages of having the students hand write the reports are that the handwritten format can be used to show student original work, handwritten reports are less easily shared and there is no financial equity involved in using pen and paper. Word-processed reports have the advantages of being easier to read and allowing for the inclusion of computer generated graphs of the data.

Once you have selected an appropriate lab and decided whether the report should be handwritten or word-processed, you should set aside some class time to go through a description of each of the components of the formal lab report. Students should be given a copy of the Lab Report Guidelines handout as well as the grading rubric. Transparencies of the Lab Report Guidelines, Sample Student Report, and grading rubric can be used to give the student clear explanations and an example of how their report should appear.

Formal Lab Report Guidelines

Prepare a written report of your experiment which includes the section titles listed below. These section titles should be used to label each section of your report.

I. Introduction
II. Hypothesis
III. Materials and Procedures
IV. Data Collection/Analysis
V. Conclusions

The following information should be included in each section of the lab report.

I. **Introduction** - In this section of the report you should give the reader background information that will help them understand the experiment that you have conducted. Important terms should be defined in the section. Additionally the purpose of the lab should be clearly stated in the introduction.

II. **Hypothesis** - This relatively short section should include a testable hypothesis written in an if-then format.

III. **Materials** - A complete listing of the materials and supplies that were used to conduct the experiment should be included in this portion of the report.

IV. **Procedures** - In this section of the report you should present the exact steps that were followed in your experiment. Clearly identify the control, variables and the measurement techniques used.

V. **Data Collection/Analysis** - All of the data that was collected during the experiment should be presented in a data table or tables. Additionally, a graph of the data should be included in this section. Make sure that the graph is appropriately titled and labeled. Include a legend if necessary.

VI. **Conclusions** - This portion of the report is used to clearly explain whether the results support or refute the hypothesis being tested.

Lab Report Grading Rubric

REPORT ITEM	POSSIBLE POINTS	EARNED POINTS/comments
Introduction	(15)	
Background information	10	
Purpose of the experiment	5	
Hypothesis (if-then)	(10)	
Written in if-then format	5	
Testable	5	
Materials	(5)	
Materials listed	5	
Procedures	(15)	
Procedures stated clearly	5	
Clearly stated measurement procedure	5	
Control present	3	
Multiple replica	2	
Data Table (design)	(15)	
Organized	5	
Readable	5	
Complete	5	
Graph	(15)	
Title	5	
Axis labels	5	
Key/legend	5	
Conclusion	(20)	
Summarizes results	5	
Explains implications	5	
Evaluates errors	5	
Recommends improvement	5	
Student answer page (rough draft) attached	(5)	
TOTAL POINTS	(100)	

SAMPLE STUDENT REPORT:

The following is a sample student report submitted for Experiment #3 Seed Germination on Seed Germination.

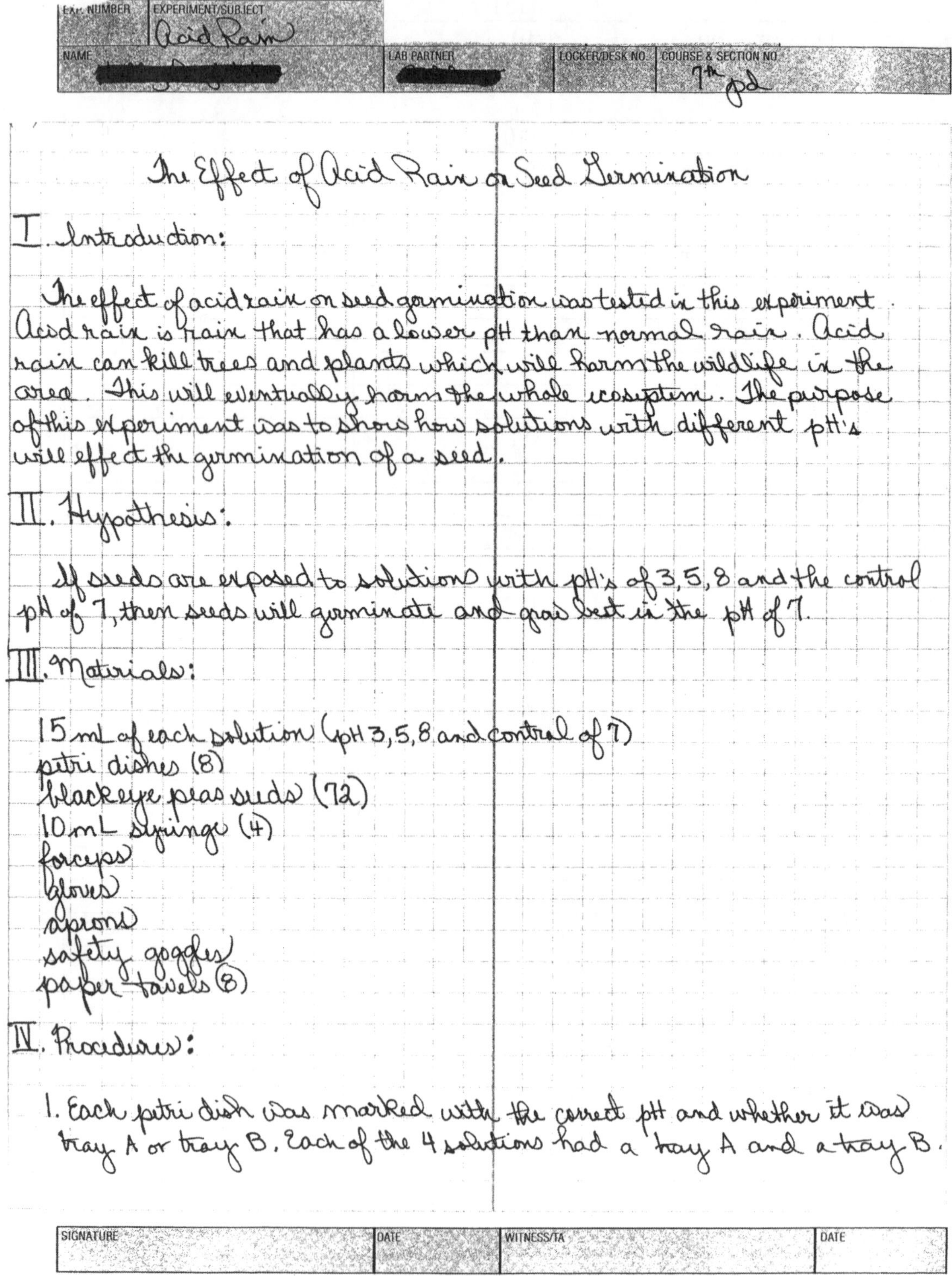

EXP. NUMBER | EXPERIMENT/SUBJECT: Acid Rain

NAME | LAB PARTNER | LOCKER/DESK NO. | COURSE & SECTION NO.: 7th pd

The Effect of Acid Rain on Seed Germination

I. Introduction:

The effect of acid rain on seed germination was tested in this experiment. Acid rain is rain that has a lower pH than normal rain. Acid rain can kill trees and plants which will harm the wildlife in the area. This will eventually harm the whole ecosystem. The purpose of this experiment was to show how solutions with different pH's will effect the germination of a seed.

II. Hypothesis:

If seeds are exposed to solutions with pH's of 3, 5, 8 and the control pH of 7, then seeds will germinate and grow best in the pH of 7.

III. Materials:

15 mL of each solution (pH 3, 5, 8 and control of 7)
petri dishes (8)
blackeye peas seeds (72)
10 mL syringe (4)
forceps
gloves
aprons
safety goggles
paper towels (8)

IV. Procedures:

1. Each petri dish was marked with the correct pH and whether it was tray A or tray B. Each of the 4 solutions had a tray A and a tray B.

SIGNATURE | DATE | WITNESS/TA | DATE

EXP. NUMBER | EXPERIMENT/SUBJECT

NAME | LAB PARTNER | LOCKER/DESK NO. | COURSE & SECTION NO.

2. Half of one paper towel (folded and torn in two) was placed in the bottom of the petri dish and three seeds were placed on the towel (centered). The second half of the paper towel was put over the seeds. This procedure was repeated in every petri dish.

3. The paper towel was left on top of the seeds, and 15 mL of the appropriate pH solutions was poured over the towel soaking the seeds and both the top and bottom paper towels. This was repeated using the corresponding solution with each petri dish.

4. After watering all the dishes and peas with the appropriate pH solutions they were put in a secure place for two days.

5. On the second day, the petri dishes were retrieved and the seeds were removed. The tail shaped radicles were measured in centimeters. The measurements were recorded in a data table. The measurements were taken each day for three days. Any dead seeds or seeds with fungus were removed and thrown away. If a seed didn't have a radicle or didn't grow, an X was recorded for that seed.

SIGNATURE | DATE | WITNESS/TA | DATE

EXP. NUMBER	EXPERIMENT/SUBJECT		
NAME	LAB PARTNER	LOCKER/DESK NO.	COURSE & SECTION NO.

V. Data Collection/Analysis

pH 3

Pea Measurements cm	Day 1	Day 2	Day 3
pea # A-1	.5	1.0	1.1
pea # A-2	.4	.5	X
pea # A-3	.4	.5	.5
pea # B-1	.4	.4	.5
pea # B-2	.2	.3	.3
pea # B-3	.5	.6	.6
#Ave.	.4	.55	.6

pH 5

pea measurements cm	Day 1	Day 2	Day 3
pea # A-1	1.7	1.8	2.0
pea # A-2	.7	1.5	2.0
pea # A-3	1.5	1.5	1.9
pea # B-1	1.7	2.0	2.8
pea # B-2	.6	1.0	1.6
pea # B-3	.9	1.5	2.6
Ave.	1.1	1.4	2.2

pH 7 control

Pea Measurements cm	Day 1	Day 2	Day 3
pea # A-1	X	X	X
pea # A-2	X	X	X
pea # A-3	X	X	X
pea # B-1	1.7	4.0	4.2
pea # B-2	3.0	4.1	4.4
pea # B-3	3.2	4.0	4.5
Ave.	2.6	4.0	4.4

pH 8

Pea Measurements cm	Day 1	Day 2	Day 3
pea # A-1	.4	.4	X
pea # A-2	.3	.4	.4
pea # A-3	.7	.8	.8
pea # B-1	.5	.5	.5
pea # B-2	.5	.5	.6
pea # B-3	.5	.5	.5
Ave.	.48	.52	.56

Ave. Growth of Pea Seeds

Growth in cm
5
4
3
2
1
0
2
3
4
Day

---- pH 3
▲▲▲ pH 5
..... pH 7
—— pH 8

SIGNATURE	DATE	WITNESS/TA	DATE

EXP. NUMBER	EXPERIMENT/SUBJECT			
NAME		LAB PARTNER	LOCKER/DESK NO.	COURSE & SECTION NO.

VI. Conclusion:

The results support the hypothesis is that if seeds are exposed to solutions with pH's of 3, 5, 8 and the control pH of 7, then the seeds will germinate and grow best in the pH of 7. The cotrol with pH 7 had the most radicle growth in comparison to the other pH's. The pH of 7 produced radicles that were 1.4 cm longer than the other leading seed.

Errors that could have accurred in this experiment include inaccurate measurements of the volumes of pH solutions applied to the seeds, inaccuracy in the measurements of the radicles. The radicles on some of the seeds were curly and hard to measure with the ruler. Additionally, there could be errors in our measurements because different group members measured the radicles each day and they may have used slightly different methods.

SIGNATURE	DATE	WITNESS/TA	DATE

McMush Lab
Testing for the Presence of Macromolecules

OBJECTIVE
Students will learn confirmation tests for the presence of glucose, starch, lipids and proteins. Students will then apply the test procedures to a slurry made from a McDonald's Happy Meal to determine the presence of these macromolecules in the sample.

LEVEL
Biology I

NATIONAL STANDARDS
UCP.1, A.1, A.2, B.2, B.3, E.1, E.2, F.1, G.2

TEKS
9(A)

CONNECTIONS TO AP
AP Biology:

I. Molecules and Cells A. Chemistry of Life 2. Organic molecules in organisms

TIME FRAME
90 minutes

MATERIALS
(For a class of 28 working in pairs)

McDonald's Happy Meal™ McMush slurry
400 mL gelatin solution
400 mL glucose solution
400 mL starch solution
56 beakers or plastic cups
14 dropper bottles Benedict's solution
14 dropper bottles of Lugol's iodine
64 test tubes (20mm x 150mm)
14 graduated cylinders
28 test tube holders
blender
hot water bath
14 dropper bottles Biuret Reagent
14 dropper bottles Sudan III

TEACHER NOTES
Preparation of solutions

Gelatin solution – Dissolve 4 g gelatin in 396 mL distilled water. Refrigerate until needed.

Glucose solution – Mix 20 g glucose (or dextrose) with 380 mL of distilled water.

Starch solution – Add 4 g of cornstarch to 396 mL of distilled water and heat until the starch dissolves. Alternately, you can use aerosol fabric spray starch. Spray the starch directly into the water, holding for a count of five.

McMush Slurry – Unwrap and place the entire contents of a Happy Meal into the blender, including the drink. Ask for a regular drink rather than a diet drink when purchasing your Happy Meal Blend thoroughly. Add 250 mL of distilled water to make the solution thin enough to be poured into the test tubes.

Benedict's Soution, Biuret reagent and Lugol's solution can be purchased from science suppliers and should be placed into dropper bottles for each lab group.

Students will need access to a hot water bath, either at their stations or in a central location.

It is possible to divide this lab over several class periods. You could present prelab information about the structure and function of a particular group of macromolecules and then move to the laboratory to perform the test for that group. The following day you could address a second macromolecule group, and so on. If this lab is going to be done over a series of days, you will need to refrigerate the gelatin solution and the McMush slurry.

POSSIBLE ANSWERS TO THE CONCLUSION QUESTION AND SAMPLE DATA

Data Table 1: Positive Tests Performed on Knowns		
Test Performed	**Substance Tested**	**Results**
Benedict's Test	Glucose solution	Orange to brick red color
Lugol's Test	Starch solution	Blue-black color
Biuret Test	Gelatin solution	Purplish color
Sudan III	Oil	Diffused orange/pink

Data Table 2: McMush Tests	
Test Performed	**Results**
Benedict's Test	Positive if you used a regular (not diet) drink
Lugol's Test	Positive
Biuret Test	Positive
Sudan III	Positive

1. How are monomers and polymers different?
   - Monomers are the smaller building blocks of the larger polymers.

2. What are the monomers for each of these macromolecules?
   a. Carbohydrates - monosaccharide
   b. Lipids - glycerol & three fatty acids
   c. Proteins - amino acids

3. Circle any of the following compounds that would be classified as carbohydrates.
   a. amino acids
   b. triglycerides
   c. glucose (circled)
   d. hemoglobin
   e. fructose (circled)
   f. hemoglobin
   g. chitin (circled)
   h. starch (circled)

4. If you were given an unknown food sample and asked to identify its contents, which test would you use to determine the presence of
   a. Lipids - Sudan III
   b. Proteins - Biuret's reagent
   c. Glucose - Benedict's test
   d. Starch - Lugol's test

5. Which macromolecule groups were found in the McMush slurry?
   - Carbohydrates, lipids, proteins

6. What portion of the Happy Meal may have provided each of these macromolecules?
   a. Lipids - oil from fries
   b. Protein - hamburger patty
   c. Glucose - drink, if not a diet drink
   d. Starch - hamburger bun

7. Jonathan and Molly performed a similar lab except they tested a slurry made from crackers. Their results show that the crackers contain both protein and fat. After checking the packaging for the crackers, the students were surprised to find that protein and fat are not listed on the nutritional label. No other groups in their class have results that show protein and fat present in the sample. Describe three factors that could contribute to their erroneous results:
   - Inaccurate measurement
   - Improper heating
   - Contamination

8. Predict which macromolecules should be present in the following food substances and indicate which test you would apply in order to detect the presence of that macromolecule. You may need to consult additional resources.

Food Substance	Predicted Macromolecule	Test to be used
a. Potato juice	Starch	Lugol's
b. Cracker	Starch	Lugol's
c. Egg white	Protein	Biuret's
d. Honey	Glucose	Benedict's

9. Design and describe an experiment to test for the presence of carbohydrates, lipids, and proteins in a taco.
   - Press for good experimental design in the answers to question 9. No control was included in the original protocol so you may need to discuss this point with your students as they write their experimental design.

REFERENCES

Bob Heun. “Re: Lab Tips at Teacher’s Corner AP Central” 3/15/01http://apcentral.collegeboard.com/members/article/1,3046,151-165-0-3895,00.html

Biology Laboratory Manual. Prentice Hall. Englewood Cliffs. 1991

McMush Lab
Testing for the Presence of Macromolecules

Carbohydrates, lipids, proteins, and nucleic acids are organic molecules found in every living organism. These macromolecules are large carbon based structures. The macromolecules are assembled by joining several smaller units, called monomers, together through a chemical reaction called dehydration synthesis. The resulting polymer can be disassembled through the complimentary process called hydrolysis.

Carbohydrates are made of carbon, hydrogen and oxygen atoms in a 1:2:1 ratio. This means that for every carbon atom present in the carbohydrate there are two hydrogen atoms and one oxygen atom present. The monomers for carbohydrates are referred to as monosaccharides. When many monosaccharides are chained together the resulting molecule is called a polysaccharide. Carbohydrates are used by living organisms as an important source of energy. Examples of carbohydrates include glucose, fructose, sucrose, galactose, ribose, deoxyribose, cellulose and chitin.

Lipids are also made of carbon, hydrogen and oxygen but the ratio of carbon, hydrogen, and oxygen is not 1:2:1. Instead, lipids have a much higher number of carbons and hydrogens with few oxygen atoms present. The nonpolar bonds that form between the carbon and hydrogen atoms of a lipid cause them to be hydrophobic, or water-repellent, molecules. This explains why water and oil do not mix. The large number of carbon to hydrogen bonds also serves to make lipids energy rich storage molecules. One gram of lipid stores twice as much energy as one gram of a carbohydrate. Lipids from animals are referred to as fats and are solids at room temperature, while those found in plants are referred to as oils which are liquids at room temperature. Fats and oils are made of smaller units called triglycerides which are composed of a glycerol and three fatty acid molecules. One important relative of true lipids are the phospholipids. Phospholipids differ in structure from regular lipids in that phospholipids are made of a glycerol and two fatty acids joined by a phosphate group. This arrangement makes phospholipid molecules have both hydrophilic and hydrophobic regions. This feature makes phospholipids an ideal structural component of the plasma membrane of cells. Steroids are another significant group of lipids. They differ slightly in structure because the carbon atoms are arranged in four rings. Examples of steroids include cholesterol, estrogen, testosterone and morphine.

Proteins are composed of amino acids which are composed of atoms of carbon, hydrogen, oxygen and nitrogen. Proteins serve as the major building blocks of organisms. Proteins are large complex molecules that combine to form various components of living organisms such as muscle fibers, enzymes, and hemoglobin. Proteins are made of unique combinations of the twenty amino acid monomers. A string of amino acid monomers joined together by peptide bonds is called a polypeptide.

PURPOSE

This lab activity provides an opportunity for the development of skills involved in chemically testing for the presence of the carbohydrates, lipids and proteins found in food samples. You will learn how to test for the presence of proteins using the Biuret test, to test for the presence of monosaccharides using the Benedicts test, to test for the presence of starches using Lugol's solution and to detect the presence of lipids using Sudan III. Once familiar with the detection techniques, you will apply those techniques to a slurry that has been made by blending a complete Happy Meal. Using the skills that you have developed you should be able to determine which organic compounds are present in the slurry.

MATERIALS

McDonald's Happy Meal™ McMush slurry
gelatin solution
glucose solution
starch solution
2 beakers or plastic cups
Benedict's solution in dropper bottle
Lugol's iodine in dropper bottle
6-8 test tubes
graduated cylinder
2 test tube holders
hot water bath
Biuret Reagent in dropper bottle
Sudan III in dropper bottle

Safety Alert

1. Goggles and aprons should be worn at all times during this lab investigation.
2. Point test tubes away from all people when heating samples.
3. Handle hot test tubes with test tube clamps.

PROCEDURE

PART I: TESTING FOR MONOSACCHARIDES

1. Benedict's solution can be used to detect the presence of monosaccharides. In the presence of a monosaccharide like glucose, Benedict's solution will change color from blue to orange when heated. Place 5 mL of the glucose solution into your test tube. Add 3 mL of Benedict's solution. Place the tube in a beaker of boiling water and boil for five minutes. Use test tube clamps to hold hot test tubes. Note any change in color.

2. Rinse out your test tube and record your results for the glucose test in Data Table 1.

3. Using the Benedict's solution test, determine whether or not the McMush slurry contains any monosaccharides and record you findings in Data Table 2.

PART II: TESTING FOR STARCHES

1. Lugol's solution can be used to test for the presence of the polysaccharide or starch. In the presence of starch, the Lugol's solution will change color from amber to a dark blue. Place 5 mL of the starch solution into your test tube. Add 5 drops of Lugol's iodine solution. Observe the change in color.

2. Rinse out your test tube and record your results for the starch test in Data Table 1.

3. Using the Lugol's solution, determine whether or not the McMush slurry contains starch. Record your findings in Data Table 2.

PART III: TESTING FOR PROTEINS

1. Biuret's reagent can be used to test for the presence of protein. Place 5 mL of the gelatin solution into your test tube. Add 10 drops of Biuret's reagent. The gelatin is a protein-rich solution and will test positive for the presence of protein. Biuret's reagent will change color from yellow to blue-violet in the presence of protein.

2. Rinse out your test tube and record your results for the protein test in Data Table 1.

3. Using the Biuret's test for protein, test the McMush slurry to determine whether or not protein is present. Record your findings in Data Table 2.

PART IV: TESTING FOR LIPIDS

1. Sudan III can be used to detect the presence of lipids. In the presence of a lipid rich solution and water, Sudan III will diffuse through the solution producing an orange-pink color. Add 5 mL of water and 5 mL of oil to a clean test tube. Add 5 drops of Sudan III to the test tube. Record your observations in Table 1.

2. Rinse out your test tube and record your results for the lipid test in Data Table 1.

3. Using the Sudan III test, determine whether or not the McMush slurry contains lipids. Record your findings in Data Table 2.

Name ___________________________________

Period __________________________________

McMush Lab
Testing for the Presence of Macromolecules

DATA AND OBSERVATIONS

Data Table 1: Positive Tests Performed on Knowns		
Test Performed	**Substance Tested**	**Results**
Benedict's Test		
Lugol's Test		
Biuret Test		
Sudan III		

Data Table 2: McMush Tests	
Test Performed	**Results**
Benedict's Test	
Lugol's Test	
Biuret Test	
Sudan III	

CONCLUSION QUESTIONS

1. How are monomers and polymers different?

2. What are the monomers for each of these macromolecules?
   a. Carbohydrates-____________
   b. Lipids-__________________
   c. Proteins-________________

3. Circle any of the following compounds that would be classified as carbohydrates.
   a. amino acids
   b. triglycerides
   c. glucose
   d. hemoglobin
   e. fructose
   f. hemoglobin
   g. chitin
   h. starch

4. If you were given an unknown food sample and asked to identify its contents, which test would you use to determine the presence of
   a. Lipids-________________________
   b. Proteins-______________________
   c. Glucose-______________________
   d. Starch-________________________

5. Which macromolecule groups were found in the McMush slurry?

6. What portion of the Happy Meal may have provided each of these macromolecules?
   a. Lipids-_________________
   b. Proteins-_______________
   c. Glucose-_______________
   d. Starch-_________________

7. Jonathan and Molly performed a similar lab except that in their lab they tested a slurry made from crackers. Their results show that crackers contain both protein and fat. After checking the cracker package, the students were surprised to find that protein and fat are not listed on the nutritional label. No other groups in their class have results that show protein and fat present in the sample. Describe three factors that could contribute to their erroneous results:

8. Predict which macromolecules should be present in the following food substances and indicate which test you would apply in order to detect the presence of that macromolecule. You may need to consult additional resources.

Food Substance	Predicted Macromolecule	Test to be used
a. Potato juice		
b. Cracker		
c. Egg white		
d. Honey		

9. Design and describe an experiment to test for the presence of carbohydrates, lipids, and proteins in a taco.

Enzyme Activity
Measuring the Effect of Enzyme Concentration

OBJECTIVE
Students will measure the time it takes for a various concentrations of catalase-soaked filter paper to float to the top of a hydrogen peroxide filled cup. The students will perform dilutions to produce the various enzyme concentrations. Additionally, the students will measure the effect of the competitive inhibitor hydroxylamine hydrochloride on the catalase reaction

LEVEL
Biology I

NATIONAL STANDARDS
UPC.2, UCP.3, UCP.5, A.1, A.2, B.2, B.3, C.1, C.5, G.2

TEKS
9(A), 9(C)

CONNECTIONS TO AP
AP Biology:
I. Molecules and Cells A. Chemistry of Life 4. Enzymes

TIME FRAME
45 minutes

MATERIALS
(For a class of 28 working in pairs)

- 148 filter paper disks
- 14 forceps
- 14 scissors
- 24 small beakers or medicine cups for dilutions
- 1 L distilled water
- paper towels
- 100 mL 10% hydroxylamine hydrochloride solution
- 100 mL catalase stock solution
- 30 small disposable cups
- timing device (seconds)
- 2 L 1.5% hydrogen peroxide (H_2O_2)
- gloves, aprons, and eye protection
- 14 marking pens

TEACHER NOTES

To prepare 1.5% hydrogen peroxide solution:

3% Hydrogen peroxide can be purchased locally at any drug store or variety store. Add equal volumes of 3% H_2O_2 and distilled water to produce a 1.5% solution. Store in a brown bottle.

To prepare the catalase stock solution:

Place a 1 cm^2 slice of beef liver in 100 mL of distilled water and macerate in a blender. Before using with students, test the catalase solution for activity by placing a few drops into 10 mL of hydrogen peroxide. Bubbles should form immediately. If you do not see bubbles, add more macerated liver to the solution. Once the catalase solution is prepared it should be refrigerated. Keep it on ice throughout the day if you need to leave it out in the lab room. The exact concentration and reactivity of the catalase is not significant for this lab.

To prepare the hydroxylamine hydrochloride solution:

Hydroxylamine hydrochloride can be purchased from a chemical supply company. Prepare a 10% solution by adding 5 grams to 45 mL of distilled water.

Prepare the filter disks by using a standard hole punch. Be careful to separate the disks if you punch multiple layers of filter paper.

Paper towels should be placed at each lab table. Students should be encouraged to wipe any excess catalase from the disks and forceps in an effort to apply a consistent amount of catalase to the disk.

POSSIBLE ANSWERS TO THE CONCLUSION QUESTIONS AND SAMPLE DATA

Data Table				
% Catalase	**Time in seconds**			
	Trial 1	Trial 2	Trial 3	Avg.
100	1	2	4	2.34
50	27	22	39	29.3
0	180+	180+	180+	180+
100% plus hydroxylamine	50	35	42	42.3

Graph

For this graph you will need to determine the following:

a. The independent variable: **catalase concentration**
   Use this to label the horizontal *x*-axis.
b. The *dependent* variable: **reaction time**
   Use this to label the vertical *y*-axis.

Graph 1 Title: The effect of catalase concentration on reaction time

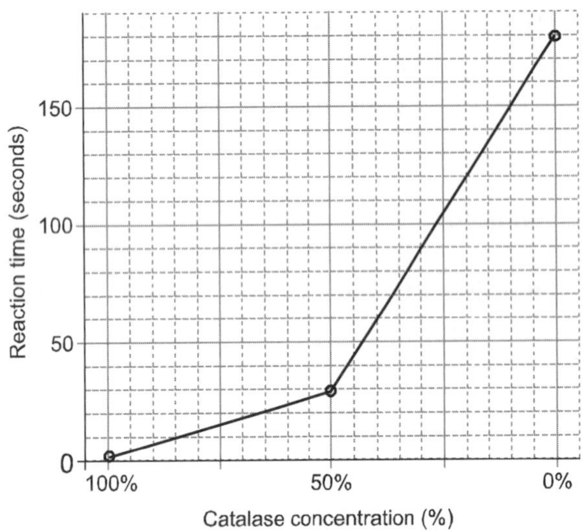

1. What causes the disks to float to the surface?
   - oxygen produced in the reaction accumulates under the disk.

2. Which concentration of catalase had the fastest reaction time?
   - 100%

3. Which concentration of catalase had the slowest reaction time?
   - 50%

4. What type of biological molecule is catalase?
   - protein

5. What does catalase do to hydrogen peroxide?
   - Temporarily binds with it causing it to be broken apart
   - H2O2 decomposes into water and oxygen gas, hence the bubbles

6. Based on the graph and overall slope of the line, what can you conclude about the effect of enzyme concentration on reaction time?
   - As concentration decreases, reaction time increases

7. How would the results be different if you repeated Part I this experiment using water instead of hydrogen peroxide?
   - The disk would not float to the top

8. Describe the effect hydroxylamine hydrochloride has on the reaction rate.
   - Hydroxylamine hydrochloride acts as an inhibitor, slowing the reaction rate

9. A student forgets to dry the tip of the forceps after dipping the disk in catalase solution. What effect will this error have on the reaction time for that trial? Explain
   - The reaction time for that trial will be FASTER than expected because there are additional catalase molecules introduced to the solution from the forceps.

Enzyme Activity
Measuring the Effect of Enzyme Concentration

Enzymes are proteins that serve as biological catalysts in a wide variety of life sustaining chemical reactions that take place in cells. As catalysts, enzymes lower the amount of energy required to make a reaction occur. We call this energy the *activation energy*. By lowering the activation energy, enzymes serve to speed up the rate at which the reactions occur.

Enzymes are said to be substrate specific. A substrate is a molecule that temporarily binds with the enzyme at an area on the enzyme called the active site. Each enzyme catalyzes one specific reaction because there is only one type of substrate molecule with the exact shape that will fit in the enzyme's active site. For example, the enzyme amylase will only act on the starch called amylose. The enzyme sucrase will only act on the sugar called sucrose because it is the only substrate that can fit in the active site of the sucrase enzyme. The enzyme and substrate temporarily join to form the enzyme substrate complex. The substrate is then converted to its products and the enzyme is freed to repeat the process with a substrate molecule. See Fig. 1.

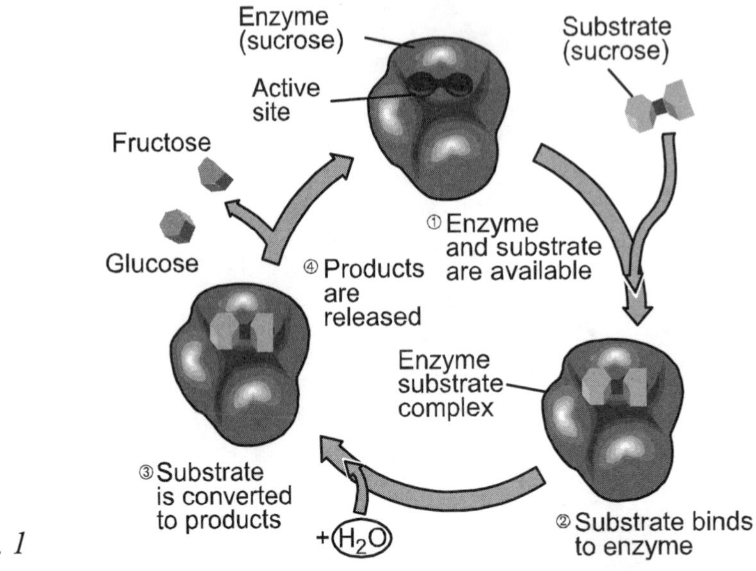

Fig. 1

Your cells, and the cells of most living organisms, contain an enzyme called catalase. Cells use an enzyme (**catalase**) to breakdown the poisonous substance (**hydrogen peroxide**) which is produced during cell reactions. You have probably seen evidence of this reaction if you have ever poured hydrogen peroxide on a cut. The catalase decomposes hydrogen peroxide into water and oxygen. The oxygen gas is released as bubbles. The rate at which this occurs depends on the number of catalase molecules that are available.

The activity of enzymes is controlled in many ways. One of the simplest ways is through the action of inhibitors. Inhibitors may compete with the substrate molecule for the active site of the enzyme. If the inhibitor gets to the active site before the substrate it will block the substrate from binding and prevent the reaction from taking place. Hydroxylamine hydrochloride is a known competitive inhibitor of the catalase/hydrogen peroxide reaction.

PURPOSE

In this lab you will measure the time it takes for a disc of filter paper soaked with varying concentrations of the enzyme catalase to float to the top of a cup filled with hydrogen peroxide. The disk will float as oxygen produced in the catalase/hydrogen peroxide reaction accumulates under the paper disk. Additionally, you will measure the effect of hydroxylamine hydrochloride on the catalase reaction.

MATERIALS

- 5 filter paper disks
- forceps
- scissors
- small beakers or medicine cups for dilutions
- 15 mL distilled water
- paper towel
- 10% hydroxylamine hydrochloride solution
- catalase stock solution
- small disposable cups
- timing device (seconds)
- 1.5% hydrogen peroxide (H_2O_2)
- gloves, aprons, and eye protection
- marking pen

Safety Alert

1. Wear goggles at all times.
2. Do not eat or drink in the laboratory.
3. Avoid unnecessary contact with chemicals.

PROCEDURE

PART I: THE EFFECT OF CATALASE CONCENTRATION ON THE DECOMPOSITION OF HYDROGEN PEROXIDE

1. On your student answer page in the space marked Hypothesis, write an if-then statement that answers the following question: What effect does increasing the concentration of catalase have on the rate of decomposition of hydrogen peroxide?

2. Using small beakers or cups, prepare the following catalase solutions.

Final Quantity Needed	Concentration of Final Solution	mL of Catalase	mL of Water
10 mL	100%	10	0
10 mL	50%	5	5
10 mL	0%	0	10

3. Use a marking pencil to label the enzyme solutions as 100%, 50% and 0%.

4. In a clean cup or beaker, pour 40 mL of 1.5% hydrogen peroxide.

5. Using your forceps, pick up one filter paper disk and submerge it in the 100% enzyme solution for 5 seconds. Do not let go of the disk.

6. Remove the disk from the solution and use a paper towel to blot it dry for five seconds. Be sure to dry the tips of the forceps.

7. Use the forceps to place the disk on the bottom of the cup. See Figure 2. **Begin timing as soon as the disk touches the surface of the hydrogen peroxide.**

Fig. 2

8. Record the time required for the disk to float to the surface of the hydrogen peroxide cup in the data table.

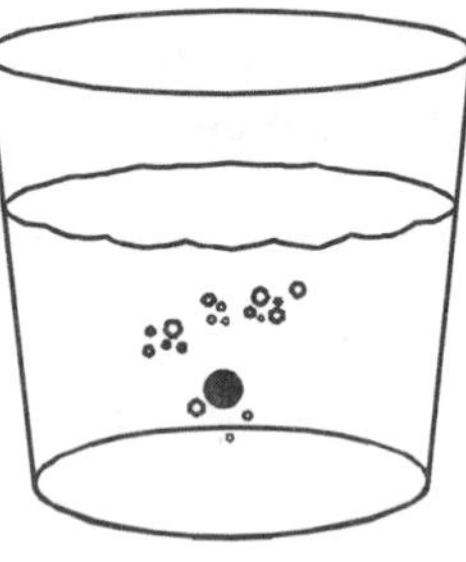

9. Conduct two additional trials with the 100% enzyme solution. Use a different filter paper disk for each trial.

10. Repeat steps 1-9 for the 50% and 0% catalase solutions. Remember to use clean filter paper each time you test. Record the times for the three trials of the remaining solutions in the appropriate column of the data table1.

11. Prepare a line graph of the average reaction time versus the enzyme concentration using the space provided on the student answer page.

PART II: THE EFFECTS OF HYDROXYLAMINE HYDROCHLORIDE ON CATALASE

1. Using your forceps, pick up one filter paper disk and submerge it in the 100% enzyme solution for 5 seconds. Do not let go of the disk.

2. Remove the disk from the solution and use a paper towel to blot it dry for five seconds. Be sure to dry the tips of the forceps.

3. Dip the disk into the hydroxylamine hydrochloride solution for 5 seconds. Remove the disk from the solution and blot it and the forceps dry using your paper towels

4. Use the forceps to place the disk on the bottom of the cup. See Figure 2. **Begin timing as soon as the disk touches the surface of the hydrogen peroxide**.

5. Record the time required for the disk to float to the surface of the hydrogen peroxide cup in the data table.

6. Repeat steps 12-16 for a total of three trials with hydroxylamine hydrochloride.

Name ______________________________

Period ______________________________

Enzyme Activity
Measuring the Effect of Enzyme Concentration

HYPOTHESIS

DATA AND OBSERVATIONS

Data Table				
% Catalase	Time in seconds			
	Trial 1	Trial 2	Trial 3	Average
100				
50				
0				
100% plus hydroxylamine				

ANALYSIS

Graph

For this graph you will need to determine the following:

a. The independent variable______________________________
Use this to label the horizontal *x*-axis.

b. The *dependent* variable______________________________
Use this to label the vertical *y*-axis.

Graph 1 Title: ____.

CONCLUSION QUESTIONS

1. What causes the disks to float to the surface?

2. Which concentration of catalase had the fastest reaction time?

3. Which concentration of catalase had the slowest reaction time?

4. What type of biological molecule is catalase?

5. What does catalase do to hydrogen peroxide?

6. Based on the graph and overall slope of the line, what can you conclude about the effect of enzyme concentration on reaction time?

7. How would the results be different if you repeated Part I this experiment using water instead of hydrogen peroxide?

8. Describe the effect hydroxylamine hydrochloride has on the reaction time.

9. A student forgets to dry the tip of the forceps after dipping the disk in catalase solution. What effect will this error have on the rate of the reaction for that trial? Explain.

Write Your Notes and Ideas Here!

The Hydrogen Peroxide Breakdown
Examining Factors that Affect the Reaction Rate of Enzymes

OBJECTIVE
Students will investigate how temperature and concentration affect enzymatic reaction rates through experimentation. Students will collect data and analyze the data to formulate reasonable conclusions.

LEVEL
Biology I

NATIONAL STANDARDS
UCP.2, UCP.3, C.1, C.5, E.1, E.2, G.2

TEKS
2 (A), 2(B), 2(C), 2(D), 9 (A)

CONNECTIONS TO AP
AP Biology:
I. Molecules and Cells A. Chemistry of Life 4. Enzymes

TIME FRAME
50 minutes

MATERIALS
(For a class of 28 working in pairs)

14 TI-83 or TI-83 + graphing calculators
(used for graphing calculator protocol)
14 computers
(used for computer protocol)
14 pressure sensor probes
14 test tube racks
14 # 4 test tube stoppers with eye droppers
28 50 mL beakers
600 mL 3% hydrogen peroxide solution
14 link cords

14 Lab Pro's or CBL's
(used for graphing calculator protocol)
14 Lab Pro's or Serial Interface Device
(used for computer protocol)
14 forceps
14 80 mL test tubes (3 cm x 20 cm)
14 10 mL graduated cylinders
200 paper filter disks
1 L catalase solutions

TEACHER NOTES
This lab can be used to supplement a unit on enzymes. Students should have background information about organic molecules like proteins and what is a chemical reaction. Demonstrations performed by the teacher with catalase prior to this experiment are useful. Use the hydrogen peroxide purchased from the store, some blood from the liver to be used in the experiment, and a potato.

1. To demonstrate that catalase is found in different types of tissue, take a slice of potato and add a few drops of hydrogen peroxide. It will fizz as it breaks down. Take 50 mL of hydrogen peroxide in a 100 mL graduated cylinder and add several drops of blood. The solution will bubble as oxygen gas is released. To demonstrate that oxygen is the gas released, a glowing splint inserted into the bubbles will cause it to reignite.

2. To demonstrate that catalase, a protein, denatures by significant increases in temperature, take a few milliliters of the blood from the liver and put it in a microwave for 10-30 seconds to "cook" the liquid. The students should notice that it appears to be different and when it is added to hydrogen peroxide there is no response. This demonstration should also reinforce the secondary structure of proteins has hydrogen bonds are broken.

3. To demonstrate that catalase, a protein, denatures by changes in pH, take a few milliters of the blood from the liver and mix it with equal amounts of 6M HCl. The students should notice that it appears to be different and actually resembles the blood after it has been cooked. When this is added to hydrogen peroxide there is no response. This demonstration should also reinforce the secondary structure of proteins has hydrogen bonds are broken.

The hydrogen peroxide is standard hydrogen peroxide purchased at the pharmacy or grocery store (3%). Part II of the lab includes hydrogen peroxide at 10° C and 35° C. Use a large beaker with ice to cool the hydrogen peroxide down to approximately 10°C and another large beaker with warm water to keep the hydrogen peroxide warm near 35°C.

To prepare the catalase solution, take 50 g of beef liver and blend it in 1 liter of water with a few ice cubes. This will last several hours on ice. Make new catalase solution for each class.

The reaction chambers are 80 mL test tubes (3 cm x 20 cm). The stopper is made using a one holed, #4 stopper and inserting the glass tubing of an eyedropper through it. Be sure to use glycerin to lubricate the glass and paper towels or other hand protection when inserting the glass through the stopper. The glass tube should be inserted so that the pointed end points out of the top of the stopper.

There are two versions of the lab protocol. The first uses calculators and the second uses computers. Below is some information on both of these devices.

1. Calculator Information

The lab protocol is based on using a LabPro® or CBL 2 (Calculator-Based Laboratory System). Students will need a TI 83+ or the TI 83, 85, 86, 89 or 92 can be easily used. Be aware that this lab can be adapted for a number of interface systems and calculators. Check with the individual manuals when making adaptations. The standard pressure probe that is needed for this lab comes from Vernier. These probes, calculators and interfaces can also be purchased from Vernier. The address is:

Vernier Software Company
13979 SW Millikan Way
Beaverton, OR 97005-2886
(503)-277-2299
www.vernier.com

2. Calculator Software Information

This activity uses DATAMATE as the data collection program. This program must be installed on the graphing calculators and can be downloaded free from Vernier. A TI-GraphLink cable is necessary for connecting the CBL2 or LabPro to a computer for download or upload processes. It is a good idea to check the Vernier site periodically for updates and update both the DATAMATE program and the operating system of your data collection devices.

3. Computer Hardware Information

Macintosh System Requirements

Power Macintosh or newer computer
At least 32 MB of RAM
System 7.5 or newer

Windows System Requirements

Windows 98/NT/ME/2000/XP
At least 32 MB of RAM
Pentium processor-base or compatible, PC

4. Computer Software Information

- The software that is used in conjunction with the pressure probe is **Logger Pro Software**. It can be purchased for the PC, or Mac.

One nice feature of Logger Pro Software is that there are templates for the probes already installed. They can be modified to fit your own experiment and then saved under your own title for the students. This lab is based on version 2.1.1. The following directions may have to be modified for other versions of this software. The following steps work nicely for this experiment:

- It is important that you try this lab and these software settings before working with students so that you can modify the templates or instructions to meet the needs of your own experiment.
- Be sure you have the experimental apparatus set up for this experiment by connecting the interface to the computer through the modem port and the pressure probe to port 1 or CH 1 on the interface.
- Pull down the File menu and click on **Open**. A menu with **Experiments** will appear
- Open the file Probes & Sensors.
- Open the file **Pressure Sensors** and select the type of pressure sensor being used, either Bio-gas, Gas Pressure, or Pressure sensor.
- Open the file that indicates units of **(mm Hg)**.
- A graph will appear. At the bottom of the graph is the pressure as being measured by the pressure sensor.
- Pull down the **Set-up Menu** on **Data Collect**, a dialog box should appear. Select **Sampling** Tab. Now type in the length of time you wish to run the experiment. Usually 3 minutes per run will be sufficient. Select minutes for the unit of time. Type in 3 to run the experiment for 3 minutes for experiment length.
- Now change the sampling speed. It should be set at 1 pts. per minute. Close this window by clicking **OK.**

- Pull down the **Data Menu** and open the **Column Options, Pressure**. Go to **Displayed Precision** and check the decimal places is check and change the numeric display to 3 decimal places. Press **OK**.
- At this time your pressure probe should be reading around 760 mm Hg. To be more accurate you could compare it to a barometric reading. The probe should not have to be calibrated. If you feel that this reading is off, you can calibrate the probe by following the directions that accompanying the pressure probe.
- Once the parameters are set, you can name and save this template to your computer be used by your students

ANSWERS TO PRE-LAB QUESTIONS

1. List four characteristics of enzymes.
   - Enzymes are proteins.
   - Enzymes are biological catalysts.
   - Enzymes can be used over and over again.
   - Enzymes react with specific reactants, or substrates.
2. What is an active site and what is its relationship to an enzyme?
   - An active site is the actual part of the enzyme involved in binding with the reactant(s) to cause the chemical reaction to take place.
3. What is the energy of activation?
   - The energy of activation is the energy that must be overcome in order to start a chemical reaction by breaking chemical bonds.
4. How does the enzyme affect the energy of activation?
   - Enzymes lower the energy of activation needed for the chemical reaction to occur.
5. What are some factors that can affect the reaction rate of an enzymatic reaction?
   - Temperature and concentration of enzyme can affect the reaction rate.

Possible answers to the conclusion questions and Sample Data

	Experiment	Minimum Pressure (Initial Pressure) (mm Hg)	Maximum Pressure (Final Pressure) (mm Hg)	Total Press Change (mm Hg)
Part I	**4 Disks**	745	1269	524
	3 Disks	745	1208	463
	2 Disks	745	1072	327
	1 Disk	745	950	205
Part II	**Room Temp.**	745	1300	555
	Cold Temp.	745	874	129
	Warm Temp.	745	1368	623

1. What is the relationship between pressure and time as the hydrogen peroxide decomposes?
   - As time passed, there was an increase in pressure as the hydrogen peroxide decomposed.

2. What gas is produced when hydrogen peroxide decomposes?
   - The gas produced when hydrogen peroxide decomposes is oxygen.

3. What is the effect of concentration of enzyme on the reaction rate of the experiment?
   - An increase in the concentration of enzyme resulted in an increase in the reaction rate.

4. What is the effect of temperature on the enzymatic decomposition of hydrogen peroxide?
   - A moderate increase in temperature results in an increase in the reaction rate.

REFERENCE

Greenbergi, Jon P., Revision Editor. *Biological Science, A Molecular Approach*. Chicago: Everyday Learning Publishing Company, 2001. pp. 704-707

The Hydrogen Peroxide Breakdown
Examining Factors that Affect the Reaction Rate of Enzymes

Using a Graphing Calculator and Data Collection Device

There are thousands of chemical reactions that occur in an organism that make life possible. Most of these chemical reactions proceed too slowly to occur by themselves. Enzymes are protein catalysts that speed up chemical reactions in a cell. Catalysts are not changed by the reactions they control, and are not used up during the reaction. Enzymes, therefore, can be used over and over again. Enzymes are large complex proteins made by the cell and allow chemical reactions to take place at the temperature of the cell. These catalysts are needed in only very small amounts because a single enzyme molecule can complete the same reaction thousands of times in one minute.

Each enzyme is very specific and can only catalyze a certain reaction. The specific reaction catalyzed by an enzyme depends on the molecular structure and shape of a small area of the enzyme's surface called the active site. The active site can attract and hold only its specific molecules. The target molecule that the enzyme attracts and acts upon is called the substrate. The substrate and the active site of the molecule must fit together very closely. Sometimes the enzyme changes its shape slightly to bring about the necessary fit.

Substrates
Product
Active Site
Enzyme
Enzyme
Enzyme-Substrate Complex
Synthesis Reaction

A chemical reaction requires that bonds in the reactants be broken. The initial energy that must be absorbed in order to break the bonds of the reactant molecule is called the energy of activation.

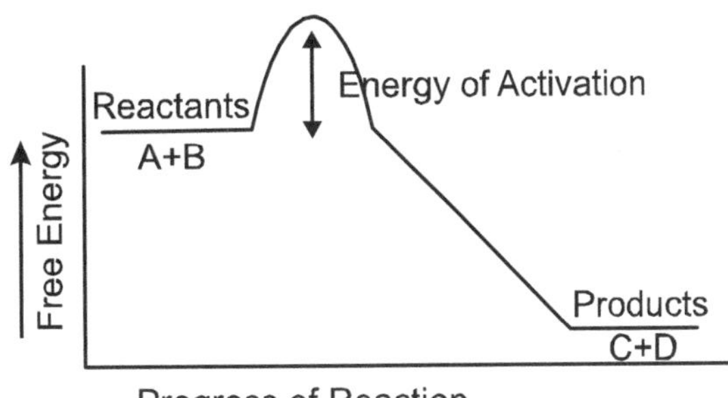

Enzymes work by lowering the energy of activation. For example, hydrogen peroxide decomposes to form water, H_2O, and oxygen gas, O_2.

$$2H_2O_2 \longrightarrow 2H_2O + O_2$$

While this is a catabolic reaction, the rate at which it occurs is slow. Light and temperature affect the reaction rate. As a result, bottles of hydrogen peroxide you may purchase at the drug store are sold in light-blocking brown bottles and have instructions to store them in a cool dark place. Hydrogen peroxide also comes with an expiration date because even with cool and dark storage, the breakdown of H_2O_2 molecules will still occur to some degree. Hydrogen peroxide is toxic to cells. This property makes it useful for treating open wounds since it kills invading bacterial cells. Interestingly enough, hydrogen peroxide is a by-product of some biochemical pathways found in many cells. Yet, the accumulation of hydrogen peroxide can kill a cell. Cells, therefore, cannot wait for hydrogen peroxide to naturally decompose because that takes too much time. Most tissues produce the enzyme, catalase, to increase the rate of hydrogen peroxide's decomposition. Catalase lowers the energy of activation needed for the decomposition and as a result, more molecules are able to be decomposed in a shorter amount of time.

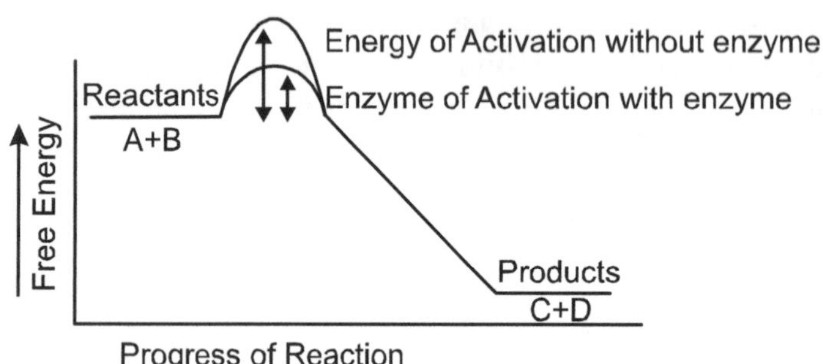

There are factors that can affect how fast an enzymatic reaction occurs. For example, an increase in the amount of enzyme will increase the reaction rate. There are more enzyme molecules available to be involved in the reaction. Another factor that can affect how fast the enzyme works is temperature. An increase in temperature causes the molecules to move faster and engage more frequently in a chemical reaction. At higher temperatures though, the enzymes will denature as the hydrogen bonding falls apart. This lab investigates the effect of enzyme concentration and temperature on an enzymatic reaction.

The reaction used in this laboratory exercise is the decomposition of hydrogen peroxide and the enzyme used is catalase. A pressure probe connected to an interface device and graphing calculator will measure the amount of oxygen gas produced. The more oxygen gas produced the greater the increase in pressure.

PURPOSE

The purpose of this laboratory exercise is to determine the reaction rate of the decomposition of hydrogen peroxide when the concentration of catalase is varies or the temperature is varied.

MATERIALS

pressure sensor probe
CBL or LabPro interface
3% hydrogen peroxide solution
forceps
10 mL pipette
2 ea 50 mL beakers
4 test tube stopper with eye dropper
graphing calculator
filter paper disks
catalase solution
test tube rack
10 mL graduated cylinder
80 mL test tube
link cord

Safety Alert
CAUTION: Take care not to spill any liquids on the interface or graphing calculator.

PROCEDURE

Note: You will either do Part I or Part II of this experiment and then share your results with another group.

PART I (EFFECT OF CONCENTRATION)

1. Answer the pre-lab questions on the student answer page.

2. Formulate two hypotheses: The first hypothesis should be about the effect of enzyme concentration on the reaction rate, and the second hypothesis should be about the effect of temperature on the enzyme reaction rate. Record this on the student answer page.

3. Slide the calculator and CBL or LabPro Interface in the bottom part of the cradle and it will click into place. Snap the calculator into the top portion of the cradle.

4. Plug the short black link cable into the link port on the bottom of the TI Graphing Calculator and the interface.

5. Plug the gas pressure probe into channel 1 of the interface. There should piece of plastic tubing from the pressure probe. Some versions of certain pressure probes have valves for opening and closing the sensor. If the pressure probe has such a valve, ensure that it is open in accordance to the directions accompanying the probe.

6. Turn on the calculator and press APPS for a TI 83+ or PRGM for the TI 83 then press the number key that precedes the DATAMATE program. At this time the interface should have automatically identified your pressure sensor. It will display the correct pressure in the upper right hand corner. If the correct pressure is not displayed do the following:
   - Select **SETUP** from the MENU by pressing 1.
   - Select “CH1” from the MENU and press ENTER.

- Press 4 for more, press 4 again for pressure.
- Select the correct type of probe.
- Select "MMHG" by pressing 2
- Press 1 to indicate OK.

7. Select SETUP from the MENU by pressing 1.
   - Select "MODE" by pressing the ▲ and then ENTER.
   - Select "TIME GRAPH" by pressing 2 and then 2 again to change the time settings
   - Enter "3" as the time between sample, in seconds, press ENTER.
   - Enter "99" as the number of sample (the interface will collect data for approximately five minutes), press ENTER.

8. Another window will appear with the summary of the probes and the length of the experiment. Press 1 to indicate OK. Press 1 or OK again to return to the main menu.

9. A new window will appear and the calculator is now ready to start the experiment. **DO NOT** press 2 until you are ready to run the experiment.

10. Place the other end of the aquarium tubing found on the pressure probe onto the eye dropper sticking out of the #4 test tube stopper.

11. Place the test tube in a test tube rack. Measure 10 mL of hydrogen peroxide with a graduated cylinder and add it to the test tube.

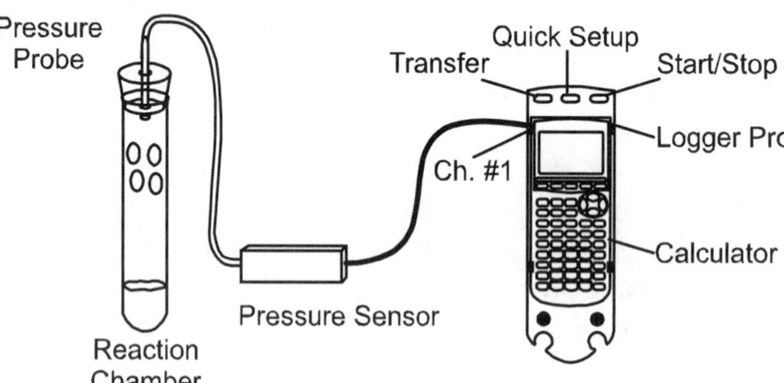

12. Pour a small amount of the catalase solution into the 50 mL beaker. Keep the catalase beaker on ice.

13. Obtain some paper filter disks and separate any paper disks that may be stuck together. Using the forceps, dip one disk into the catalase solution. Drain the disk against the wall of the beaker several times to remove the excess solution. With the forceps, transfer the disk to the test tube and place it on the interior wall of the test tube. It will stick to the wall of the test tube. Using the forceps carefully push the disks 1/2 to 1/3 of the way down the wall of the test tube. Repeat this procedure until you have four disks stuck to the inside wall of the test tube.

14. Place the stopper that is connected to the pressure probe onto the test tube.

15. Press [2]. There should be 4 short beeps and the quick setup light will flash. The experiment will run for approximately 5 minutes. You should notice that the data is being graphed as it is being collected.

16. Immediately, tip the test tube slightly on its side so that the hydrogen peroxide will bring the disks down into the solution and the reaction will begin. Right the test tube up again.
    - **CAUTION: Pressure is building in the test tube. During the course of the experiment, it is important that you keep your thumb on the stopper to prevent it from popping off as the pressure builds.**

17. When the experiment is complete, 4 short beeps will sound and the quick setup light will flash. Now a labeled, fitted graph will be displayed.
    - Use the [◄] and [►] keys to move the cursor. View the data points will be displayed at the bottom of the graph. Use these keys to determine the minimum or initial pressure and the maximum or final pressure. Record this information in your data table on the student answer page.

18. Press [ENTER] and the screen will tell you which Lists contain your data. Press [ENTER] again and the program is done.

19. Repeat the experiment three more times, but each time using one less disk. Trial 2 should contain 3 disks; Trial 3 should contain 2 disks, and Trial 4 should contain 1 disk. Be sure to wash the test tube thoroughly between trials, making sure all the catalase is removed. Also when starting DATAMATE do **not** press [CLEAR], and it will retain the last parameters set, so that you do not have to reset the program. Be sure to record the maximum/final and minimum/initial pressure measurements in your data table.

20. Clean up your area and return your equipment to its original condition.

PART II (EFFECT OF TEMPERATURE)

1. Answer the pre-lab questions on your student answer page.

2. Formulate two hypotheses: The first hypothesis should be about the effect of enzyme concentration on the reaction rate, and the second hypothesis should be about the effect of temperature on the enzyme reaction rate. Record this on the student answer page.

3. Slide the calculator and CBL 2 or LabPro Interface in the bottom part of the cradle and it will click into place. Snap the calculator into the top portion of the cradle.

4. Plug the short black link cable into the link port on the bottom of the TI Graphing Calculator and the interface.

5. Plug the gas pressure probe into channel 1 of the interface. There should piece of plastic tubing from the pressure probe. Some versions of certain pressure probes have valves for opening and closing the sensor. If the pressure probe has such a valve, ensure that it is open in accordance to the directions accompanying the probe.

6. Turn on the calculator and press [APPS] for a TI 83+ or [PRGM] for the TI 83 then press the number key that precedes the DATAMATE program. At this time the interface should have automatically identified your pressure sensor. It will display their correct pressure in the upper right hand corner. If the correct pressure is not displayed do the following:
   - Select **SETUP** from the MENU by pressing.[1].
   - Select "CH1" from the MENU and press [ENTER].
   - Press [4] for more, press [4] again for pressure.
   - Select the correct type of probe.
   - Select "MMHG" by pressing [2].
   - Press [1] to indicate OK.

7. Select SETUP from the MENU by pressing [1].
   - Select "MODE" by pressing the [▲] and then [ENTER].
   - Select "TIME GRAPH" by pressing [2] and then [2] again to change the time settings.
   - Enter "3" as the time between sample, in seconds, press [ENTER].
   - Enter "99" as the number of sample (the interface will collect data for approximately 5 minutes), press [ENTER].

8. Another window will appear with the summary of the probes and the length of the experiment. Press [1] to indicate OK. Press [1] or OK again to return to the main menu.

9. A new window will appear and the calculator is ready to start the experiment. **DO NOT** press [2] until you are ready to run the experiment.

10. Place the other end of the aquarium tubing found on the pressure probe onto the eye dropper sticking out of the #4 test tube stopper.

11. Place the test tube in a test tube rack. Measure 10 mL of hydrogen peroxide with a graduated cylinder and add it to the test tube.

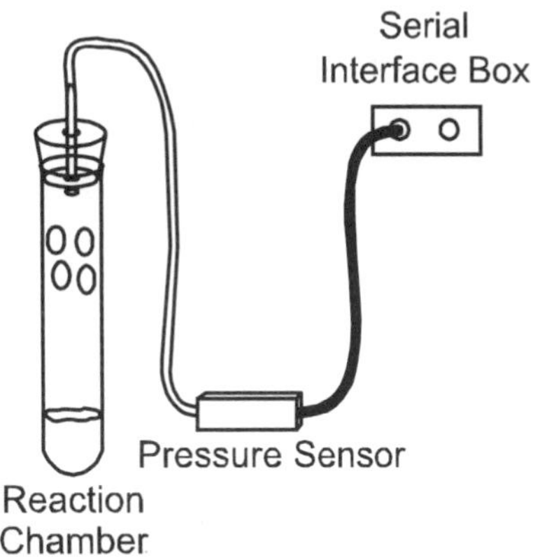

Setup Connected to the Computer

12. Pour a small amount of the catalase solution into the 50 mL beaker. Keep this catalase beaker on ice.

13. Obtain some paper filter disks and separate any paper disks that may be stuck together. Using the forceps, dip one disk into the catalase solution. Drain the disk against the wall of the beaker several times to remove the excess solution. With the forceps, transfer the disk to the test tube and place it on the interior wall of the test tube. It will stick to the wall of the test tube. Using the forceps carefully push the disks 1/2 to 1/3 of the way down the wall of the test tube. Repeat this procedure until you have four disks stuck to the inside wall of the test tube.

14. Place the stopper that is connected to the pressure probe on to the test tube.

15. Press [2]. There should be 4 short beeps and the quick setup light will flash. The experiment will run for 5 minutes. You should notice that the data is being graphed as it is being collected.

16. Immediately, tip the test tube slightly on its side so that the hydrogen peroxide will bring the disks down into the solution and the reaction will begin. Right the test tube up again.
    - **CAUTION: Pressure is building in the test tube. During the course of the experiment, it is important that you keep your thumb on the stopper to prevent it from popping off as the pressure builds.**

17. When the experiment is complete, 4 short beeps will sound and the quick setup light will flash. Now a labeled, fitted graph will be displayed.
    - Using the ◄ or ► keys to move the cursor and the data points will be displayed at the bottom of the graph. Use these keys to determine the minimum or initial and the maximum or final pressure. Record this information in your data table on the student answer page.

18. Press ENTER and the screen will tell you which Lists contain your the data. Press ENTER again and the program is done.

19. Repeat the experiment, but this time use hydrogen peroxide that has been cooled to 10° C. Be sure to wash the test tube thoroughly, making sure all the catalase is removed. Also when starting DATAMATE do not press CLEAR, and it will retain the last parameters set, so that you do not have to reset the program.

20. Repeat the experiment, but this time use hydrogen peroxide that has been warmed to 35° C. Also when starting DATAMATE do not press CLEAR, and it will retain the last parameters set, so that you do not have to reset the program.

21. Clean all your equipment and return it to its original condition.

The Hydrogen Peroxide Breakdown
Examining Factors that Affect the Reaction Rate of Enzymes

Using a Computer

There are thousands of chemical reactions that occur in an organism that make life possible. Most of these chemical reactions proceed too slowly to occur by themselves. Enzymes are protein catalysts that speed up chemical reactions in a cell. Catalysts are not changed by the reactions they control, and are not used up during the reaction. Enzymes, therefore, can be used over and over again. Enzymes are large complex proteins made by the cell and allow chemical reactions to take place at the temperature of the cell. These catalysts are needed in only very small amounts because a single enzyme molecule can complete the same reaction thousands of times in one minute.

Each enzyme is very specific and can only catalyze a certain reaction. The specific reaction catalyzed by an enzyme depends on the molecular structure and shape of a small area of the enzyme's surface called the active site. The active site can attract and hold only its specific molecules. The target molecule that the enzyme attracts and acts upon is called the substrate. The substrate and the active site of the molecule must fit together very closely. Sometimes the enzyme changes its shape slightly to bring about the necessary fit.

Substrates

Product

Active Site

Enzyme

Enzyme

Enzyme-Substrate Complex

Synthesis Reaction

A chemical reaction requires that bonds in the reactants be broken. The initial energy that must be absorbed in order to break the bonds of the reactant molecule is called the energy of activation.

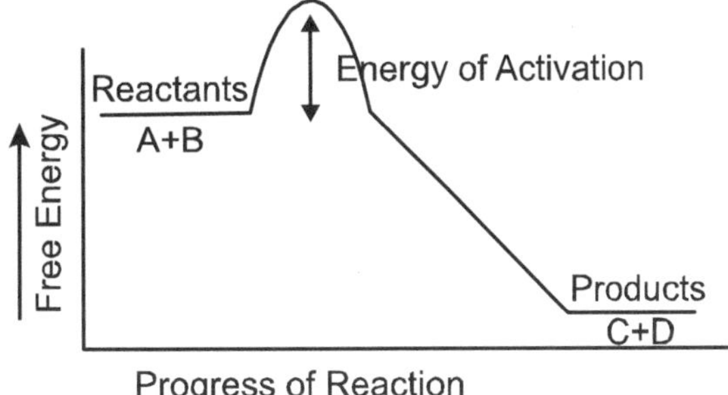

Enzymes work by lowering the energy of activation. For example, hydrogen peroxide decomposes to form water, H_2O, and oxygen gas, O_2.

$$2H_2O_2 \longrightarrow 2H_2O + O_2$$

While this is a catabolic reaction, the rate at which it occurs is slow. Light and temperature affect the reaction rate. As a result, bottles of hydrogen peroxide you may purchase at the drug store are sold in light-blocking brown bottles and have instructions to store them in a cool dark place. Hydrogen peroxide also comes with an expiration date because even with cool and dark storage, the breakdown of H_2O_2 molecules will still occur to some degree. Hydrogen peroxide is toxic to cells. This property makes it useful for treating open wounds since it kills invading bacterial cells. Interestingly enough, hydrogen peroxide is a by-product of some biochemical pathways found in many cells. Yet, the accumulation of hydrogen peroxide can kill a cell. Cells, therefore, cannot wait for hydrogen peroxide to naturally decompose because that takes too much time. Most tissues produce the enzyme, catalase, to increase the rate of hydrogen peroxide's decomposition. Catalase lowers the energy of activation needed for the decomposition and as a result, more molecules are able to be decomposed in a shorter amount of time.

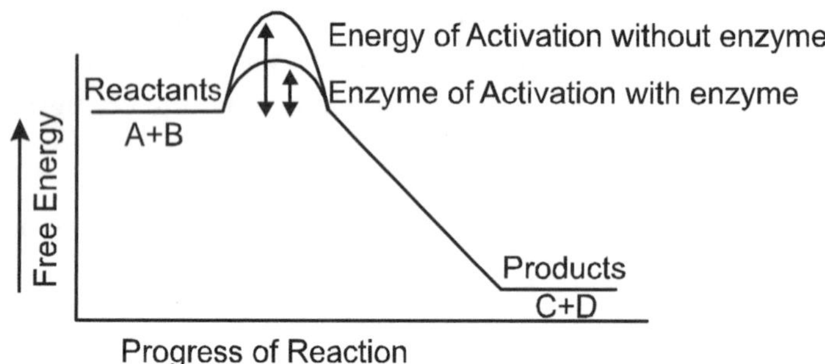

There are factors that can affect how fast an enzymatic reaction occurs. For example, an increase in the amount of enzyme will increase the reaction rate. There are more enzyme molecules available to be involved in the reaction. Another factor that can affect how fast the enzyme works is temperature. An increase in temperature causes the molecules to move faster and engage more frequently in a chemical reaction. At higher temperatures though, the enzymes will denature as the hydrogen bonding falls apart. This lab investigates the effect of enzyme concentration and temperature on an enzymatic reaction.

The reaction used in this laboratory exercise is the decomposition of hydrogen peroxide and the enzyme used is catalase. A pressure probe connected to an interface device and graphing calculator will measure the amount of oxygen gas produced. The more oxygen gas produced the greater the increase in pressure.

PURPOSE

The purpose of this laboratory exercise is to determine the reaction rate of the decomposition of hydrogen peroxide when the concentration of catalase is varies or the temperature is varied.

MATERIALS

pressure sensor probe
catalase solution
test tube rack
10 mL graduated cylinder
80 mL test tube
paper filter disks
computer with Logger Pro installed
3% hydrogen peroxide solution
forceps
10 mL pipette
2 ea 50 mL beakers
4 test tube stopper with eye dropper
Lab Pro or serial interface box
link cord

Safety Alert
CAUTION: Electricity is being used.
Take care not to spill any liquids on any of the computer equipment or electrical outlets.

PROCEDURE

Note: You will either do Part I or Part II of this experiment and then share your results with another group.

PART I (EFFECT OF CONCENTRATION)

1. Answer the pre-lab questions on student answer page.

2. Formulate two hypotheses: The first hypothesis should be about the effect of enzyme concentration on the reaction rate, and the second hypothesis should be about the effect of temperature on the enzyme reaction rate. Record this on the student answer page.

3. Plug the pressure sensor into Port 1 of the serial box or Ch 1 of the LabPro. This box should already be plugged into the modem port and AC outlet. Plug the gas pressure probe into channel 1 of the interface. There should piece of plastic tubing from the pressure probe. Some versions of certain pressure probes have valves for opening and closing the sensor. If the pressure probe has such a valve, ensure that it is open in accordance to the directions accompanying the probe.

4. Now click on the **LoggerPro** and open the file titled "Catalase".

5. A graph should appear and you should notice that at the top you can read both time and pressure readings. Make sure that the pressure probe is reading between 730 and 790 mm Hg. If it is not, tell your teacher.

6. Place the other end of the tubing found on the pressure probe onto the eyedropper sticking out of the #4 test tube stopper.

7. Place the test tube into a test tube rack. Measure 10 mL of hydrogen peroxide with a graduated cylinder and add it to the test tube.

8. Pour a small amount of the catalase solution into the 50 mL beaker. Keep this catalase beaker on ice.

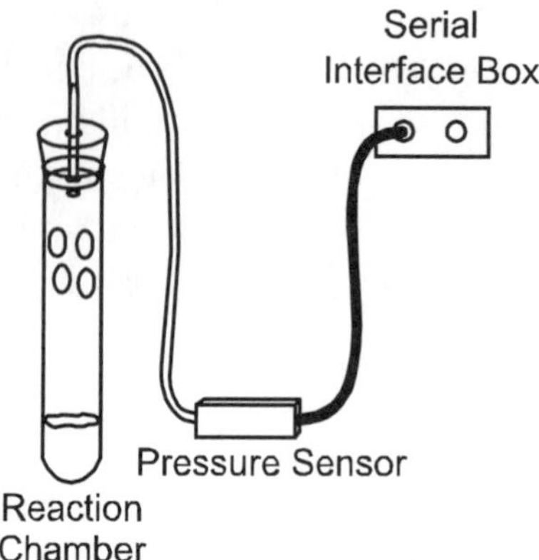

Setup Connected to the Computer

9. Obtain some paper filter disks and separate any paper disks that may be stuck together. Using the forceps, dip one disk into the catalase solution. Drain the disk against the wall of the beaker several times to remove the excess solution. With the forceps, transfer the disk to the test tube and place it on the interior wall of the test tube. It will stick to the wall of the test tube. Using the forceps carefully push the disks 1/2 to 1/3 of the way down the wall of the test tube. Repeat this procedure until you have four disks stuck to the inside wall of the test tube.

10. Place the stopper that is connected to the pressure probe on to the test tube.

11. Press the enter key, or click on **Collect**. You should notice that the data is being graphed as it is being collected.

12. Immediately, tip the test tube slightly on its side so that the hydrogen peroxide will bring the disks down into the solution and the reaction will begin. Right the test tube up again.
    - **CAUTION: Pressure is building in the test tube. During the course of the experiment, it is important that you keep your thumb on the stopper to prevent it from popping off as the pressure builds.**

13. When the experiment is complete, pull down the **Analyze menu** and highlight **Statistics**. This will display the minimum or initial pressure and the maximum or final pressure. Record this information in your data table on the student answer page.

14. Pull down the **Data Menu** and click on **Store Latest Run**. This will allow you to compare this run to the subsequent runs of the experiment. The red line should become a thinner red line.

15. The effects of concentration of enzyme on the reaction rate can be tested by repeating the experiment three more times. Each time reducing the number of disks using three disks, two disks, and one disk respectively. Steps 7-12 are the steps that you should follow in repeating the experiment. Be sure to wash out the test tube thoroughly making sure all the catalase is removed.

16. After you have finished close all windows on the computer. Clean up your area and return your equipment to its original condition.

PART II (EFFECT OF TEMPERATURE)

1. Answer the pre-lab questions on your student answer page.

2. Formulate two hypotheses: The first hypothesis should be about the effect of enzyme concentration on the reaction rate, and the second hypothesis should be about the effect of temperature on the enzyme reaction rate. Record this on the student answer page.

3. Plug the pressure sensor into Port 1 of the serial box or Ch 1 of the LabPro. This box should already be plugged into the modem port and AC outlet. Plug the gas pressure probe into channel 1 of the interface. There should piece of plastic tubing from the pressure probe. Some versions of certain pressure probes have valves for opening and closing the sensor. If the pressure probe has such a valve, ensure that it is open in accordance to the directions accompanying the probe.

4. Now click on the **LoggerPro** and open the file titled "Catalase".

5. A graph should appear and you should notice that at the top you can read both time and pressure readings. Make sure that the pressure probe is reading between 730 and 790 mm Hg. If it is not, tell your teacher.

6. Place the other end of the tubing found on the pressure probe onto the eyedropper sticking out of the #4 test tube stopper.

7. Place the test tube into a test tube rack. Measure 10 mL of hydrogen peroxide with a graduated cylinder and add it to the test tube.

8. Pour a small amount of the catalase solution into the 50 mL beaker. Keep this catalase beaker on ice.

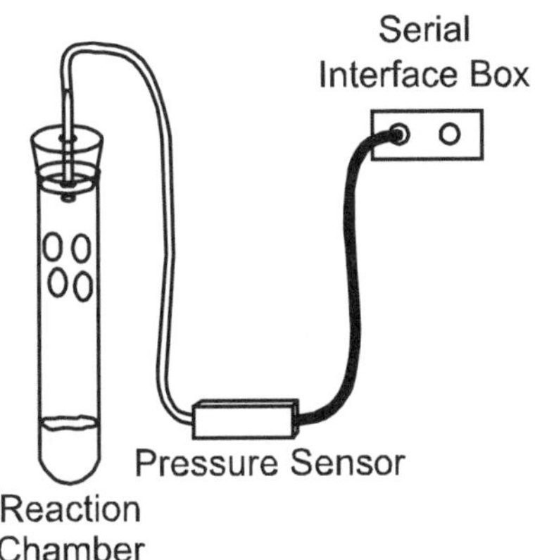

Setup Connected to the Computer

9. Obtain some paper filter disks and separate any paper disks that may be stuck together. Using the forceps, dip one disk into the catalase solution. Drain the disk against the wall of the beaker several times to remove the excess solution. With the forceps, transfer the disk to the test tube and place it on the interior wall of the test tube. It will stick to the wall of the test tube. Using the forceps carefully push the disks 1/2 to 1/3 of the way down the wall of the test tube. Repeat this procedure until you have four disks stuck to the inside wall of the test tube.

10. Place the stopper that is connected to the pressure probe on to the test tube.

11. Press the enter key, or click on **Collect**. You should notice that the data is being graphed as it is being collected.

12. Immediately, tip the test tube slightly on its side so that the hydrogen peroxide will bring the disks down into the solution and the reaction will begin. Right the test tube up again.
    - **CAUTION: Pressure is building in the test tube. During the course of the experiment, it is important that you keep your thumb on the stopper to prevent it from popping off as the pressure builds.**

13. When the experiment is complete, pull down the **Analyze menu** and highlight **Statistics**. This will display the minimum or initial pressure and the maximum or final pressure. Record this information in your data table on the student answer page.

14. Pull down the **Data Menu** and click on **Store Latest Run**. This will allow you to compare this run to the subsequent runs of the experiment. The red line should become a thinner red line.

15. The effects of temperature on the enzyme reaction rate can be tested by repeating the experiment two more times. The first time use hydrogen peroxide that has been cooled to 10° C and the second time use hydrogen peroxide that has been warmed to 35° C. Steps 7-14 are the steps that you should follow in repeating the experiment. Be sure to wash out the test tube thoroughly making sure all the catalase is removed.

16. After you have finished close all windows on the computer. Clean up your area and return your equipment to its original condition

Name ______________________________

Period ______________________________

The Hydrogen Peroxide Breakdown

HYPOTHESES

DATA AND OBSERVATIONS

	Experiment	Minimum Pressure (mm Hg)	Maximum Pressure (mm Hg)	Total Press Change (mm Hg)
Part I	4 Disks			
	3 Disks			
	2 Disks			
	1 Disk			
Part II	Room Temp.			
	Cold Temp.			
	Warm Temp.			

PRE-LAB QUESTIONS

1. List four characteristics of enzymes.

2. What is an active site and what is its relationship to an enzyme?

3. What is the energy of activation?

4. How does the enzyme affect the energy of activation?

5. What are some factors that can affect the reaction rate of an enzymatic reaction?

CONCLUSION QUESTIONS

1. What is the relationship between pressure and time as the hydrogen peroxide decomposes?

2. What gas is produced when hydrogen peroxide decomposes?

3. What is the effect of concentration of enzyme on the reaction rate of the experiment?

4. What is the effect of temperature on the enzymatic decomposition of hydrogen peroxide?

Microscopic Measurement
Using a Light Microscope to Determine an Object's Size

OBJECTIVE
Students will demonstrate the proper technique in using a light microscope and measure various microscopic objects. The students will determine the area and volume of various objects using the light microscope.

LEVEL
Biology I

NATIONAL STANDARDS
UCP.2, UCP.3, C.1, E.1, E.2, G.2

TEKS
1(A), 2 (B), 2 (C), 2 (D), 4 (A)

CONNECTIONS TO AP
AP Biology:
I. Molecules and Cells B. Cells 1. Prokaryotic and eukaryotic cells

TIME FRAME
50 Minutes

MATERIALS
(For a class of 28 working in pairs)

14 light microscopes
42 cover slips
14 clear metric rulers 10 cm long
14 prepared slides
42 microscope slides
14 bottles of Lugol's iodine
newspapers

TEACHER NOTES
This lesson can be used at the beginning of the year as an introduction to the microscope. It includes measuring with the microscope and determining volume, using micrometers as units.

When selecting prepared slides to be used in Part III, select slides with relatively large specimen that are visible to the naked eye.

When obtaining the letters and period from the newspaper, use the classified section. The print in the other part of the newspaper is much too large.

You may want to prepare some permanent slides of the letters and hairs prior to the lab. This can be done either by using clear fingernail polish to seal the outside cover slip or transparent tape along the edges of the coverslip to secure in place.

The Lugol's iodine (iodine potassium iodide) will stain the nucleus of the onion cells.

To prepare the Lugol's iodine solution:

- Add 6 g of potassium iodide, KI to 300 mL of distilled water.
- Add 0.6 g of iodine to the potassium iodide solution. The iodine will take some time to dissolve.
- Dispense 15 mL into the 14 brown dropper bottles.
- Keep the bottle tightly capped and in the dark.
- Be sure to use rubber gloves when making the above solution.

ANSWERS TO PRE-LAB QUESTIONS

1. Fill in the diagram of the microscope below.

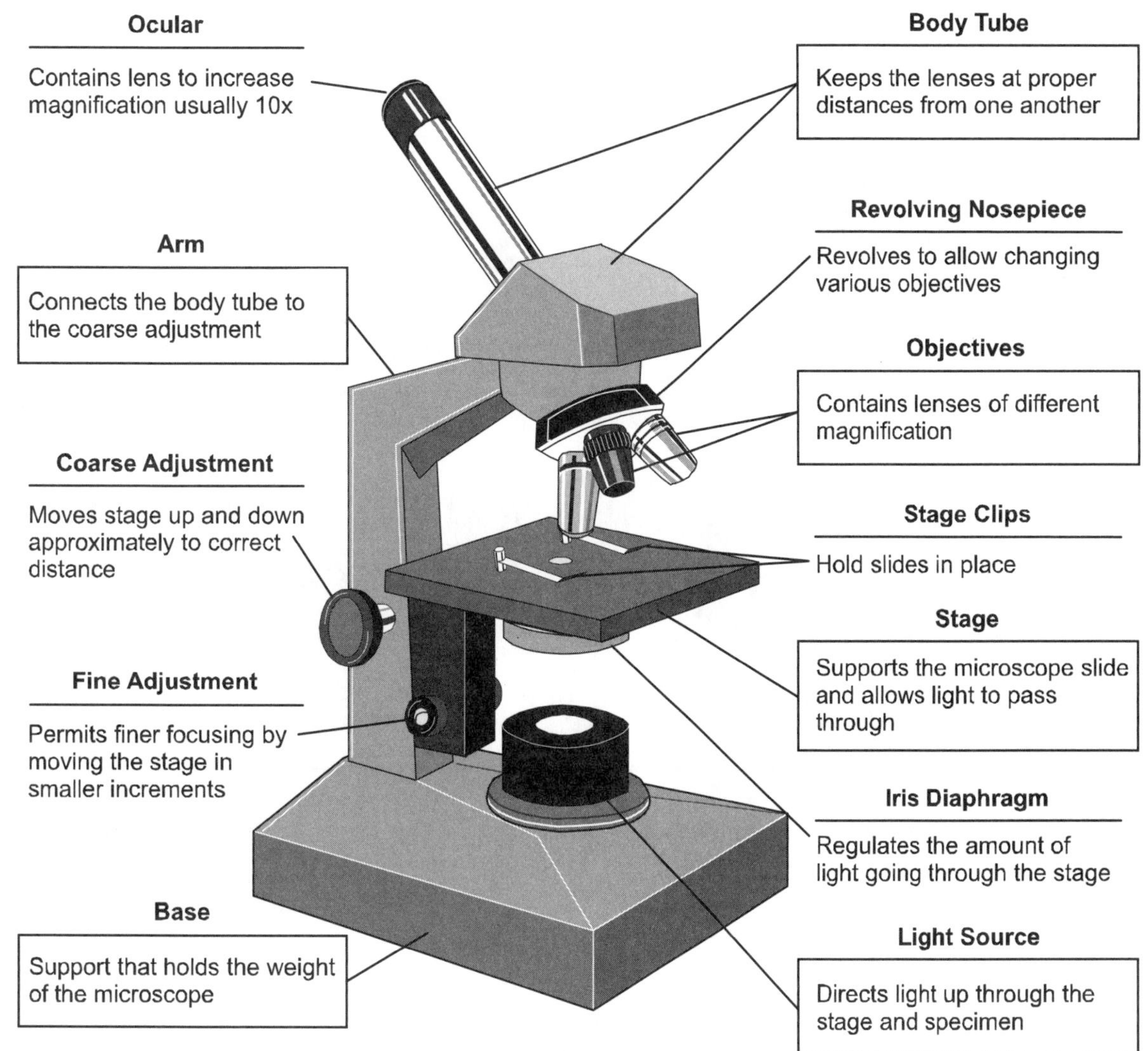
Ocular
Contains lens to increase magnification usually 10x
Arm
Connects the body tube to the coarse adjustment
Coarse Adjustment
Moves stage up and down approximately to correct distance
Fine Adjustment
Permits finer focusing by moving the stage in smaller increments
Base
Support that holds the weight of the microscope
Body Tube
Keeps the lenses at proper distances from one another
Revolving Nosepiece
Revolves to allow changing various objectives
Objectives
Contains lenses of different magnification
Stage Clips
Hold slides in place
Stage
Supports the microscope slide and allows light to pass through
Iris Diaphragm
Regulates the amount of light going through the stage
Light Source
Directs light up through the stage and specimen

POSSIBLE ANSWERS TO THE CONCLUSION QUESTIONS AND SAMPLE DATA

PART IV: VIEWING THE LETTER "E"

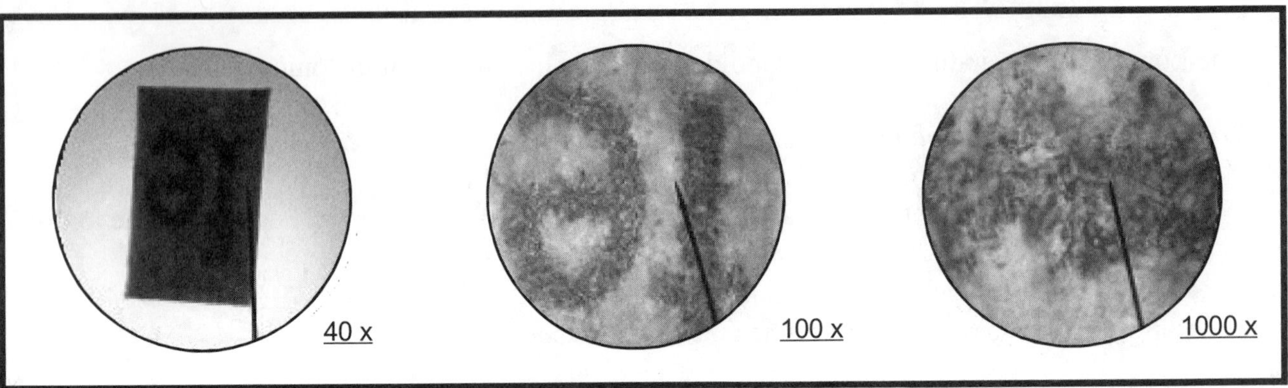

List three things that the microscope did to the letter "e" when viewing under the microscope.

1. Increased magnification and increased detail.
2. Turned the "e" upside down.
3. Reversed the "e" from left to right.

PART V: MEASURING WITH THE MICROSCOPE

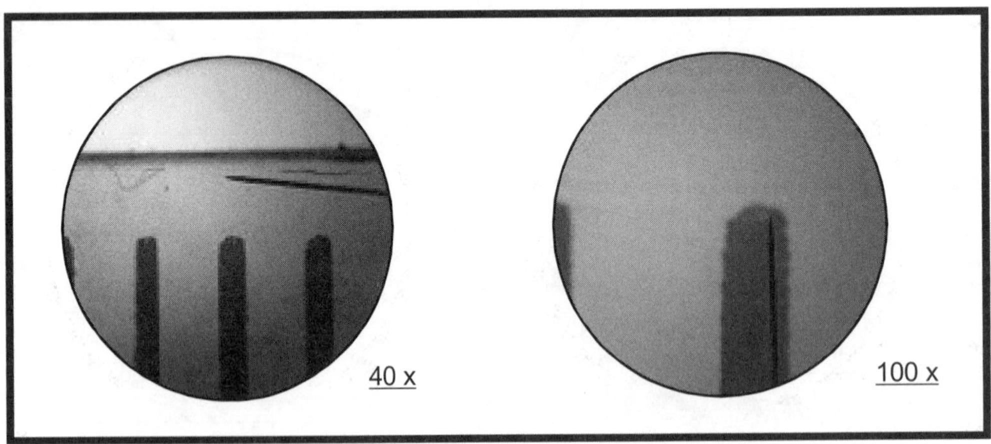

For the field of view(s) that could not be measured with a ruler on the stage, determine the diameter using the formula and the indirect method.

Magnification	Diameter of field of view (micrometers, μm)	Can be measured with a ruler (yes / no)
40X	4000	yes
100X	1750	yes
400X	375	no

On 100X power, the diameter of the field of view should be between 1.5 and 1.75 mm depending on how it is measured. This assumes 1.5 for this answer.

Diameter on medium (100X) = 1.5 mm or 1500 μm

Ratio of high to low $= \frac{400}{100} = 4.0$ then $\frac{1500}{4.0}\ \mu m = 375\ \mu m$

PART VI: MEASURING THE AREA OF A PERIOD

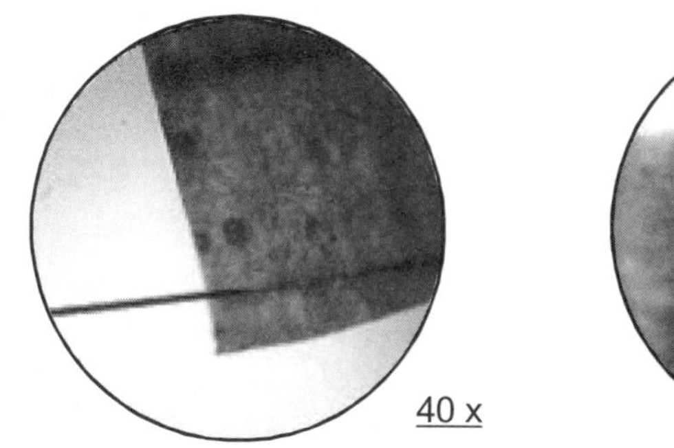
40 x

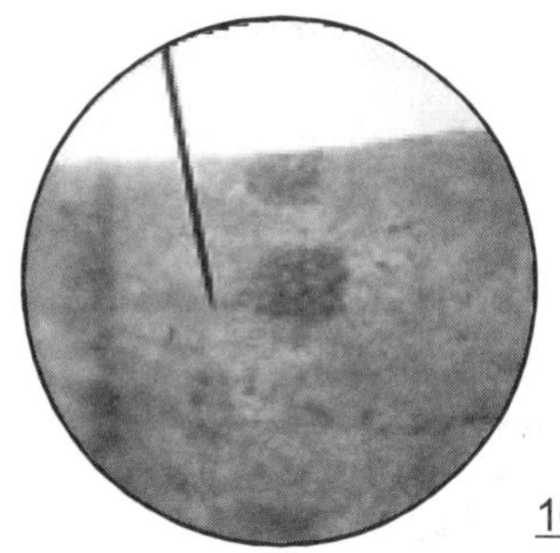
100 x

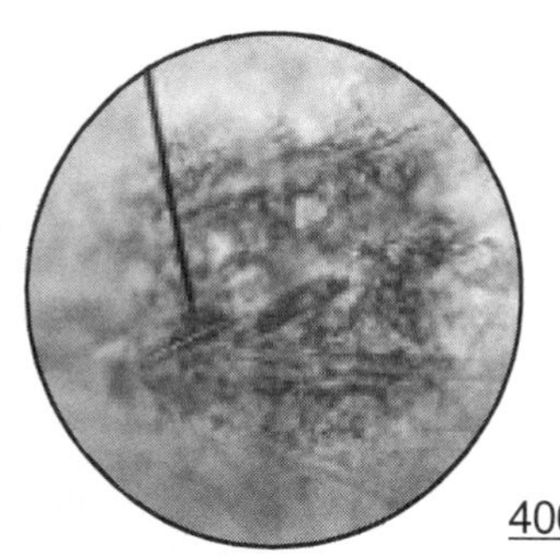
400 x

Determine the area of a period from the classified section of the newspaper. Show your work.

The period occupies approximately 2/3 of the field of view on high. The diameter on high is 375 μm so therefore the diameter of the period is 2/3 X 375 μm = 250 μm.

The radius of the period is 125 μm. The area of the period is

$$A = \pi r^2$$

$$A = \pi(125)^2$$

$$A = 49{,}087\ \mu m^2$$

PART VII: MEASURING THE VOLUME OF A CYLINDER

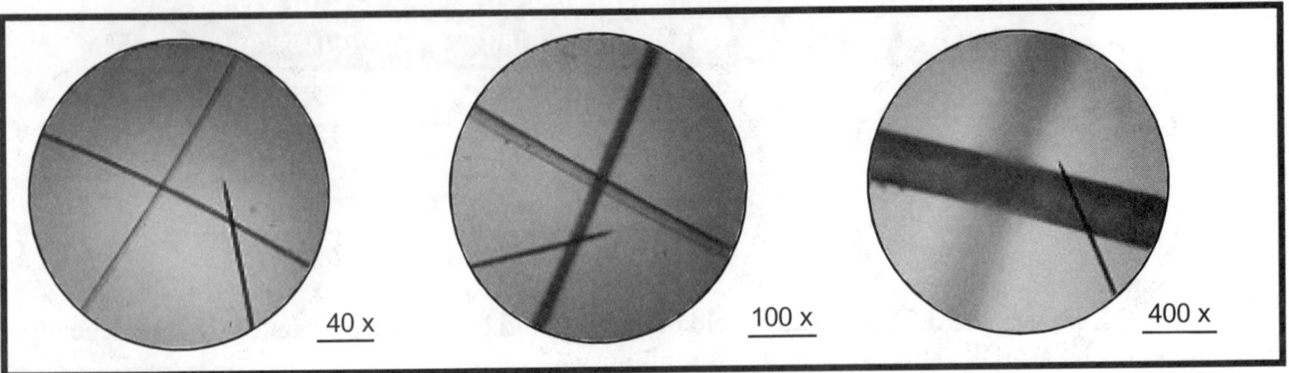

Determine the volume of a cylinder from one of the hairs. Show your work.

The hair occupies approximately 1/5 of the field of view on high magnification or 400X. The diameter on high magnification is 375 μm so therefore the diameter of the hair is 1/5 X 375 μm = 75 μm. The length of the cylinder is the entire length of the hair in the field of view or 375 μm

$V = H\pi r^2$ where H is 375 μm and r= 75 μm

$V = 375\ \mu m \times \pi \times (75\ \mu m)^2$

$V = 6{,}626{,}797\ \mu m^3$

PART VIII: MEASURING THE VOLUME OF A SPHERE AND BLOCK

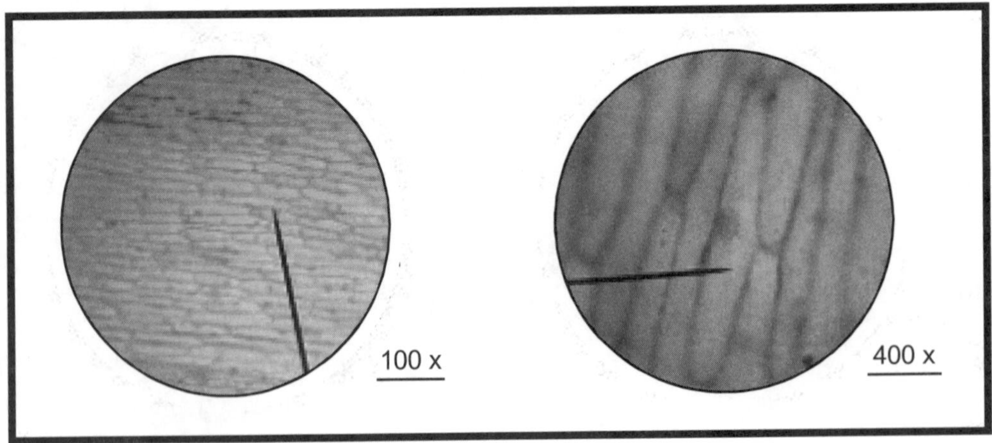

Determine the volume of the onion cells or block. Show your work.

Ten onion cells fit across the field of view on 400X and the diameter of this field of view is 375 μm. Therefore, the width of one cell is approximately 38 μm. The height or depth of the onion cell equals the width of the cell. The length of the cell is approximately 9/10 of the diameter of the field of view. Therefore, the length is 9/10 x 375 μm or 337 μm.

The volume of the onion cell is equal to

V = L x W x H

L = 337 μm W = 38 μm H = 38 μm

V = 337 μm x 38 μm x 38 μm

V = 487,350 μm^3

Determine the volume of the nucleus or sphere. Show your work.

V = $(4/3)\pi r^3$. The nucleus occupies about half the width of the onion cell, so therefore the diameter of the nucleus is 1/2 X 38 μm or 19 μm. The radius of the nucleus is one half of that value or 9.5 μm.

The volume of the nucleus is equal to

V = $(4/3)\pi r^3$ The radius is equal to 9.5μm.

V = $(4/3)\pi$ x $(9.5\ \mu m)^3$

V = 3,591 μm^3

CONCLUSION QUESTIONS

1. What is the advantage of using high power?
   - The advantage of using high power is being able to increase the detail that cannot be seen on low power.

2. What is the advantage of using low power?
   - The advantage of using low power is that a greater portion of the slide can be viewed perhaps revealing more information about the interrelationship of objects.

3. If a slide has 28 yeast cells in a field of view on 100X, approximately how many yeast cells will be seen when the magnification is increased to 400X?
   - If the magnification increases by a factor of four then the number of objects viewed should decrease by a factor of four. There will be seven cells visible.

4. What is the resolving power with regard to a microscope?
   - Resolving power is the measurement of how close two points can be and still be distinguished as separate.

REFERENCES

Abramoff, Peter and Robert G. Thompson. *Laboratory Outlines in Biology*. New York: W.H. Freeman and Company, 1994. pp. 17-25

King, Jack, Gerald Sanders, Robert Wallace. *Biology, the Science of Life*. Dallas: Scott, Foresman and Company, 1981. pp. 96-97

Milani, Jean P., Revision Coordinator. *Biological Science, A Molecular Approach.* Dubuque: Kendall Hunt Publishing Company, 1996. pp. T56, 614-617, 645

Microscopic Measurement
Using a Light Microscope to Determine an Object's Size

The microscope is a valuable tool used by biologists. It magnifies materials such as cells that the human eye cannot distinguish. We cannot see objects much smaller than 0.1 mm in size. The most commonly used compound microscope is the monocular (one eyepiece) light microscope. The microscopes found in most high school laboratories magnify objects from 40X – 1000X. The resolving power is the limiting factor that determines how much a microscope can magnify. *Resolving power* is the measurement of how close two points can be and still be distinguished as separate. The resolving power of the human eye is approximately 0.1 mm. This value is somewhat variable as some humans are capable of making much finer distinctions than others and this ability can change with age.

A microscope is basically a tube with lenses at both ends. The lens that is closest to the eye is the *ocular lens*. It is not unusual for this lens to magnify 10X by itself. The level of magnification is found on the side of the ocular. Some oculars will include built-in pointers or measuring devices.

The lenses that are found on the revolving nosepiece are the *objectives*. Most microscopes will have two or more objectives. The magnification of the objective lens is stamped on the side of the lens. The total magnification of an object can be found by multiplying the magnification of the objective lens with that of the ocular lens. For example, a microscope with a 10X ocular lens and a 10X low power objective lens has a low power total magnification of 100X. The objectives are attached to a revolving nosepiece so that turning the nosepiece can change the objectives. The advantage of using an objective with higher magnification is an increase in detail than can be viewed. The disadvantage of viewing at a higher magnification is that less of the slide can be viewed. For example, if there are 20 evenly distributed yeast cells in the field of view at 50X, then when the microscope objective is increased to a magnification to 100X, then, on the average, there should be only 10 cells visible. These yeast cells however, will appear twice as large. The other disadvantage of using higher magnification is that the depth of focus is much more difficult to control. For example, on 40X two crossed threads on a microscope slide can both be brought into focus. However, when the magnification is increased to 100X only one of the threads can be brought into focus. The other thread will be out of focus.

Underneath the stage is the *condenser lens* which has a diaphragm. This lens regulates the amount of light passing through the specimen. Specimens to be viewed are usually thin enough that the light passes right through them. Light reaches the eye after being passed through the objects to be examined. There are times when the amount of light passing through the specimen is too much and the amount of light needs to be reduced. The iris of the microscope removes any stray light that might cause the image to be blurry.

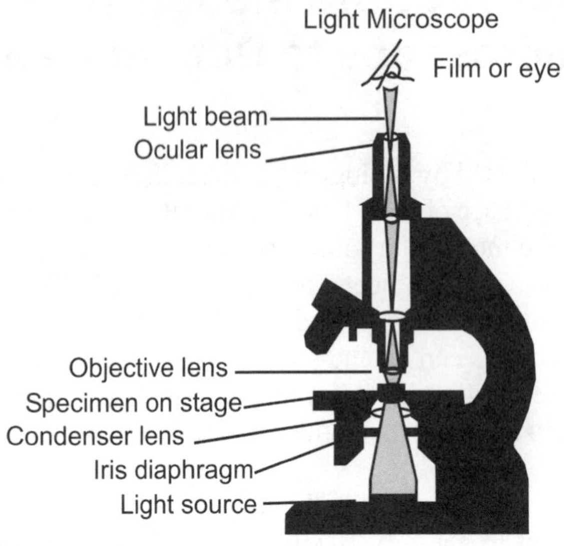

PURPOSE

In this investigation, you will learn how to use and care for a microscope.

MATERIALS

- cover slips
- 3 microscope slides
- scissors
- newspaper
- dropping pipet
- compound microscope
- transparent metric ruler

> **Safety Alert**
> 1. **Caution: Scissors are sharp. Use care when handling.**

PROCEDURE

PART I: CARE OF THE MICROSCOPE

1. It is important to take proper care of the microscope; it is probably one of the most expensive pieces of equipment in the laboratory. When moving the microscope, always carry the microscope with both hands, placing one hand on the arm while holding the base with the other hand.

2. Always set the microscope down gently and away from the edge of the table. If a lamp is attached to the microscope, keep its wire out of any water. Remove all of your materials from the table except those items needed for the lab.

3. If you wear mascara hold your eyes at a distance from the ocular lens. When your eye blinks, your eyelashes can transfer some of the mascara to the ocular lens, making it difficult to see the specimen.

4. Before using the microscope, clean the lenses carefully with lens paper. The lenses of the microscope are the most expensive items on the microscope. Always clean lenses with the lens paper designed for this task. Using filter paper, paper towel or any other substitute may scratch the lenses.

5. To prevent damage to the high power objective, ***always*** return the revolving nosepiece to the low power setting before putting away the microscope.

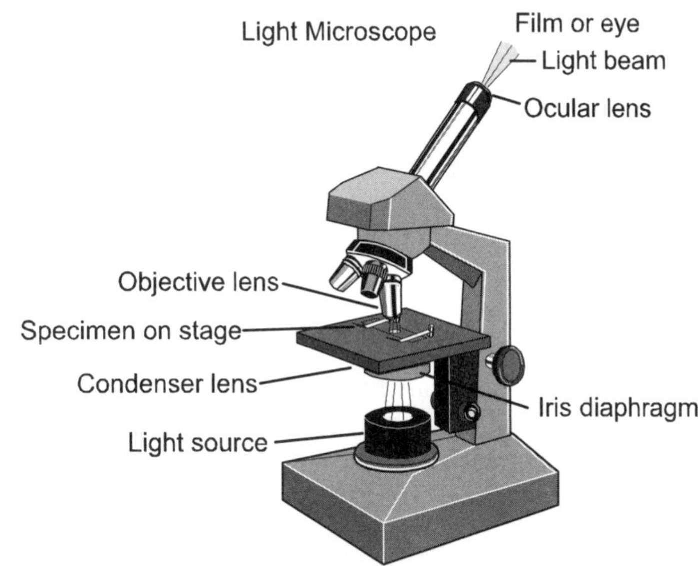

PART II: IDENTIFYING THE PARTS OF THE MICROSCOPE

1. Obtain a microscope and use the diagram above to guide you as you locate the various parts. Read about the function of each part of the microscope below. Use this information to complete the pre-lab activity.
   a. **Ocular or eyepiece** - Contains lenses to increase magnification, usually 10X.
   b. **Arm** - Connects body tube to the base where stage and adjustment knobs are located.
   c. **Revolving nosepiece** - Allows changing of various objectives.
   d. **Objectives** - Contains lenses of different magnifications, usually 4X, 10X, and 40/43X.
   e. **Stage** - Holds microscope slides and has an opening to allow light to pass through.
   f. **Stage clips** - hold the slide in place.
   g. **Adjustment knobs** - Can be found as one knob with two parts or as two separate knobs. The outer knob or the larger knob is the coarse adjustment and is used to bring the slide into focus. The fine adjustment is the inner knob or the smaller knob and is used to sharpen the focus.
   h. **Diaphragm** - Regulates the amount of light passing through the stage.
   i. **Light source** - Directs light upward through the diaphragm.
   j. **Base** - Supports the microscope.

PART III: USING THE MICROSCOPE

1. Plug in the microscope. Turn on the lamp by using the lamp switch. This will allow light through the stage. Most microscopes are equipped with a diaphragm for regulating light. Some materials are best viewed in dim light, others in bright light.

2. Rotate the nosepiece to bring the low-power objective into place. When changing from one objective to another you will hear a click as the objective snaps into position.

3. Using only lens paper, wipe the lenses to make sure that they are dry and free of fingerprints and debris.

4. Obtain a prepared slide and look at it to locate the specimen. Place the slide on the stage so that the specimen is over the opening on the stage.

5. When focusing, start with the objective with the lowest magnification. Make sure that **both** the coarse and fine adjustment knobs are lowered down as far as possible. Do not allow the objectives to touch the cover slip.

6. Adjust the light with the diaphragm so that an evenly distributed circle of light is visible.

7. Look through the ocular and slowly turn the coarse adjustment knob to raise the nosepiece until the specimen comes into rough focus. Use the fine adjustment knob to sharply focus the specimen.

8. To increase the magnification, revolve the nosepiece to the higher objective. Be sure to snap this lens in place. You should only have to sharpen the focus with the fine-adjustment knob. You should **not** focus using the coarse-adjustment knob after changing to a higher magnification.

9. Sketch the specimen as it appears under high power magnification in the space provided on your student answer page. Indicate the magnification power in the lower right of your sketch.

10. Remove the slide and return to the low power objective.

PART IV: VIEWING THE LETTER "E"

1. Cut a lowercase "e" from the classified section of the newspaper. The smaller the letter, the better. Place it right side up on a clean slide.

2. This is a dry mount slide, so just place a cover slip over the newspaper.

3. Focus the letter "e" using steps 3 - 7 from Part III.

4. Notice how this letter appears in the field of view compared to how it appears on the slide. Draw this letter as it appears in the field of view on your student answer page. In making microscope drawings keep the following points in mind.
   a. Microscope drawings are made in circles to represent the field of view.
   b. Be sure to label the total magnification outside the circle to the lower right-hand side.

c. Draw the field of view as it appears in the microscope and with the proper proportions. If an object occupies half of the field of view when viewing it with the microscope, then when the object is drawn, make sure that it occupies half the circle.
d. Include as much detail as possible.
e. When labeling, draw straight lines with a ruler, and print the label.

5. Slowly move the slide to the right. Observe which direction the "e" moves in the field of view. Slowly move the slide away from you. Again, observe which direction the "e" moves in the field of view.

6. Following step # 8 from Part III view the "e" on high power and draw the image as it appears in the field of view.

PART V: MEASURING WITH THE MICROSCOPE

Because objects examined with a microscope are usually quite small, biologists measure objects viewed under the microscope in units called micrometers, which is one thousandth of a millimeter. The symbol for micrometer is μm, the Greek letter μ (called mu) followed by m.

1. You can estimate the size of a microscopic object by comparing it with the size of the field of view. Determine the size of the field by placing a plastic mm ruler on the stage. Use the low power objective to focus the divisions on the ruler.

2. Carefully move the ruler until its marked edge passes through the center of the field of view.

3. Count the number of divisions that you can see in the field of view. One mm or 1000 μm is the distance from the center of one mark to the center of the next.

4. Record the diameter of the low power field of view for your microscope, in micrometers, on your student answer page. This process can be used for objectives as great as 10X.

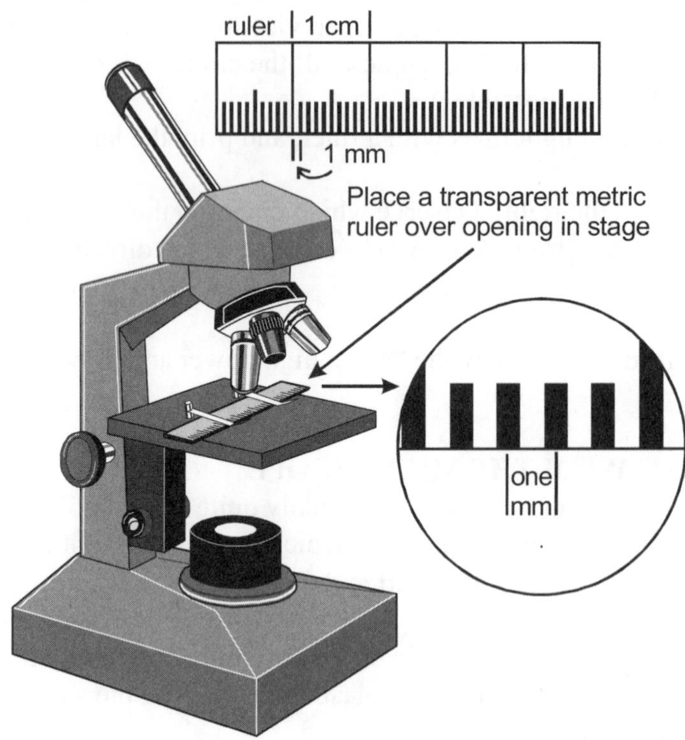

The above field of view measures approximately 6750μm

The diameter of the high power (40X or 43X) cannot be determined using the process described above. This is because the high power diameter is usually less than one millimeter. The high power diameter can be determined indirectly. To determine the diameter on high power, you need to know the low power field diameter and the magnifying power of both objectives. Since the magnification of the objectives is inversely proportional to the field size, you can use the formula:

$$\text{High Power Field Diameter} = \frac{\text{Low Power Field Diameter} \times \text{Low Power Magnification}}{\text{High Power Magnification}}$$

5. Use the formula above and determine the diameter of the field of view on high power. Record this in the space provided on your student answer page.

6. Knowing the diameter of the field of view will allow you to estimate the sizes of objects viewed under the microscope with both low and high power, by comparing them with the diameter of the field of vision. For example, if a tiny organism takes up approximately one-half of a field of view that is 1000 micrometers in diameter, then the size of the organism is one-half of 1000 micrometers, or 500 micrometers.

PART VI: MEASURING THE AREA OF A PERIOD

1. Cut a period from the classified section of the newspaper. For the best results, use the smallest period you can find. The smaller the period, the better the results will be. Place the period on the microscope slide.

2. This is another dry mount slide, so just place a cover slip over the newspaper. Follow steps 3-13. View this on high magnification and make a drawing of the field of view on the student answer page.

3. Using the information and calculations determined in steps 5 and 6 in part V determine the diameter of the period on high magnification. Next, calculate the area of the period in micrometers.
   - Remember that the area of a circle is $A = \pi r^2$ where r is the radius of the circle.

PART VII: MEASURING THE VOLUME OF A CYLINDER

1. Obtain two different-colored hairs, one light and one dark. Place both hairs on a clean glass slide. Cross one hair over the other and place a cover slip over them. Put the slide on the stage so that where the hairs cross is in the middle of the field of view.

2. Follow steps 3-13 in part III. View the hairs on high magnification and make a drawing of the field of view on the student answer page. Notice that on low power both of the hairs can be brought into focus. This is not true on high magnification.

3. Observe the hairs using high power. Draw these crossed hairs on your student answer page.

4. Focus on one of the hairs and imagine that what is viewed in the microscope is a cylinder. Determine the volume of the cylinder, using the information in steps 5 and 6 in part V measure the diameter of the of a hair and use the formula below to determine the volume of a cylinder.
   - Remember the volume of a cylinder is $V = H\pi r^2$ where r is the radius of the circle and H is the height of the cylinder.
   - Record your volume calculations on your student answer page.

PART VIII: MEASURING THE VOLUME OF A SPHERE AND A BLOCK

1. Obtain a layer of an onion; tear the onion layer in half. Looking at the concave side, you should be able to pull off a thin layer of epidermal cells. This layer of epidermal cells is usually one layer thick and can be seen with the light microscope. Place this layer of epidermal cells on the slide. Add a drop of iodine and place a cover slip on top of the epidermal cells. When placing the cover slip on top of the slide, place one end of the cover slip on top of the slide and keep the cover slip at about a 45° angle. Allow the cover slip to drop down. This should eliminate many air bubbles.

2. View this slide using steps 3-13. The cells may be too large on 400X to measure, if that is the case continue using 100X. The cells have a block-like shape. The length and width can be measured by using the microscope. The height or depth of the cell is approximately equal to the width of the cell (or whichever dimension was smaller). Estimate the length and width of the onion plant cells. Draw this field of view on your student answer page.

3. Determine the volume of the block or cell, using the information in steps 5 and 6 in part V.
   - Remember the volume of the block is V = L x W x H.
   - Record this calculation on your student answer page.

4. The nucleus of the cell can be visualized because of the iodine stain. The nucleus is in the shape of a sphere. Estimate the diameter of the nucleus and then determine the volume of the nucleus using the information in steps 5 and 6 in part V.
   - Remember the volume of a sphere is $V = (^4/_3)\pi r^3$.
   - Record this calculation on your student answer page.

5. Remove the slide from the stage, turn off the light with the switch, unplug and return your microscope to its storage position. Clean your work area and return your lab supplies as directed by your teacher.

Name ______________________________

Period ______________________________

Microscopic Measurement
Using a Light Microscope to Determine an Object's Size

PRE LAB QUESTIONS

1. Fill in the diagram of the microscope below.

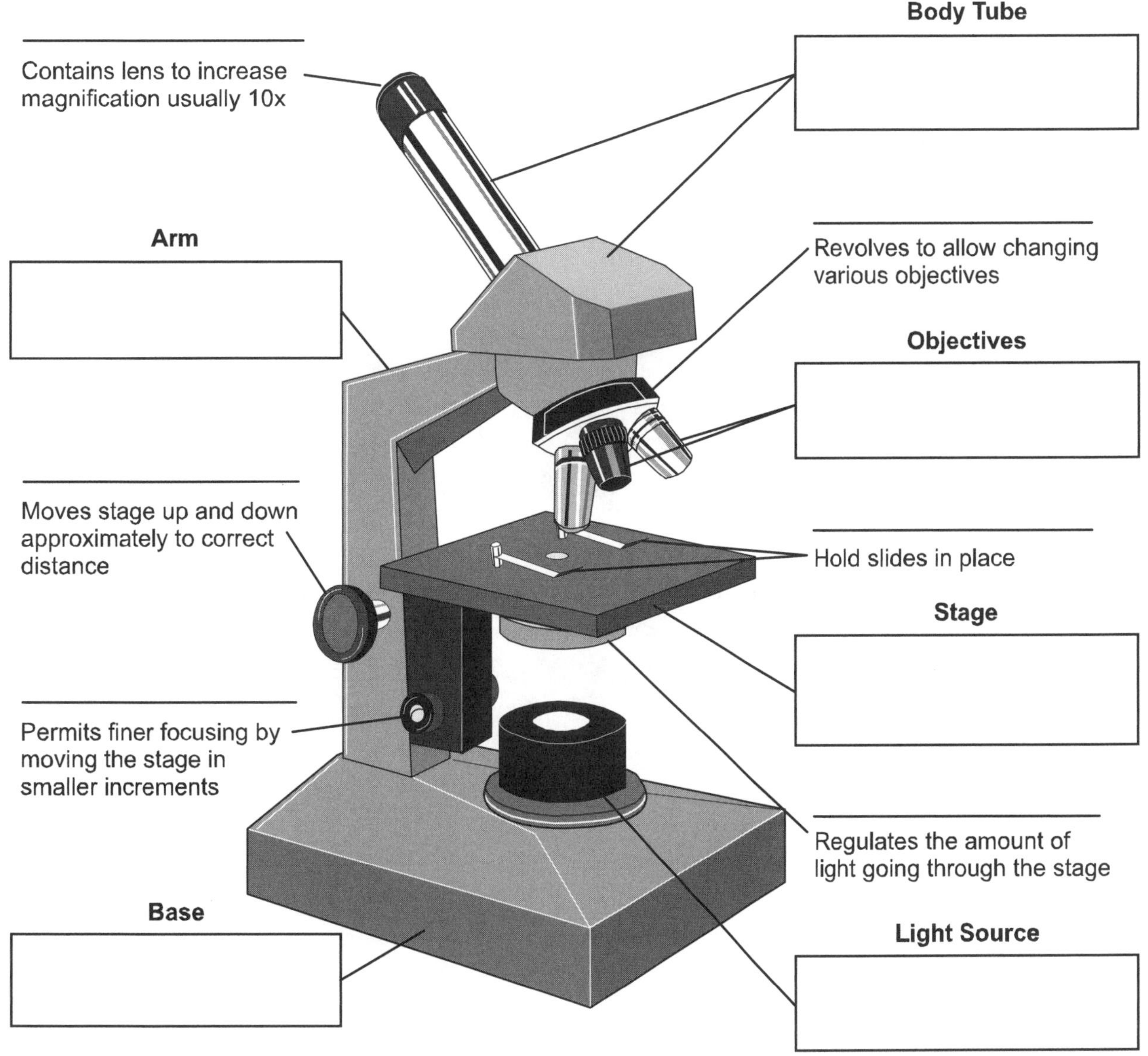

DATA AND OBSERVATIONS

PART III: USING THE MICROSCOPE

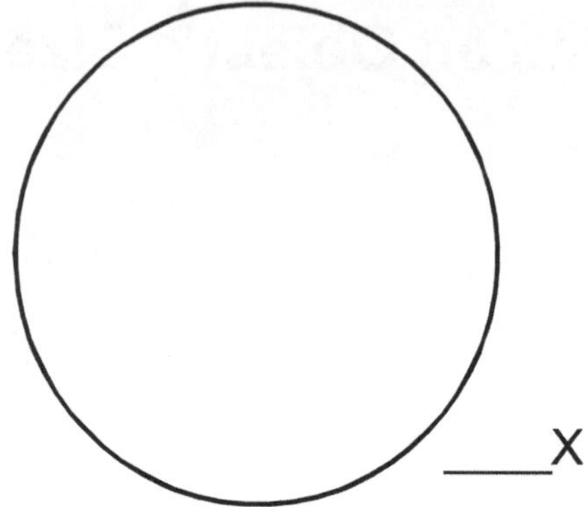

PART IV: VIEWING THE LETTER "E"

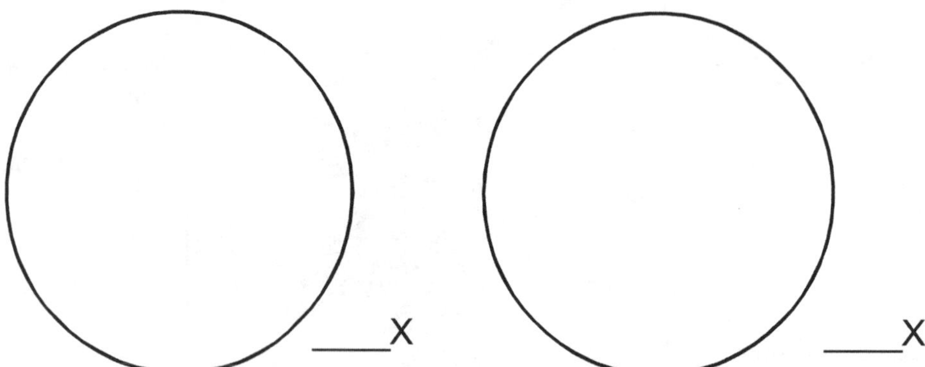

List three things that the microscope did to the letter "e" when viewing under the microscope.

1.

2.

3.

PART V: MEASURING WITH THE MICROSCOPE

For the field of view(s) that could not be measured with a ruler on the stage, determine the diameter using the formula and the indirect method.

Magnification	Diameter of field of view (micrometers)	Can be measured with a ruler (yes / no)
40X		
100X		
400X		

PART VI: MEASURING THE AREA OF A PERIOD

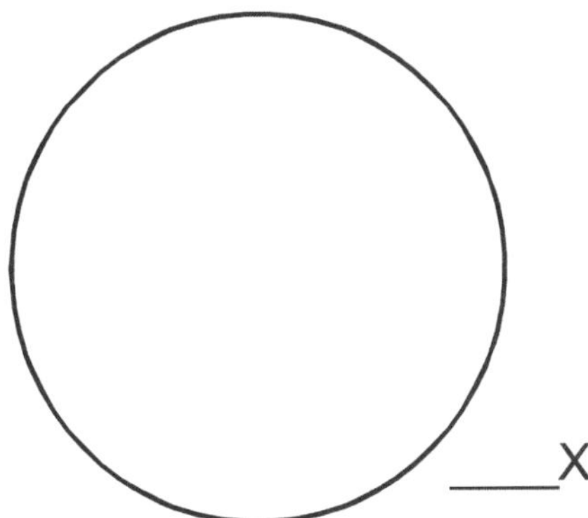

Determine the area of a period from the classified section of the newspaper. Show your work.

PART VII: MEASURING THE VOLUME OF A CYLINDER

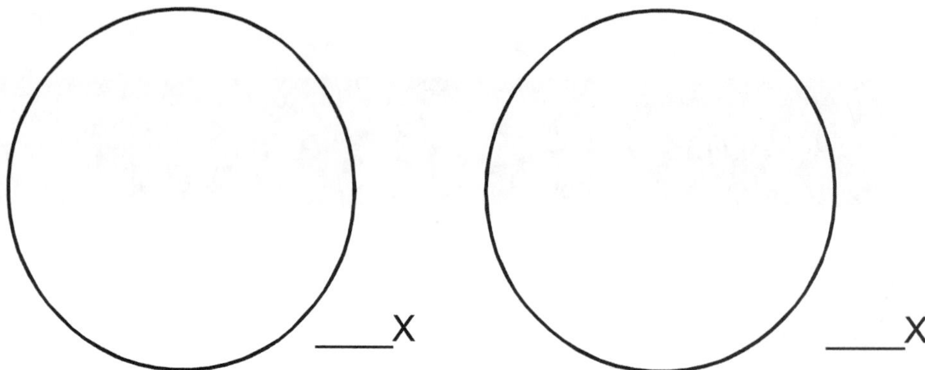

Determine the volume of a cylinder from one of the hairs. Show your work.

PART VIII: MEASURING THE VOLUME OF A SPHERE AND BLOCK

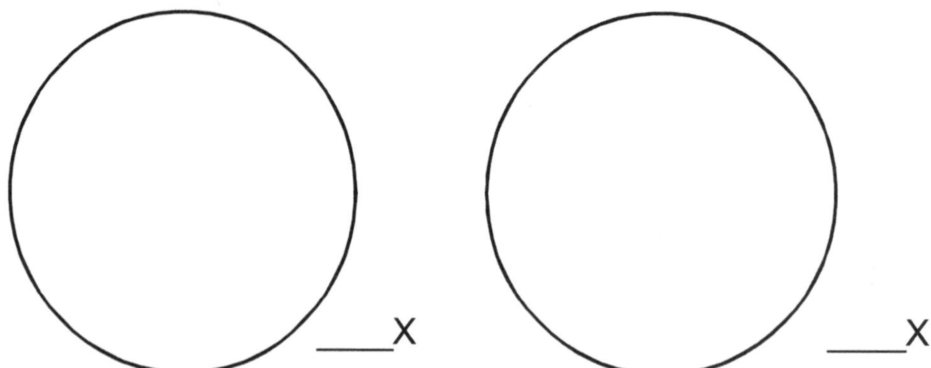

Determine the volume of the onion cells or block. Show your work.

Determine the volume of the nucleus or sphere. Show your work.

CONCLUSION QUESTIONS

1. What is the advantage of using high power?

2. What is the advantage of using low power?

3. If a slide has 28 yeast cells in a field of view on 100X, approximately how many yeast cells will be seen when the magnification is increased to 400X?

4. What is the resolving power with regard to a microscope?

Larger Is Not Always Better
Examining Cell Size and Rates of Diffusion

OBJECTIVE
Students will investigate the relationship between cell size and the total surface area-to-volume ratio. Additionally, students will investigate the rate of diffusion and its relationship to cell size.

LEVEL
Biology I

NATIONAL STANDARDS
UCP.1, UCP.2, UCP.3, C.1, G.2

TEKS
2(A), 2(B), 2(C), 2(D), 4(B)

CONNECTIONS TO AP
AP Biology:
  I. Molecules and cells B. Cells 2. Membranes

TIME FRAME
50 Minutes

MATERIALS
(For a class of 28 working in pairs)

- 28 pairs of safety goggles
- 28 pairs plastic gloves
- 28 millimeter rulers
- 28 plastic table knives
- 3 L of 0.1% HCl
- 14 TI-83 graphing calculators (optional)
- 28 lab aprons
- 28 250 mL beakers
- 28 plastic spoons
- several rolls of paper towels
- 14 blocks of phenolphthalein agar
- 0.1 M sodium hydroxide, NaOH

Safety Alert
Caution: 0.1 M NaOH and 0.1% HCL is a mild irritant. Avoid skin/eye contact; do not ingest. Immediately run water over any skin that the liquid comes in contact with. Flush the skin for 10 minutes.

Label: CAUTION: 0.1% HCl, Mild irritant.

TEACHER PAGES

TEACHER NOTES

The day before class, prepare enough phenolphthalein agar to make at least 14 blocks measuring 3 cm x 3 cm x 6 cm. Do not prepare more than 1 day in advance. (The carbon dioxide in the air will combine with the water in the cubes, forming carbonic acid and turn the pink cubes white.)

To Prepare Phenolphthalein Agar:

Mix 30 g of plain agar per liter of water and bring to a boil while stirring continuously. Let the mixture cool, but before it solidifies stir in 1 g phenolphthalein powder per liter of agar solution made. Intensify the pale pink color by slowly adding 0.1 M NaOH until it is a deep pink. If you do not have 0.1 M NaOH, it can be made by adding 4 grams of NaOH pellets dissolved in enough water to make 1.0 L of solution. Take care in mixing this solution as NaOH is a strong base. Pour the mixture into a flat-bottomed pan to a depth of 3 cm. When the agar has solidified, cut into blocks measuring 3 cm x 3 cm x 6 cm

Alternative Preparation:

Plastic containers can be bought at some discount stores which measure 7 in x 10 in x 2 in. This converts to 18 cm x 25 cm x 4 cm. This allows for 18 blocks of agar to be cut measuring approximately 3 cm x 3 cm x 6 cm. (Standard dimensions given in length X width X height.)

1.5 L of agar must be prepared to make enough agar blocks to fill this container. Mix 45 g of agar with 1.5 liter of water. The agar can be prepared using a microwave. Place ingredients into a 2 L beaker or similar microwaveable container. Stir the mixture every three minutes until it begins to boil. This usually takes about 15-20 minutes. Allow the mixture to cool for a few minutes before stirring in 1.5 g of phenolphthalein powder. Intensify the pale pink color by slowly adding 0.1 M NaOH until a deep pink color appears. Pour this mixture into the plastic container and allow it to solidify. When the agar has solidified, cut into blocks 3 cm x 3 cm x 6 cm blocks.

To prepare 0.1% HCl:

Use proper safety precautions when making this solution: Prepare this solution in a fume hood while wearing a face shield over goggles and nitrile rubber gloves. Slowly add 4 mL of concentrated HCl to 1 L of distilled water. Repeat two more times to make 3 L of 0.1% HCl.

An optional calculator section is included in the procedure. Students will be instructed in use of the graphing calculator to create a graph of their results. Using Foundation Lesson VIII with the students will enable them to analyze their graph.

POSSIBLE ANSWERS TO THE CONCLUSION QUESTIONS AND SAMPLE DATA

Cube dimension	Distance HCl diffused in the cube	Rate of diffusion	Distance from center of cube
1 cm	0.5 cm	0.05 cm/min	0.1 cm
2 cm	0.5 cm	0.05 cm/min	0.5 cm
3 cm	0.5 cm	0.05 cm/min	1.0 cm

Cube Dimension	Surface Area	Volume (cm^3)	Simplest Ratio
0.01 cm	0.0006 cm^2	0.000001 cm^3	600:1
1 cm	6 cm^2	1 cm^3	6:1
2 cm	24 cm^2	8 cm^3	3:1
3 cm	54 cm^2	27 cm^3	2:1

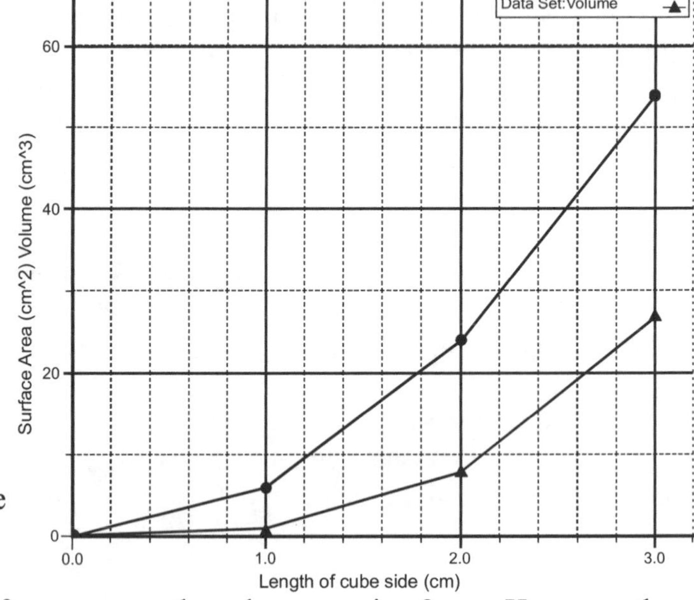

1. Which cube had the greatest surface area? Which cube had the greatest volume? Be sure to consider the hypothetical cell as well.
    - The cube which has the greatest surface area is the cube measuring 3 cm in length and the cube which has the greatest volume also measured 3 cm in length

2. Which cube had the greatest total surface area-to-volume ratio? Write a statement describing the relationship between the total surface area-to-volume ratio and increasing cell size. Be sure to consider the hypothetical cell as well.
    - Question 1 points out that the cube that had the greatest volume and greatest surface area was the cube measuring 3 cm. However, the cube that has the greatest *total surface area-to-volume ratio* is the hypothetical cell of 0.01 cm. The ratio was 600:1. In examining the data table, it is obvious that the surface area does not increase a fast as the volume. The volume of a cell grows at a faster rate than its surface area.

3. What physical evidence was observed which suggested that the acid entered the cell?
    - The cube turned from pink to white because phenolphthalein is an indicator that turns from pink to colorless in acid solutions. As the acid diffused into the cube, the cube turned colorless.

4. What is the distance the acid traveled in the three agar cubes? How much farther did the acid have to travel to reach the center of the cube?
   - The acid diffused approximately 0.5 cm. in the 1 cm cube, the acid had almost reached the center. In the 2 cm cube, it still had 0.5 cm to go before reaching the center and in the 3 cm cube, the acid still had a 1 cm to go before reaching the center.

5. Determine the rate of diffusion for each of the agar cells. Write a statement describing the relationship between the rate of diffusion and cell size.
   - For all three cubes, the rate of diffusion was the same, 0.05 cm/min. This implies that the larger the cell, the longer it takes for substances to diffuse to the center of the cell.

REFERENCES

Ferl, Robert, Gerald P. Sanders, and Robert Wallace. *Biology the Science of Life*. New York: Harper Collins Publishers, 1990. pp. 78-79

Greenberg, Jon, Revision Editor. *Biological Science, A Molecular Approach*. Chicago: Everyday Learning, 2001. pp. 712-713, T38, T42, T88

Larger Is Not Always Better
Examining Cell Size and Rates of Diffusion

During the course of natural selection as cells evolved from prokaryotic to eukaryotic, cells increased in size. The average size of a prokaryotic cell is approximately 1mm in diameter whereas the average size of eukaryotic cell usually ranges from 10 mm to 100 mm in diameter. There are some cells that are exceptionally large. For example, a nerve cell can be meters long and an ostrich egg is technically one cell. In these exceptions, the cells have modifications that allow them to still function effectively. A nerve cell is long but the diameter is small so that all of the cytoplasm is close to the surface. And, although an ostrich egg is very large in three dimensions, the vast majority of the ostrich egg is inert. By having only a small area on the surface of the egg that is metabolically active the cell can still function despite its large size.

There are two generally accepted reasons why cells remain small. First, a given amount of metabolically active cytoplasm requires a minimum amount of cell membrane for the exchange of materials. As a cell increases in size, the volume does not increase as fast as the cell membrane. Mathematically, as the radius of a hypothetical sphere is doubled, the surface area is squared while the volume is cubed. This explanation for cell size limitation is known as the surface-volume hypothesis.

The second reason why cells remain small has to do with the rate of diffusion and the distance materials must travel to reach the center of the cell. The rate of diffusion of materials in a liquid will remain constant as cells increase in size. This means that it will take a longer period of time for needed materials to reach the center of the cell and it will also take a longer period of time for materials to exit the cell.

PURPOSE

This lab investigates how rate of diffusion and total surface area-to-volume ratio are related to cell size. Three different sized cubes of agar are used to represent cells of varying sizes. Each cube has been made with phenolphthalein which is an indicator that turns from pink to colorless in the presence of an acid.

MATERIALS

- 2 pairs safety goggles
- 2 pairs plastic gloves
- millimeter ruler
- plastic table knife
- 150 mL 0.1% HCl
- TI-83 graphing calculator (optional)
- 2 lab aprons
- 250 mL beaker
- plastic spoon
- paper towels
- block of phenolphthalein agar

Safety Alert
Caution: 0.1% HCl is a mild irritant. Avoid skin/eye contact; do not ingest. Immediately flush any contaminated area with water for 10 minutes. Call your teacher.

PROCEDURE

1. Write two hypotheses for this experiment. The first describing what will happen to the surface area-to-volume ratio that occurs as the size of a cube increases and the second describing what will happen to the rate of diffusion when the size of a cube increases.

2. Get a block of agar from your teacher. Be sure to wear gloves while handling the block. Using the plastic knife cut the block into three pieces. The first cube should be 3 cm on each side, the second 2 cm on each side, and the last 1 cm on each side.

3. Put all three cubes into a beaker and cover with 0.1% HCl (hydrochloric acid). Allow the cubes to remain in the acid for 10 minutes. Stir occasionally with the plastic spoon taking care not to damage your cubes.
   - **CAUTION: HCl is an irritant and can destroy clothing. Avoid skin/eye contact; do not ingest. Immediately flush spills and splashes with water for 15 minutes, rinse mouth with water. Notify your teacher.**

4. Create a data table that displays the surface area, volume, and total surface area-to-volume ratio of four cubes (3 cm, 2 cm, 1cm, and a hypothetical cube measuring 0.01 cm).
   a. Remember that area is $A = l \times w$ and that there are 6 faces to a cube.
   b. Remember that volume is $V = l \times w \times h$.
   c. The total surface area-to-volume ratio is calculated as follows:

$$\text{Ratio of surface area to volume} = \frac{\text{surface area}}{\text{volume}}$$

   d. This ratio also may be written "surface area: volume." The ratio should be expressed in its simplest form (for example, 3:1 rather than 24:8).

5. Draw a graph that illustrates the relationship between both the length of one side of the cube (found on the *x* axis) versus both volume and surface area (on the *Y* axis). There will be two curves displayed.

6. Wear gloves and use the plastic spoon to remove the agar cubes from the HCl after 10 minutes. Use paper towels to blot them dry. Continue wearing your gloves and avoid handling the cubes until they are blotted dry. Use the plastic knife to slice each cube in half. Record your observations of the sliced surface. Measure the depth of diffusion of the HCl in each of the three cubes. Measure the distance remaining that the acid would have to continue diffusing in order to reach the center of the cube.

7. Create a data table for the three cubes that compares the length of the side of the cube, the distance the acid traveled, the distance the acid would have to continue diffusing to the reach the center of the cube, and the rate of diffusion for all three cubes.

$$\text{remember that Rate of Diffusion} = \frac{\text{Distance the acid traveled}}{\text{Time in the acid}}$$

8. Dispose of the acid as directed by your teacher and place the agar cubes into the trash.

9. Optional—Graphing Calculator Exercise

   The graphing calculator can be used to generate the graph by doing the following:

   a. Turn on your calculator and press CLEAR to clear the screen.
   b. Clear all lists by pressing 2nd, + [mem]. Move cursor to ClrAllLists (by pressing the ▼ key OR press 4) and then press ENTER twice. Done should appear on the screen.
   c. Press STAT, ENTER (Figure 1). This is the data table. In list 1 or L1, enter the length of the cubes and be sure to include the hypothetical cube of 0.01 cm. (Figure 2)

Figure 1

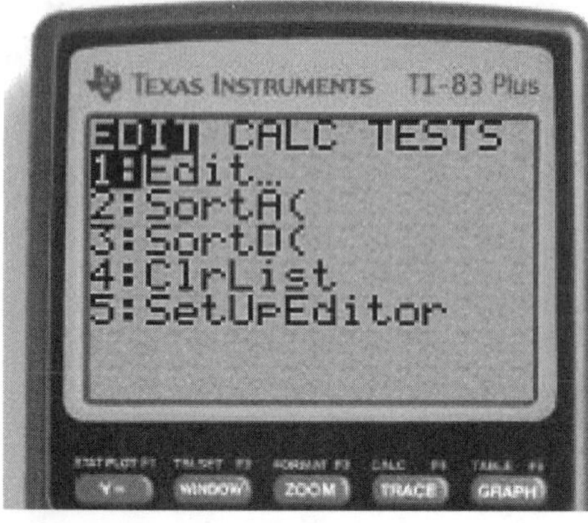

Figure 2

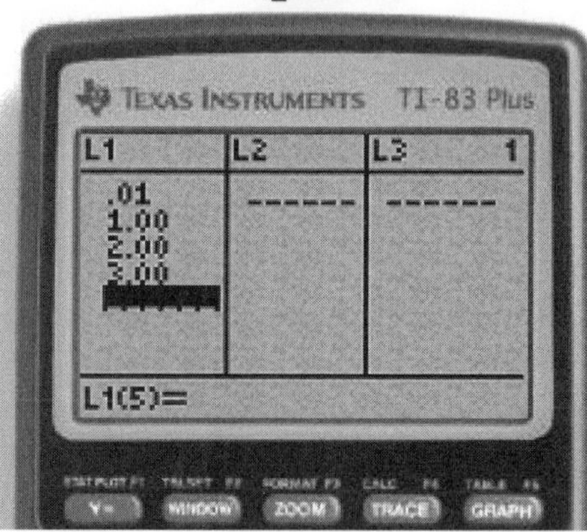

   d. Put the cursor at the top of L2 and press ENTER and there should be a blinking cursor at the bottom of the screen.
   e. Now key in the equation for the surface area of the cubes by pressing 6, X, 2nd, 1 [L1], ^, 2. This will square the length of the cube and then multiply it by six because there are six sides. See Figure 3.

Figure 3

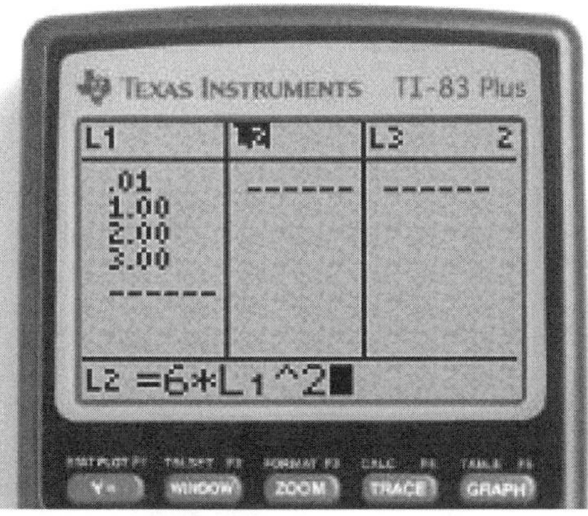

Figure 4

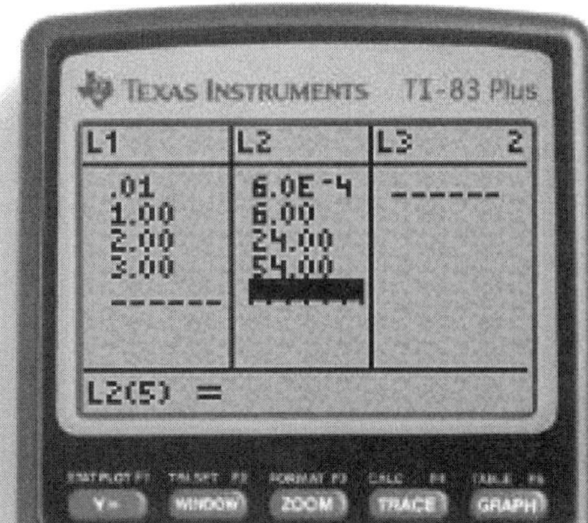

f. Press ENTER and the surface area of the cubes should appear in L2. (Figure 4)

g. To determine the volume of the cubes, place the cursor at the top of L3 and press 2nd, 1 [(L1], ^, 3, ENTER. Figure 5.

h. Press ENTER and the volume of the cubes should appear in L3. Figure 6.

Figure 5

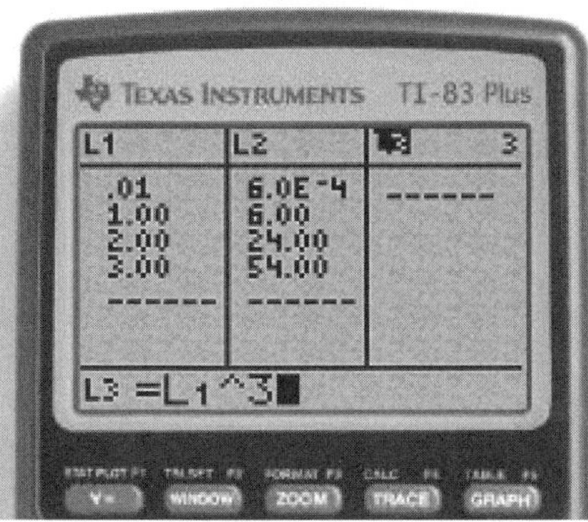

Figure 6

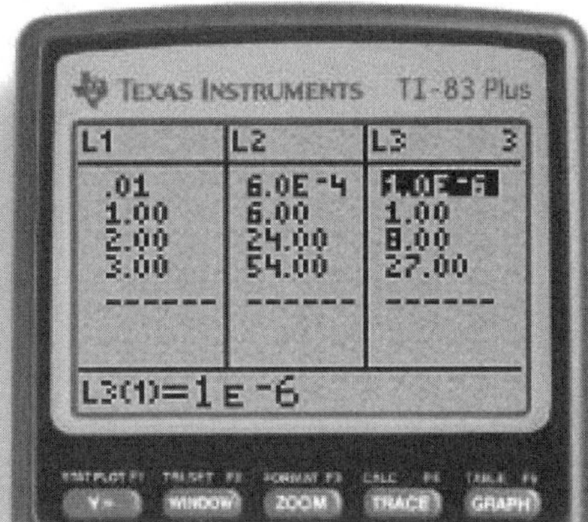

i. To examine the total surface area-to-volume ratio, place the cursor at the top of F4 and press ENTER, 2nd, 2 [L2], ÷, 2nd, 2, 3 [L3]. (Figure 7)

Figure 7

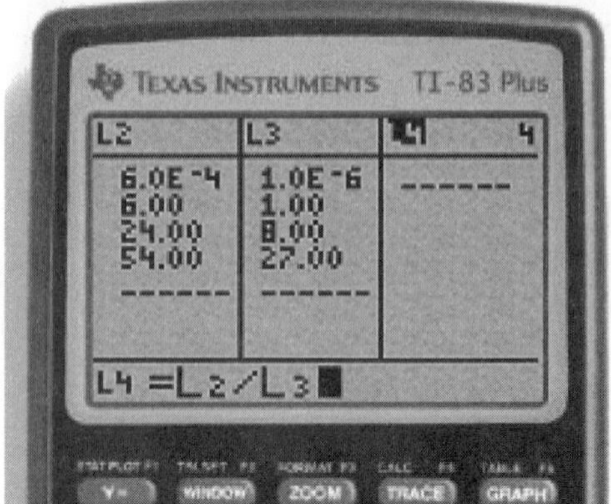

Figure 8

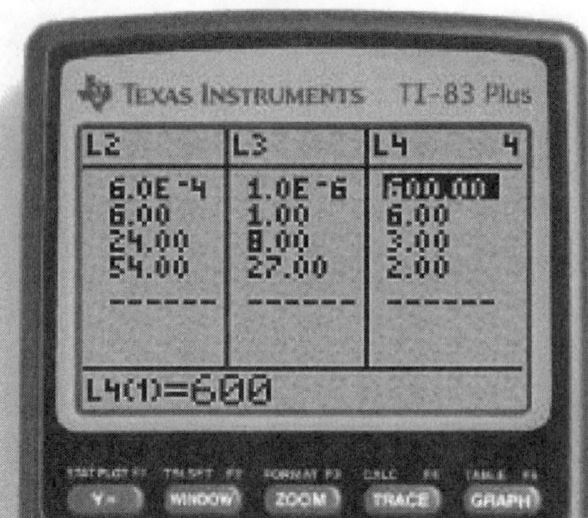

j. Press ENTER. This will display the surface to volume ratio. (Figure 8)

k. To view this graphically press 2nd, Y=, ENTER. (Figure 9)

Figure 9

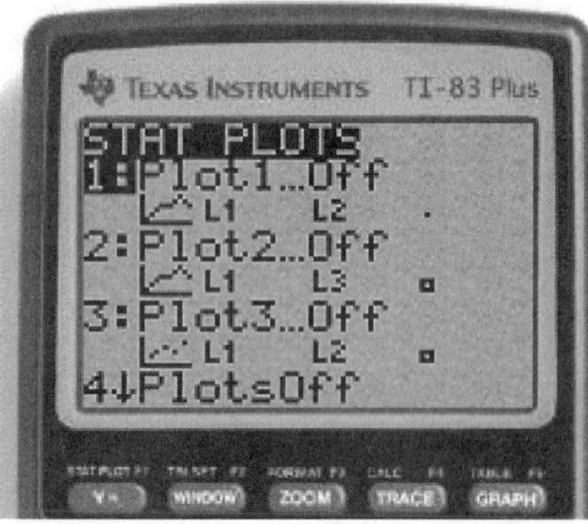

Figure 10

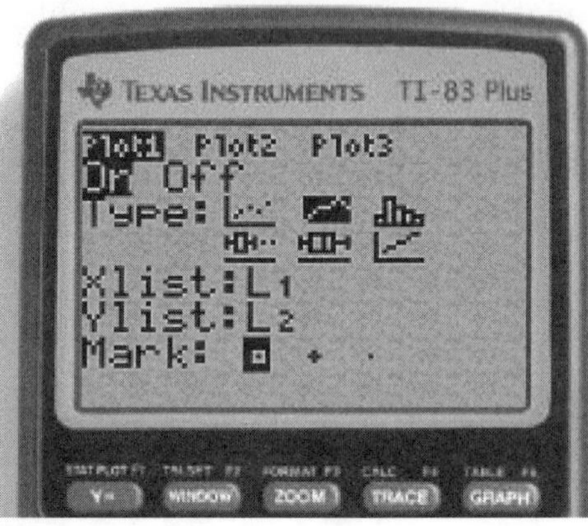

l. Put your cursor on PLOT1 and press ENTER and then put the cursor on ON and press ENTER. Both PLOT 1 and ON should be highlighted. All other plots should be inactivated.

m. Place the cursor on the line graph and press ENTER.

n. The X-List will be L1 and the Y-List will be L2. Activate this by placing the cursor on X-List and pressing 2nd, 1 [L1] and then place the cursor on the Y-List and press 2nd, 2 [L2]. (Figure 10)

o. To activate a second line go back and highlight PLOT 2 and press ENTER, and set all the parameters the same as PLOT 1 except the Y-List will have L3 in it. This is done by placing the cursor on the Y-List and pressing 2nd, 3 [L3]. (Figure 11)

Figure 11

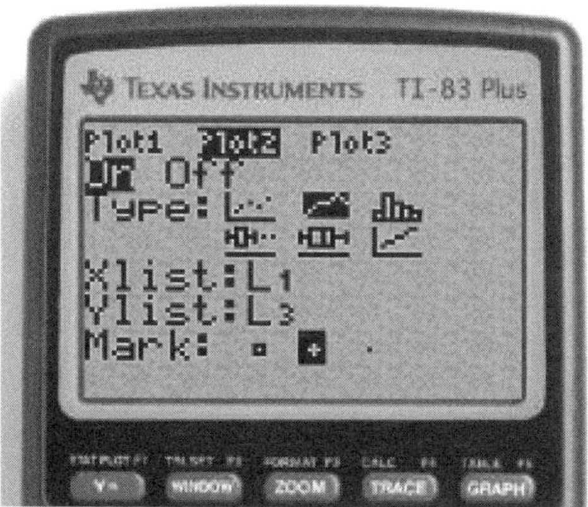

Figure 12

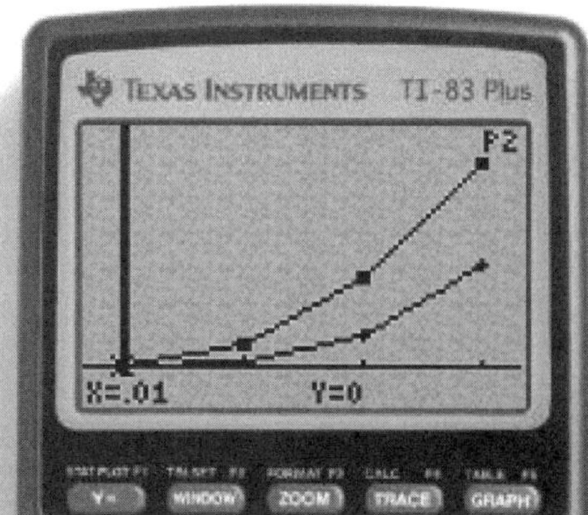

p. To display the graph press ZOOM, 9 and pressing TRACE will display the value for the points plotted. (Figure 12)

q. You can print your graph using TI Connect or you can import your data using Graphical Analysis 3® or Logger Pro 3®.

Name ______________________________

Period ______________________________

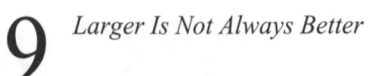

Larger Is Not Always Better
Examining Cell Size and Rates of Diffusion

HYPOTHESIS

DATA AND OBSERVATIONS

Cube dimension	Distance HCl diffused in the cube (cm)	Rate of diffusion (cm/min)	Distance from center of cube (cm)
1 cm			
2 cm			
3 cm			

Cube Dimension	Surface Area (cm^2)	Volume (cm^3)	Simplest Ratio
0.01 cm			
1 cm			
2 cm			
3 cm			

CONCLUSION QUESTIONS

1. Which cube had the greatest surface area? Which cube had the greatest volume? Be sure to consider the hypothetical cell as well.

2. Which cube had the greatest total surface area-to-volume ratio? Write a statement describing the relationship between the total surface area-to-volume ratio and increasing cell size. Be sure to consider the hypothetical cell as well.

3. What physical evidence was observed which suggested that the acid entered the cell?

4. What is the distance the acid traveled in the three agar cubes? How much farther did the acid have to travel to reach the center of the cube?

5. Determine the rate of diffusion for each of the agar cells. Write a statement describing the relationship between the rate of diffusion and cell size.

The Fluid Mosaic Membrane
Modeling Membrane Structure and Osmosis

OBJECTIVE
Students will identify the structure and function of the components of the fluid mosaic model of cell membranes. Students will identify those components on a diagram of the model. They will use the models to demonstrate hypotonic, hypertonic and isotonic conditions.

LEVEL
Biology I

NATIONAL STANDARDS
UCP.1, UCP.2, UCP.3, UCP.5, B.2, C.1, C.5, G.2

TEKS
Biology 4(A), 4(B)

CONNECTIONS TO AP
AP Biology:

I. Molecules and Cells B. Cells C. Cell membranes

TIME FRAME
Two 45 minute periods

MATERIALS

28 copies of membrane components pattern
28 copies of paper glucose molecules pattern
scissors
copies of student answer pages
teacher set of membrane components

TEACHER NOTES
This lesson is designed to be used in conjunction with the plasmolysis lab activity.

Teaching procedures:

1. Photocopy and enlarge a set of membrane components to be used on the chalkboard. Magnetic tape or masking tape can be used to adhere the pieces to the board. Color your pieces or photocopy the model pieces on colored paper so they will be visible. Laminate them for added durability.

2. As you check roll and take care of opening procedures, have the students cut out the membrane components and glucose molecules. Provide envelopes or paperclips for the student to use to keep up with their models when the activity is completed.

3. Describe the structure and function of the fluid mosaic cell membrane model components. Place the membrane component pieces on the board as you proceed through your descriptions. Important points to include are:
   a. Membrane proteins—there are two main types of proteins in the membrane, peripheral and integral. Integral proteins span the entire width of the lipid bilayer. Peripheral proteins are not embedded and are loosely attached to the surface of the membrane. Proteins in the membrane may serve as transport proteins, chemical receptors, enzymes, regulators for cell to cell recognition, cell connections, and attachment sites for cytoskeletal structures. These proteins are irregularly distributed throughout the membrane and for this reason the membrane is described as a mosaic.
   b. Phospholipids—are arranged in a double layer. These phospholipids are composed of a phosphate head region and a hydrocarbon tail region. The phospholipids are not static but can move laterally within the membrane. This is why the membrane is said to be fluid.
   c. Cholesterol—helps keep the phospholipids spaced apart thereby adding to the fluidity of the membrane.
   d. Surface carbohydrates—the surface carbohydrates function in cell recognition, cell signaling, and cell adhesion.
   e. Collectively the structure of the membrane allows it to be selectively permeable, allowing small, uncharged particles to move by passive transport through the membrane while preventing the passage of large or charged substances. Large or charged substances must have a special pathway through the membrane.

4. To check student understanding have the student hold up the correct model component in response to each of the following questions. Confirm the correct answer to each question before moving to the next.
   a. Which membrane component forms the bilayer? (phospholipids)
   b. Which membrane component could serve in cell transport? (integral protein)
   c. Which structure helps keep the membrane fluid? (cholesterol)
   d. Which structures function in cell adhesion? (surface carbohydrates, proteins)
   e. Which structure could serve an enzyme? (integral protein)
   f. Which structure can serve as a site for cytoskeletal structure attachment? (peripheral proteins)
   g. Which structure lends fluidity to the membrane? (cholesterol and phospholipids)
   h. Which structures are spread in a mosaic throughout the membrane? (integral proteins)

5. Explain that small, uncharged molecules like water, carbon dioxide, and oxygen can move into the cell by passing between the fluid phospholipid molecules. Larger compounds or charged substances move through the membrane by passing through an integral, transport protein.

6. Have the students assemble their components into a segment of membrane on their desktop and use the water and glucose arrows to indicate where these substances can enter the cell.

7. The students should now label and give the function of each of the structures indicated on the diagram of the fluid mosaic membrane.

8. Explain that osmosis, the movement of water through the semipermeable membrane, will occur from an area of high water concentration to an area of lower concentration. Use transparency masters 1, 2, and 3 to explain the differences between hypertonic, hypotonic and isotonic conditions.

9. Ask the students to use their model to demonstrate each of the situations listed below. Move around the room to observe the students' responses.
   a. A cell that is hypertonic to its environment.
   b. A cell that is isotonic to its environment.
   c. A cell that is hypotonic to its environment.
   d. A blood cell placed in distilled water.
   e. A blood cell in 10% saline solution.

10. Explain that when animal cells are placed in hypertonic solutions they will lose water and shrivel or crenate. When animal cells are placed in hypotonic solutions they will gain water and can burst. Plant cells, on the other hand, have a cell wall surrounding the cell membrane so when a plant cell is placed in a hypotonic solution they will gain water until they are full or turgid. When plant cells are placed in hypertonic solutions they will lose water and go through plasmolysis but the cells do not shrivel because the cell wall is in place.

11. Have the students label the osmosis diagrams located on the student answer page. They are to label both sides of the membrane as hypertonic, hypotonic or isotonic and draw an arrow showing the overall pathway of water.

12. Students should now answer the multiple choice questions independently. These questions may also be used as a quiz at the conclusion of the activity.

13. Follow up with Experiment #11 Plasmolysis.

Model pieces – Membrane components

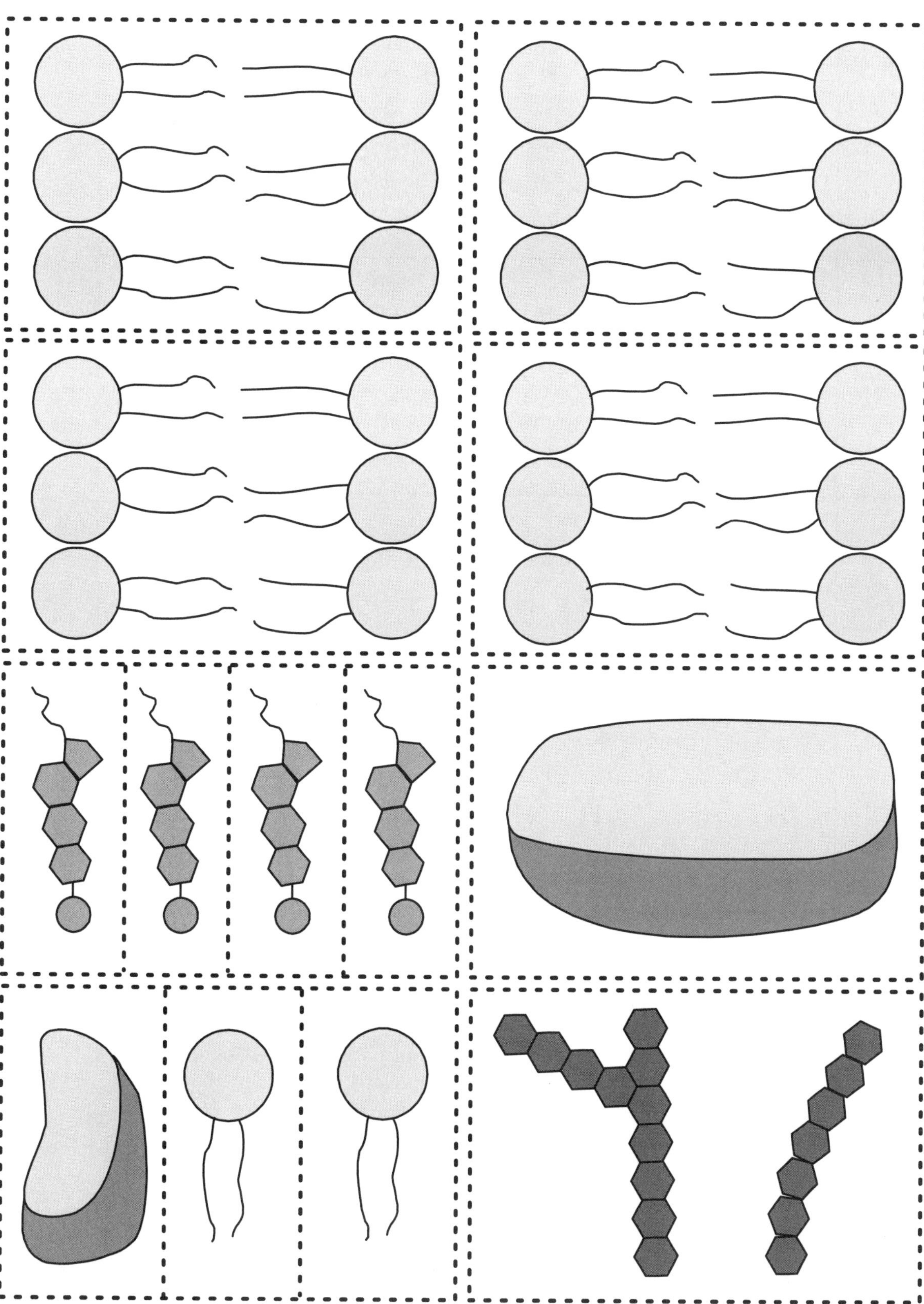

Model pieces – Glucose, water, and pathway arrows

Glucose	Glucose	Glucose	Glucose	Glucose
Glucose	Glucose	Glucose	Glucose	Glucose
Water	Water	Water	Water	Water
Water	Water	Water	Water	Water

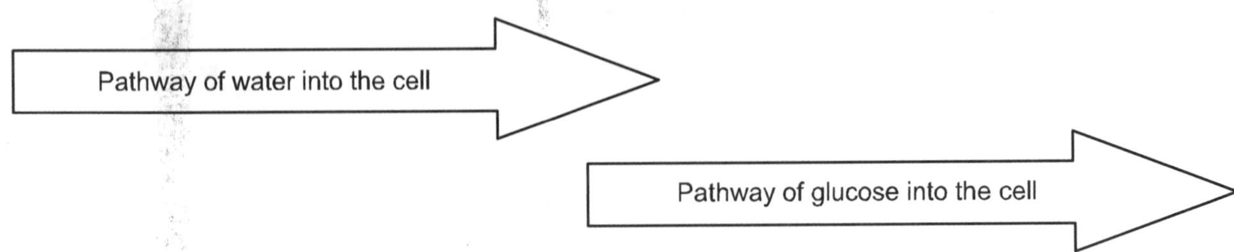

TRANSPARENCY MASTER 1: CELL IN A HYPERTONIC ENVIRONMENT

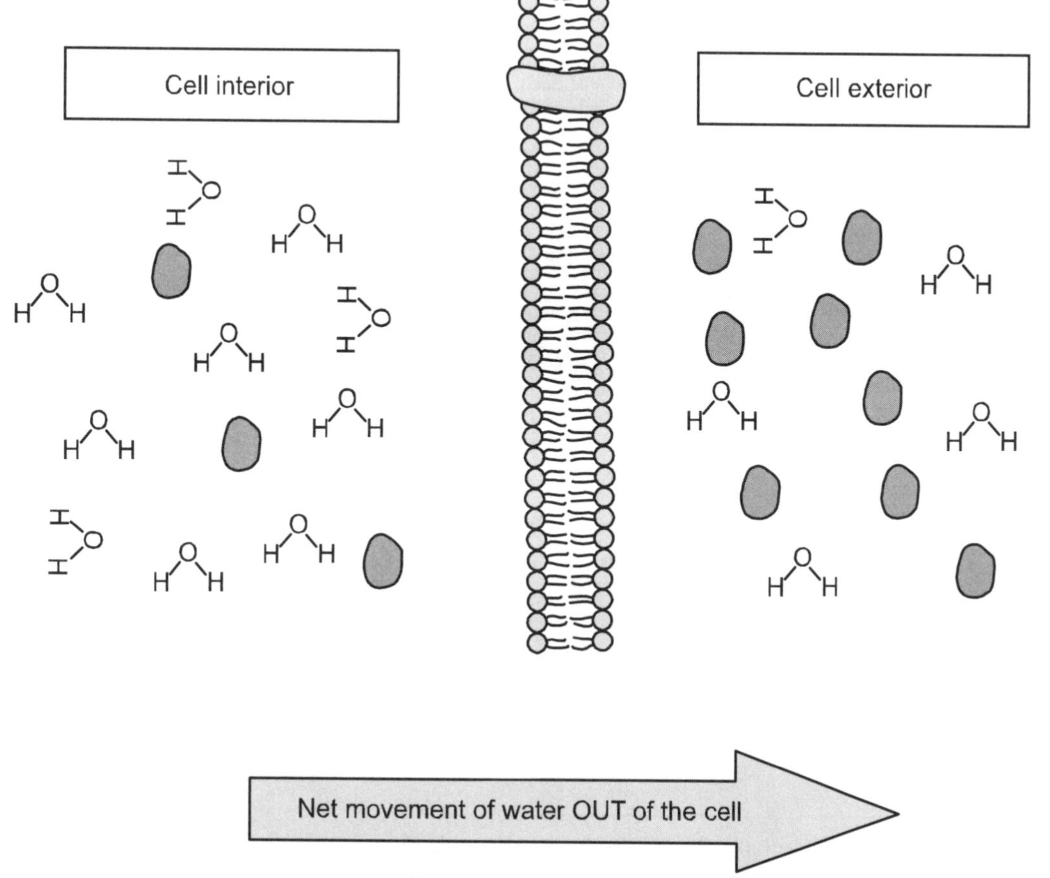

The solution in the cellís cytoplasm is hypotonic in comparison to the exterior solution.

The solution outside the cell is hypertonic in comparison to the interior solution.

When placed in a hypertonic solution, the cell will lose water as water moves from an area of high concentration of water to a lower concentration of water.

TRANSPARENCY MASTER 2: CELL IN A HYPOTONIC ENVIRONMENT

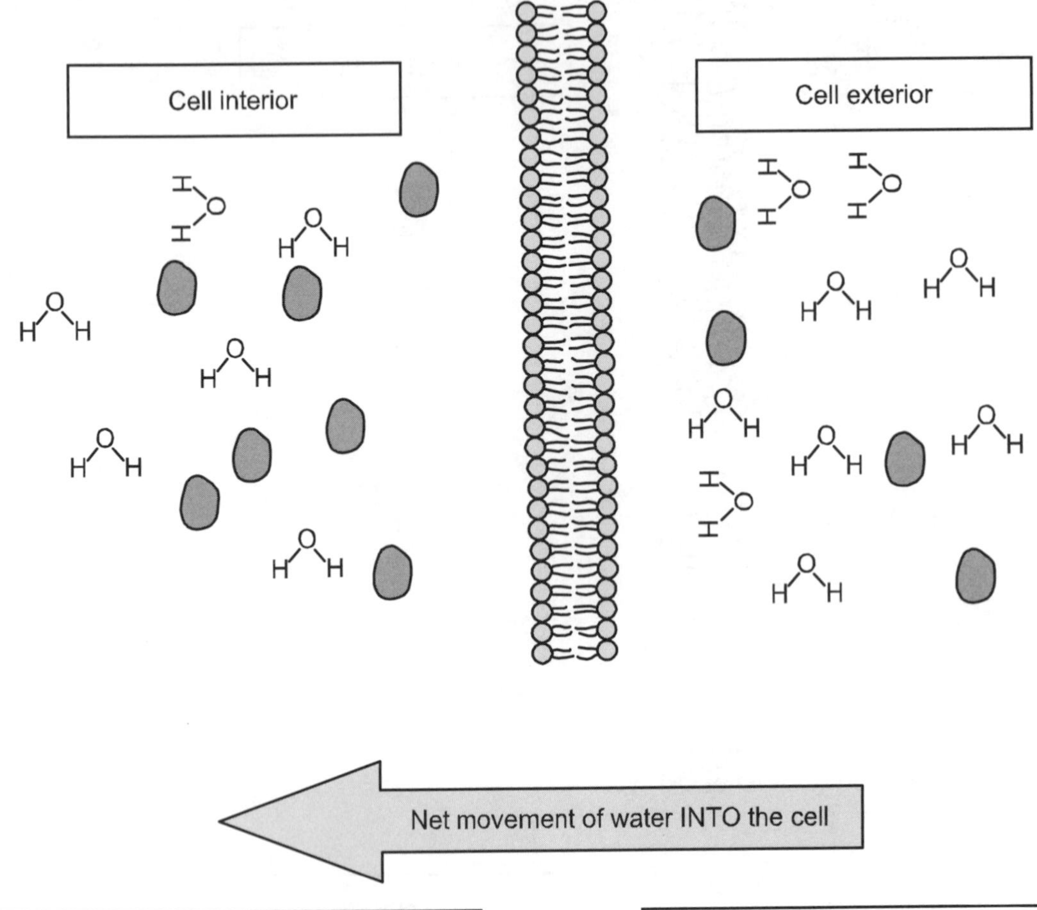

The solution in the cell's cytoplasm is hypertonic in comparison to the exterior solution.

The solution outside the cell is hypotonic in comparison to the interior solution.

When placed in a hypotonic solution, the cell will gain water as water moves from an area of high concentration of water to a lower concentration of water.

TRANSPARENCY MASTER #3: CELL IN AN ISOTONIC ENVIRONMENT

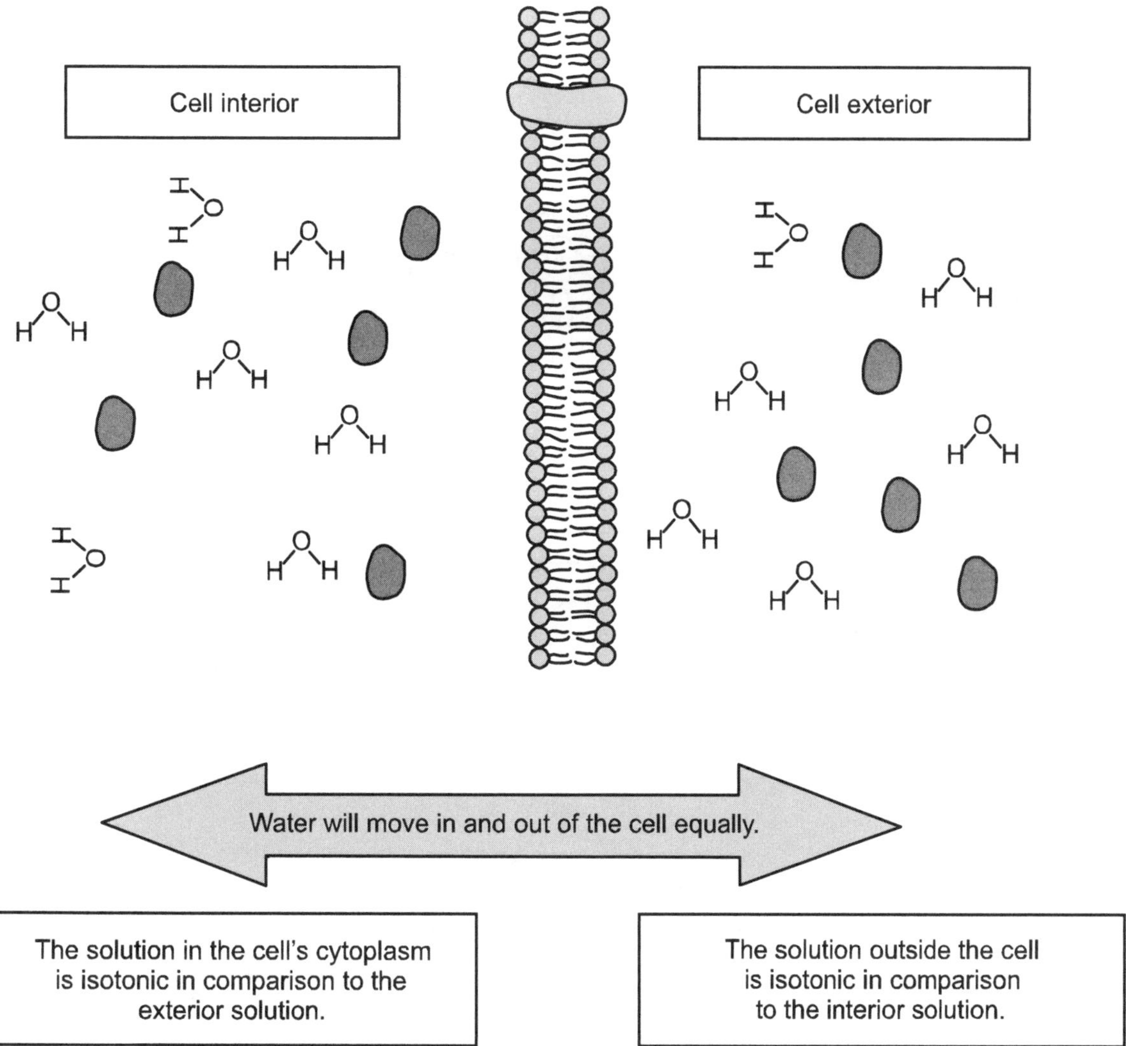
Cell interior
Cell exterior
Water will move in and out of the cell equally.
The solution in the cell's cytoplasm is isotonic in comparison to the exterior solution.
The solution outside the cell is isotonic in comparison to the interior solution.

When placed in an isotonic solution, the cell will have an equal movement of water in and out of the cell.

POSSIBLE ANSWERS TO THE CONCLUSION QUESTIONS AND SAMPLE DATA

PART I

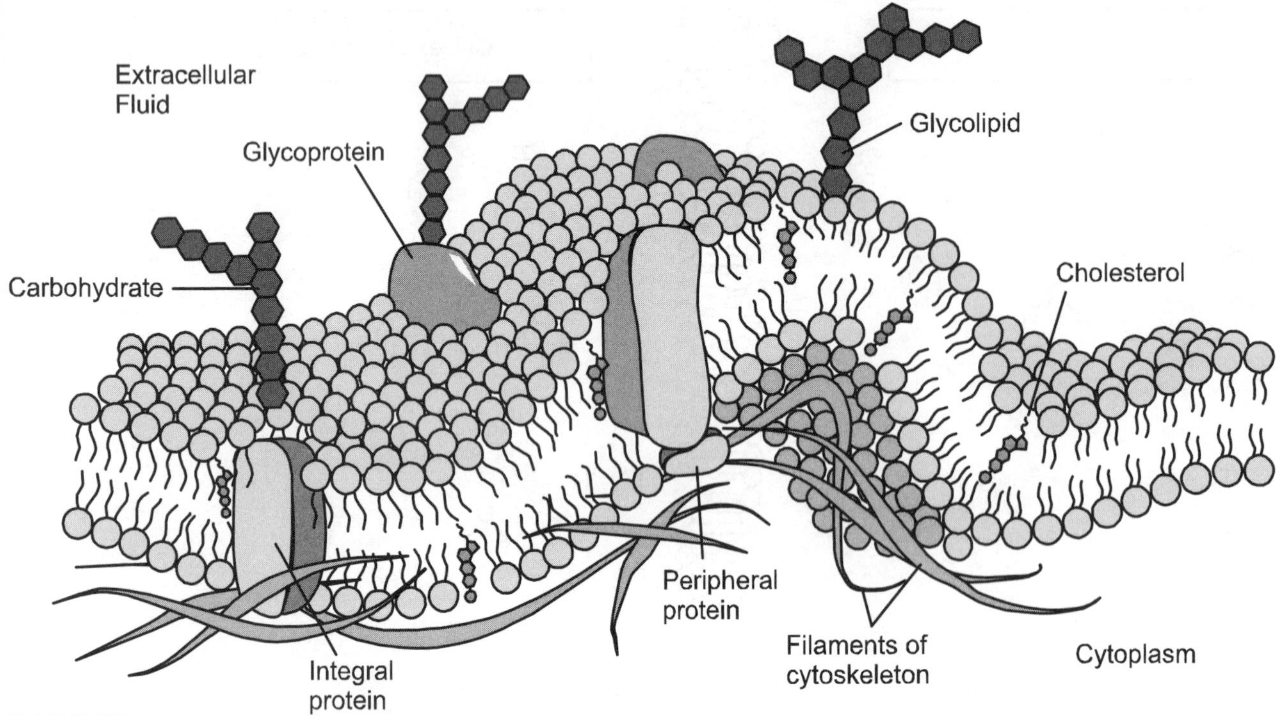

PART II

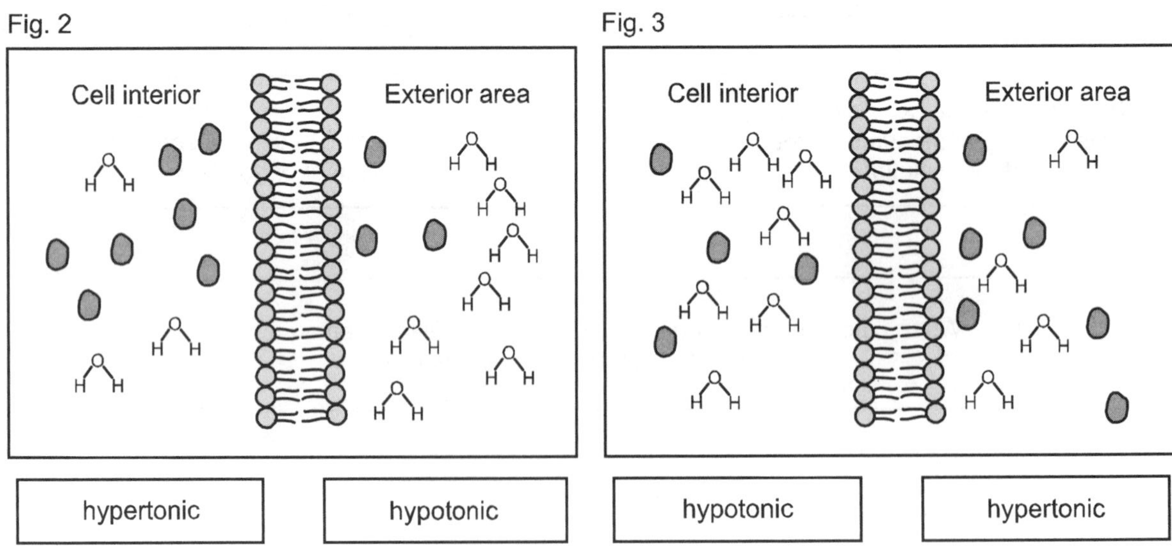

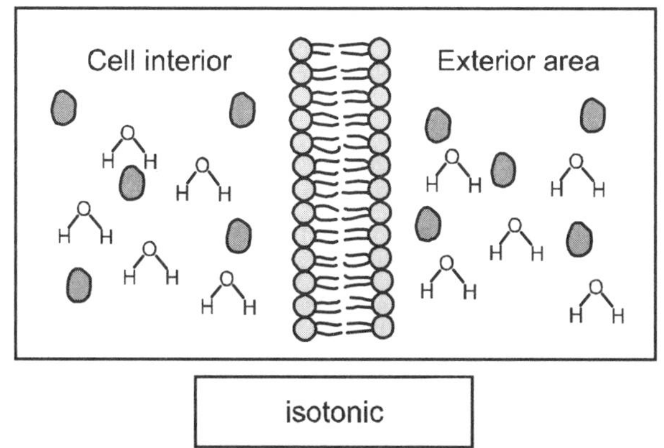

Fig. 4

isotonic

ANALYSIS

PART I: MEMBRANE STRUCTURE CHART

Functional cellular event	Membrane structural component involved
Hydrogen ions (H^+) are being pumped to the inside of the membrane	Integral transport protein
Glucose is entering the cell.	Integral transport protein
Water is entering the cell.	phospholipids
Carbon dioxide is diffusing out of the cell	phospholipids
The cell is recognized as belonging to a specific tissue.	Carbohydrate tags
Intermediate filaments of the cytoskeleton are anchored in place.	Peripheral protein

PART II: OSMOTIC PREDICTIONS

Cell Type	If placed in this solution	Will the cell gain or lose water?
Liver cell	Hypotonic	gain
Onion cell	Hypertonic	lose
Cheek cell	Isotonic	neither
Red blood cell	Hypotonic	gain
Potato cell	Hypertonic	lose

CONCLUSION QUESTIONS

__d__ 1. Which of the following statements is supported by the fluid-mosaic model of membrane structure?
a. The cell membrane is a phospholipid layer divided by carbohydrates.
b. The cell membrane is a protein layer in which large lipids are found.
c. The cell membrane is composed of carbohydrates floating in a sea of lipids.
d. The cell membrane is a lipid layer in which proteins float.

__b__ 2. A red blood cell placed in distilled water will swell and burst due to the movement of
a. salt from the distilled water diffusing into the cell
b. water molecules moving by osmosis into the cell
c. water from the red blood cell moving into the distilled water
d. salt from the red blood cell moving into the distilled water

__c__ 3. The pathway taken by water molecules into the cell is
a. through the cholesterol molecules
b. between the globular proteins
c. between the fluid phospholipids
d. through the peripheral proteins

__a__ 4. If excess fertilizer is placed around the root of a tomato plant, the leaves of the plant will shrivel and turn brown. All of the statements help explain why EXCEPT
a. The fertilizer makes the soil solution hypotonic to the root cells.
b. The water moves out of the root cells by osmosis into the soil.
c. The plant's roots are in a hypertonic solution.
d. Water is moving from an area of high water concentration to low water concentration.

__c__ 5. Which of the following terms is most closely associated with the selective permeability of the cell membrane?
a. hydrolysis
b. hypothesis
c. homeostasis
d. homologous

__d__ 6. A cell that has deformity or irregularities in transport proteins may not be able to
a. allow water to enter the cell
b. prevent carbon dioxide from entering the cell
c. move small particles out of the cell.
d. move large particles into the cell

__b__ 7. Which of the following is a true statement regarding the following situation?
a. the exterior is hypotonic
b. there will be a net movement of water out of the cell.
c. this diagram could be of an animal cell in distilled water
d. the cell's internal solution is hypotonic

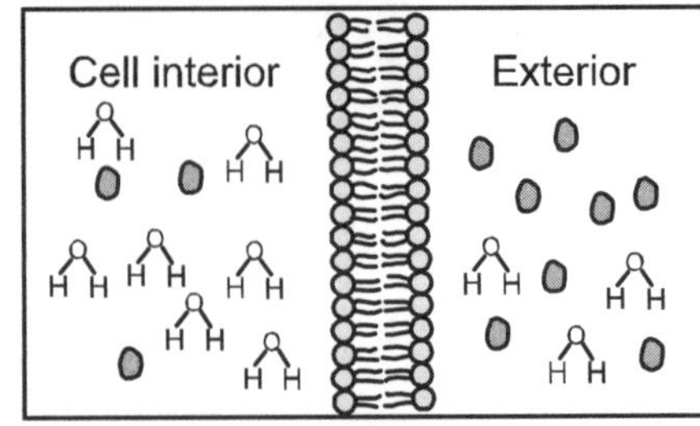

The Fluid Mosaic Membrane
Modeling Membrane Structure and Osmosis

Living cells are surrounded by a cell membrane. The structure of the membrane allows it to function as a selectively permeable barrier separating the cell's internal cytoplasmic solution from the external environment. The currently accepted model of structure for this membrane is referred to as the fluid-mosaic model. The major components of the cell membrane are described below.

a. Membrane proteins—there are two main types of proteins in the membrane, peripheral and integral. Integral proteins span the distance of the lipid bilayer. Peripheral proteins are not embedded and are loosely attached to the surface of the membrane. Proteins in the membrane may serve as transport proteins, chemical receptors, enzymes, regulators of cell to cell recognition, cell connections, and attachment sites for cytoskeletal structures. These proteins are irregularly distributed throughout the membrane and for this reason the membrane is described as a mosaic.

b. Phospholipids—are arranged in a double layer. These phospholipids are composed of a phosphate head region and a hydrocarbon tail region. The phospholipids are not static but can move laterally within the membrane. This is why the membrane is said to be fluid.

c. Cholesterol—helps keep the phospholipids spaced apart which adds to the fluidity of the membrane.

d. Surface carbohydrates—the surface carbohydrates function in cell recognition, cell signaling, and cell adhesion.

This selectively permeable membrane is important in the cell's ability to maintain homeostasis or the condition of equilibrium. Collectively, the components of the cell membrane allow it to be selectively permeable, allowing small, uncharged particles to move by passive transport through the membrane while preventing the passage of large or charged substances. Large or charged substances must have a special pathway through the membrane.

Water will move through the membrane with relative ease from an area of high water concentration to an area of low water concentration. In comparing two solutions, a solution is said to be hypertonic if it contains a higher concentration of solutes than another. The solution with the smaller number of dissolved substances (or solutes) is called hypotonic. When comparing two solutions that are of equal solute concentration, they are referred to as isotonic. Hypertonic solutions have lower water concentrations and will gain water from hypotonic solutions. Cells placed in distilled water, for example, will gain water as it moves through the selectively permeable membrane from an area of high water concentration to an area of lower water concentration. An understanding of this phenomenon will allow us to explain why cells will gain or lose water in various settings.

PURPOSE
In this activity, you will model and demonstrate your understanding of the structure of the fluid-mosaic membrane and the effects of the membrane's permeability to water.

MATERIALS
scissors
membrane component sheets
envelope

PROCEDURE
PART I
1. Cut out all of the items on the two pages of the membrane modeling pages by cutting along the dotted lines. Your teacher will provide a paper clip or envelope for storage of your cut out pieces.

2. Listen as your teacher describes the fluid mosaic membrane components. Use your membrane component pieces to respond as your teacher asks you to identify various membrane structures.

3. Assemble your components into a simulated membrane on your desk top. Place the pathway of water arrow so that it passes through the phospholipids. Place the pathway of glucose arrow so that it passes through an integral protein.

4. Label the diagram of the fluid mosaic membrane found on the student answer page.

5. Locate the membrane structure chart on the student answer page. Using the information you have learned during this segment of the activity, identify the membrane component involved for each of the cell functions listed.

PART II
1. Listen as your teacher explains the meaning of hypertonic, hypotonic, and isotonic conditions.

2. Observe Fig. 2 and label the cell interior and exterior as hypertonic, hypotonic or isotonic. Also, draw an arrow to indicate the direction water will move.

3. Repeat step 7 for Fig. 3 and Fig. 4.

4. Locate the osmotic predictions chart on the student answer page. Using the information you have gained from this activity, predict what will occur for each cell and condition listed.

5. Upon your teacher's instruction, read and answer each multiple choice question in the conclusion section of the student answer page.

Name ______________________________

Period ______________________________

The Fluid Mosaic Membrane
Modeling Membrane Structure and Osmosis

PART I

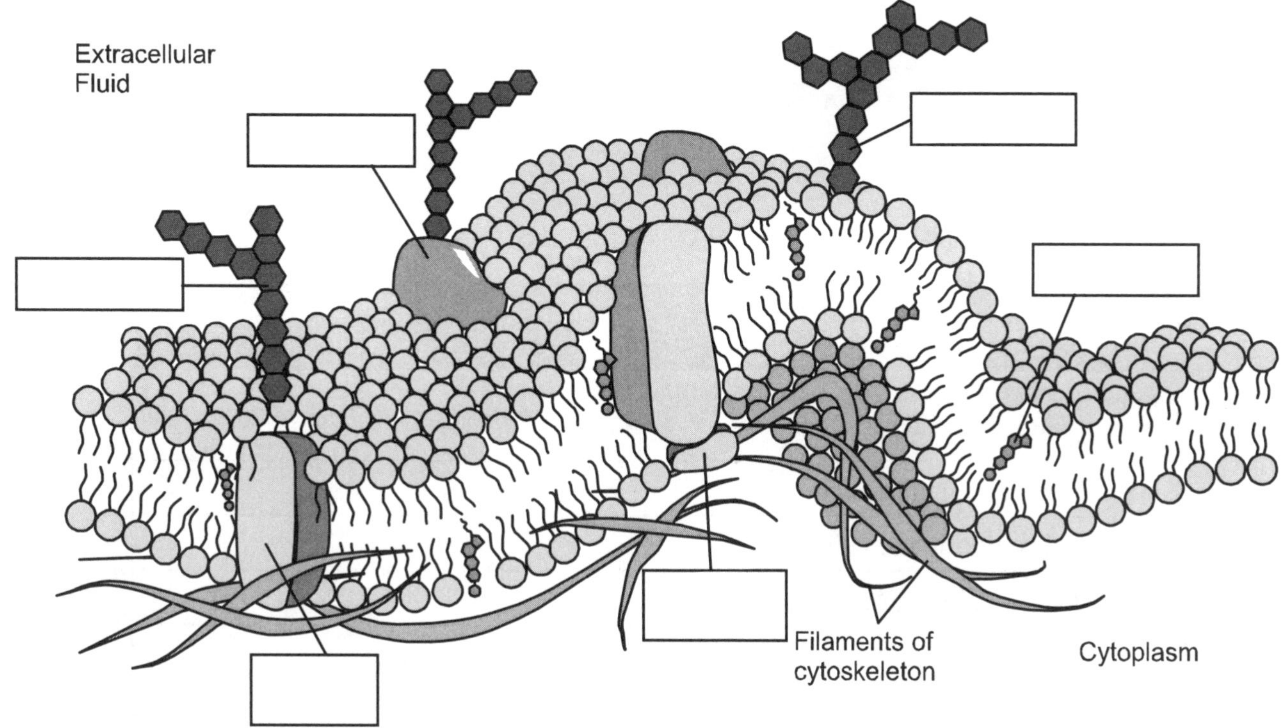

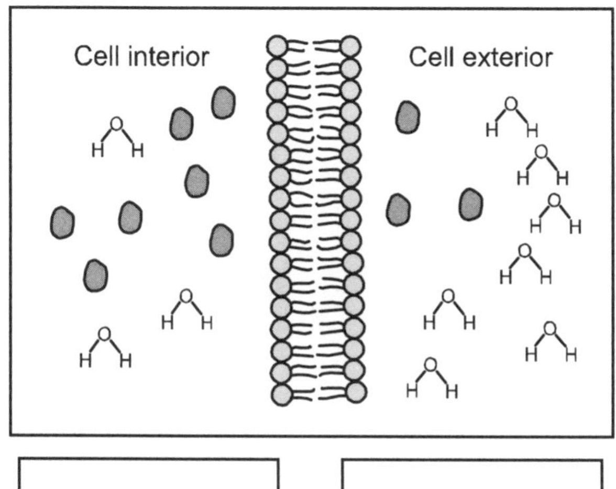

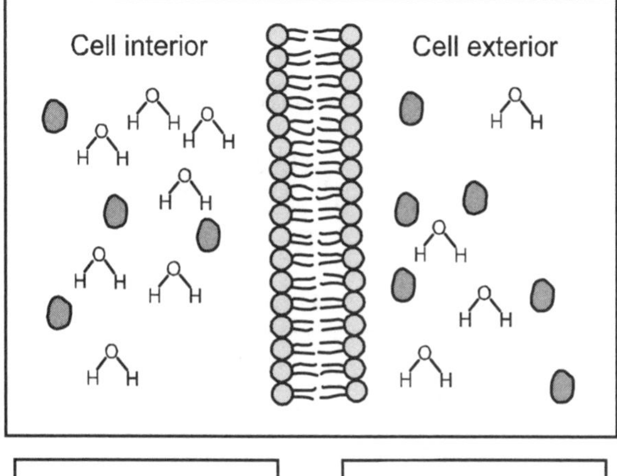

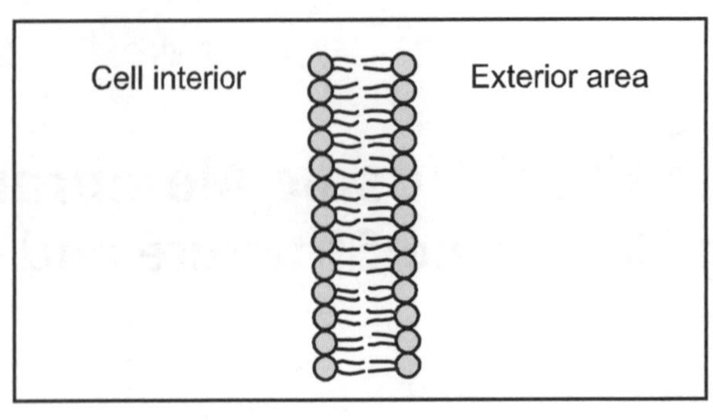

Fig. 4

ANALYSIS

PART I: MEMBRANE STRUCTURE CHART

Functional cellular event	Membrane structural component involved
Hydrogen ions (H^+) are being pumped to the inside of the membrane	
Glucose is entering the cell.	
Water is entering the cell.	
Carbon dioxide is diffusing out of the cell	
The cell is recognized as belonging to a specific tissue.	
Intermediate filaments of the cytoskeleton are anchored in place.	

PART II: OSMOTIC PREDICTIONS

Cell Type	If placed in this solution	Predicted results
Liver cell	Hypotonic	
Onion cell	Hypertonic	
Cheek cell	Isotonic	
Red blood cell	Hypotonic	
Potato cell	Hypertonic	

CONCLUSION QUESTIONS

______ 1. Which of the following statements is supported by the fluid-mosaic model of membrane structure?

a. The cell membrane is a phospholipid layer divided by carbohydrates.
b. The cell membrane is a protein layer in which large lipids are found.
c. The cell membrane is composed of carbohydrates floating in a sea of lipids.
d. The cell membrane is a lipid layer in which proteins float.

______ 2. A red blood cell placed in distilled water will swell and burst due to the movement of

a. salt from the distilled water diffusing into the cell
b. water molecules moving by osmosis into the cell
c. water from the red blood cell moving into the distilled water
d. salt from the red blood cell moving into the distilled water

______ 3. The pathway taken by water molecules into the cell is

a. through the cholesterol molecules
b. between the globular proteins
c. between the fluid phospholipids
d. through the peripheral proteins

______ 4. If excess fertilizer is placed around the root of a tomato plant, the leaves of the plant will shrivel and turn brown. All of the statements help explain why EXCEPT

a. The fertilizer makes the soil solution hypotonic to the root cells.
b. The water moves out of the root cells by osmosis into the soil.
c. The plant's roots are in a hypertonic solution.
d. Water is moving from an area of high water concentration to low water concentration.

______ 5. Which of the following terms is most closely associated with the selective permeability of the cell membrane?

a. hydrolysis
b. hypothesis
c. homeostasis
d. homologous

______ 6. A cell that has deformity or irregularities in transport proteins may not be able to

a. allow water to enter the cell
b. prevent carbon dioxide from entering the cell
c. move small particles out of the cell
d. move large particles into the cell

______ 7. Which of the following is a true statement regarding the following situation?

a. the exterior is hypotonic
b. there will be a net movement of water out of the cell
c. this diagram could be of an animal cell in distilled water
d. the cell's internal solution is hypotonic

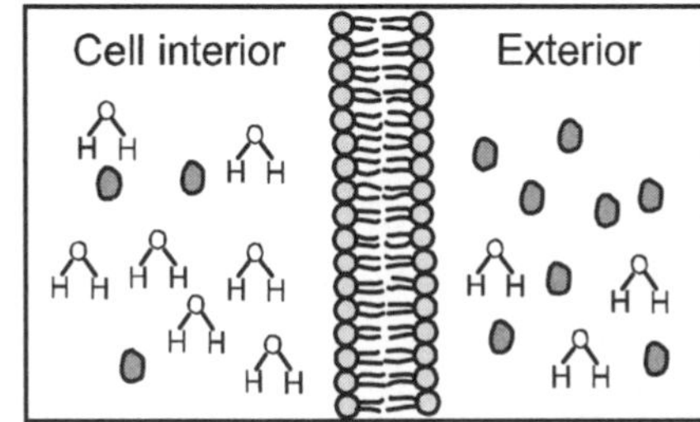

Plasmolysis
Comparing *Elodea* and Onion Cell Plasmolysis

OBJECTIVE
Students will observe the process of plasmolysis by placing *Elodea* and onion cells in hypertonic solutions. Students will observe turgidity in *Elodea* cells placed in distilled water.

LEVEL
Biology I

NATIONAL STANDARDS
UCP.3, UCP.5, A.1, A.2, C.1, E.1, E.2, G.2

TEKS
2(A), 4(B), 5(A)

CONNECTIONS TO AP
AP Biology:
I. Molecules and Cells A. Chemistry of Life B. Cells

TIME FRAME
45 minutes

MATERIALS
(For a class of 28 working in pairs)

100 mL of 10% salt solution
1 large red onion
14 droppers
paper towels
14 forceps
28 slides
28 coverslips
14 microscopes
100 mL distilled water

TEACHER NOTES
The observation of plasmolysis is one section of AP Biology's Lab 1 which can be effectively presented in the first year course.

Red onion epidermal cells are used rather than plain white onions due to the pigmentation which allows a much better visualization of the process. If red onions, sometimes called purple onions, are unavailable in your area, you can use white onions if you stain the epidermal cells with neutral red, a cytoplasmic stain. Neutral red stain can be purchased from scientific supply companies. If using white onions, have the students apply a drop of neutral red to the side of the prepared slide and draw the stain onto the cells using paper towel between steps 4 and 5.

In your pre-lab remarks, mention to the students that during the process of drawing water across the slide they may see particles moving in the water and that they should not let this movement distract them. Focusing on the moving particles will cause them to miss the events of plasmolysis that are occurring at the same time on the slide.

The students should place the epidermis in water on the slide as quickly as possible to prevent the sample from desiccating. When peeling the onion epidermis, the students should use the forceps rather than their fingers to avoid the onion smell getting on their hands.

Elodea or *Anacharis* can be purchased at local pet stores that sell aquarium plants. You may want to call the pet store ahead of time to find out when a fresh shipment will arrive. Fresh, green, vigorous *Elodea* works best for this activity.

10% salt solution can be prepared by combining 10 grams of salt and 90 mL of distilled water.

POSSIBLE ANSWERS TO THE CONCLUSION QUESTIONS AND SAMPLE DATA

HYPOTHESIS # 1

If onion cells are exposed to a 10% salt solution, then the cells will undergo plasmolysis.

HYPOTHESIS #2

If *Elodea* cells are exposed to a 10% salt solution, then the cells will undergo plasmolysis.

DATA AND OBSERVATIONS

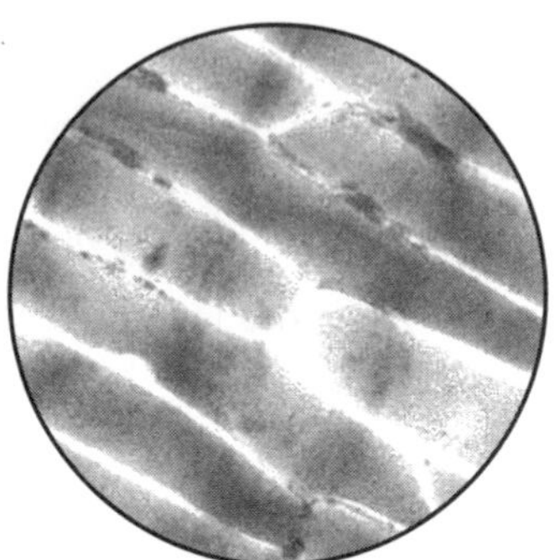

Onion Cells: Tap water

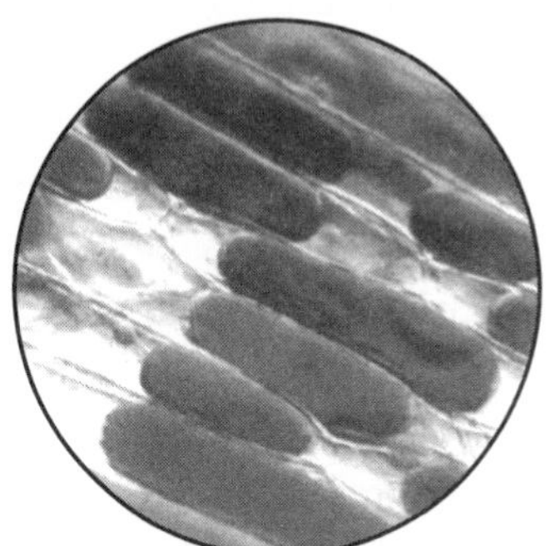

Onion Cells: 10% salt solution

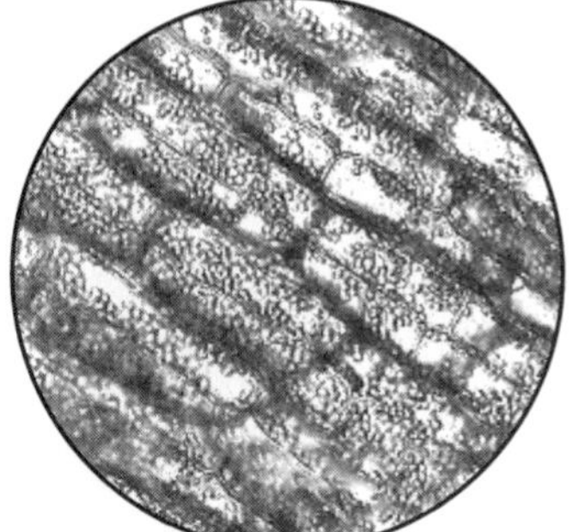

Elodea Cells: Tap water

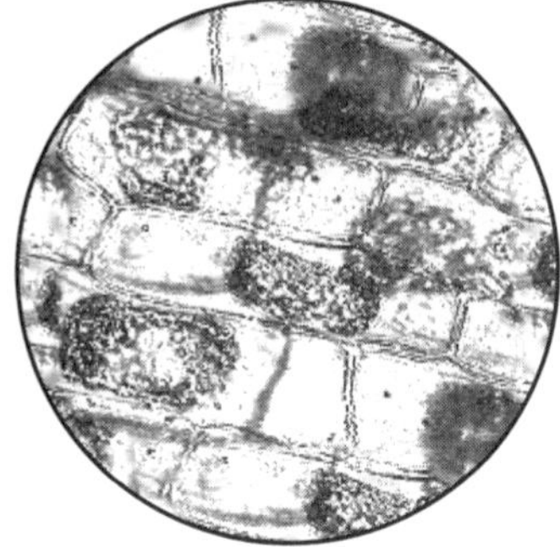

Elodea Cells: 10% salt solution

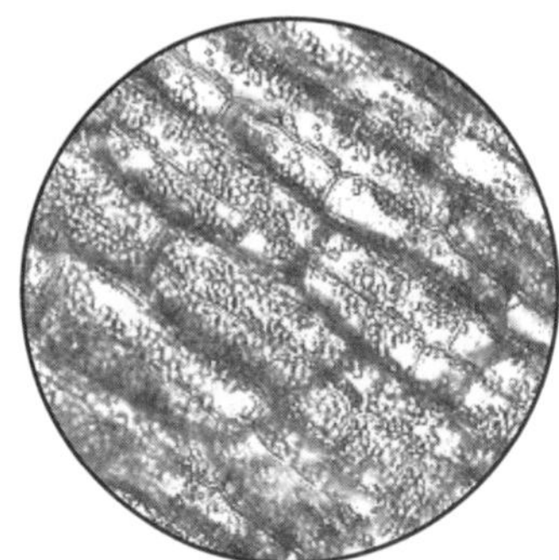

Elodea Cells: Distilled water

1. Describe the effects of placing an onion cell in a hypertonic solution.
   - The central vacuole loses water and the cell membrane shrinks inward and the cells became flaccid.

2. Explain what happened to the *Elodea* cells when they were exposed to distilled water.
   - The central vacuoles gained water and the cells became turgid.

3. In which solution were the onion cells most turgid?
   - Distilled water

4. In which solution were the *Elodea* cells most turgid?
   - Distilled water

CONCLUSION QUESTIONS

1. How do onion and Elodea cells compare in their response to being placed in a 10% salt solution? Why?
   - Both are plant cells and will lose water in a 10% salt solution.
   - They will become flaccid because water is moving out of the central vacuole.

2. If a human blood cell is placed in distilled water it will eventually rupture and go through lysis. Why did the onion and Elodea cells not rupture when placed in distilled water?
   - The plant cells have a cell wall which prevents rupturing.

3. Predict what would happen if cells of yeast, a fungus, had been used in this experiment.
   - Yeast, a fungus, also has a cell wall and would have lost water but would not rupture.

4. After a family picnic, Sharlonda dumped the ice and rock salt from the ice cream maker in the back yard. That area of the yard now contains dead, brown grass. Explain why this happened. Use the words hypotonic, hypertonic and plasmolysis in your explanation.
   - Sharlonda dumped a hypertonic salt solution onto the grass. The hypotonic cells in the leaves lost water went through plasmolysis and died.

5. Using your understanding of plasmolysis and osmosis, explain why grocery stores frequently spray the produce and vegetables with a fine mist of water.
   - The frequent spraying of produce and vegetables prevents excessive loss of water through osmosis and prevents plasmolysis that occurs in the produce.

REFERENCES

Allen, Dorothea. *The Biology Teacher's Deskbook*. West Nyack: Parker Publishing, 1979.

Campbell, Neil and Jane B. Reece. *Biology*. San Francisco: Benjamin Cummings, 2002. pp. 752-753

McFadden, Carol H. and William Keeton. *Biology: An Exploration of Life*. New York: WW Norton & Company, 1995. pg. 109

Plasmolysis
Comparing *Elodea* and Onion Cell Plasmolysis

INTRODUCTION

Have you ever seen a plant with wilted leaves? Plant leaves wilt in response to a loss of water from individual cells. When the cells lose too much water, the cell membrane will shrink away from the cell wall in a process called plasmolysis. The leaf appears wilted because the individual cells are flaccid, meaning that their central vacuole is no longer filled with water. In a healthy plant cell, the large central vacuole is filled with water creating an internal pressure, or turgor pressure, which helps keep the cell membrane pressed against the cell wall. A plant cell with a water filled central vacuole will be stiff or turgid See Figure 1. A plant cell whose central vacuole is not filled will have a lower internal turgor pressure and will be flaccid See Figure 1.

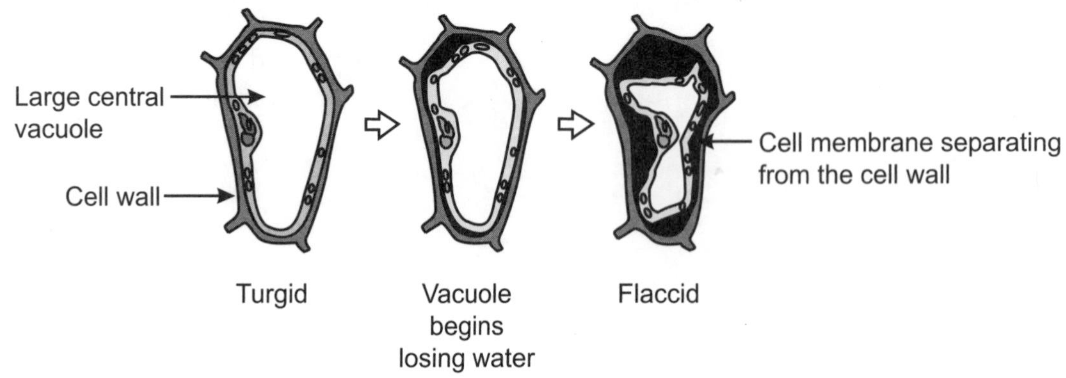

Fig. 1

Water moves across the plasma membrane by osmosis from an area of high water concentration to an area with lower water concentration. This movement of water effects cell homeostasis. Plant cells are homeostatic when the central vacuole is filled with water. Plant cells placed in hypotonic solutions tend to exhibit turgidity while plant cells in hypertonic solutions will lose water and become flaccid. Bacteria and fungus, which also have cell walls, will also experience plasmolysis in hypertonic solutions. Plasomlysis can be observed in the laboratory by surrounding plant cells with hypertonic and hypotonic solutions and observing the effects on the cell.

PURPOSE

In this lab activity, you will expose onion and *Elodea* cells to a solution of salt to observe plasmolysis.

MATERIALS

10% salt solution	2 slides
red onion epidermal cells	2 coverslips
dropper	microscope
paper towel	forceps
distilled water	

Safety Alert

1. Handle and carry microscope properly.
2. When focusing the microscope on high power, use the fine adjustment knob to avoid breaking the slide.
3. Onion and onion juice may be an irritant to the eye. Avoid contact with the eye.

PROCEDURE

1. Read the introduction section of the lab.

2. Formulate a hypothesis explaining what you think will happen when onion cells are placed in a 10% salt solution. Write your hypothesis on the student answer page.

3. Using forceps, remove a small segment of epidermis from a piece of red onion. Prepare a wet mount slide by adding the onion epidermis to a drop of tap water placed in the center of a clean glass slide. Cover with a cover slip

4. Focus the slide under low power and then switch to high power. Adjust the microscope's diaphragm to the amount of light that allows you to visualize the cell wall and the vacuole of the cell. Make a labeled sketch of your observations in the space provided on the student answer page.

5. Leaving the slide on the microscope stage, place a drop of 10% salt solution on the left hand side of the slide. The drop should touch the side of the coverslip. Place a small piece of paper towel on the right hand side of the slide to draw the salt water across the slide See Figure 2. This will expose the onion epidermis to the hypertonic salt solution.

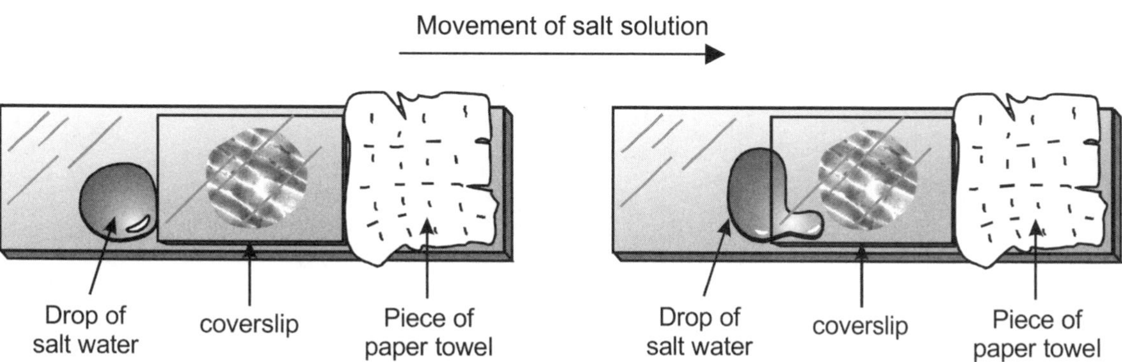

Fig. 2

6. Observe the effects of the salt solution on the onion cells. You may notice the movement of particles in the water as the water is wicked to the opposite side of the slide. Do not let these particles distract your attention. Focus on what occurs inside the onion cells. Notice any changes in color, size, or shape of the cell structures. Make a labeled sketch of your observations in the space provided on the student answer page.

7. Flood the onion cells with a hypotonic solution by placing a drop of distilled on the left hand side of the slide. The drop should touch the edge of the coverslip. Place a small piece of paper towel on the right hand side of the slide to draw the distilled water across the slide.

8. Observe the effects of the distilled water on the onion cells. Make a labeled sketch of your observations in the space provided on the student answer page.

9. Formulate a hypothesis explaining what you think will happen when *Elodea* cells are placed in a 10% salt solution. Write your hypothesis on the student answer page.

10. Repeat steps 3 through 6 using the cells found in one leaf of *Elodea* instead of onion cells.

11. Flood the *Elodea* cells with a hypotonic solution by placing a drop of distilled on the left hand side of the slide. The drop should touch the edge of the coverslip. Place a small piece of paper towel on the right hand side of the slide to draw the distilled water across the slide.

12. Observe the effects of the distilled water on the *Elodea* cells. Make a labeled sketch of your observations in the space provided on the student answer page.

13. Remove the slide from the stage of the microscope, clean all slides and coverslips. Store your microscope as instructed by your teacher.

Name ________________________________

Period ________________________________

Plasmolysis
Comparing *Elodea* and Onion Cell Plasmolysis

HYPOTHESIS # 1

HYPOTHESIS #2

DATA AND OBSERVATIONS

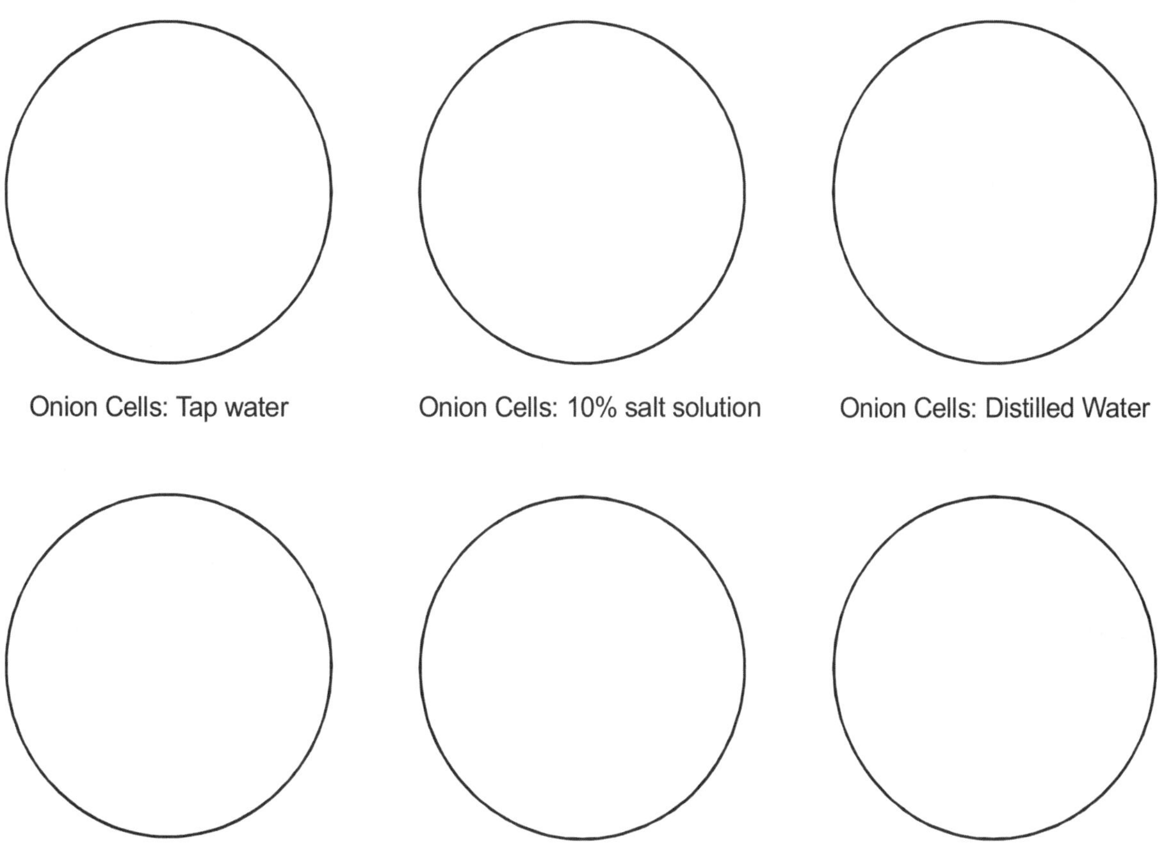

ANALYSIS

1. Describe the effects of placing an onion cell in a hypertonic solution.
2. Explain what happened to the *Elodea* cells when they were exposed to distilled water.
3. In which solution were the onion cells most turgid?
4. In which solution were the *Elodea* cells most turgid?

CONCLUSION QUESTIONS

1. How do onion and Elodea cells compare in their response to being placed in a 10% salt solution?

2. If a human blood cell is placed in distilled water, it will eventually rupture and go through lysis. Why did the onion and Elodea cells not rupture when placed in distilled water?

3. Predict what would happen if cells of yeast, a fungus, had been used in this experiment.

4. After a family picnic, Sharlonda dumped the ice and rock salt from the ice cream maker in the back yard. That area of the yard now contains dead, brown grass. Explain why this happened. Use the words hypotonic, hypertonic and plasmolysis in your explanation.

5. Using your understanding of plasmolysis and osmosis, explain why grocery stores frequently spray the produce and vegetables with a fine mist of water.

Write Your Notes and Ideas Here!

The Gate Keepers
Examining Osmosis and Selective Diffusion

OBJECTIVE
Students will explain how membranes are semi-permeable and how that relates to plasma membranes. The students differentiate between hypertonic, hypotonic, and isotonic conditions and how it relates to the process of osmosis. Students will collect data, and determine the percentage of corn syrup that is isotonic to the egg.

LEVEL
Biology I

NATIONAL STANDARDS
UCP.1, UCP.2, UCP.3, C.1, E.1, E.2, G.2

TEKS
2(A), 2(B), 2(C), 2(D), 4(B)

CONNECTIONS TO AP
AP Biology:

I. Molecules and Cells B. Cells 2. Membranes

TIME FRAME
50 Minutes day 1
15 Minutes days 2 and 3

MATERIALS
(For 28 students working in pairs)

Part I
14 dialysis tubing sections 15 cm long
14 12 cm dialysis tubing diameter 2.2 cm
150 mL of 1% starch-15% glucose solution
14 vials of glucose test tape
14 10 cc syringes
200 mL of iodine solution
14 250 mL beakers

Part II
42 250 mL beakers or cups
3 L corn syrup
several balances
aluminum foil
3 L vinegar
28 uncooked eggs
14 100 mL graduated cylinders
14 plastic spoons

Part III
3 L vinegar
14 uncooked eggs
14 100 mL graduated cylinders
14 plastic spoons
3 L corn syrup
several balances
aluminum foil
14 TI-83 graphing calculators (optional)

TEACHER NOTES

This lab activity is designed to supplement a unit on the cell and homeostasis.

Part I of this lab is to demonstrate the semi-permeable nature of cell membranes. It is recommended that the class does either Part II or Part III. It is time consuming to do both Parts II and III. There is a strong math component to Part III. Part II of this lab demonstrates the process of osmosis. In Part III of this lab the student investigates the relationship between osmosis and varying amounts of corn syrup. This activity needs two periods to complete. Sample data for Part III includes both 24 and 48 hour data. The trend is the same but more dramatic for 48 hours than 24. The relationship is not linear and therefore a linear regression line or best fit line should not be drawn.

To prepare 500 mL Lugol's iodine solution:

Dissolve 10 g of potassium iodide in 100 mL of distilled water. Add 5 g of iodine crystals to this solution. Add an additional 400 mL of distilled water. Store the solution in an opaque or dark brown bottle. Be sure to use rubber gloves when making the above solution.

To prepare 200 mL of 15% glucose-1% starch:

Dissolve 30 g of glucose and 2 g of soluble starch in enough distilled water to make 200 mL of solution

Hints

To save on the expense of the glucose test paper, you may want to perform the test as a demonstration. Show them that the iodine water does not have glucose and that the 15% glucose-1% starch solution does. Also the glucose test strips can be cut in half.

If you do not have enough 250 mL beakers, use clear plastic cups that can be purchased at the local store.

Students can bring in the eggs and corn syrup.

Use weigh boats or Petri dishes on the balance. Corn syrup can harm your balance.

Safety Alert

Be sure to warn the students of the following:

Warning: Lugol's iodine solution is a poison if ingested. It is also a strong irritant and can stain clothing. Avoid skin/eye contact; do not ingest. If contact occurs, flush affected area with water for 10 minutes; rinse mouth with water; notify your teacher immediately.

Warning: Be sure to wash your hands after handling raw eggs. Salmonella is bacteria commonly found in poultry and egg. To avoid food poisoning, one should always wash their hands after handling raw eggs.

POSSIBLE ANSWERS TO THE CONCLUSION QUESTIONS AND SAMPLE DATA

PART I

Part I Data Table				
Substance	**Present in the beaker at the beginning**	**Present in the dialysis tubing at the beginning**	**Present in the beaker at the end**	**Present in the dialysis tubing at the end**
Water	yes	yes	yes	yes
IKI	yes	no	yes	yes
Glucose	no	yes	yes	yes
Starch	no	yes	no	yes

1. What substances were permeable to the dialysis membrane? How do you know?
   - H2O was permeable because the amount of liquid increased in the tubing.
   - Glucose was permeable because the test tape showed that initially no glucose was in the beaker yet at the end of 30 minutes glucose appeared in the water in the beaker.
   - Iodine was permeable because it crossed the membrane and reacted with the starch turning it purple.

2. Which substance was impermeable to the dialysis membrane? How do you know?
   - Starch was impermeable because the water in the beaker remained a golden brown color. If starch had crossed the membrane into the beaker of water, the water would have turned purple.

3. Explain the concept of a selectively permeable membrane and how this relates to the dialysis tubing.
   - There are pores in the dialysis tubing, and it is the size the molecules and the size of the pore that will determine what is permeable to the membrane. Large molecules cannot cross because they are too large for the pores. This is why starch cannot cross because it is a macromolecule and is too large for the pore. On the other hand, smaller molecules can cross because they fit through the pore of the dialysis tubing.

4. This lab used glucose because it is permeable to the dialysis membrane. Glucose is a monosaccharide. Sucrose cannot be used because it impermeable to the membrane. Sucrose is a disaccharide. Explain why sucrose is impermeable to the membrane and how the results of the experiment would change if sucrose were used.
   - Sucrose, being a disaccharide, is twice as large as glucose and exceeds the pore diameter of the dialysis tubing. The results would have changed in that there would not be any sugar found in the water of the beaker after 30 minutes.

PART II

Part II Data Table	
Mass of egg in vinegar	77.0 g
Mass of original egg	57.3 g
Difference in mass	+ 19.7 g
Percent change in mass	+ 34.0 %
Mass of egg in corn syrup	44.3 g
Mass of original egg	57.3 g
Difference in mass	– 13.0 g
Percent change in mass	– 23.0 %
Mass of egg in water	59.5 g
Mass of original egg	59.3 g
Difference in mass	+ 0.2 g
Percent change in mass	+ 0.34 %

1. What happened to the shell of the egg when it was placed in the vinegar? What caused this to happen?
   - The vinegar, acetic acid, interacted with calcium carbonate in the shell to release carbon dioxide [hence the bubbles] and as result the outer shell softens since all of the carbon is removed. The shell was no longer present since it is essentially dissolved. The complete reaction is as follows:

     $CaCO_3 + HC_2H_3O_2 \rightarrow CO_2 + CaC_2H_3O_2$; the carbon dioxide bubbles away and the calcium acetate is soluble in water solutions. If you leave the egg out for 24 hours or so, the shell will harden again as it absorbs carbon from carbon dioxide from the air.

2. What happened to the mass of the egg after it was left in vinegar? Explain what accounts for the change in the mass of the egg in terms of osmosis.
   - The mass of the egg increased as water entered the egg because the water was more concentrated on the outside of the egg than on the inside. The vinegar was hypotonic relative to the material inside the egg.

3. What happened to the mass of the egg after it was left in corn syrup? Explain what accounts for the change in the mass of the egg in terms of osmosis.
   - The mass of the egg decreased as water left the egg because the water was more concentrated on the inside of the egg than on the outside of the egg. The water inside the egg was hypotonic relative to the corn syrup.

4. What happened to the mass of the egg after it was left in water? Explain what accounts for the change in the mass of the egg in terms of osmosis.
   - There was very little change in the mass of the egg because the calcium shell of the egg is waterproof — not because the two liquids were isotonic.

5. If carrot sticks are put into water and refrigerated, they become turgid or stiff. If red blood cells are given the same treatment, they burst or lyse. Account for the difference in the results.
   - Plant cells have cell walls which prevent them from bursting when water enters the plant cell. Animals do not have cell walls therefore as water enters the cell, the cell will burst.

6. A patient comes into the emergency room. She is unconscious and is obviously dehydrated. Explain what sort of intravenous solution (IV) you would inject into your patient and why. Remember that pure distilled water would be hypotonic to the patient blood.
   - She would be given an isotonic solution relative to blood plasma. If she were given just plain water, that is hypotonic relative to the blood cells, the blood cells would burst. If she is given a solution that is hypertonic to the plasma, the blood cells and tissues would lose water which would just aggravate the condition.

PART III

Part III Data Table

Results after 24 hours

Egg	1	2	3	4	5	6	7	8	9	10	11
Percent Syrup	0 %	10 %	20 %	30 %	40 %	50 %	60 %	70 %	80 %	90 %	100 %
Final Mass (g)	846.6	77.3	79.1	73.7	61.9	56.4	56.8	55.5	57.9	56.7	50.9
Initial Mass (g)	79.5	76.9	85.7	87.8	81.5	80.4	85.4	85.4	91.3	91	83.1
Change in Mass (g)	5.1	0.4	-6.6	-14.1	-19.6	-24	-28.6	-29.9	-33.4	-34.3	-32.2
Percent Change in Mass (%)	6.42	$5e^{-1}$	-7.7	-16.1	-24	-29.9	-33.5	-35	-36.6	-37.7	-38.75

Results after 48 hours

Egg	1	2	3	4	5	6	7	8	9	10	11
Percent Syrup	0 %	10 %	20 %	30 %	40 %	50 %	60 %	70 %	80 %	90 %	100 %
Final Mass (g)	85.5	81	82	77.5	59.5	52.6	50.7	47	50	45.1	41.8
Initial Mass (g)	79.5	76.9	85.7	87.8	81.5	80.4	85.4	85.4	91.3	91	83.1
Change in Mass (g)	6	4.1	-3.7	-10.3	-22	-27.8	-34.7	-38.4	-41.3	-45.9	-41.3
Percent Change in Mass (%)	7.55	5.33	-4.32	-11.7	-26.9	-34.6	-40.6	-44.9	-45.2	-50.5	-49.69

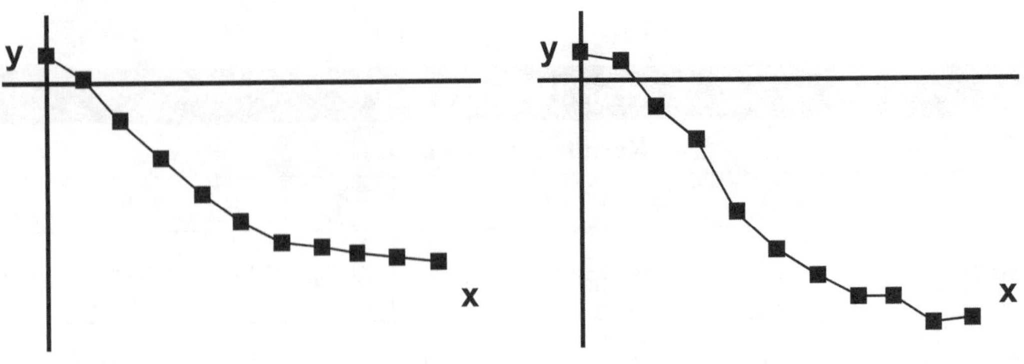

Results after 24 hrs.

Results after 48 hrs.

1. Use your graph to determine the percent corn syrup that is isotonic to the egg.
   - The place where the line crosses the *x* axis is the point where there is no change in the mass of the egg. This is the point where the egg and corn syrup are isotonic.

2. Design a procedure to support that the interpolated value for the percent of corn syrup that is isotonic to the egg is correct?
   - First, mix up the percent of corn syrup that is supposed to be isotonic to the egg. Now weigh an egg without the shell and submerge it into the corn syrup solution. After 24 hours, weigh the egg again to see if there is a change in mass. If isotonic, there should be no change in mass.

3. What is the relationship between the percent change in mass and increasing amounts of corn syrup?
   - With an increase in the percent of corn syrup, there is an increasing gain in percent change in mass.

4. At 100% corn syrup, was the egg hypertonic or hypotonic relative to the corn syrup? How do you know?
   - The egg was hypotonic relative to the syrup, because the egg lost mass.

5. In distilled water, was the egg hypertonic or hypotonic relative to the corn syrup? How do you know?
   - The egg was hypertonic relative to pure water because the egg gained mass.

6. Why would be harmful to drink the ocean water if you were in a life boat on the ocean and thirsty?
   - Sea water is hypertonic relative to plasma. Because sea water is hypertonic, the body would actually lose water to the urinary system. Drinking sea water would make a person become more dehydrated.

REFERENCES

"Diffusion and Cell Membranes", *Biology: Principles and Exploration, Laboratory Experiments, Teacher's Edition.* Austin: Holt, Rinehart and Winston, 1996. pp. 15-20

Haverson, Michael. http://www.the-aps.org/education outreach/outreach/acts-labs/halversn1.htm. "How Do Hypotonic, Hypertonic, and Isotonic Solution Affect the Water Movement of a Cell" (viewed October 1, 2003).

Greenberg, Jon, Revision Editor. *BSCS, A Molecular Approach.* Chicago: Everyday Learning, 2001. pp. T41, 709-711

The Gate Keepers
Examining Osmosis and Selective Diffusion

The cell membrane is a selectively permeable membrane that regulates what materials enter and leave the cell. There are some substances that are permeable to the cell membrane, such as water, oxygen, and carbon dioxide. Their ability to move into and out of the cell is a function of the Second Law of Thermodynamics and free energy.

If a skunk sprays its "perfume" in a classroom, a student walking into the room can smell this odor. The student will be able to locate the source of the odor by tracing the odor along an increasing gradient to its source or the skunk. However, after enough time has passed, another student entering the room may be able to detect the odor but will not be able to locate the skunk. The preceding example is an illustration of the Second Law of Thermodynamics and free energy. When the spray is first released, it forms a small cloud of molecules that is relatively ordered. These molecules are in constant random motion and now have the freedom to move in any direction. It seems intuitive that out of the all the possible directions that the spray molecules will take, they will move away from the center of the cloud rather than towards it. These molecules are moving from an area of high concentration to an area of lower concentration. It is true that a small percentage of the spray molecules will move toward the center of the cloud, but the majority will move away from the center. The net movement of the molecules is away from the center of the cloud. In doing so, the spray forms a concentration gradient that the first student could follow to locate its source. As the molecules continue to move, they become more random, and they will become relatively equidistant from one another and a concentration gradient will no longer exist. At that time the system is in equilibrium; the perfume molecules will continue to move but there will be no net movement of the molecules and the second student entering the room will not be able to locate the source of the spray or the skunk.

This example follows the Second Law of Thermodynamics as this system over time becomes more disorderly as the molecules randomly move. The free energy of the molecules then decreases as they become more random and disorganized.

Scientists summarize the movements of diffusion in a rule: substances tend to move from areas of higher concentration to areas of lower concentration. This difference in concentrations between two places is called a *diffusion gradient.*

When a substance is able to pass through a membrane, we say that the membrane is *permeable* to that substance. Membranes may be more permeable to some substances than to others: they are said to be *differentially permeable*. In other words, these membranes have different permeability to different substances; perhaps a small urea molecule will pass easily, but not a large starch molecule. Sometimes membranes do not permit substances to pass through at all. They are said to *impermeable* to that substance.

Water is also permeable to the membrane and can cross freely. Whether the net movement of water is into or out of the cell is a function of the osmotic gradient. Osmosis is the special process of water moving across a membrane along a concentration gradient. When materials are impermeable to the cell membrane and are not in equilibrium, there is a net movement of water across the membrane. The rule of thumb is "water likes to dilute". Water, like other substances, will cross the membrane from where the water is most concentrated to an area where it is least concentrated.

If a semi-permeable membrane separates two solutions, and those solutions are different in their concentrations, one can expect that there will be a net movement of water. The solution that has the greatest concentration of solutes is said to be *hypertonic* relative to the other side. The solution that has the least concentrations of solutes is said to be *hypotonic* relative to the other side. The net movement of water will be from the hypotonic side of the membrane to the hypertonic side of the membrane as "water dilutes" the side with greater amount of solutes.

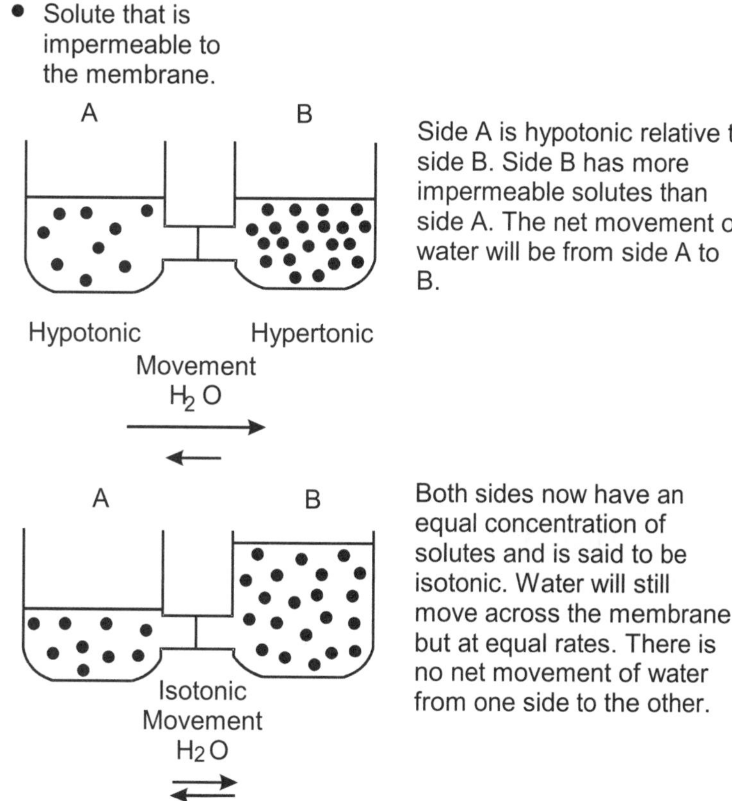
Solute that is impermeable to the membrane.
A
B
Side A is hypotonic relative to side B. Side B has more impermeable solutes than side A. The net movement of water will be from side A to B.
Hypotonic
Hypertonic
Movement
H_2O
A
B
Both sides now have an equal concentration of solutes and is said to be isotonic. Water will still move across the membrane but at equal rates. There is no net movement of water from one side to the other.
Isotonic
Movement
H_2O

PURPOSE

The purpose of this lab is to investigate the process of diffusion and osmosis through a semi-permeable membrane. It also explores the change in the mass of an egg with a change in the concentration of corn syrup through the process of osmosis. Your teacher may direct you to do either part II or part III or both. This depends on the amount of time available to the class.

MATERIALS

Part I

dialysis tubing (15 cm long)
12 cm of dialysis tubing (diameter 2.2 cm)
15 cc of 1% starch-15%glucose solution
1 vial glucose test tape
10 cc syringe
10 cc of iodine solution
1 250 mL beaker

Part II

3 250 mL beakers
200 mL corn syrup
balance
aluminum foil
plastic spoon
200 mL vinegar
2 uncooked eggs
100 mL graduated cylinder
rubber bands
lab apron and goggles

Part III

1 uncooked egg
200 mL vinegar
balance
TI-83 graphing calculator
100 mL graduated cylinder
2 250 mL beakers
200 mL corn syrup
paper towels
lab apron and goggles
plastic spoon

> **Safety Alert**
> **Lugol's iodine solution is a poison if ingested. It is also a strong irritant and can stain clothing. Avoid skin/eye contact; do not ingest. If contact occurs, flush affected area with water for 10 minutes; rinse mouth with water; call your teacher immediately.**
>
> **Warning: Be sure to wash your hands after handling raw eggs. Salmonella is a bacteria commonly found in poultry and eggs. To avoid food poisoning, one should always wash their hands after handling raw eggs.**

PROCEDURE

PART I

1. Obtain one piece of dialysis tubing and tie a knot in one end. Open the other end of the tubing. This is best done with wet fingers rubbing the end of the tubing.

2. Use the syringe to put 10 cc of 15% glucose and 1% starch solution into the dialysis tubing bag. Using glucose test tape, test the solution in the dialysis tubing for presence of glucose. Record your findings in the data table.

3. Tie the open end of the bag shut and wipe off the outside of the bag.

4. Fill a 250-mL beaker with 200 mL of water. Add 10 cc of iodine solution or enough that the water appears golden yellow. Using glucose test tape, test the solution in the beaker for presence of glucose. Record your findings in the data table.

5. Submerse the bag into the beaker of iodine and water. Allow bag to remain in the solution for 30 minutes and observe the results. After time has elapsed, test the beaker and the dialysis tubing for the presence of glucose.

6. Observe the dialysis bag and the solution in the beaker for evidence of the presence of starch. Remember that a blue to blue-black color indicates the presence of starch in an iodine containing solution. Record your findings in the data table

PART II

1. Obtain 2 raw eggs. Measure their mass to the nearest 0.1 of a gram.

2. Pour 200 mL of vinegar into a 250 mL beaker and label it *vinegar*. Using a spoon, lower the egg into the beaker of vinegar.

3. Pour 200 mL of water into a second 250 mL beaker and label it *water*. Using a spoon, lower the second egg into the beaker of water.

4. Observe the eggs for a few minutes and record your observations. Cover both beakers with aluminum foil.

5. After 1-2 days, observe what has happened to the eggs and how they have changed. Carefully remove the egg in water, dry it with a soft paper towel and weigh it. Return the egg back to the beaker of water. Record your results in the table on your student answer page.

6. Carefully remove the egg in the vinegar, dry it with a soft paper towel, and weigh it. Record your results in the table on your student answer page.

7. Pour 200 mL of corn syrup in a clean beaker and label it *syrup*. Carefully put the vinegar soaked egg in to the beaker of corn syrup.

8. Cover both beakers with aluminum foil. Let them rest for 1-2 days. Clean your work station and wash your hands.

9. After 1-2 days, observe what has happened to the eggs and how they have changed. Carefully remove the eggs from the beakers and weigh them.

10. Record your results in the table on your answer sheet. Determine the % change in mass by using the following equation:

$$\%\text{ change in mass} = \frac{(\text{Final mass} - \text{Original mass})}{\text{Original mass}} \text{ X } 100$$

11. Dispose of the eggs according to your teacher's instructions and clean the beakers and your work station.

12. Be sure to wash your hands after handling the eggs.

PART III

1. Obtain a raw egg. Measure its mass to the nearest 0.1 of a gram.

2. Pour 200 mL of vinegar into a 250 mL beaker and label it *vinegar*. Using a spoon, lower the egg into the beaker of vinegar.

3. After 1-2 days, observe what has happened to the egg.

4. Your teacher will assign you a percent of corn syrup solution to make. Make the assigned solution by following the appropriate recipe below. Use a 250 mL beaker for your solution.

Percent Corn Syrup	Amount of Corn Syrup	Amount of Water
0%	0 mL	200 mL
10%	20 mL	180 mL
20%	40 mL	160 mL
30%	60 mL	140 mL
40%	80 mL	120 mL
50%	100 mL	100 mL
60%	120 mL	80 mL
70%	140 mL	60 mL
80%	160 mL	40 mL
90%	180 mL	20 mL
100%	200 mL	0 mL

Mix the solution thoroughly until the solution is homogeneous. If you are using a high concentration of corn syrup (80% or 90%), it is easier to mix 20 mL of the corn syrup with the water and then add the remaining corn syrup.

5. Carefully remove the egg from the vinegar, carefully dry it with a soft paper towel, and weight it. Record this as the original weight in the data table.

6. Carefully place this egg in to your assigned corn syrup solution.

7. Clean up your work station. Be sure to wash your hands after handling the eggs.

8. After 1-2 days, observe what has happened to the egg and how it has changed. Carefully remove the egg from the beaker and carefully dry it taking care not to break the membrane.

9. Weigh the egg and record this as the final mass.

10. Determine the percent change in mass by using the following formula:

$$\% \text{ change in mass} = \frac{(\text{Final mass} - \text{Original mass})}{\text{Original mass}} \text{ X } 100$$

11. Collect the class data for all the eggs in the class.

12. Dispose of your eggs as instructed by your teacher. Clean up your work station. Be sure to wash your hands after handling the eggs.

Optional - The data can be graphed on a TI-83 graphing calculator by doing the following:

13. To make a data table press STAT, then select EDIT (Figure 1) and press ENTER. Notice that there are columns or lists to record data.

Figure 1

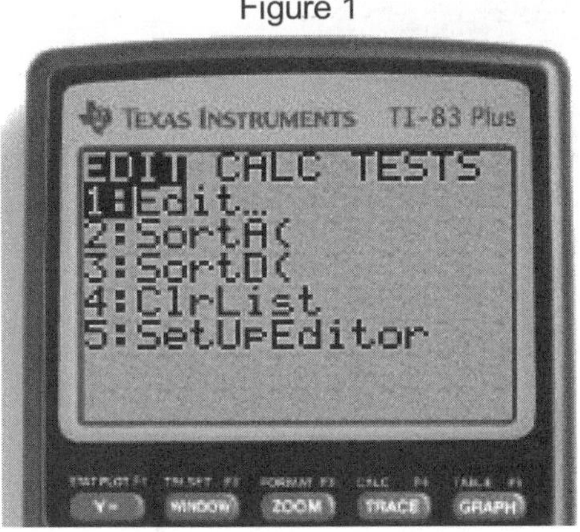

Figure 2

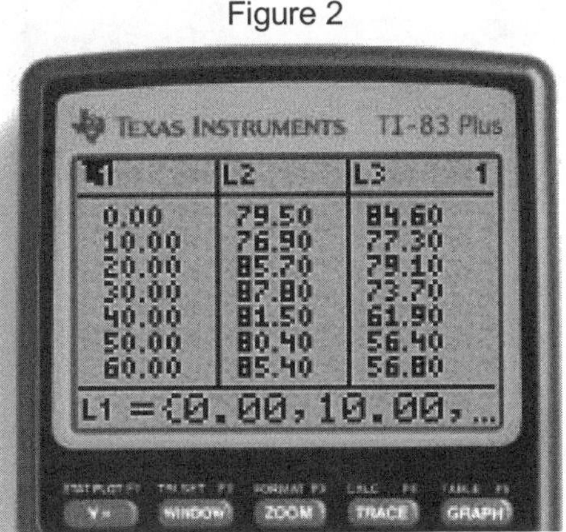

14. To clear a list that might have data in it, put the cursor at the very top of the list so that the name of the column is highlighted. Press CLEAR followed by the ▼.

15. Now enter the percent of corn syrup in L1 starting at 0 for the first entry and ending at 100 percent for the last entry. In L2 record the corresponding initial mass. In L3 record the corresponding final mass. See Figure 2.

16. Calculate the percent change in mass in L4 by doing the following:
    a. Position the cursor at the top of L4 and press ENTER. Key in (, (, 2nd, 3 [L3], −, 2nd, 2 [L2],), ÷, 2nd, 2 [L2],), X, 1, 0, 0, (see Figure 3) and then press ENTER (see Figure 4).
    b. To view this graphically, press 2nd, Y=, ENTER. At this time make sure to put your cursor on PLOT 1 and press ENTER and move the cursor down to ON and press ENTER. Both PLOT 1 and ON should be highlighted. All other plots should be inactivated. Highlight the line plot (the second of graph displayed) and press ENTER.

Figure 3

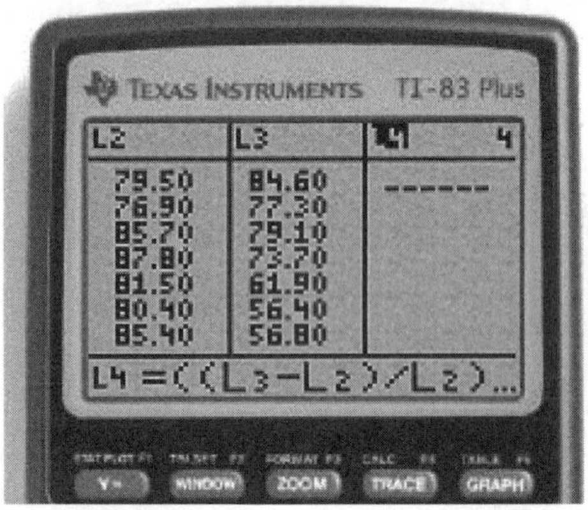

Figure 4

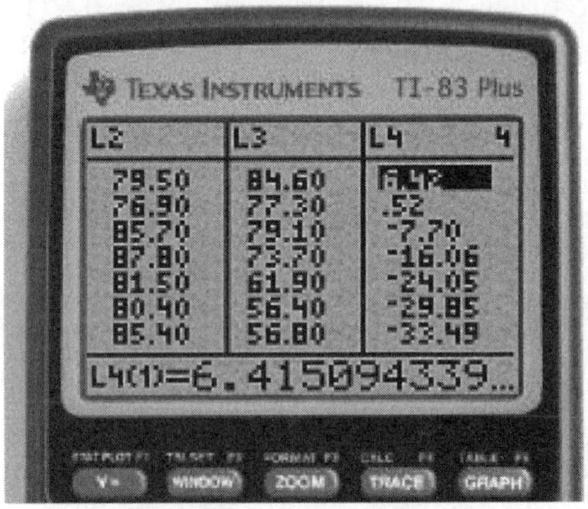

17. Highlight the Xlist and press 2nd, 1 [L1].

18. Highlight the Ylist and press 2nd, 4 [L4]. See Figure 5.

19. Press ZOOM then press 9. A graph should appear that will automatically adjust the axes so that they fit the window. See Figure 6.

Figure 5

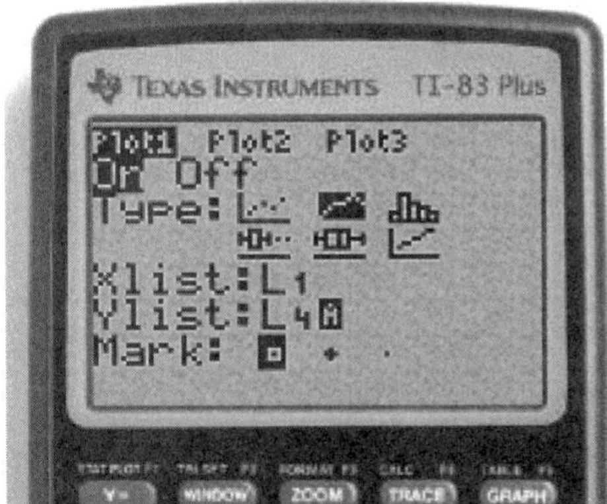

Figure 6

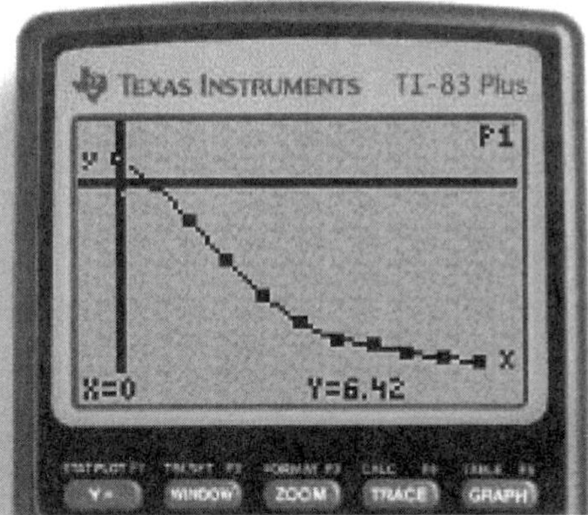

Name ______________________________

Period ______________________________

The Gate Keepers
Examining Osmosis and Selective Diffusion

DATA AND OBSERVATIONS

PART I

Part I Data Table				
Substance	**Present in the beaker at the beginning**	**Present in the dialysis tubing at the beginning**	**Present in the beaker at the end**	**Present in the dialysis tubing at the end**
Water				
IKI				
Glucose				
Starch				

Part II Data Table	
Mass of egg in vinegar (g)	
Mass of original egg (g)	
Difference in mass (g)	
Percent change in mass (%)	
Mass of egg in corn syrup (g)	
Mass of original egg (g)	
Difference in mass (g)	
Percent change in mass (%)	
Mass of egg in water (g)	
Mass of original egg (g)	
Difference in mass (g)	
Percent change in mass (%)	

Part III Data Table											
Egg	**1**	**2**	**3**	**4**	**5**	**6**	**7**	**8**	**9**	**10**	**11**
Percent Syrup	0 %	10 %	20 %	30 %	40 %	50 %	60 %	70 %	80 %	90 %	100 %
Final Mass (g)											
Initial Mass (g)											
Change in Mass (g)											
Percent Change in Mass (%)											

CONCLUSION QUESTIONS

PART I

1. What substances were permeable to the dialysis membrane? How do you know?

2. Which substances were impermeable to the dialysis membrane? How do you know?

3. Explain the concept of a selectively permeable membrane and how this relates to the dialysis tubing.

4. This lab used glucose because it is permeable to the dialysis membrane. Glucose is a monosaccharide. Sucrose can not be used because it impermeable to the membrane. Sucrose is a disaccharide. Explain why sucrose is impermeable to the membrane and how the results of the experiment would change if sucrose were used.

PART II

1. What happened to the shell of the egg when it was placed in the vinegar? What caused this to happen?

2. What happened to the mass of the egg after it was left in vinegar? Explain what accounts for the change in the mass of the egg in terms of osmosis.

3. What happened to the mass of the egg after it was left in corn syrup? Explain what accounts for the change in the mass of the egg in terms of osmosis.

4. What happened to the mass of the egg after it was left in water? Explain what accounts for the change in the mass of the egg in terms of osmosis.

5. If carrot sticks are put into water and refrigerated, they become turgid or stiff. If red blood cells are given the same treatment, they burst or lyse. Account for the difference in the results.

6. A patient comes into the emergency room. She is unconscious and is obviously dehydrated. Explain what sort of intravenous solution (IV) you would inject into your patient and why. Remember that pure distilled water would be hypotonic to the patient blood.

PART III

1. Use your graph to determine the percent corn syrup that is isotonic to the egg.

2. Design a procedure to support that the interpolated value for the percent of corn syrup that is isotonic to the egg is correct?

3. What is the relationship between the percent change in mass and increasing amounts of corn syrup?

4. At 100% corn syrup, was the egg hypertonic or hypotonic relative to the corn syrup? How do you know?

5. In distilled water, was the egg hypertonic or hypotonic relative to the corn syrup? How do you know?

6. Why would it be harmful to drink the ocean water if you were in a life boat on the ocean and thirsty?

Write Your Notes and Ideas Here!

Chromosome Manipulative
Demonstrating Mitosis

OBJECTIVE
Students will demonstrate an understanding of the terms chromosome, chromatid, homologous pair, independent assortment, and segregation using paper models of chromosomes.

LEVEL
Biology I

NATIONAL STANDARDS
UCP.1, UCP.2, UCP.5, C.1, C.2, G.1, G.2

TEKS
6(E)

CONNECTIONS TO AP
AP Biology:
I. Molecules and Cells B. Cell 4. Cell cycle

TIME FRAME
20 minutes

MATERIALS
(For a class of 28 working individually)

56 copies of chromosome #1
56 copies of chromosome #2
28 scissors
28 pink and blue map colors
28 meters of yarn or string

TEACHER NOTES
The use of inexpensive manipulatives in the classroom will allow you to periodically check the students understanding of abstract concepts. This chromosome modeling activity is designed to help you assess student understanding efficiently and promptly.

In lieu of having the students color the chromosomes, you could copy the chromosomes on pink and blue copy paper.

Suggested teaching procedures:

1. Have the students cut out and color four chromosomes as follows:
   a. One large chromosome – blue
   b. One large chromosome – pink
   c. One small chromosome – blue
   d. One small chromosome – pink

2. Cut out a set for you to use during the demonstration portion of the activity.

3. Ask students to fold all their chromosomes in half lengthwise, make a circle on top of their desk using the string, and place the chromosomes inside the circle.

4. Explain the terms chromatin, chromosome, replicated chromosome, and homologous pair using your paper model. Check student understanding by having the students show you the structure as you randomly call out one of the four terms. This allows you to check student understanding from your location.

5. Have the students simulate replication by unfolding each chromosome.

6. Instruct students to draw chromatin, chromosome, replicated chromosome, and homologous pairs on their answer page.

7. Explain the main events of the mitosis stages while having the students model the stages on their desk tops.

8. Check for student understanding by randomly calling out the phase name and having the students demonstrate the stage at their desk.

9. Divide the students into pairs and have them explain to their partner the stages of mitosis. They should use their paper chromosomes and draw the stages on their answer page.

10. Instruct students to complete the conclusion questions.

POSSIBLE ANSWERS TO THE CONCLUSION QUESTIONS AND SAMPLE DATA

DATA AND OBSERVATIONS

CHROMATIN	CHROMOSOME	REPLICATED CHROMOSOME	HOMOLOGOUS CHROMOSOME

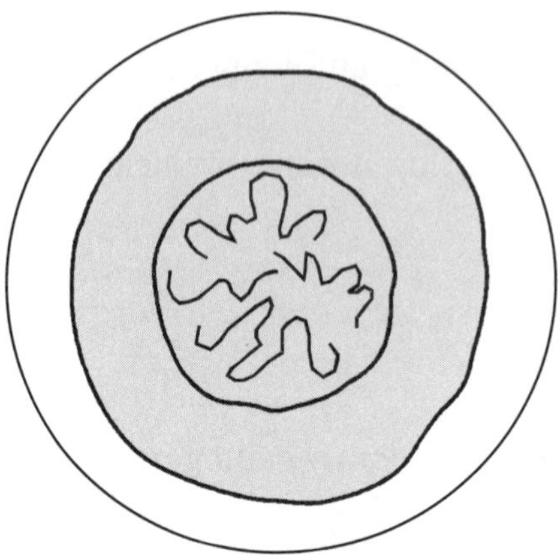

Model cell during Interphase

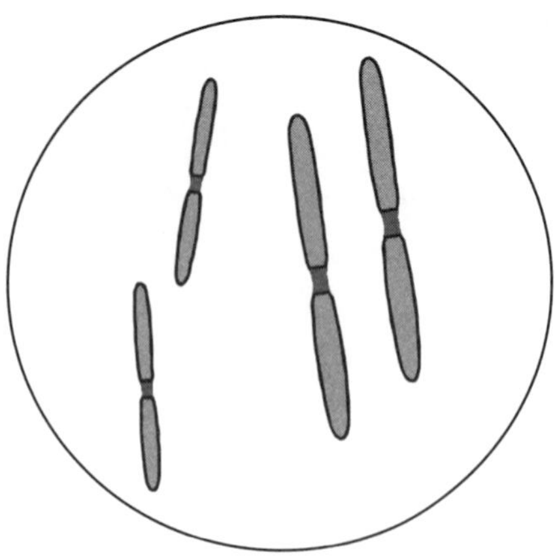

Model cell during Prophase

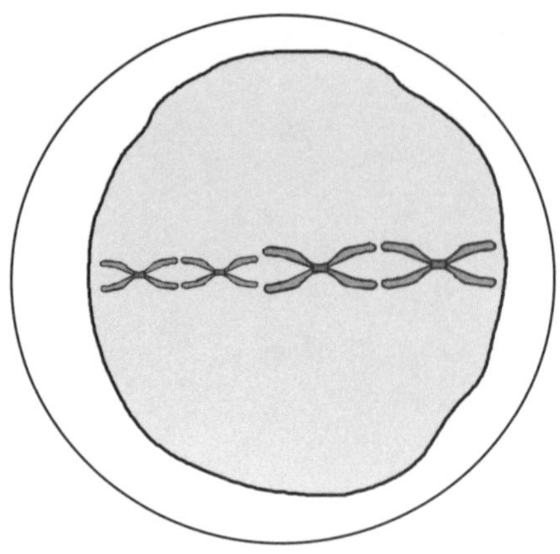

Model cell during Metaphase

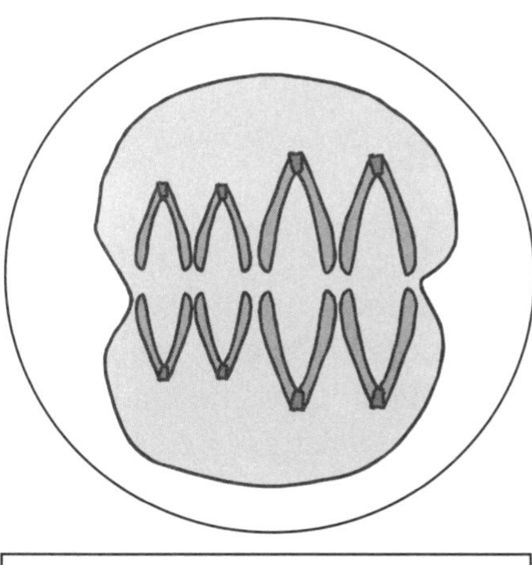

Model cell during Anaphase

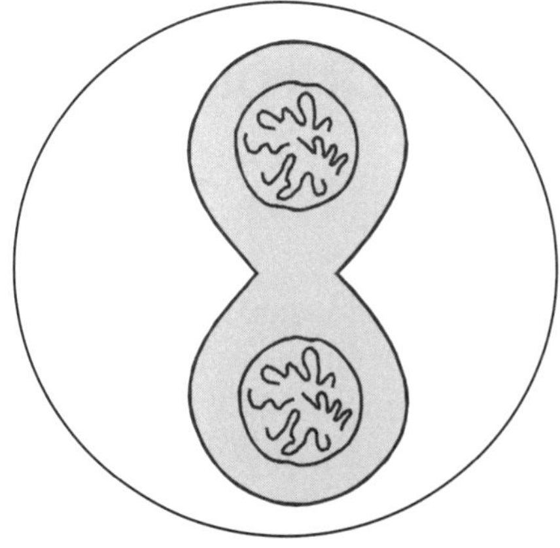

Model cell during Telophase

CONCLUSION QUESTIONS

1. What is the purpose of mitosis?
   - To produce two genetically identical daughter cells

2. What event produces copies of the DNA to ensure genetic continuity in the daughter cells?
   - DNA Replication

3. If a cell normally had a total of 6 chromosomes, how many chromosomes would be present in the cell during prophase?
   - 12

4. Draw the cell mentioned in question three as it would appear in metaphase:
   - Diagram should show 6 replicated chromosomes on the equator

5. Draw the cell mentioned in question three as it would appear in telophase:
   - Diagram should show 6 chromosomes on one side of cell and 6 chromosomes on the other side

Chromosome Manipulative
Demonstrating Mitosis

Genetic information, housed inside the nucleus of each cell, is carried in the form of chromosomes. Chromosomes transmit genetic information found in their DNA sequences to the next generation of cells through the process of mitosis. Mitosis produces offspring cells that contain the same kind and amount of genetic information found in the original cell. During mitosis the cells undergo an exact duplication of the parent nucleus, forming two new cells, or daughter cells, of identical genetic makeup. For example, if the original parent cell's nucleus contained 12 chromosomes, each of the new daughter cells produced through mitosis will contain 12 chromosomes. Normal body cells in humans contain 46 chromosomes. In humans, the process of mitosis results in the production of two new daughter cells each contains 46 chromosomes.

Several different terms are used to describe the chromosome as it exists in the various stages of this division process. *Chromatin* is a term used to describe the relaxed state of the DNA and its proteins. *Replicated chromosome* is a term used to identify a chromosome that has completed the process of DNA replication and now exists in duplicates that are attached at an area called the *centromere*. These duplicates or replicas are referred to as *sister chromatids*.

Prior to the onset of cell division, during the interphase of the cell's life cycle, the genetic information found within the nucleus of the cell will be copied through a process known as *DNA replication*. During DNA replication each strand of DNA is duplicated forming two copies of the chromosome. These copies, or *chromatids*, will remain attached to each other at the centromere region until they become separated from one another through the events of mitosis. In human cells where the original chromosome count is 46, the cell that has completed DNA replication will contain say 46 chromosomes consisting of 2 sister chromatids for a total of 92 chromatids. The overall purpose mitosis is to separate these replicated chromosomes, portioning them into two, new daughter cells.

The events of mitosis are divided into four main stages. The following events occur in each stage.

Prophase – The long, stringy, unwound chromatin fibers coil and condense into thick threads of visible genetic material called chromosomes. As the cell enters prophase, the chromosomes have already been replicated forming sister chromatids. The sister chromatids are connected to each other at the centromere. The spindle apparatus begins to form. The nuclear membrane breaks down and the nucleolus disappears.

Metaphase – The centromeres of the sister chromatids line up along the center, or metaphase plate, of the cell bringing the genetic material to the center of the cell. Microtubules connect the centromere of each chromosome to the spindle.

Anaphase – The centromere of each chromosome divides, separating the sister chromatids from each other. The chromatids of each pair will be moved by the spindle fibers toward opposite poles of the cell. The separated chromatids are now called chromosomes. This separation allows one copy of each chromosome to be placed on opposite sides of the dividing cell. The chromosomes continue to move the poles of the spindle forming two separate groups.

Telophase – The final stage of mitosis occurs as new nuclear membranes are formed around both groups of chromosomes. The result is two separate nuclei, each containing the same genetic information at the original cell's nucleus. The chromosomes will uncoil and relax to form chromatin threads. The spindle begins to break apart and the nucleoli are reformed.

PURPOSE

The purpose of this activity is to demonstrate the stages of mitosis using chromosome models.

MATERIALS

2 copies of replicated chromosome #1
2 copies of replicated chromosome #2
scissors
pink and blue map colors
1 meter piece of yarn or string

> **Safety Alert**
> 1. Use care when handling sharp or pointed instruments.

PROCEDURE

1. Cut out two copies of replicated chromosome #1 and two copies of replicated chromosome #2.

2. Color one copy of replicated chromosome#1 pink to represent the maternal copy of the chromosome.

3. Color the second copy of replicated chromosome#1 blue. It will represent the paternal copy of the chromosome.

4. Color one copy of replicated chromosome#2 pink to represent the maternal copy. Color the second copy of replicated chromosome #2 blue to represent the paternal copy of the chromosome.

5. Using the piece of string, make a circular shape on the top of your desk to represent a cell membrane.

6. Fold each of the 4 chromosomes in half at the centromere.

7. Place the chromosomes inside the cell membrane you have made on your desk top.

8. Locate the data table on your student answer page. Complete the table by drawing pictures of the objects listed.

9. Listen carefully as your teacher describes the events of the stages of mitosis.

10. At the conclusion of the teacher's description of the stages, go through the steps of mitosis once again with your partner and draw the stages in the space provided on the answer sheet.

11. Complete the questions on the student answer page.

Name ______________________________

Period ______________________________

Chromosome Manipulative
Demonstrating Mitosis

DATA AND OBSERVATIONS

CHROMATIN	CHROMOSOME	REPLICATED CHROMOSOME	HOMOLOGOUS CHROMOSOMES

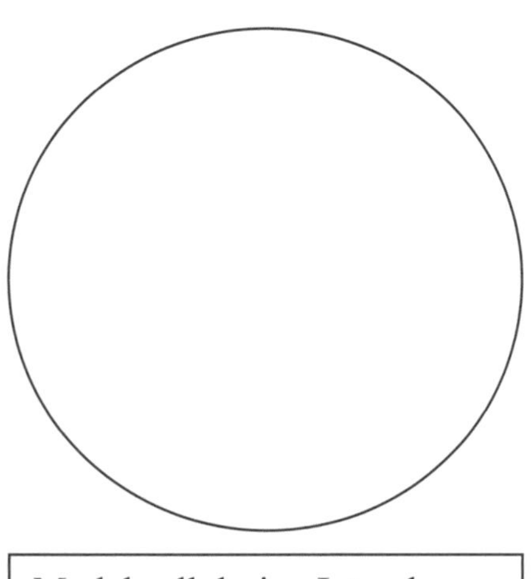

Model cell during Interphase

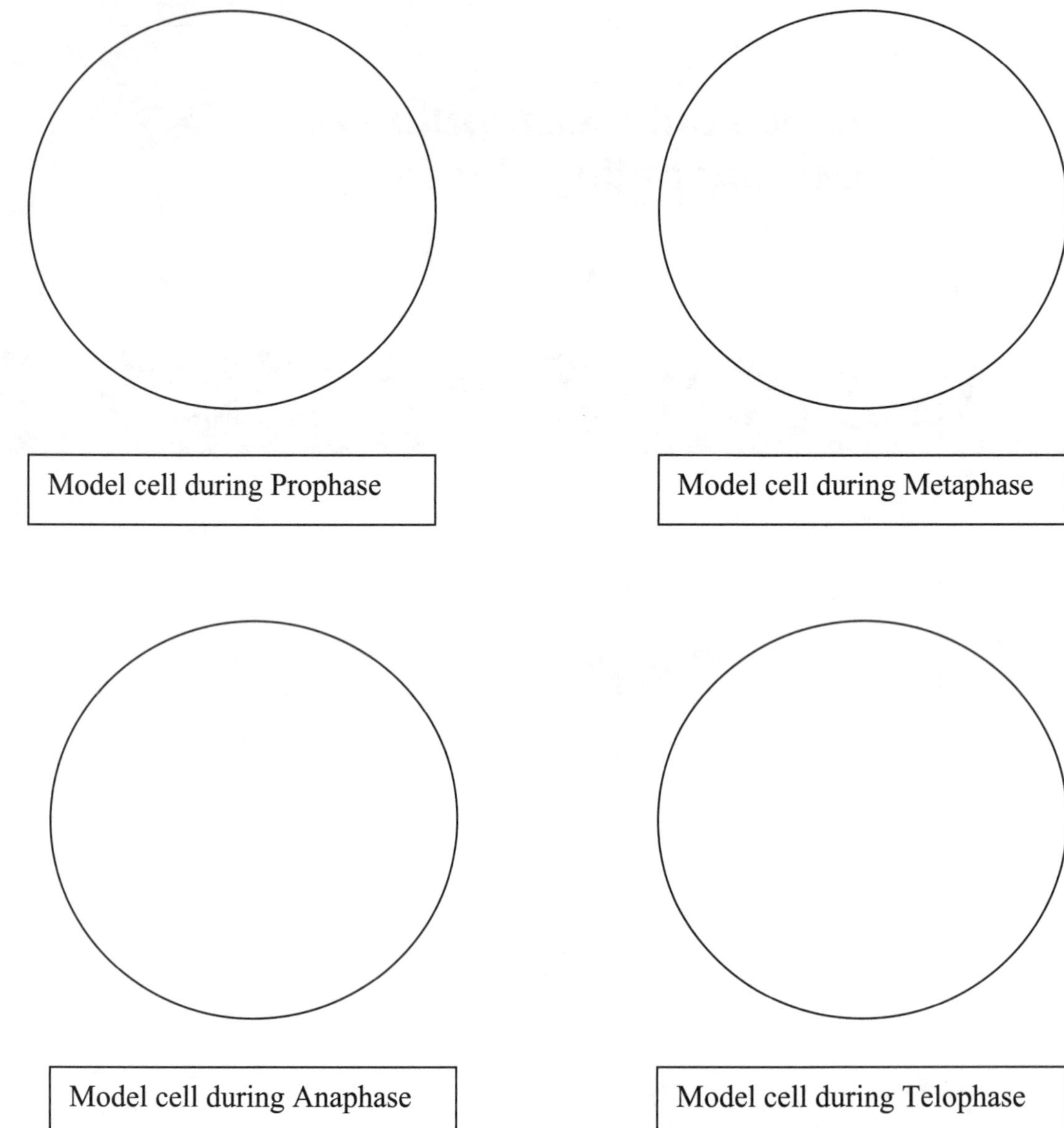

CONCLUSION QUESTIONS

1. What is the purpose of mitosis?

2. What cellular event produces copies of the DNA to ensure genetic continuity in the daughter cells?

3. If a cell normally had a total of 6 chromosomes, how many chromosomes would be present in the cell during prophase?

4. Draw the cell mentioned in question 3 as it would appear in metaphase:

5. Draw the cell mentioned in question 3 as it would appear in telophase:

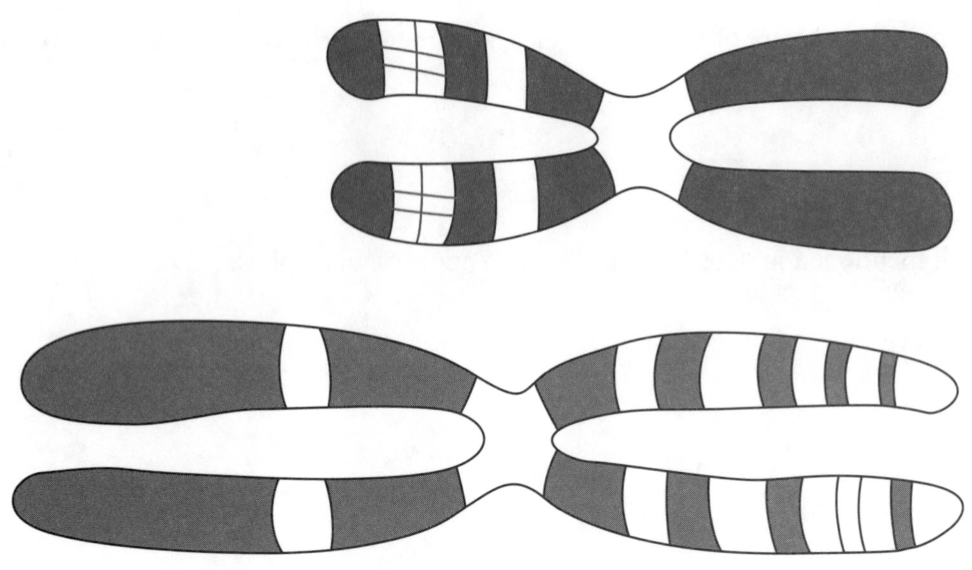

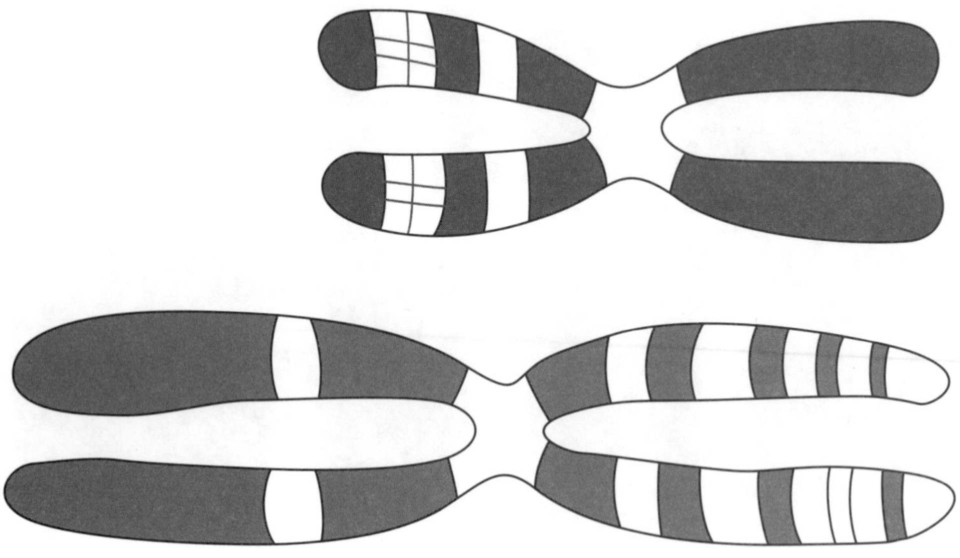

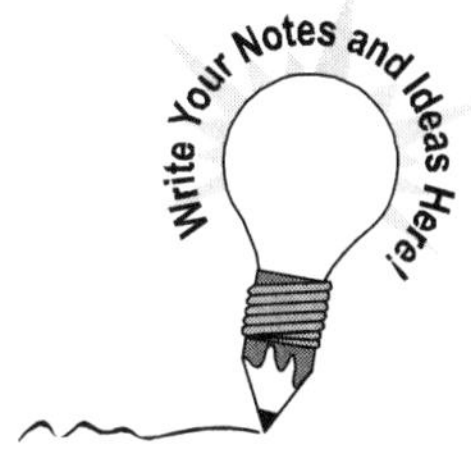
Write Your Notes and Ideas Here!

Cell Division
Observing Mitosis in a Root Tip

OBJECTIVE
Students will prepare and stain a wet mount of an onion root tip. The students will then observe the stages of mitosis in the root tip squash.

LEVEL
Biology I

NATIONAL STANDARDS
UCP.1, UCP.2 UCP.5, C.1, C.2, E.1, E.2, G.1, G.2

TEKS
Biology 1(A), 2(B), 6(E)

CONNECTIONS TO AP
AP Biology:
  Cells – Cell cycle, mitosis

TIME FRAME
45 minutes

MATERIALS
(For a class of 28 working in pairs)

- 14 vials of treated onion root tips
- 14 forceps
- 42 microscope slides
- 50 mL aceto-orcein stain
- 14 treating dishes
- 14 wooden macerating sticks
- 14 scalpels
- 14 test tubes
- 14 microscopes
- paper towel
- 42 coverslips
- goggles & aprons
- 100 mL1 M HCl
- 7 green onions
- water bath

TEACHER NOTES
To prepare the root tips:

<u>At least one week prior to lab</u>:

Scrape away the old, dried roots from several green onion bulbs. Wrap each onion bulb in moist paper towels and place in a dark, warm area. Fresh, new roots should sprout in 2-3 days.

At least 2-3 days prior to lab:

To prepare fixative solution:

Combine 25 mL of glacial acetic acid ($HC_2H_3O_2$) and 75 mL of 95% ethanol (C_2H_5OH). Safety Caution: Mix this solution in the fume hood to avoid inhalation of the fumes from glacial acetic acid.

You will need enough root tips for each lab group to have at least three tips. Remove the root tips using a clean scalpel. Place the root tips in 100 mL of fixative solution. Allow the root tips to remain in this solution for 48 hours.

Prior to the lab:

Remove the root tips from the fixative solution and place them in 100 mL of 70% ethanol until ready for use. A solution that is approximately 70% ethanol can be prepared by mixing 74 mL of 95% ethanol diluted to 100mL with distilled water. Root tips can be stored in a small vial of 70% ethanol solution for 2 months. When ready to use, place the root tips into a test tube with enough 1 M HCl to cover the tips. To prepare 1M HCl, add 8.3 mL of 12M HCl to 91.7 mL of distilled water. **Safety Caution**: This solution should be prepared in the fume hood while wearing goggles and an apron. Place the tube into a 60° C water bath for 15 minutes. Decant or use a pipet to draw off as much HCl as possible from the tube. Add enough aceto-orcein stain to the test tube to completely cover the root tips. After 10-15 minutes the root tips will turn pink and are ready to be used by the student. Alternately, you could have students prepare their own tips in advance of the squash and observation portion of the lab.

Students will need to be patient while searching for mitotic cells on their slides. By having the students prepare more than one squash, the chances of success are increased. However, you may want to have some prepared slides of root tips on hand for students who are not able to successfully prepare a squash.

You may want to display slide images of the root tips. Images of onion cells in the various stages of mitosis can be found at http://www.lima.ohio-state.edu/biology/mitosis.html. These images could be placed into a power point presentation and used during a pre-lab discussion of the stages. Additionally, you may want to print out a paper copy of an image such as this for the students to use in the event that they are unable to locate mitotic cells in their samples. Pointing out the stages on slide images such as those found at this site will help students better recognize the stages found on their own slides.

POSSIBLE ANSWERS TO THE CONCLUSION QUESTION AND SAMPLE DATA

Data Table 1			
Mitotic Stage	Viewing Area		Total Number of Cells per stage
	Area 1	Area 2	
Prophase	8	12	20
Metaphase	2	4	6
Anaphase	4	5	9
Telophase	1	3	4
Non-dividing Interphase	110	126	236
Total cells counted in viewing area	125	150	275

Data Table 2				
Sketch of mitotic stage	$\% = \frac{\text{number of cells in stage}}{\text{total number of cells observed}} \times 100$			
Name of stage	prophase	metaphase	anaphase	telophase

ANALYSIS

1. Calculate the percentage of cells that you observed that were undergoing mitosis. Use the formula shown below to calculate your answer. Show your work in the space provided.

$$\text{\% cells in mitosis} = \frac{\text{total number of cells in all phases of mitosis}}{\text{total number of cells}} \times 100$$

$$\% = \frac{39}{275} \times 100 = 14.18\%$$

Stage of Mitosis	Percentage of cells observed to be in this stage
Prophase	7.27%
Metaphase	2.18%
Anaphase	3.27%
Telophase	1.45%

2. Using the data found in data table 1, determine the percent of cells in each of the mitotic stages listed below:

$$\% = \frac{\text{number of cells in stage}}{\text{total number of cells observed}} \times 100$$

CONCLUSION QUESTIONS

1. What are the stages of the cell cycle? In which stage of the cell cycle were most of the cells that you observed?
   - G1, S, G2, M
   - G1 of interphase

2. Explain why the tip of the root was observed in this activity.
   - The root tip contains the meristem tissue which is rapidly growing, through mitosis.

3. Based on the number of cells observed in each stage of mitosis, which stage do you think takes the longest amount of time to complete? The least amount of time to complete?
   - Prophase
   - Telophase

4. What is the role of mitosis in the distribution of genetic information to new cells?
   - Mitosis allows for the even distribution of the chromosomes into the new cells.

REFERENCES

Biology Laboratory Manual. College Entrance Examination Board. New York: Revised, 2001. pp. 19-21

Greenberg, John, Revision Editor. *BSCS Biology, A Molecular Approach*. Chicago: Everyday Learning, 2001.

Cell Division
Observing Mitosis in a Root Tip

Individual cells within an organism go through various stages of growth and division. These stages are referred to as the cell cycle. The life cycle of a cell, or the cell cycle, can be separated into four main phases; G_1, S, G_2, and M as shown in figure 1. The G1, S, and G_2 stages, collectively, make up the *Interphase* portion of the cell's life cycle. The first gap stage, or G_1 stage, is one in which the cell experiences most of its growth and metabolic activity. The synthesis, or S stage, follows the G_1stage. In the S stage, the cell's DNA is replicated in preparation for cell division. After replication is complete, the cell will contain two connected copies of each chromosome. The third stage, G_2, is usually the shortest of the three stages of interphase. During this second gap stage many of the organelles and molecules required for cell division are produced. When the cell enters the final stage of the cell cycle, the M stage, the cell will go through mitosis. Mitosis is the process of dividing the nucleus into two equal portions. Cytokinesis, the process of dividing the cytoplasm of the cell, will occur after mitosis is complete. Some cells, like muscle cells, may not go through cytokinesis following each mitotic episode.

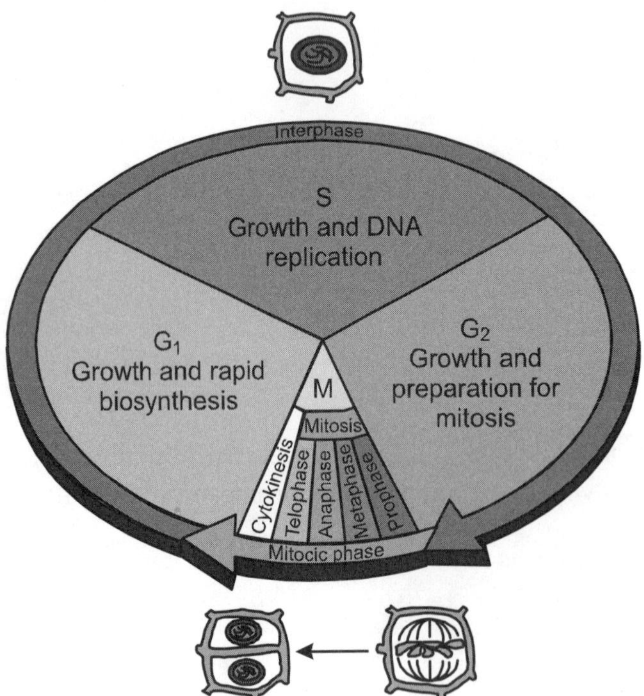

Figure 1

Plants and animals go through the process of mitosis for growth and replacement of cells. Plants contain rapidly growing areas called meristems in the tips of the roots and shoots. The cells in these rapidly growing areas are actively engaged in the process of mitosis. The events of mitosis can be divided into four phases: prophase, metaphase, anaphase and telophase. The following events occur in each stage.

Prophase – The long, stringy, unwound chromatin fibers coil and condense into thick threads of visible genetic material called chromosomes. As the cell enters prophase, the chromosomes have already been replicated forming sister chromatids. The sister chromatids are connected to each other at the centromere. The spindle apparatus begins to form. The nuclear membrane breaks down and the nucleolus disappears.

Metaphase – The centromeres of the sister chromatids line up along the center, or metaphase plate, of the cell bringing the genetic material to the center of the cell. Microtubules connect the centromere of each chromosome to the spindle.

Anaphase – The centromere of each chromosome divides, separating the sister chromatids from each other. The chromatids of each pair will be moved by the spindle fibers toward opposite poles of the cell. The separated chromatids are called chromosomes. This separation allows one copy of each type of chromosome to be placed on opposite sides of the dividing cell. The chromosomes continue to move to the poles of the spindle forming two separate groups.

Telophase – The final stage of mitosis occurs as new nuclear membranes are formed around both groups of chromosomes. The result is two separate nuclei, each containing the same genetic information at the original cell's nucleus. The chromosomes will uncoil and relax to form chromatin threads. The spindle begins to break apart and the nucleoli are reformed.

The events of mitosis have resulted in the production of two identical nuclei. The cell may now undergo cytokinesis in which the cytoplasm of the cell is divided. In animal cells, the onset of cytokinesis is marked by the presence of a cleavage furrow. The cell membrane is drawn inward until the cytoplasm is split into two separate parts forming two distinct cells. In plant cells cytokinesis results from the formation of a cell plate between the two newly formed nuclei. As the cell wall grows, it separates the nuclei into two distinct cells.

PURPOSE

In this activity you will prepare squashes of onion root tips which have been going through the process of mitosis. Using slides of the onion root tip, you will observe the mitotic stages in actively dividing cells.

MATERIALS

- vial of treated onion root tips
- forceps
- microscope slide (3)
- prepared slide of onion root tip
- microscope
- paper towel
- cover slip (3)

Safety Alert

1. Use proper procedure for carrying and focusing the microscope.

PROCEDURE

1. Using forceps carefully remove an onion root tip from the vial and place the tip on a clean microscope slide.

2. Place the slide on a smooth, flat surface. Add a drop of water and a cover slip to the slide to make a wet mount. Place the wet mount slide between two pieces of paper towel.

3. Use the eraser end of a pencil to press down on the cover slip. Apply only enough pressure to squash the root tip into a single cell layer. Be careful not to move the cover slip while you are pressing down with the eraser. If you press too hard, you might break the glass slide and tear apart the cells in the onion root tip.

4. Repeat steps 1, 2, and 3 to make two additional root tip squashes.

5. View each slide that you have prepared using a compound light microscope. Begin with the low power lens and then switch to the high power objective. This wet mount slide will be relatively thick so you will need to take caution when switching to the high power lens. Once on high power, use the fine-adjustment knob to bring the image into focus. You will find more mitotic cells in the lower, tip-end of the root.

6. From your three slides, select the one that contains the greatest number of cells undergoing mitosis. While viewing the slide under high power, count or estimate the number of cells that you see in the viewing area. Record this number in the Data Table 1. (If none of your slides contain mitotic cells, notify your teacher who may provide you with a prepared slide to observe.)

7. Without moving the slide, count the number of cells that are undergoing mitosis. Record the number that you see that are in prophase, metaphase, anaphase and telophase. Record these numbers in Data Table 1.

8. Move the slide to a completely new viewing area near the one you just observed. Count the total number of cells present and then count those that are in prophase, metaphase, anaphase and telophase. Record these numbers in Data Table 1.

9. In the space provided on the student answer sheet, prepare a sketch of each stage of mitosis that you observed on your slides. Label each sketch with the appropriate stage name.

10. Dispose of your slides and materials according to your teacher's instructions. Clean up your work area before leaving the lab.

Name ______________________________

Period ______________________________

Cell Division
Observing Mitosis in a Root Tip

DATA AND OBSERVATIONS

Data Table 1

Mitotic Stage	Viewing Area		Total number of cells per stage
	Area 1	Area 2	
Prophase			
Metaphase			
Anaphase			
Telophase			
Non-dividing Interphase			
Total cells counted in viewing area			

Data Table 2

Sketch of mitotic stage				
Name of stage				

ANALYSIS

1. What percentage of the cells that you observed were undergoing mitosis? Use the formula shown below to calculate your answer. Show your work in the space provided.

$$\%\text{ cells in mitosis} = \frac{\text{total number of cells in all phases of mitosis}}{\text{total number of cells}} \times 100$$

2. Using the data found in Data Table 1, determine the percent of cells in each of the stages listed below:

$$\% = \frac{\text{number of cells in stage}}{\text{total number of cells observed}} \times 100$$

Stages of Mitosis	Percentage of cells observed to be in this stage
Prophase	
Metaphase	
Anaphase	
Telophase	

CONCLUSION QUESTIONS

1. What are the stages of the cell cycle? In which stage of the cell cycle were most of the cells that you observed?

2. Explain why the tip of the root was observed in this activity.

3. Based on the number of cells observed in each stage of mitosis, which stage do you think takes the longest amount of time to complete? The least amount of time to complete? Explain your reasoning.

4. What is the role of mitosis in the distribution of genetic information to new cells?

Write Your Notes and Ideas Here!

Yeast and Molasses
Examining the Effect of Food Concentration on Fermentation

OBJECTIVE
Students will determine the concentration of molasses that will yield the greatest amount of energy by yeast cells. Students will make a hypothesis and then evaluate the validity of that hypothesis based on collected data.

LEVEL
Biology I

NATIONAL STANDARDS
UCP.1, UCP.2, UCP.3, A.1, A.2, B.2, B.3, C.1, C.5, F.2, G.1, G.2

TEKS
2 (A), 2 (B), 2 (C), 2 (D), 9 (A)

CONNECTIONS TO AP
AP Biology:

I. Molecules and Cells, C. Cellular Energetics 2. Fermentation and cellular respiration.

TIME FRAME
30 min day 1

45 min day 2

MATERIALS
(For 28 students working in groups of 4)

56 ea test tubes 25 x 200 mm (70 mL)
7 ea test tube racks
28 ea # 4 test tube stoppers
500 mL of 10 % molasses solution
500 mL of 40 % molasses solution
500 mL of 80 % molasses solution
500 mL distilled water
56 ea graduated centrifuge tubes 17 mm x 120 mm (15 mL) 0.1 mL graduations
100 mL yeast solution
500 mL of 5 % molasses solution
500 mL of 20 % molasses solution
500 mL of 60 % molasses solution
500 mL of 100 % molasses solution
graduated cylinder 100 mL

TEACHER NOTES

This lab activity supplements a unit on cellular respiration.

Make the following solutions by mixing:

Percentage	Amount of molasses	Amount of water
0 %	0 mL	500 mL
5 %	25 mL	475 mL
10 %	50 mL	450 mL
20 %	100 mL	400 mL
40 %	200 mL	300 mL
60 %	300 mL	200 mL
80 %	400 mL	100 mL
100 %	500 mL	0 mL

If time permits, you may want the students to make their own molasses solution by mixing the following:

Percentage	Amount of molasses	Amount of water
0 %	0 mL	40 mL
5 %	2 mL	38 mL
10 %	4 mL	36 mL
20 %	8 mL	32 mL
40 %	16 mL	24 mL
60 %	24 mL	16 mL
80 %	32 mL	8 mL
100 %	40 mL	0 mL

It may take some time to get the molasses and the water thoroughly mixed.

Make the yeast solution by adding 1 package of brewer's yeast (7g) to 1 L of warm water about 15 min before class. When the yeast is needed, dilute 30 mL of the stock solution with 70 mL of warm water.

Part I of this lab is to investigate the relationship between energy production using fermentation and increasing concentration of food. This food is molasses. Students should predict that with increasing concentrations of molasses there should be a corresponding increase in the production of energy. This is indicated by the amount of carbon dioxide produced. Students will have to modify their hypothesis because when the concentration of molasses is above 80%, there is a decrease in the amount of energy produced because there is not enough water for the cells to live.

Prepare a transparency of the data table to facilitate the sharing of data.

Part II is a pen and paper exercise to examine the specific events of glycolysis and fermentation. While the instructions tell the students to cut and paste the missing words and phrases, an alternative to this is just to write the missing information in the boxes.

POSSIBLE ANSWERS TO THE CONCLUSION QUESTIONS AND SAMPLE DATA

Amount of CO_2 Collected (mL)								
Test Tube #	1	2	3	4	5	6	7	8
Percent of Molasses	0 %	5 %	10 %	20 %	40 %	60 %	80 %	100 %
Individual Team Data	0	5	11	14	15	15	7.5	0
Team # 1	0	5.5	10.5	15	15	15	7	0
Team # 2	0	5	10	13.5	15	15	7	1
Team # 3	0	6	10	12.5	15	15	8	0
Team # 4	0	4	10.5	15	15	15	7.5	0
Team # 5	0	5.5	12	15	15	15	7	0
Team # 6	0	4	10.5	15	14.5	15	8	0
Team # 7	0	5.5	11	14	15	13	7.5	0
Class Average	0.0	5.1	10.6	14.4	14.9	14.7	7.4	0.1

1. What happened to the amount of gas produced as the concentration of molasses increased?
   - In the beginning, an increase in the concentration of molasses resulted in an increase in the production of carbon dioxide, however, after a certain point, an increase in the concentration of molasses resulted in a decrease of carbon dioxide production. This is because there is insufficient water to support life for the yeast cells.

2. What percentage of molasses produced the greatest amount of energy? Does this support your hypothesis?
   - The individual data indicated that the greatest amount of energy produced occurred when the molasses was concentrated between twenty and sixty percent. The data supported the hypothesis up to sixty percent and then after that, an increase in the concentration of molasses resulted in a decrease in the amount of energy produced.

3. Design an experiment based on this protocol that would investigate the effect of temperature on fermentation.
   - This is an open-ended question that will result in variable answers but the following is a possible answer: The data indicated that a molasses concentration of 20-60% resulted in the greatest amount of energy production. This lab could use the same protocol with 40% molasses for three sets of test tubes. One set could be put into the refrigerator, the second in an incubator and the third at room temperature for 24 hours. Check and insure the students to include control in their experimental design.

PART II

Diagram Key — Biochemical Pathway for Glycolysis and Fermentation.

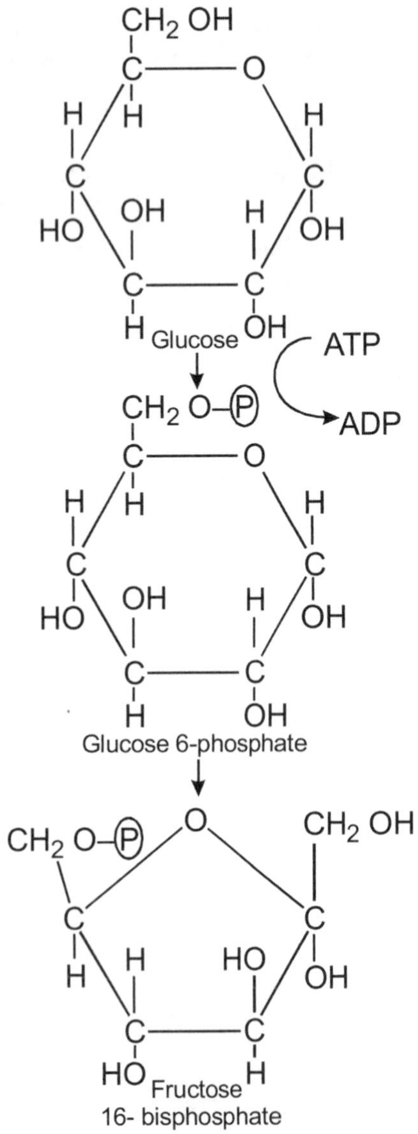

Glucose

ATP

ADP

1. A phosphate is added to glucose. It comes from ATP. This phosphate increases the amount of energy of glucose.

Glucose 6-phosphate

2. Atoms are rearranged and glucose 6-phosphate is turned into fructose 6-phosphate.

Fructose 16- bisphosphate

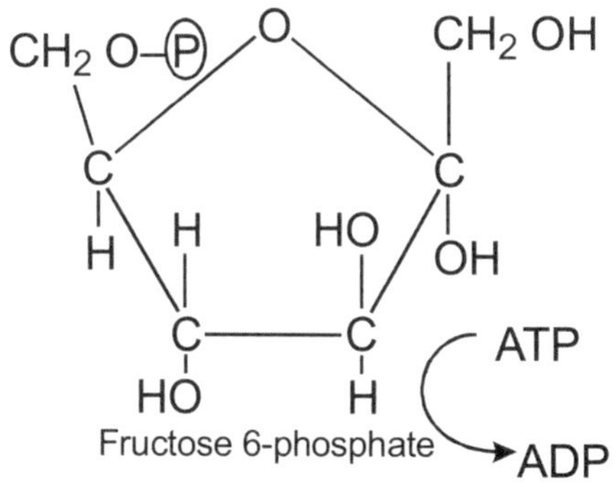

Fructose 6-phosphate

ATP → ADP

3. Another phosphate is added to fructose 6-phosphate. It comes from ATP. This phosphate increases the amount of energy of fructose.

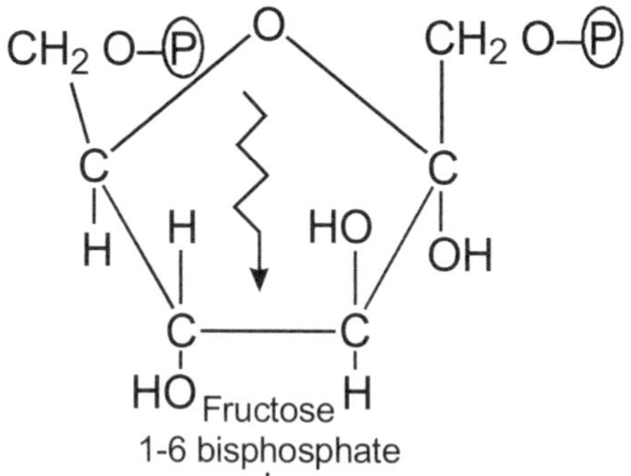

Fructose 1-6 bisphosphate

4. Fructose 1-6 bisphosphate has so much energy and is so unstable that this hexose is cleaved into two trioses, phosphoglyceralaldehyde or PGAL and dihydroxacteone phosphate.

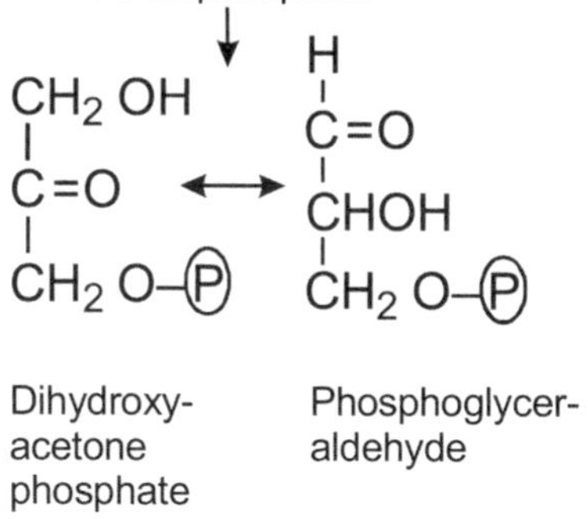

Dihydroxy-acetone phosphate ⟷ Phosphoglycer-aldehyde

5. Atoms are rearranged and dihydroxy-acetone phosphate is turned into phosphoglyceraldehyde, PGAL. From This point in time, everything is multiplied by a factor of two because there are two trioses.

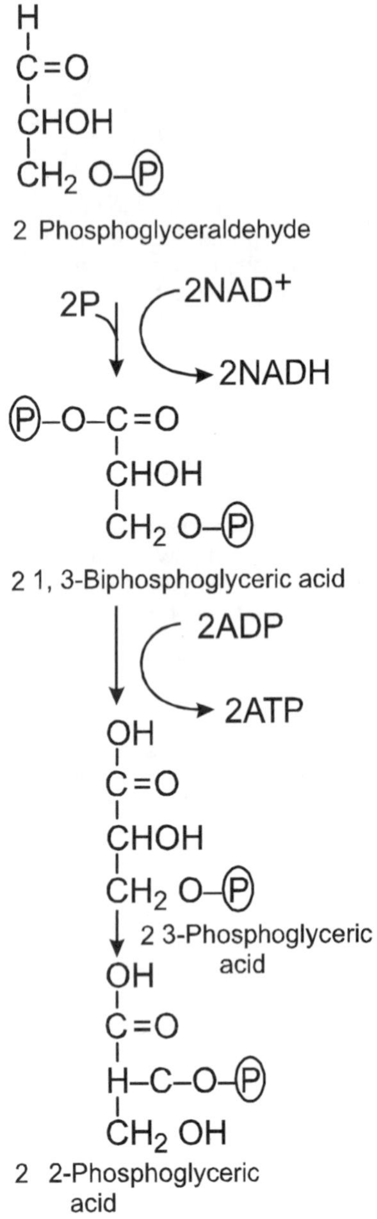

H
|
C=O
|
CHOH
|
CH_2 O–(P)

2 Phosphoglyceraldehyde

2P ↓ 2NAD+ → 2NADH

(P)–O–C=O
|
CHOH
|
CH_2 O–(P)

2 1, 3-Biphosphoglyceric acid

↓ 2ADP → 2ATP

OH
|
C=O
|
CHOH
|
CH_2 O–(P)

2 3-Phosphoglyceric acid

↓

OH
|
C=O
|
H–C–O–(P)
|
CH_2 OH

2 2-Phosphoglyceric acid

6. Hydrogens are stripped from phosphoglyceral aldedhyde transferred to NAD^+. In addition, an inorganic phosphate group is added to the molecule. This phosphate group comes from the cytoplasm. This produces 1, 3-biphosphoglyceric acid.

7. 1-3 Biphosphoglyceric acid transfers one of its phosphates to ADP to make ATP. This produces 3-phoshoglyceric acid.

8. The phosphate group found on carbon number three is transferred to carbon number two. This produces 2-phosphoglyceric acid.

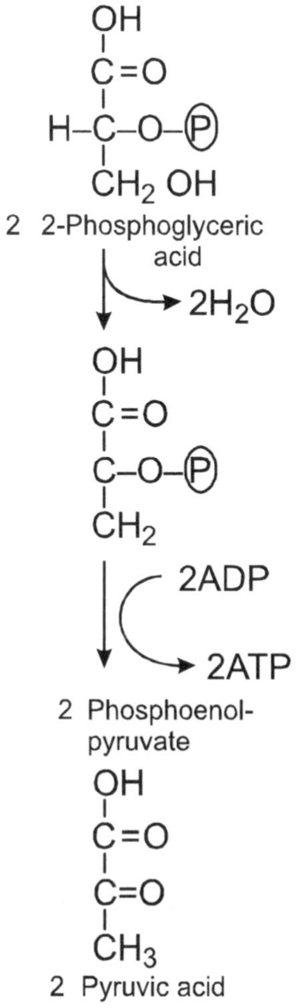

$$\begin{array}{c} OH \\ | \\ C{=}O \\ | \\ H{-}C{-}O{-}\text{Ⓟ} \\ | \\ CH_2\ OH \end{array}$$

2 2-Phosphoglyceric acid

↓ → $2H_2O$

9. A dehydration reaction occurs as a water molecule is removed to form phosphoenolpyruvic acid or PEP.

$$\begin{array}{c} OH \\ | \\ C{=}O \\ | \\ C{-}O{-}\text{Ⓟ} \\ | \\ CH_2 \end{array}$$

2 Phosphoenol-pyruvate

↓ 2ADP → 2ATP

10. Phosphoenolpyruvic acid transfers its phosphate to ADP to form ATP. This produces pyruvic acid. If oxygen is present, then the pyruvic acid is used in the Krebís cycle. If NO oxygen is present, then fermentation occurs.

$$\begin{array}{c} OH \\ | \\ C{=}O \\ | \\ C{=}O \\ | \\ CH_3 \end{array}$$

2 Pyruvic acid

TEACHER PAGES

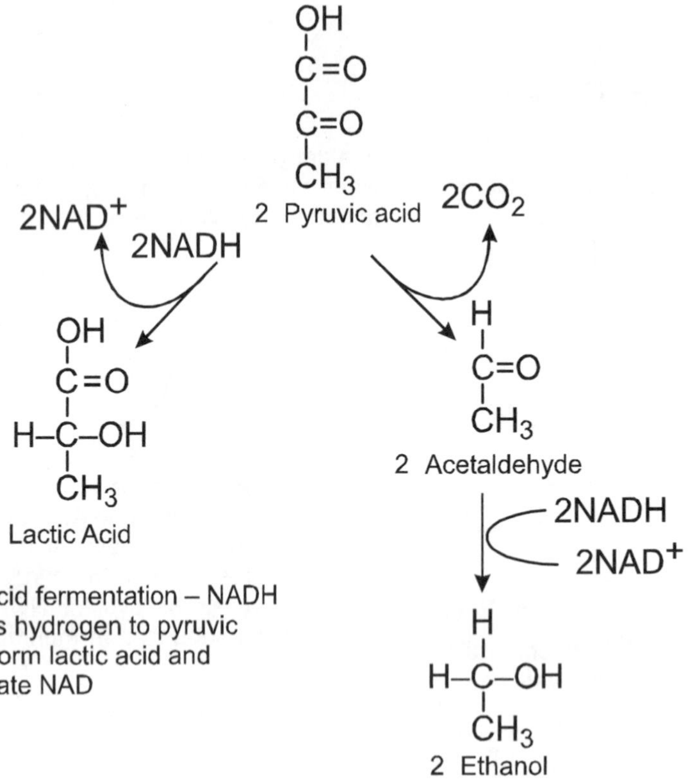

OH
|
C=O
|
C=O
|
CH_3
2 Pyruvic acid

$2NAD^+$ ← 2NADH

$2CO_2$

OH
|
C=O
|
H–C–OH
|
CH_3
Lactic Acid

Lactic acid fermentation – NADH transfers hydrogen to pyruvic acid to form lactic acid and regenerate NAD

H
|
C=O
|
CH_3
2 Acetaldehyde

2NADH → $2NAD^+$

H
|
H–C–OH
|
CH_3
2 Ethanol

Alcohol fermentation – Carbon dioxide is removed and NADH transfers hydrogen to the acetylaldhyde to form ethanol

REFERENCES

Biological Science, Interaction of Experiments and Ideas. Englewood Cliffs: Prentice-Hall, Inc., 1983. pp. 16-22

Yeast and Molasses
Examining the Effect of Food Concentration on Fermentation

All cells need energy, and the most common form of energy used by cells is ATP. The full name given to ATP by chemists is adenosine triphosphate. ATP is a molecule that contains the monosaccharide, ribose which is a pentose sugar. Bonded to ribose is the nitrogenous base, adenine. This is the same nitrogenous base found in DNA and RNA. Also attached to ribose are three phosphate groups. Two of the bonds connecting the phosphates are considered high-energy meaning that the phosphate groups are easily removed. This is due to the negative charges found on the phosphate groups. One or more of these phosphate groups can transfer to another molecule. Remove one phosphate from ATP, and the molecule becomes adenosine diphosphate or ADP. Remove two phosphates from ATP and the molecule becomes adenosine monophosphate or AMP.

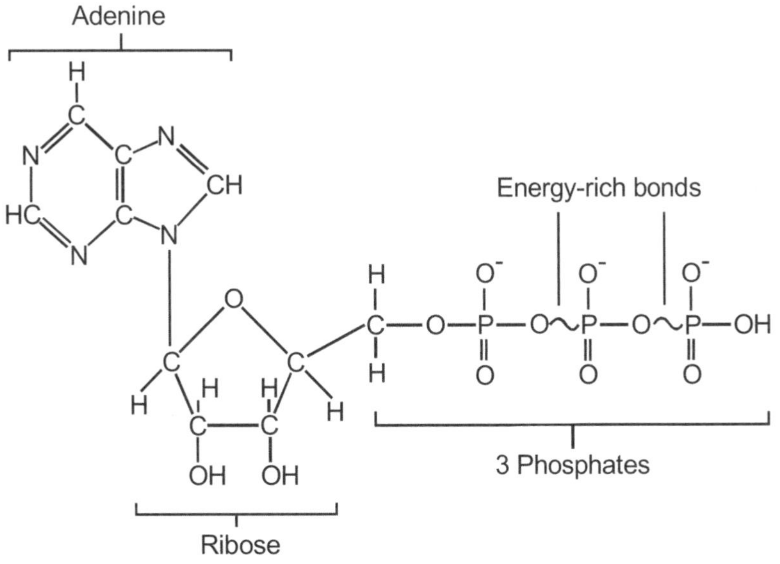

Adenine

Energy-rich bonds

3 Phosphates

Ribose

Many biochemical reactions require the addition of phosphates to one or more reactants in order to proceed. The addition of these phosphates increases the energy content of the molecule. An example of this is glucose-phosphate. Glucose-phosphate has more energy than just plain glucose because of the addition of a phosphate group. Cells need a plentiful supply of ATP. Once the ATP is used and converted into ADP, the cells need to regenerate ATP by adding a phosphate to ADP. Since energy was released during the breaking of the phosphate bond, the reverse process of forming a phosphate bond requires an energy input.

$$\text{ADP} + \text{P} \xrightarrow{\text{Energy needed}} \text{ATP}$$

You might be wondering where the cell will obtain this energy. This energy comes from the cell breaking down or oxidizing high-energy food molecules like glucose, sucrose, or other such organic compounds. Glucose has considerably more energy than ATP. One molecule of ATP has approximately 16 kcal/mole whereas glucose has approximately 680 kcal/mole. You may ask, why not use glucose instead of ATP as the cell energy currency? The reason that glucose cannot be used directly as an energy source is that glucose has too much energy. Releasing it all at once is like putting a match into a gas can. The cell cannot handle the release of all that energy at once as the increase in temperature would denature the enzymes and kill the cell. So instead, cell respiration releases the energy in small amounts at a time and this involves many steps. Another analogy that illustrates using glucose as a direct energy source in the cell involves using a thousand dollar bill to buying gasoline. You have money but it is unusable money, and the bill has to be taken to the bank and exchanged for useable money such as ten-dollar bills. ATP then represents ten-dollar bills. The cell can use ATP directly, easily. The chemical equation below summarizes the process of cellular respiration.

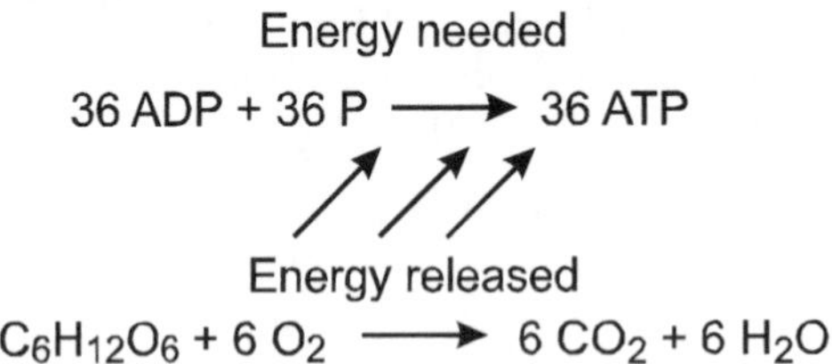

There are three major parts to cell respiration. The three parts to cellular respiration are glycolysis, the Kreb's cycle, and chemiosmosis. Glycolysis occurs in the cytoplasm of the cell. The major events in the process of glycolysis are the following:

1. Glucose $\longrightarrow$ 2 pyruvic acid
2. 2 NAD + $2H^+$ $\longrightarrow$ 2 NADH
3. 2 ATP $\longrightarrow$ 2 ADP + 2 P
4. 4 ADP + 4 P $\longrightarrow$ 4 ATP

Net 2 ATP made

During the process of glycolysis no oxygen is required.

The other 34 molecules of ATP are made in the Krebs cycle and chemiosmosis. These processes occur in the inner compartment of the mitochondria. It is at the very end of these processes that oxygen is needed. Respiration is often referred to as aerobic respiration because oxygen is required. If there is no oxygen present, then the Krebs cycle and chemiosmosis will not occur.

If oxygen is not present, then glycolysis can continue to make pyruvic acid and two molecules of ATP. After all, the synthesis of two ATP molecules is better than making none. The limiting factor in this process is having enough NAD to make the NADH. In order to regenerate NAD, several additional steps are needed. These additional steps complete the process known as fermentation. There are several types of fermentation. The most common types of fermentation are lactic acid fermentation and alcohol fermentation. Lactic acid fermentation is performed by muscle cells when muscles are vigorously contracting and are unable to obtain enough oxygen. Yeast cells, plant cells and certain bacteria perform alcoholic fermentation in the absence of oxygen. The alcohol produced is ethanol and during this reaction a molecule of carbon dioxide is released.

This lab exercise uses yeast cells to investigate the relationship between fermentation and food concentrations. If yeast cells have more food available, will they produce more energy and ultimately more ATP? Yeast cells undergo alcoholic fermentation and as a result produce carbon dioxide as a by-product. This lab uses the amount of carbon dioxide released as an indicator for the amount of fermentation occurring. Below are the final steps added to glycolysis to complete the process of fermentation.

2 Pyruvic acid

$2NAD^+$ ← 2NADH

$2CO_2$

Lactic Acid

2 Acetaldehyde

2NADH → $2NAD^+$

2 Ethanol

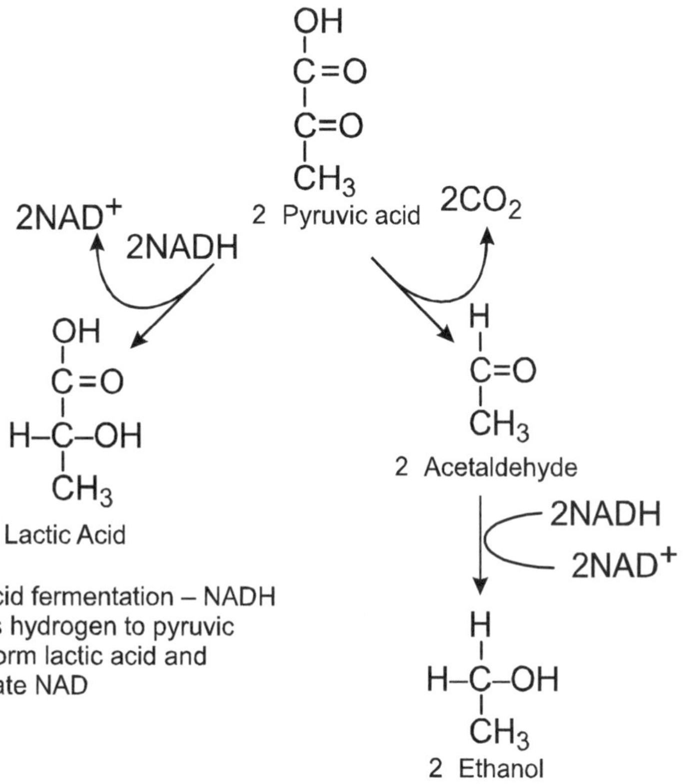

Lactic acid fermentation – NADH transfers hydrogen to pyruvic acid to form lactic acid and regenerate NAD

Alcohol fermentation – Carbon dioxide is removed and NADH transfers hydrogen to the acetylaldhyde to form ethanol

PURPOSE

In this activity you will investigate the process of fermentation and its relationship to the availability of food for respiration.

MATERIALS

Part I

100 mL graduated cylinder
8 ea graduated centrifuge tubes 17 x 120 mm (0.1 mL graduations)
stock yeast solution
5 % molasses solution
20 % molasses solution
60 % molasses solution
100 % molasses solution
8 ea test tubes 25 x 200 mm (70 mL)
test tube rack
4 ea # 4 test tube stoppers
10 % molasses solution
40 % molasses solution
80 % molasses solution
distilled water

Part II

scissors
glue stick

PROCEDURE

PART I

1. Formulate a hypothesis that explains the relationship between the amount of energy produced through fermentation and increasing amount of food available. State your hypothesis on your student answer page.

2. Obtain the above materials and label the large test tubes 1-8.

3. Add 40 mL of the indicated molasses solution to each of the following test tubes:
   # 1 — 0 % molasses/ only distilled water
   # 2 — 5 % molasses
   # 3 — 10 % molasses
   # 4 — 20 % molasses
   # 5 — 40 % molasses
   # 6 — 60 % molasses
   # 7 — 80 % molasses
   # 8 — 100 % molasses

4. Add 10 mL of stock yeast solution to each test tube.

5. Stopper each tube and shake thoroughly to ensure a uniform mixture.

6. Remove the stopper and rinse the stopper with water.

7. Obtain a small centrifuge tube and notice that it has markings on the sides of the tube in mL. The small tube needs to be filled with the yeast-molasses solution. Do this by inverting the small centrifuge tube and sliding it into the large test tube. Then, put the large stopper into the large tube and hold it on its side. When the small tube is completely filled with the suspension, slowly move the large tube back to its upright position. If there is any air bubble in the small tube, repeat the procedure until no air is present.

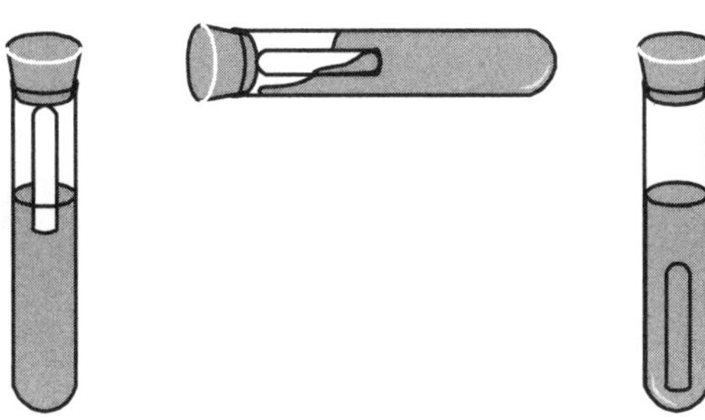

8. Allow the tubes to sit for 24 hours. After 24 hours, measure the gas in the centrifuge tube for each tube by observing the amount of gas in the tube using the gradations on the side of the centrifuge tube. Record this in the data table. Collect data for each group in the classroom and average the data.

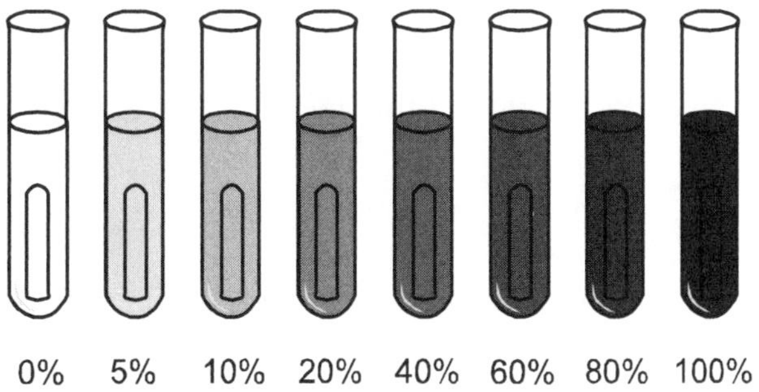

9. Graph your data and the class-averaged data.

Optional — These calculations can be done on a TI-83 calculator by doing the following:

1. To make a data table press STAT, the select EDIT (Figure 1) and press ENTER. Notice that there are columns or lists to record data.

Figure 1

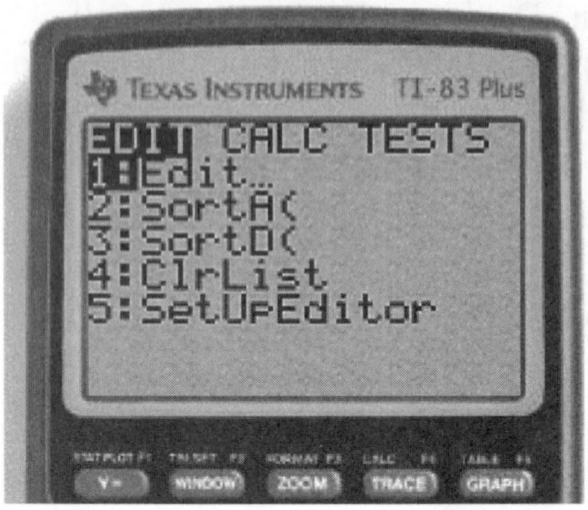

Figure 2

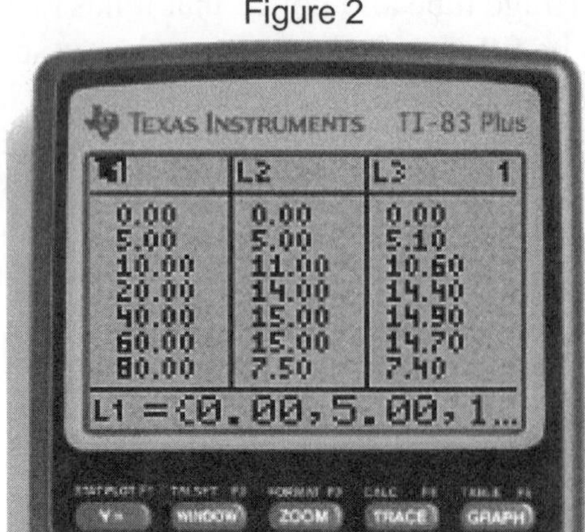

2. To clear a list that might have data in it, put the cursor at the very top of the list so that the name of the column is highlighted. Press CLEAR followed by the ▼.

3. Now enter the percent of molasses in L1 starting at 0 for the first entry and ending at 100 percent for the last entry. In L2, record the amount of carbon dioxide collected. In L3, record the class average for the amount of carbon dioxide collected. (Figure 2). To view this graphically, press 2nd, Y=, ENTER. At this time make sure to put your cursor on PLOT 1 and press ENTER. Then move the cursor down to ON and press ENTER. Both PLOT 1 and ON should be highlighted. All other plots should be inactivated. Highlight the line graph (Figure 3) and press ENTER.

4. Highlight the Xlist and press 2nd, 1 [L1].

5. Highlight the Ylist and press 2nd, 2 [L2].

6. Highlight the box symbol for the Mark and press ENTER (Figure 3).

Figure 3

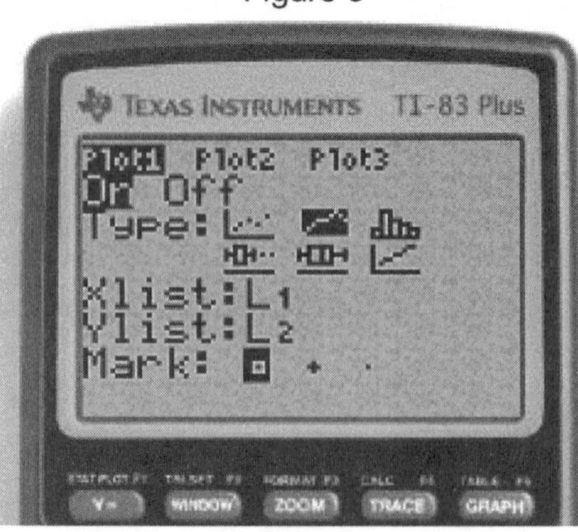

Figure 4

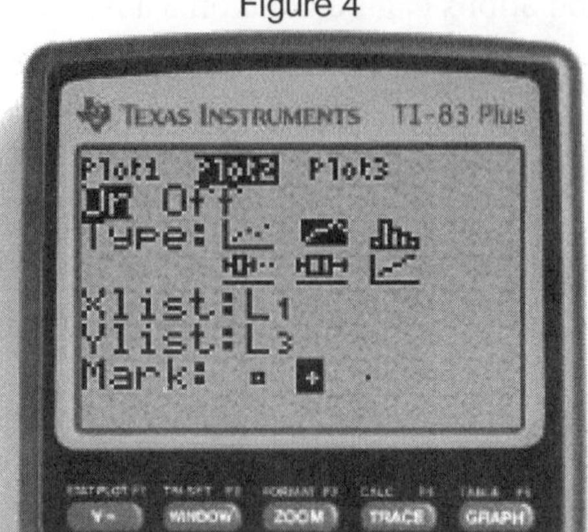

7. To put a second line on the graph, position the cursor on Plot 2 and press ENTER. Move the cursor down to ON and press ENTER. Both PLOT 2 and ON should be highlighted. Highlight the line graphs (Figure 4) and press ENTER.

8. Highlight the Xlist and press 2nd, 1 [L1].

9. Highlight the Ylist and press 2nd, 3 [L3].

10. Highlight the cross hairs symbol for the Mark and press ENTER (Figure 4).

11. Press, ZOOM then press 9. A graph should appear that will have automatically adjusted the axes so that they fit the window. (Figures 5 and 6).

Figure 5

Figure 6

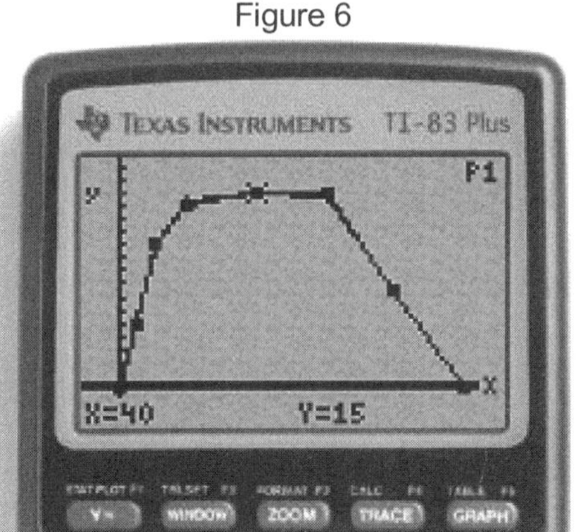

It may appear that there is only one line on the graph if your data is close to the class average. To demonstrate that both lines are present press TRACE and then use the ▲ and ▼ to differentiate between the points. Look at the figures above. In figure 5, the data point, Y=14.9, is class averaged data and in figure 6, the data point Y=15, is the student's data.

PART II

Below are the steps of glycolysis and fermentation. As you read about the steps of fermentation, look at the accompanying diagram on the student answer sheet. You will notice that there are names of products and descriptions of the reaction missing. The empty boxes indicate missing items. At the end of the diagram is a list of missing parts. Using scissors and a glue stick, fill in the missing items to make the biochemical pathway complete. Be sure to place either the missing step or molecule in the correct sequence.

1. A phosphate is added to glucose. It comes from ATP. This phosphate increases the amount of energy of glucose.

2. Atoms are rearranged and glucose 6-phosphate is turned into fructose 6-phosphate.

3. Another phosphate is added to fructose 6-phosphate. It comes from ATP. This phosphate increases the amount of energy of fructose.

4. Fructose 1-6 bisphosphate has so much energy and is so unstable that this hexose will be cleaved into two trioses, phosphoglyceraldehyde or PGAL and dihydroxacteone phosphate.

5. Atoms are rearranged and dihydroxyacetone is turned into a second phosphoglyceraldehyde PGAL molecule. From this point in time, everything is multiplied by a factor of two because there are two trioses.

6. Hydrogens are stripped from phosphoglyceraldedhyde and transferred to NAD^+. In addition, an inorganic phosphate group is added to the molecule. This phosphate group comes from the cytoplasm. This produces 1, 3-biphosphoglyceric acid.

7. 1-3 Biphosphoglyceric acid transfers one of its phosphates to ADP to make ATP. This produces 3-phoshoglyceric acid.

8. The phosphate group found on carbon number three is transferred to carbon number two. This produces 2-phosphoglyceric acid.

9. A dehydration reaction occurs as a water molecule is removed to form phosphoenolpyruvic acid or PEP.

10. Phosphoenolpyruvic acid transfers it phosphate to ADP to form ATP. This produces pyruvic acid. If oxygen is present then the pyruvic acid is used in the Kreb's cycle. If NO oxygen is present, then fermentation occurs.

11. *Lactic acid fermentation*- Hydrogens are transferred to pyruvic acid from NADH to form lactic acid and NAD^+. *Alcoholic fermentation*- Hydrogens are transferred to pyruvic acid from NADH to form lactic acid and NAD^+ and a molecule of carbon dioxide is removed.

Name ________________________________

Period ________________________________

Yeast and Molasses
Examining the Effect of Food Concentration on Fermentation

HYPOTHESIS

DATA AND OBSERVATIONS

Amount of CO_2 Collected (mL)								
Test Tube #	1	2	3	4	5	6	7	8
Percent of Molasses	0 %	5 %	10 %	20 %	40 %	60 %	80 %	100 %
Individual Team Data								
Team # 1								
Team # 2								
Team # 3								
Team # 4								
Team # 5								
Team # 6								
Team # 7								
Class Average								

DIAGRAM OF FERMENTATION

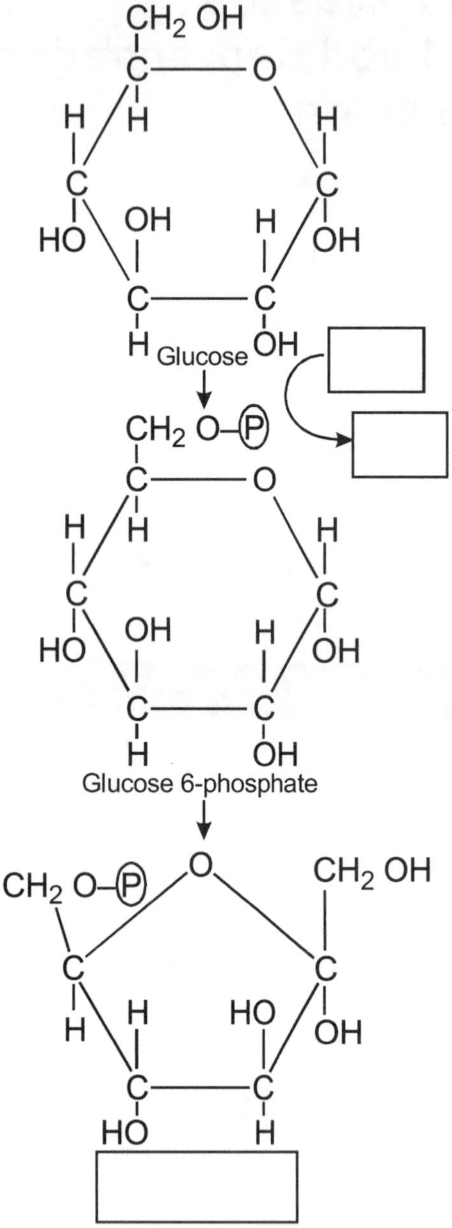

Glucose

1. A phosphate is added to glucose. It comes from ATP. This phosphate increases the amount of energy of glucose.

Glucose 6-phosphate

2. Atoms are rearranged and glucose 6-phosphate is turned into fructose 6-phosphate.

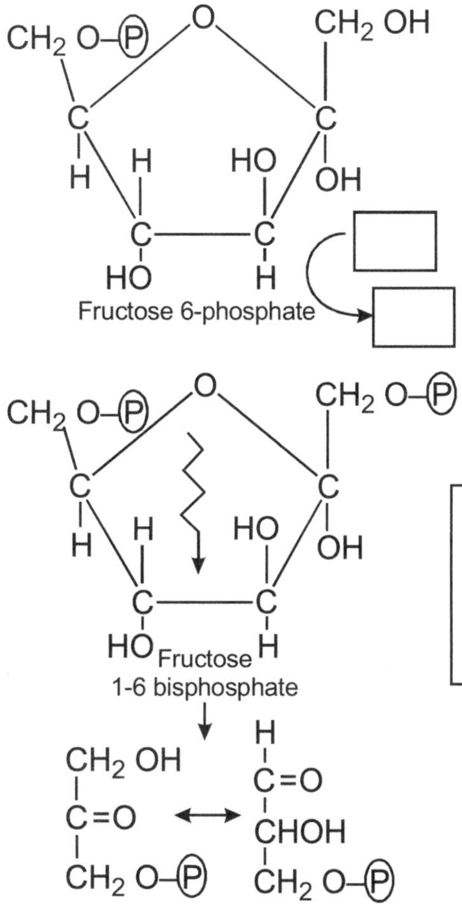

CH_2O–(P) O CH_2OH C C H H HO OH C C HO H

Fructose 6-phosphate

3. Another phosphate is added to fructose 6-phosphate. It comes from ATP. This phosphate increases the amount of energy of fructose.

CH_2O–(P) O CH_2O–(P) C C H H HO OH C C HO H

Fructose 1-6 bisphosphate

CH_2OH		H
C=O	⟷	C=O
CH_2O–(P)		CHOH
		CH_2O–(P)
Dihydroxy-acetone phosphate		Phosphoglycer-aldehyde

5. Atoms are rearranged and dihydroxy-acetone phosphate is turned into phosphoglyceraldehyde, PGAL. From This point in time, everything is multiplied by a factor of two because there are two trioses.

H
C=O
CHOH
CH_2 O–Ⓟ

2 Phosphoglyceraldehyde

6. Hydrogens are stripped from phosphoglyceral aldedhyde transferred to NAD^+. In addition, an inorganic phosphate group is added to the molecule. This phosphate group comes from the cytoplasm. This produces 1, 3-biphosphoglyceric acid.

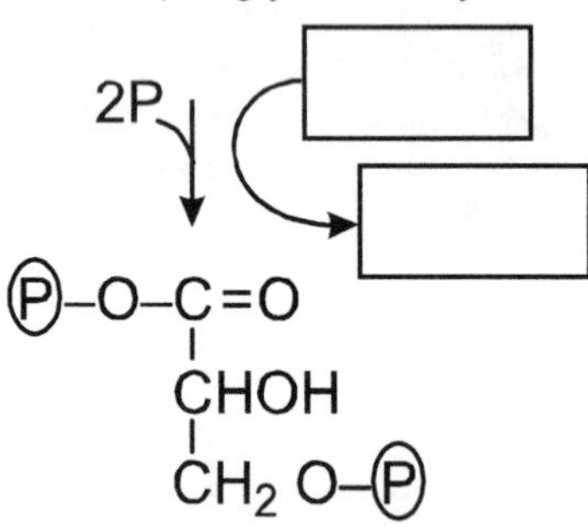

2 1, 3-Biphosphoglyceric acid

7. 1-3 Biphosphoglyceric acid transfers one of its phosphates to ADP to make ATP. This produces 3-phoshoglyceric acid.

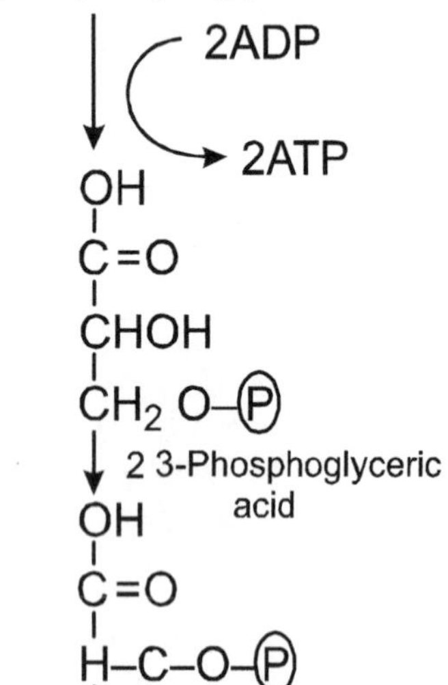

CH_2 OH

2 2-Phosphoglyceric acid

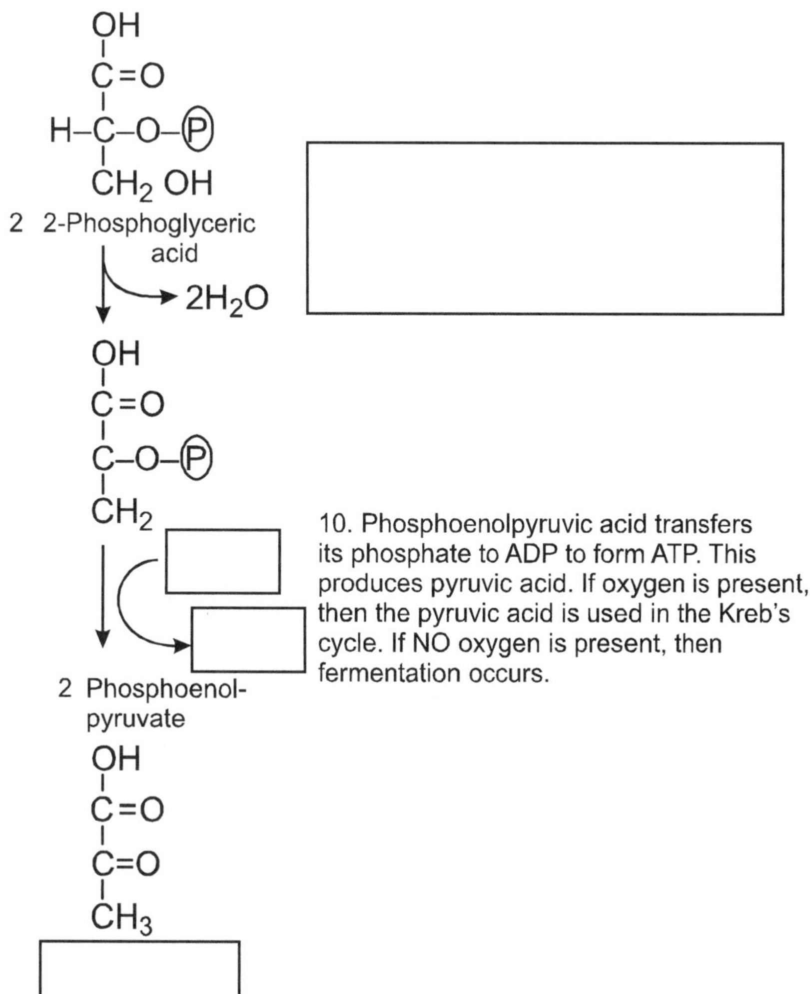
OH
C=O
H–C–O–(P)
CH2 OH
2 2-Phosphoglyceric acid
2H2O
OH
C=O
C–O–(P)
CH2
2 Phosphoenol-pyruvate
OH
C=O
C=O
CH3
10. Phosphoenolpyruvic acid transfers its phosphate to ADP to form ATP. This produces pyruvic acid. If oxygen is present, then the pyruvic acid is used in the Kreb's cycle. If NO oxygen is present, then fermentation occurs.

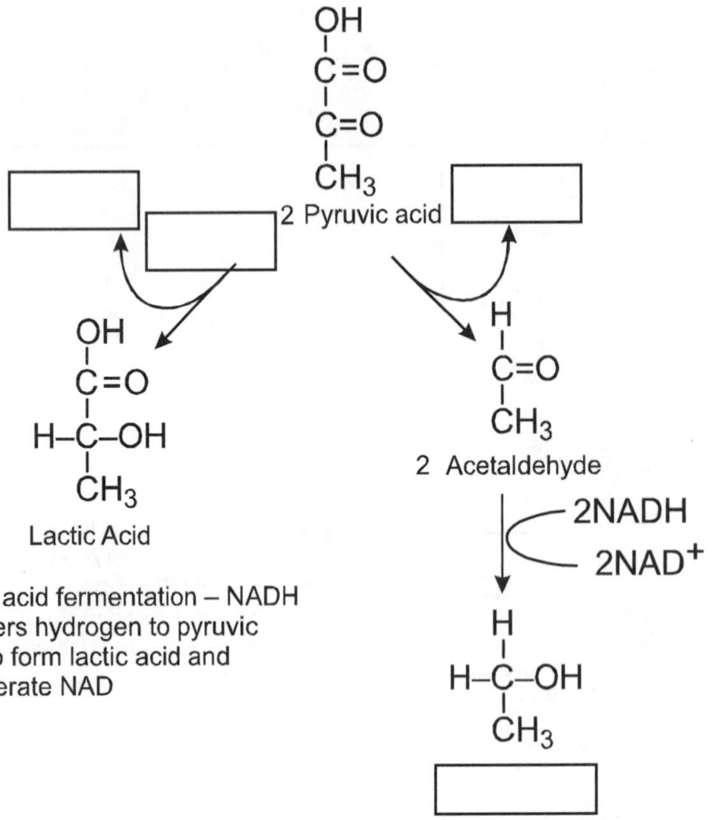

OH
|
C=O
|
C=O
|
CH_3
2 Pyruvic acid

OH
|
C=O
|
H–C–OH
|
CH_3
Lactic Acid

Lactic acid fermentation – NADH transfers hydrogen to pyruvic acid to form lactic acid and regenerate NAD

H
|
C=O
|
CH_3
2 Acetaldehyde

2NADH
$2NAD^+$

H
|
H–C–OH
|
CH_3

Alcohol fermentation – Carbon dioxide is removed and NADH transfers hydrogen to the acetylaldhyde to form ethanol

Here are the missing items to make glycolysis and fermentation complete:

2 Pyruvic acid

2 Ethanol

Fructose 1-6 bisphosphate has so much energy and is so unstable that this hexose is cleaved into two trioses, phosphoglyceral aldehyde or PGAL and dihydroxacteone phosphate.

Fructose 1-6 bisphosphate

ADP

ADP

ATP

2NADH

$2NAD^+$

ATP

ATP

ADP

$2NAD^+$

2NADH

A dehydration reaction occurs as a water molecule is removed to form phosphoenolpyruvic acid or PEP.

$2\ CO_2$

The phosphate group found on carbon number three is transferred to carbon number two. This produced 2-phosphoglyceric acid.

CONCLUSION QUESTIONS

1. What happened to the amount of gas produced as the amount of molasses increased?

2. What percentage of molasses produced the greatest amount of energy? Does this support your hypothesis?

3. Design an experiment based on this protocol that would investigate the effect of temperature on fermentation.

Write Your Notes and Ideas Here!

Picking out the Pigments
Isolating and Comparing Plant Pigments

OBJECTIVE
Students will isolate plant pigments on chromatography paper using a given solvent. In Part II of the activity, the students will design and use a protocol to determine which solvent combination produces the most bands on a chromatogram using *Coleus* or Swiss chard.

LEVEL
Biology I

NATIONAL STANDARDS
UCP.1, UCP.2, UCP.5, A.1, A.2, B.2, B.6, C.1, C.5, E.1, E.2, G.1, G.2, G.3

TEKS
5(A)

CONNECTIONS TO AP
AP Biology:
I. Molecules and Cells C. Cell Energetics, Photosynthesis

TIME FRAME
50 minutes

MATERIALS
(For a class of 28 working in pairs)

84 strips of chromatography paper
42 large test tubes (25x200 mm)
rubber stopper with hook or push pin
14 leaves from spinach
14 small glass beakers
14 rulers
100 mL isopropyl alcohol
100 mL each of various solutions to serve as solvents from which the students may choose ethanol, acetone, methanol, water
14 leaves from *Coleus* or swiss chard
14 graduated cylinders, 10 mL

Safety Alert
1. Aprons and goggles must be worn during this activity.
2. CAUTION: Acetone, alcohols, and organic solvents are flammable.
3. Avoid inhalation of fumes from solvents.

TEACHER NOTES

These chromatograms are run in test tubes to allow for the use of relatively small quantities of solvent. The chromatography paper hangs from a hook located on the bottom of the stopper. Prepare the stoppers with hooks as follows:

Using pliers, insert a T-pin through the center top of the stopper. The pin should extend completely through the stopper with enough of the tip protruding to bend into a hook for suspending the chromatography paper. See Fig. 1

Fig.1 *Fig. 2*

Alternately, a pushpin can be used to attach the chromatography paper to the bottom of the stopper. See Figure 2.

Precut the chromatogram strips to save time.

In the pre-lab instructions, stress the relationship between solubility and movement of the pigment up the chromatogram.

Prepare solvent choices as follows:

Solvent A = 9 parts petroleum ether/1 part acetone
Solvent B = Acetone
Solvent C = 70% isopropyl alcohol

POSSIBLE ANSWERS TO THE CONCLUSION QUESTIONS AND SAMPLE DATA

Solvent A Chromatogram with spinach				
Band #	Color	Distance Traveled	Pigment Type	R_f*
1 solvent front	n/a	8.8 cm	n/a	n/a
2	Yellow-orange	8.7 cm	carotene	.98
3	Light Yellow	7.5 cm	xanthophyll	.85
4	Green blue green	6.6 cm	Chlorophyll a	.75
5	Green-olive green	5.0 cm	Chlorophyll b	.57

Part II

Data Table 2: Solvent B Chromatogram w/*Coleus*

Band #	Color	Distance Traveled	Pigment Type	R_f*
1	solvent	8.4	n/a	n/a
2	Green	8.3	Chlorophyll a,b	.98
3	Red	1.0	Anthocyanin	.11

Data Table 3

Solution C Isopropyl Chromatogram w/swiss chard

Band #	Color	Distance Traveled	Pigment Type	R_f*
1	Solvent front	3.4	n/a	n/a
2	Green	1.6	chlorophylls	.47
3	Reddish purple	.4	Anthocyanin	.12

CONCLUSION QUESTIONS

1. What types of pigments are typically found in leaves?
   - Chlorophyll α and chlorophyll β, carotenoids, xanthophylls and anthocyanins.

2. What causes the pigments to move up the chromatogram different distances?
   - Some pigments are more soluble in acetone than others causing them to move farther.
   - Some pigments are attracted to the fibers in the paper causing them to travel shorter distances.

3. List the pigments in order of solubility from most soluble to least soluble in solution A.
   - Xanthophyll, carotene, chlorophyll b, chlorophyll a.

4. Why do some of the pigments appear yellow to our eyes while others appear green?
   - Yellow pigments reflect yellow wavelengths of light and absorb all other wavelengths.
   - Green pigments reflect green wavelengths of light and absorb all other wavelengths.

5. How is an action spectrum different from an absorption spectrum?
   - Action spectra are narrower and stimulate photosynthesis.
   - An absorption spectrum includes all of the wavelengths of light absorbed.

6. Why are all of the pigments not visible in a typical leaf?
   - Chlorophyll pigments are more numerous and mask the presence of the carotenes, xanthophylls and anthocyanins, however, in a purple leaf the amount of anthocyanin is greater than the amount of chlorophyll so the leaf appears purple.

7. Compare the bands produced in solutions A, B, and C. How are they alike? How are they different?
   - All three show chlorophyll solubility.
   - Solutions B and C do not separate the two types of chlorophylls or the yellow pigments.

8. Explain why the solvents you chose gave the results obtained.
   - The pigments were more soluble in this combination than the other.

REFERENCES

Helms, Doris R., Carl Helms, Robert Kosinski, and John Cummings. *Biology in the Laboratory*. New York: Freeman, 1998.

Morgan, Judith Giles and M. Eloise Brown Carter. *Investigating Biology*. San Francisco, 2002.

Picking out the Pigments
Isolating and Comparing Plant Pigments

Plants contain a variety of pigments that vary in color and chemical characteristics. Chlorophyll α and chlorophyll β, carotenoids, and xanthophylls are four pigments found in the chloroplasts of plants. These pigments play important roles in the process of photosynthesis. Chlorophyll α has a blue-green appearance. The yellow-green pigment is chlorophyll β. The orange-yellow pigment is carotene and the light yellow pigments are called xanthophylls. These four pigments are non-polar and are not soluble in water. A fifth pigment type, the anthocyanins, have a redish purple color, are polar and soluble in water. The anthocyanins, found in the vacuoles of leaves, serve a protective role, help to attract pollinators, and are thought to be distasteful to predators.

Chlorophyll α appears bright green to a bluish green color to the human eye. The color detected by human eye results from the green wavelength of light being reflected by this pigment. As sunlight strikes the leaf, the other wavelengths of light in the visible light spectrum (red, orange, yellow, blue, indigo, and violet) are absorbed by the leaf while the chlorophyll pigments reflect the green wavelengths. The wavelengths that are absorbed by the various pigments in the plant's leaves are collectively referred to as the absorption spectrum. Some of the wavelengths that have been absorbed by the plant will energize the plant's photosynthetic process, setting energy transfer events into action. The wavelengths of light that stimulate the plant's chemical processes are referred to as the plant's action spectrum. The action spectrum for many plants is limited to the red and blue wavelengths of light. See Figure 1.

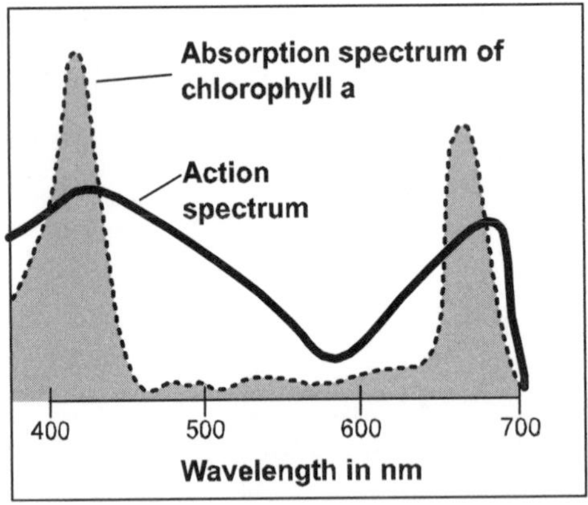

Fig. 1

The various pigments in a cell extract are separated and identified using a technique called paper chromatography. In this technique, the solvent moves up the chromatography paper and carry the dissolved pigments with it. The pigments move up the paper at unequal rates. One reason for this unequal rate is that the pigments vary in their solubility. Another reason for this unequal rate is due to the different degrees of attraction between the pigments and the paper. The fewer intermolecular attractive forces formed with the paper, the faster the rate of movement of the pigment. For example, when cell extracts containing beta carotene are placed in an acetone/ether solvent, few hydrogen bonds form between the paper and the pigment and beta carotene is very soluble in acetone/ether. As a result beta carotene will move rapidly up the chromatogram.

Plant leaves contain varying amounts of chlorophyll, carotene, xanthophylls and anthocyanin. However, most plants have a higher concentration of chlorophyll than the other pigments giving them an overall green appearance. Some plants like *Coleus* have leaves that reveal a variety of colors including green, yellow, and red due to the variation in pigments. During the fall, deciduous plants will decrease their levels of photosynthesis in response to reduced hours of sunlight per day and the amount of chlorophyll present will decline. This results in revealing the carotenes and xanthophylls which make the leaves appear orange and yellow. The bright red and purple colors come from anthocyanin pigments. Brown colors come from tannin, a bitter waste product. Different combinations of these pigments give us a wide range of colors each fall.

The arrangement of these five types of pigments on the chromatography paper and the relative locations of the pigments on the paper will change in different solvents. For example, solvents containing water will produce produce anthocyanin bands when other solvents do not.

PURPOSE

In this activity you will first prepare a chromatogram using pigments of swiss chard leaves and the solvent acetone. In the second portion of the activity, you will devise a plan to make a chromatogram containing as many bands as possible.

MATERIALS

3 strips of chromatography paper
3 large test tubes (25 x 200mm)
3 rubber stopper with hook or pin
1 leaf from spinach
1 small glass beaker 14 rulers
100 mL isopropyl alcohol
100 mL each of various solutions to be chosen from in Part II.
isopropyl alcohol, acetone, ethanol, water
1 leaf from *Coleus* or swiss chard
10 mL graduated cylinder

Safety Alert

1. Aprons and goggles must be worn during this activity.
2. CAUTION: Acetone, alcohols, and organic solvents are flammable.
3. Avoid inhalation of fumes from solvents.

PROCEDURE

PART I

1. Three solvents are provided for you to use to make a chromatogram from spinach leaves. Solvent A is made of petroleum ether and acetone, Solvent B is made of acetone, and Solvent C is acetone and water. Which solvent will produce the most bands on a chromatogram of spinach leaf pigment? Write your answer in the form of a hypothesis on the student answer page.

2. Obtain a piece of chromatography paper that has been precut to fit the large test tube.

3. Use a pencil to draw a line across the width of the chromatography paper 1.5 cm from the bottom of the paper. This will be your starting line. See Figure 2.

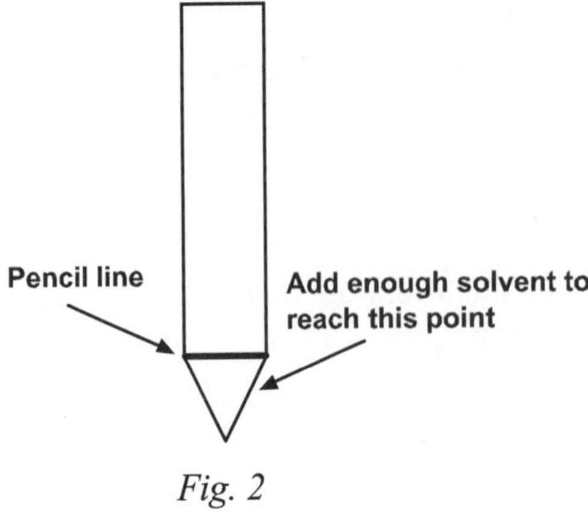

Fig. 2

4. Obtain a spinach leaf from your teacher. Place the spinach leaf on top of the line on the chromatography paper. Using a coin, press the pigment into the chromatography paper by rolling the coin over the surface of the leaf several times.

5. Obtain a large test tube and stopper to serve as your chromatography chamber.

6. Attach your pigment stained chromatography paper to the stopper and insert the paper into the test tube. Observe the position of the paper. It should be suspended in such a way that the tip is almost touching the bottom of the test tube. Do not allow your chromatography paper to touch the sides of the test tube. Adjust the position of your chromatogram as needed.

7. Remove the stopper and paper from the tube, and place approximately 5 mL of Solvent A in the bottom of the test tube. You will need enough solvent to wet the bottom of the paper without covering the pigment line. See Figure 2 above. Avoid inhaling the solvent fumes.

8. Repeat steps 4 through 7 for Solvent B and Solvent C.

9. Place the test tubes in an upright position and leave them undisturbed until the solvent has wicked at least 3/4 of the way up the chromatography paper. DO NOT LET THE SOLVENT RISE TO THE TOP OF THE PAPER.

10. Remove the stopper and chromatography paper from the tube. Quickly mark the level that the solvent has traveled, using a pencil.

11. Use a pencil to mark the location of each pigment on your chromatogram. Sketch your chromatogram in the data section of the student answer page. Include the colors of the pigments in your diagram.

12. Using a ruler, measure the distance the solvent moved from the starting line to the solvent pencil mark. Record this distance in the data table on the student answer page.

13. Measure the distance traveled by each of the pigments from the starting line. Record the measurements in the data table.

14. Using the information provided in the introduction, determine the type of pigment found in each band on the chromatogram.

15. Answer the Part I conclusion questions on the student answer page.

PART II

1. Using the chromatography technique learned in Part I, determine which solvent combination will allow you to extract the largest number of pigments from *Coleus.*

2. Write your hypothesis in the space provided on the student answer sheet.

3. Design an experiment to test your hypothesis. Describe your experiment in the space provided on the student answer page. Limit your experimentation for this portion of the lab to two chromatograms.

4. Record the distanced traveled by the pigments in your chromatograms in the data table provided on the student answer page.

5. Label the probable pigment types for each band in your chromatograms. Place the pigment names in the data table.

Name ______________________________

Period______________________________

Picking out the Pigments
Isolating and Comparing Plant Pigments

HYPOTHESIS

Part I Hypothesis

Part II Hypothesis

DATA AND OBSERVATIONS

Part I Data: Sketch your chromatogram(s) in the space below:

Part II Data: Sketch your chromatogram(s) in the space below:

Part II: Experimental Design

ANALYSIS

Data Table 1: Acetone Chromatogram Measurements				
Band #	Color	Distance Traveled	Pigment Type	R_f*
1 (top)				
2				
3				
4				
5				

Data Table 2: Part II Chromatogram #1 Measurements				
Band #	Color	Distance Traveled	Pigment Type	R_f*

Data Table 3: Part II Chromatogram #2 Measurements				
Band #	Color	Distance Traveled	Pigment Type	R_f*

$$*R_f = \frac{\text{Distance pigment migrated}}{\text{Distance solvent front migrated}}$$

CONCLUSION QUESTIONS

1. What types of pigments are typically found in leaves?

2. What causes the pigments to move up the chromatogram different distances?

3. List the pigments in order of solubility from most soluble to least soluble in solution A.

4. Why do some of the pigments appear yellow to our eyes while others appear green?

5. How is an action spectrum different from an absorption spectrum?

6. Why are all of the pigments not visible in a typical leaf?

7. Compare the bands produced in solutions A, B, and C. How are they alike? How are they different?

8. How do the chromatograms made from *Coleus* (or swiss chard) compare to those made from spinach leaves?

Write Your Notes and Ideas Here!

Light, Dark, Does It Really Matter?
Examining the Factors of the Light Reaction

OBJECTIVE
Students will investigate factors that affect the light reaction of photosynthesis and model the process of the light reaction.

LEVEL
Biology I

NATIONAL STANDARDS
UCP.1, UCP.2, UCP.5, B.2, B.3, B.6, C.1, C.5

TEKS
1(A), 2(B), 2(C), 2(D), 9(B)

CONNECTIONS TO AP
AP Biology:
I. Molecules and Cells C. Cellular Energetics 3. Photosynthesis

TIME FRAME
Part A 30 minutes
Part B 30 minutes

MATERIALS
(For a class of 28 working in pairs)

56 test tubes 13 x 100 mm	14 test tube racks
1 L phosphate buffer	1 L distilled water
14 5 cc syringes	14 Beral disposable pipets
chloroplasts suspension	1 roll of aluminum foil

Safety Alert
CAUTION: Be sure to warn your students about the fact that DPIP may stain their skin or clothing.

TEACHER NOTES

This lab activity supplements a unit of photosynthesis. It investigates the importance of light and intact chloroplasts on the reaction. In addition there is a paper and pen activity to reinforce the process of chemiosmosis. It suggests students cut and tape the missing phrases from the list provided. Students can also write them in as an alternative.

To make the chloroplast solution, use 50 g of fresh spinach with 250 mL of a 0.5M ice-cold sucrose solution. Make the sucrose solution by dissolving 171 g of sucrose in distilled water and diluting to a total volume of l liter. Place both the spinach leaves with stems removed and the sucrose solution into a blender. You may have to tear the leaves. Blend the spinach with three 5-10 second bursts. Pour the mixture through several layers of cheesecloth. Keep the solution on ice. This will last only 1-2 hours, after which new chloroplast suspensions should be made.

To make the chlorophyll solution, grind 50 g of fresh spinach leaves with 250 mL of methanol or ethanol with a mortar and pestle until dark green. Pour the mixture through several layers of cheesecloth. Avoid using a blender as any leaks in the seals of the blender may result in an electrical fire.

0.1- M Phosphate Buffer is made by dissolving 174 g K_2HPO_4 (dibasic) in distilled H_2O and dilute to a total solution volume of 1 L. Make a second solution by dissolving 136 g KH_2PO_4 (monobasic) in distilled H_2O and diluting to a total solution volume of 1 L. Mix 685 mL of KH_2PO_4 (monobasic) with 315 K_2HPO_4 (dibasic). The pH should be 6.5, if not adjust accordingly using a pH meter and drops of an acid or base. Since this is a 1 M solution, it must be diluted to 0.1 M by taking 100 mL of the 1 M phosphate buffer solution and diluting it to 1 L by adding distilled water.

DPIP (2-6 Diphosphoindol phenol or 2,6-dichlorophenol-indophenol) solution is made by dissolving 0.072 g of DPIP in distilled water to total solution volume of 1 liter. This solution in its oxidized state is a blue dye.

CAUTION: DPIP may stain clothing and skin. Use care when handling this solution.

Light will reduce the DPIP solution so it needs to be stored in the dark either in amber bottles or in the refrigerator. The effect of light on the DPIP during the laboratory period is negligible. Also, if you are just playing around with this lab and leave the DPIP out in an open beaker, the amount of water that evaporates will affect concentration of DPIP. This will make the DPIP much more concentrated thus darker and will affect the results.

POSSIBLE ANSWERS TO THE CONCLUSION QUESTIONS AND SAMPLE DATA

	# 1 Control	# 2 Light Test Tube Chloroplast	# 3 Dark Test Tube Chloroplast	# 4 Light Test Tube Chlorophyll
Beginning Color	Blue	Blue	Blue	Blue
Final Color	Blue	Clear	Blue	Blue
Light (+,-) Reaction		+	-	-

1. Why are ATP and NADPH needed for photosynthesis?
   - ATP and NADPH provide the chemical energy needed to make the sugar in the Calvin cycle.

2. Is light needed for photosynthesis? How do you know?
   - Yes. Light is needed to excite the chlorophyll molecules. The solution remained blue when left in the dark without light.

3. Are chloroplasts needed for the light reaction or is chlorophyll by itself enough? How do you know?
   - For the light reaction to occur, intact chloroplasts are needed. When chlorophyll was used instead of chloroplasts, the solution remained blue since the light reaction did not take place.

4. Explain how the thylakoid is analogous to a battery.
   - The electron transport chain is used to separate charges across a membrane. The inside of the thylakoid is positive relative to the stroma which is negative. This is analogous to a battery, which also has a separation of charge. Any separation of charge creates an electric potential, commonly called a voltage.

5. Explain how ATP is produced during the light reaction.
   - ATP is produced as hydrogen ions flows across a CF1 particle to phosphorylate ATP.

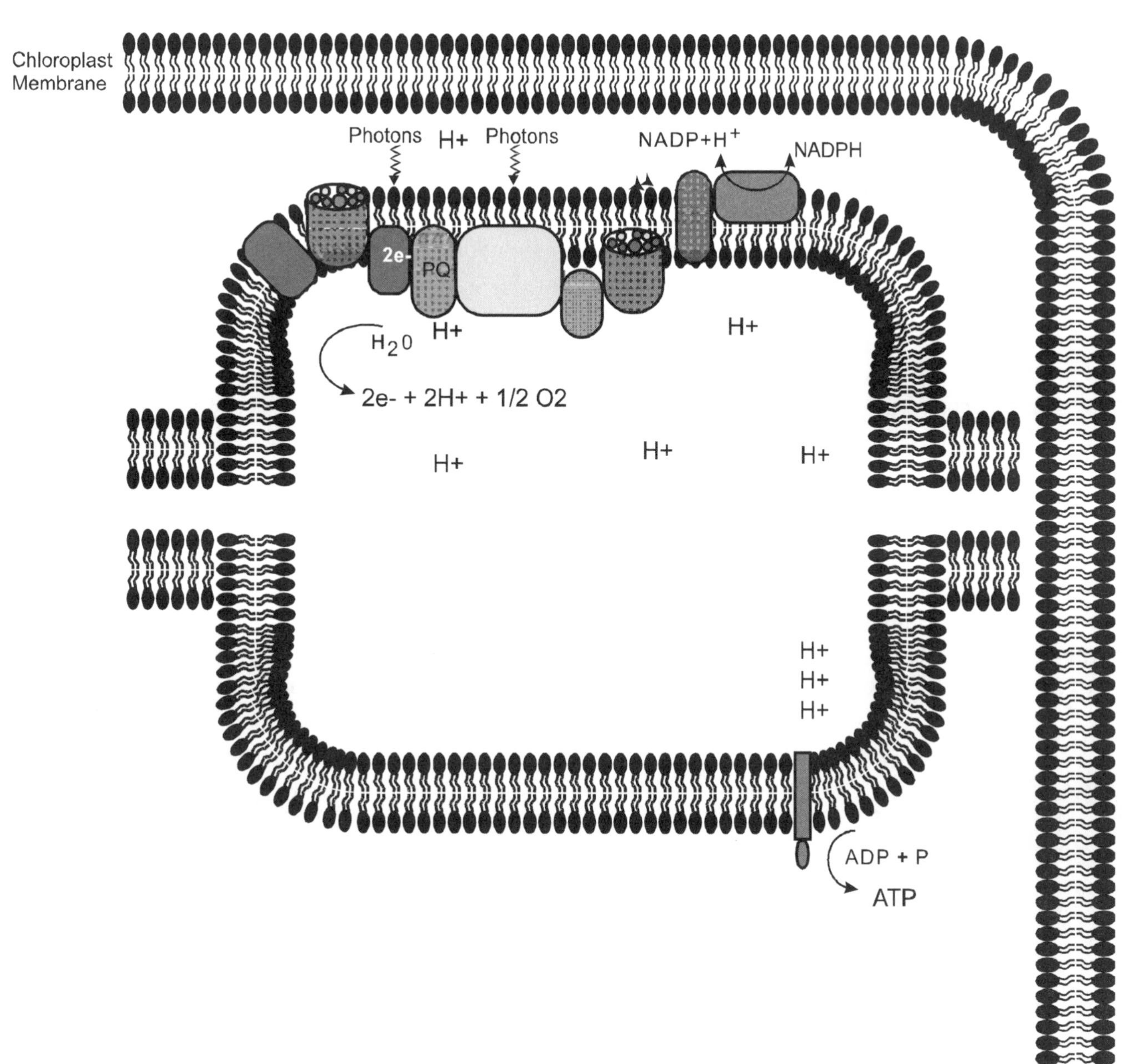

REFERENCES

Ferl, Robert, Gerald Sanders, and Robert Wallace. *Biology the Science of Life*. New York: Harper Collins Publisher, 1991. pp. 980-1007

Advanced Placement Biology Laboratory Manual for Teachers. New York: Educational Testing Service, Revised 2001. pg. 27

Light, Dark, Does It Really Matter?
Examining the Factors of the Light Reaction

Photosynthesis is a most wonderful process in which the chloroplasts of plants make sugar from carbon dioxide and water. Glucose has more energy than carbon dioxide. This is because the glucose molecule has hydrogen.

$$6CO_2+6H_2O \longrightarrow C_6H_{12}O_6+6O_2$$

Photosynthesis converts solar energy into the chemical energy needed to make glucose. This chemical energy is temporarily stored in the bonds of ATP and NADPH through the events of the light reactions.

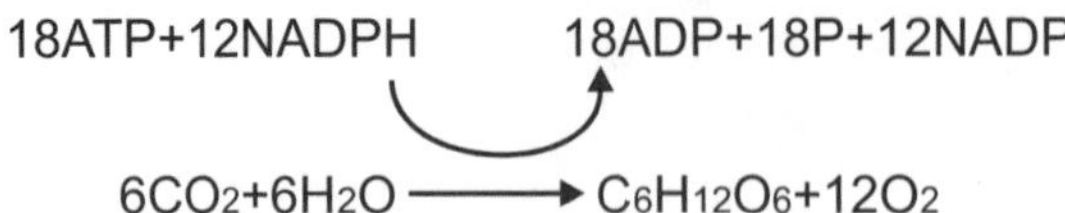

In order for this reaction to continuously occur, the plant cell must regenerate both the ATP (put the phosphate back on ADP) and NADPH (put hydrogen on NADP). This regeneration also requires energy, but this energy comes from light and chlorophyll molecules found in the chloroplasts.

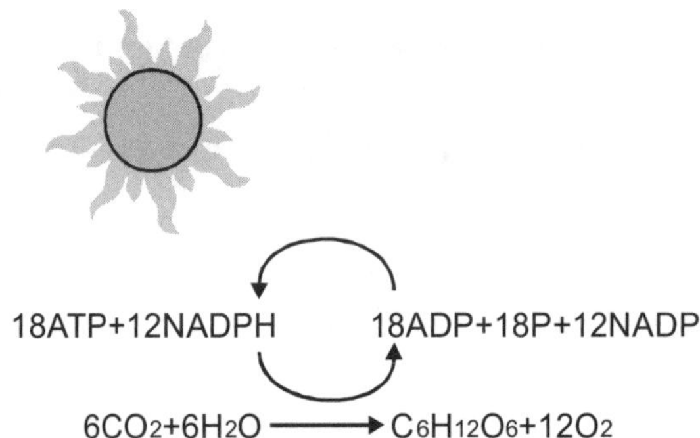

Since photons of light are required, this is called the light reaction. The purpose of the light reactions is to make the chemical energy needed to make glucose in the Calvin cycle. The light reaction occurs in the thylakoid of the chloroplast.

PURPOSE

The purpose of this lab is to investigate the factors that affect the light reaction of photosynthesis. These factors include investigation of the importance of light and the importance the structure of the chloroplasts. The light reaction is also simulated with a model.

To investigate this reaction, a dye DPIP is used. DPIP is blue but will turn clear if it is mixed with chloroplasts and the light reaction is allowed to occur. This color change allows us to determine whether or not the light reaction is indeed occurring.

MATERIALS

4 test tubes 13 x 100 mm
phosphate buffer
5 cc syringe
aluminum foil
test tube rack
distilled water
Beral disposable pipet

Safety Alert
CAUTION: DPIP and chlorophyll may stain skin or clothing.

	# 1 Control	# 2 Light Test Tube Chloroplast	# 3 Dark Test Tube Chloroplast	# 4 Light Test Tube Chlorophyll
Phosphate Buffer	1 cc	1 cc	1 cc	1 cc
Distilled Water	3 cc	3 cc	3 cc	3 cc
DPIP	1 cc	1 cc	1 cc	1 cc

PROCEDURE

1. Formulate a hypothesis that will test the factors that affect photosynthesis. Record your hypothesis in the space provided on the student answer page.

2. Obtain the materials needed above. Label the test tubes 1-4.

3. Put the solutions into each of the test tubes as indicated in the chart above. Compare the colors and record the beginning colors on the student answer sheet.

4. Wrap test tube #3 it in foil and make a foil cap, so that no light is allowed into the tube.

5. In test tubes #2 and #3, add three drop of chloroplasts. Mix by swirling the test tubes. Observe the color and compare it to test tube #1. Return the #3 test tube to the aluminum foil.

6. In test tube #4 add three drop of CHLOROPHYLL not chloroplasts. Swirl the test tubes. Observe the color and compare it to test tube #1.

7. Every five minutes observe the color of tests tubes and compare them to test tube #1 for fifteen minutes. Record the final color of each test tube on the student answer sheet.

The Light Reaction of Photosynthesis

Read about the steps of the light reaction in following text. On your student answer sheet is a diagram of the light reaction. As you read about the light reaction, cut out the missing and place them in the proper sequence. The thylakoid membrane has built into it collections of pigment molecules, which include chlorophylls and carotenoids. This collection is called a photosystem. When a photon of light is absorbed by one of the pigment molecules, electrons are excited and elevated to a higher energy level. The energy is passed from pigment to pigment until it reaches an "antenna" molecule.

1. The electron transport chain captures excited electrons. The electrons move from one electron carrier to another. Each time the electron is transferred, it loses a small amount of energy.

2. As the electrons move through the electron transport chain, one electron carrier in particular has special properties. This carrier has the ability to "pump" hydrogen ions, H^+, across the thylakoid membrane from the outside to the inside of the thylakoid.

3. To finish the trip, the electron must be energized again at another photosystem with photons of light.

4. Once energized, the electron continues it trip down the electron transport chain. The ultimate electron acceptor at the end of the electron transport chain is NADP. NADP will also combine with H+ to form NADPH.

5. Once this trip is complete, the system needs replacement electrons. These replacement electrons come from the splitting of water molecules. This reaction will produce 2 H^+ ions, $2e^-$, and ½ of an O_2 molecule. The oxygen gas leaves the thylakoid, diffusing out the chloroplasts and eventually out of the leaf.

6. The e^- are used by the photosystem as replacement electrons.

7. The H^+ ions accumulate, to make the interior of the thylakoid acidic relative to the stroma.

8. This separation of charge is used to phosphorylate ADP and make ATP as 3 H^+ ions move through the CF1 particle to make ATP.

Name ______________________________

Period ______________________________

Light, Dark, Does It Really Matter?
Examining the Factors of the Light Reaction

HYPOTHESIS

DATA AND OBSERVATIONS

	# 1 Control	# 2 Light Test Tube Chloroplast	# 3 Dark Test Tube Chloroplast	# 4 Light Test Tube Chlorophyll
Beginning Color				
Final Color				
Light (+,-) Reaction				

CONCLUSION QUESTIONS

1. Why are ATP and NADPH needed for photosynthesis?

2. Is light needed for photosynthesis? How do you know?

3. Are intact chloroplasts needed for the light reaction or is chlorophyll by itself enough? How do you know?

4. Explain how the thylakoid is analogous to a battery.

5. Explain how ATP is produced during the light reaction.

LIGHT REACTION DIAGRAM

Below are missing parts to the light reaction with a diagram of the thylakoid. Supply the missing parts to the light reaction in the thylakoid.

$2e^- + 2H^+ + 1/2\ O_2$

NADPH

ATP

$H^+\ H^+\ H^+\ H^+\ H^+$

$2e^-$

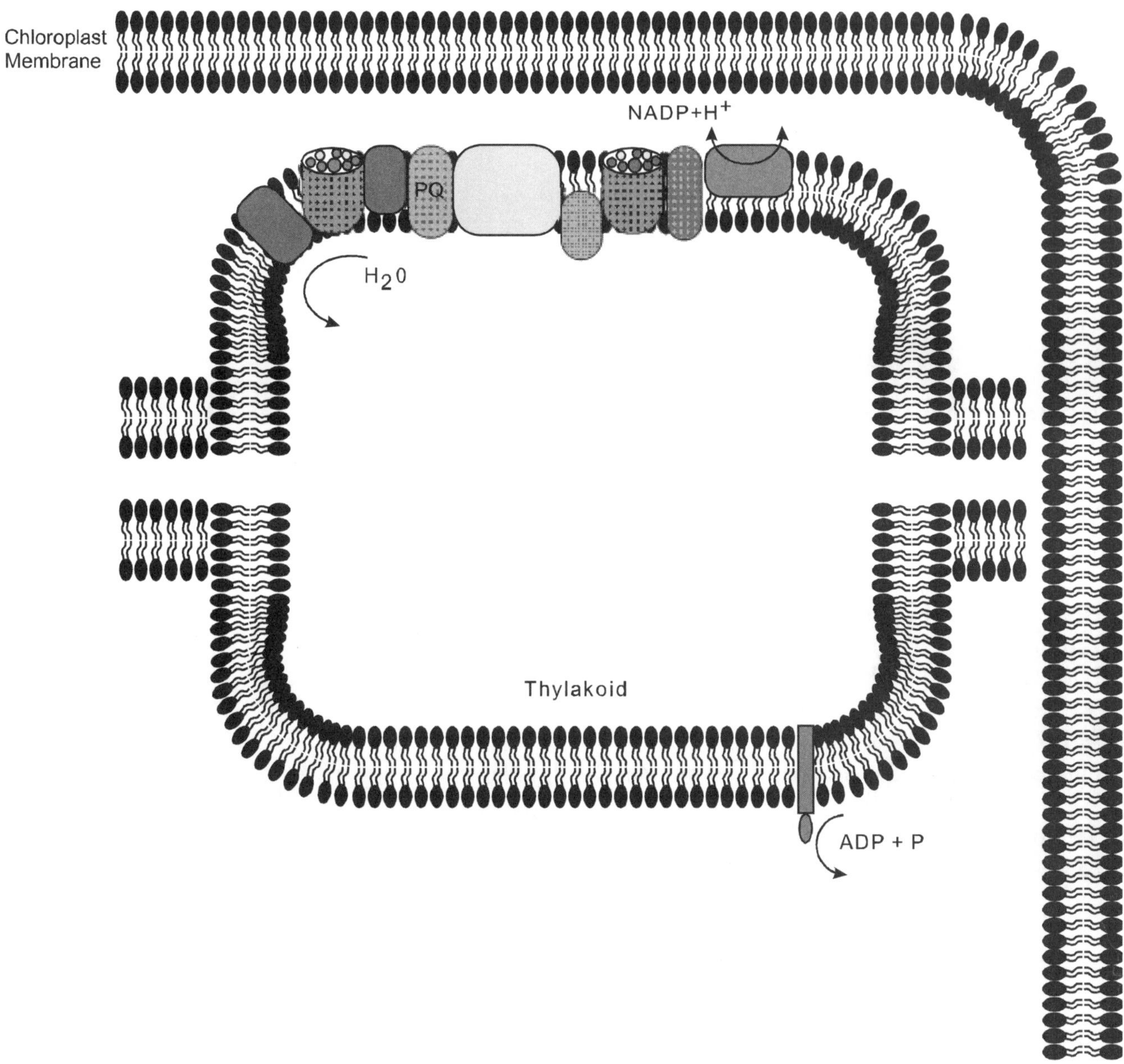
Chloroplast
Membrane
NADP+H+
PQ
H20
Thylakoid
ADP + P

Lights Out
Demonstrating Dark Reactions

OBJECTIVE
Students will determine the effect of limited light on the amount of starch produced by the dark reaction in the leaves of plants.

LEVEL
Biology I

NATIONAL STANDARDS
UCP.1, UCP.2, UCP.3, UCP.5, A.1, A.2, B.3, B.6, C.4, G.1, G.2

TEKS
5(A), 9(A), 9(B), 10(C)

CONNECTIONS TO AP
AP Biology:
I. Molecules and Cells C. Cell Energetics 2. Photosynthesis

TIME FRAME
50 minutes one day and an additional 30 minutes 2-3 days later

MATERIALS
(For class of 28 working in groups of 4)

plant with at least 28 leaves that has been in the dark for 48 hours
1000 mL beaker (7) or other suitable heat proof container for water bath
150 mL of ethanol
Lugol's iodine solution in dropper bottle (7)
4" strip of foil (7)
scissors (7)
250 mL beaker (7)
copies of blackline master of hierarchy cut in strips
Calvin cycle transparency
cereal bowl with cereal or small single serving box of cereal
hot plates (several)
access to a plant light or fluorescent light source for 48 consecutive hours
1.4 L tap water
Petri dish bottoms (14)
forceps (7)
paper clips (28)
container for used iodine
hierarchy transparency
tape (1 roll)
packet of sugar

TEACHER NOTES

This lab can be used in conjunction with the *Light, Dark, Does It Really Matter?* lab to provide a thorough presentation of photosynthesis.

The cereal and sugar are used to help students see the relevance of the dark reaction to their own world. You could use most any food that contains sugar and starch for this portion of the lesson.

The plants used in this experiment need to be kept in the dark for 2 days prior to the beginning of the experiment. Coleus and geranium are good choices for plants to be used in this activity because they have large leaves and are relatively inexpensive. Once the students attach their initials, the plants should be well watered and kept in the light for two to three days.

Lugol's solution can be purchased from a chemical supplier or prepared by dissolving 10 g potassium iodide and 5 g of iodine in 1L of distilled water. Dispense in amber dropper bottles.

You will need to provide a container in which the students can pour off their excess Lugol's solution in step 15.

Due to the abstract nature of the concepts regarding the light and dark reactions of photosynthesis, students benefit from making concrete connections to their everyday world. Making structure and function connections for the students will also help them retain the content. For example, explain that the chloroplast membrane follows the fluid mosaic membrane model. The membranes permeability to carbon dioxide and water is due to its structure. The process of photosynthesis is dependent upon the permeability of the membrane to carbon dioxide for the dark reactions and water for the light reactions. In addition to helping the students understand photosynthesis, this connection to previous learning will emphasize to the students that they are learning this content for later use not just because "it will be on the next test".

Suggested Teaching Procedures:

Day One

1. Introduce this lesson by showing the students a bowl (or box) containing corn flakes and a packet of sugar. Ask them to think about these questions:
   a. Is there energy in this bowl? *(yes)* In the sugar? *(yes)*
   b. Where is the energy? *(tied up in the chemical bonds of the sugar and cereal)*
   c. How did the energy get there? *(plants used solar energy to bind carbon dioxide molecules together with hydrogens in the process of photosynthesis)*
   d. Why do we eat foods like these? *(so that we can get the stored energy out of the bonds)*

2. Go over the correct responses to the questions and explain that the part of photosynthesis where the actual formation of the bonds takes place is the dark reaction, the topic for this lesson.

3. Use the photosynthesis hierarchy transparency to present the structures involved in photosynthesis and specifically the location of the events of the Calvin cycle. Prior to presenting the light or dark reactions in any detail, students need to have a clear understanding of the location of the events of the Calvin's cycle in order to grasp the significance of this rather abstract concept.

4. Have the students cut out the diagrams representing the structures in the hierarchy and tape them in descending order in the space provided on their student answer page.

5. Have the students name a plant that they see in their everyday world. Call on 8 or 10 of the students to tell you where their plant is located. Press for real examples! By starting with concrete knowledge of plants that actually exist in their world the students can build an understanding of the abstract concepts of photosynthesis. Have the students get in pairs and using their favorite plant, practice naming the structures in the hierarchy in order to explain where photosynthesis occurs. One partner can explain where light reactions occur using their hierarchy from large to small, the other partner can sequence their's from small to large to explain where the dark reactions occur. Emphasize the use of their favorite plant as they state their hierarchies. Student responses to this activity should sound like "The dark reactions takes place in the stroma surrounding the thylakoids found in a chloroplast in a mesophyll cell located in the mesophyll tissue of the leaf of the St. Augustine grass growing in my front yard."

6. The students should then write down the names of the hierarchical structures in the space provided on the student answer page.

7. Have the students read through the pre-laboratory information and answer the pre-lab questions on the student answer page. Alternately, you may want to have the students read through the information as a warm-up prior to your presentation on the hierarchical arrangements.

8. Explain the significant events of the Calvin cycle using the transparency. After your explanation, check student understanding by going through questions such as:
   a. What is the main purpose of the Calvin cycle? *(to produce energy rich carbohydrates)*
   b. Where does the Calvin cycle occur? *(in the stroma of the chloroplast of a mesophyll cell in the mesophyll tissue in the leaf of the rose bush in my back yard)*
   c. What chemicals enter into the Calvin cycle? *(carbon dioxide, ATP, and NADPH)*
   d. Where do these chemicals come from? *(Carbon dioxide diffuses in through the stoma, ATP and NADPH come most directly from the light reactions)*
   e. Where does the C in glucose come from? The H? The O? C from carbon dioxide, H from NADPH, and O from carbon dioxide.
   f. What does the Calvin cycle have to do with the cereal I showed you at the beginning of class? *(Calvin cycle events produced the energy rich carbohydrates found in the flakes)*

9. Explain that the lab is designed to compare the carbohydrate production in the presence of light to that in the dark. Here you will need to spend a little time explaining that although the Calvin cycle events don't directly require light, they are directly dependent on the ***products*** of the light reactions.

10. Give a brief overview of the lab activity and explain the safety precautions that must be taken. You may want to have a sample of foil-cut out initials of the appropriate size to cover a large portion of the leaf's surface. If the cut outs used are too small the results are difficult to distinguish. Let the students know that they do not need to spend much time cutting out intricate, elaborate designs. Simple block letters work best. However, this is often times the students' favorite part of the lab. To save class time, you could have the students cut out their initials at home. They do not have to be cut out of foil. Any opaque material will suffice. Foil is used in this activity because it folds easily allowing ease of attachment. You can also use film negatives to block the light on the leaves. If you try this, select picture negatives that have large, contrasting images, like a photo of a truck, car or house.

11. Have the students perform Part I of the lab.

Day Two

12. Set up the water baths prior to class and have the students perform Part II of the lab. Inexpensive sauce pans make good water bath containers.

13. In your post lab discussion, review the main events of the Calvin cycle using the transparency.

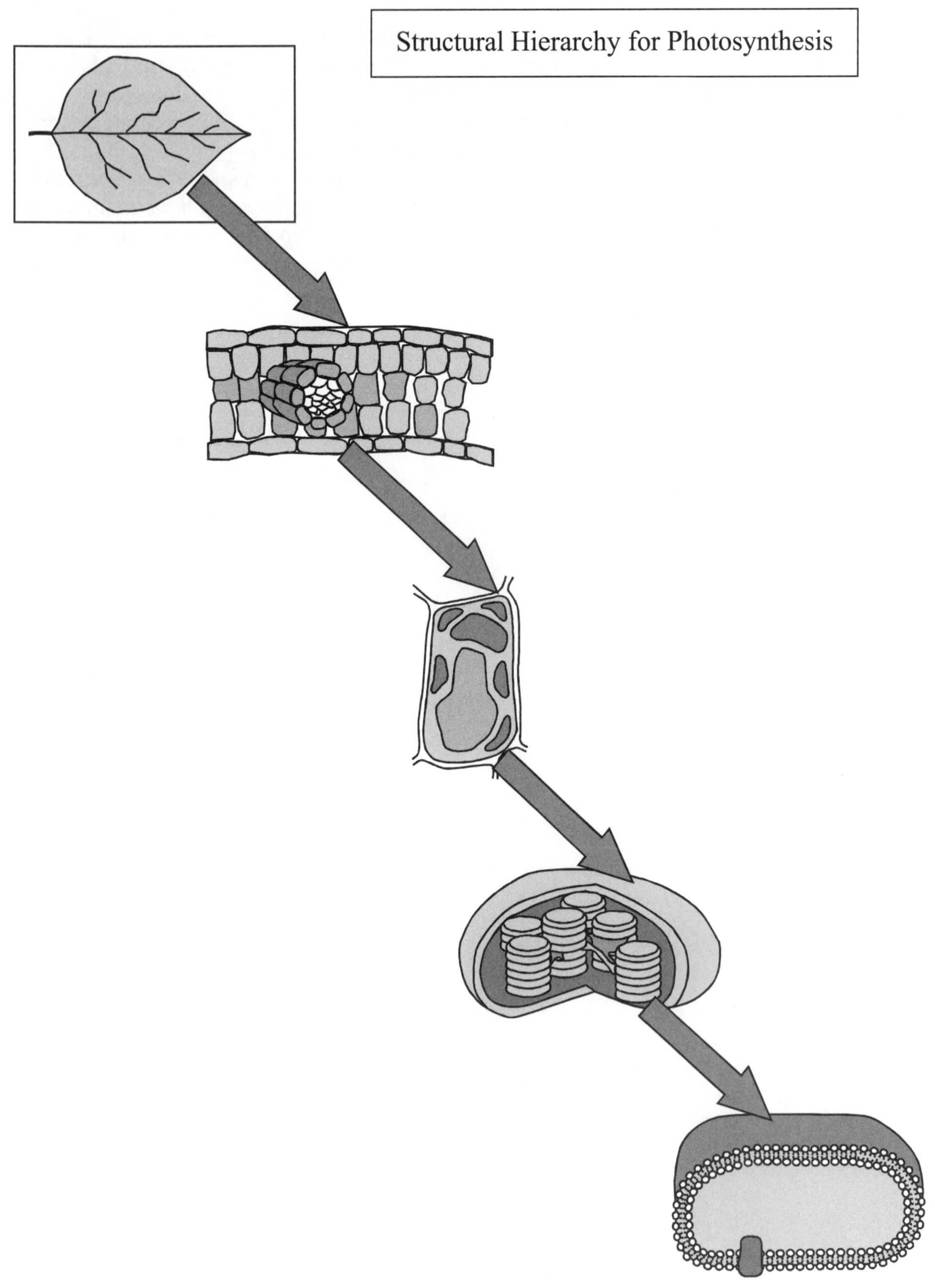
Structural Hierarchy for Photosynthesis

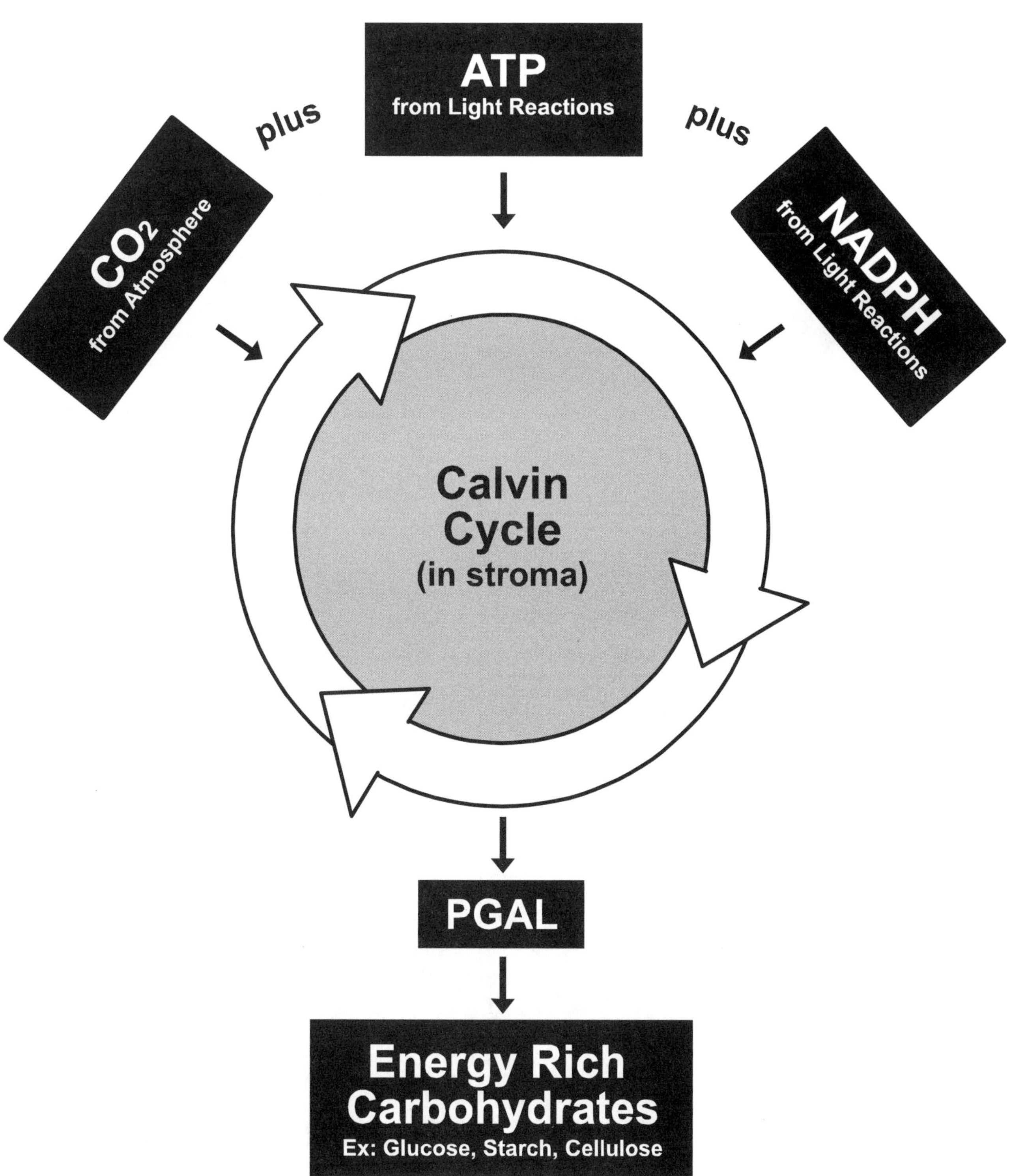
ATP
from Light Reactions
plus
plus
CO_2
from Atmosphere
NADPH
from Light Reactions
Calvin
Cycle
(in stroma)
PGAL
Energy Rich
Carbohydrates
Ex: Glucose, Starch, Cellulose

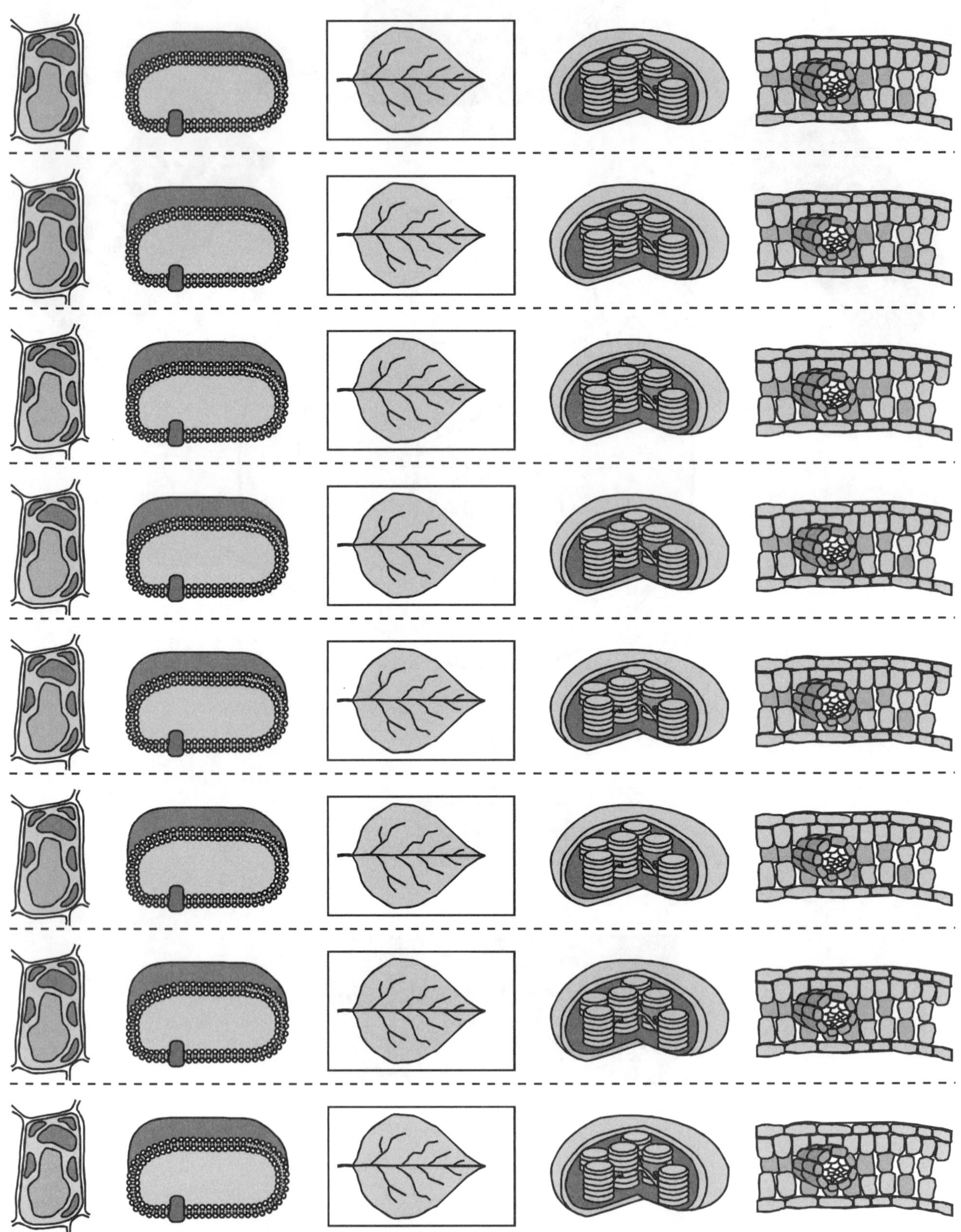

POSSIBLE ANSWERS TO THE CONCLUSION QUESTIONS AND SAMPLE DATA

HIERARCHY OF PHOTOSYNTHESIS DIAGRAMS

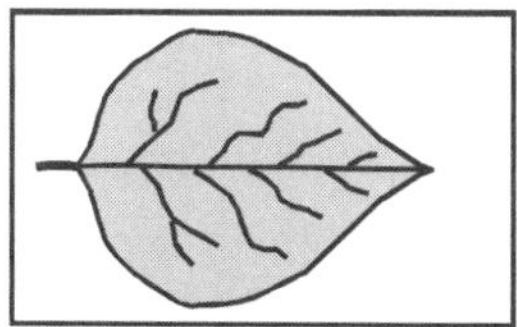 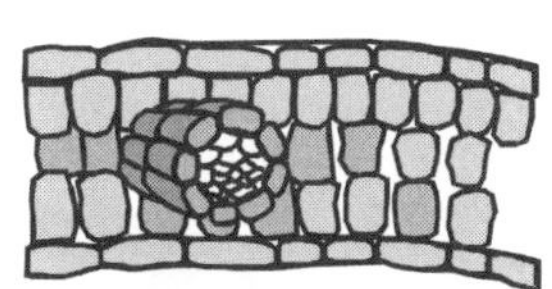 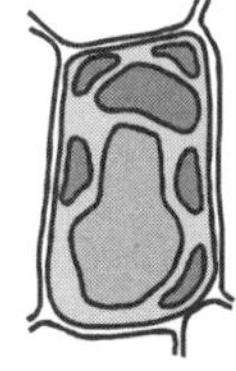  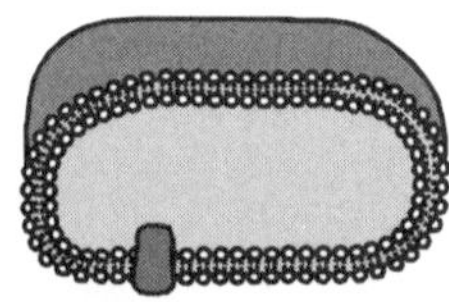

Hierarchy of photosynthesis structures for my favorite plant:

- stroma, chloroplast, mesophyll cell, mesophyll tissue, leaf of my favorite plant –the rosebush in my back yard.

PRE-LAB QUESTIONS:

1. What are the two main events of photosynthesis?
   - Light reactions, Calvin cycle

2. Where, specifically, do the Calvin cycle reactions occur?
   - stroma — surrounding the thylakoids in the chloroplast of a mesophyll cell in the mesophyll tissue in a leaf of my favorite plant — the rosebush in my back yard.

3. Name three chemicals that go into the Calvin cycle.
   - Carbon dioxide, ATP, NADPH

4. How many carbon dioxides must enter the Calvin cycle in order to form a single glucose molecule? How many molecules of ATP and NADPH are needed to form a single glucose molecule?
   - Six molecules carbon dioxides are needed. 18 molecules ATP and molecules of 12 NDAPH are needed.

5. Give three examples of energy rich end products of the dark reactions of photosynthesis:
   - glucose, starch, cellulose

PART II

Diagram of leaf with initials after staining: (covered area will not stain where the cut out are)

Diagram of plain, non-treatment leaf: will be blue all over

ANALYSIS

1. Describe the similarities in the two leaves after they have been boiled and stained with iodine.
   - Both contain areas stained blue.

2. Describe the differences in the two leaves after they have been boiled and stained with iodine.
   - The leaf with the foil cut outs does not stain blue.

3. Which portion of the leaf contains the most starch, the part that had been covered with foil or the part that was not covered? Explain your answer using evidence from the lab.
   - the most starch is located in the darkest stained areas which are outside the area covered by the foil

CONCLUSION QUESTIONS

1. What is the purpose of removing, boiling and staining the second leaf in this experiment?
   - The second leaf serves as a control.

2. Did the Calvin cycle take place in the mesophyll cells located underneath your group's foil cut out initials? How do you know?
   - No, not much because there is little blue-black staining there which indicates very little, if any starch production.

3. Photosynthesis produces glucose. Lugol's iodine solution tests for starch. What is the relationship between starch and glucose?
   - Starch is made from rings of glucose. When a plant makes excess glucose through the process of photosynthesis, it will chemically bond the glucose rings to form chains of starch.

4. Why is it important to primary consumers, like you, that plants store their energy as starch?
    - Plants store the energy which primary consumers obtain when they eat the part of plant which is storing starch..

5. What iodine test results would have been obtained from a leaf that had been entirely covered with foil?
    - There would have been very little blue staining indicating low levels of starch.

6. Give an example of how structure is related to function in a chloroplast of your favorite plant.
    - The phospholipid membrane of the chloroplast is semipermeable allowing water to easily enter the chloroplast.
    - The structures of the thylakoids are little compartments. The proteins inserted into to the structure of the thylakoid membrane is the electron transport chain. The compartment nature of the thylakoid allows for the separation of charge analogous to a battery this important to the process of chemiosmosis. The stroma provides a matrix or environment for the enzymes needed for the Calvin cycle to occur.

7. Describe how the Calvin cycle is dependent upon the events of the light reactions.
    - The energy for the Calvin cycle (ATP molecules) and the hydrogens (NADPH) for PGAL are provided by the light reactions.

8. Write a chemical equation that describes the process of photosynthesis.

$$12\ NADPH \longrightarrow 12\ NADP + 12\ H$$

$$18\ ATP \longrightarrow 18\ ADP + 18\ P$$

$$6\ CO_2 + 6\ H_2O \longrightarrow C_6H_{12}O_6 + 6\ O_2$$

Lights Out
Demonstrating Dark Reactions

The ultimate source of energy used by living things comes from the sun. Autotrophs, such as plants produce energy rich carbon compounds by converting radiant energy to chemical energy in the process of photosynthesis. The primary site of photosynthesis in most plants is the leaves which are structurally arranged to effectively perform this function. The leaf contains photosynthetic *mesophyll tissues*. Within the mesophyll tissue there are mesophyll cells which typically contain 30-40 chloroplasts. The chloroplast is surrounded by a double membrane on the outside and stacks of membranes on the inside called *grana*. Each granum is made of stacks of sac-like membranes called *thylakoids*. Surrounding the grana is a gel-like matrix called the *stroma*. The stroma and the thylakoid membranes are directly involved in the processes of photosynthesis.

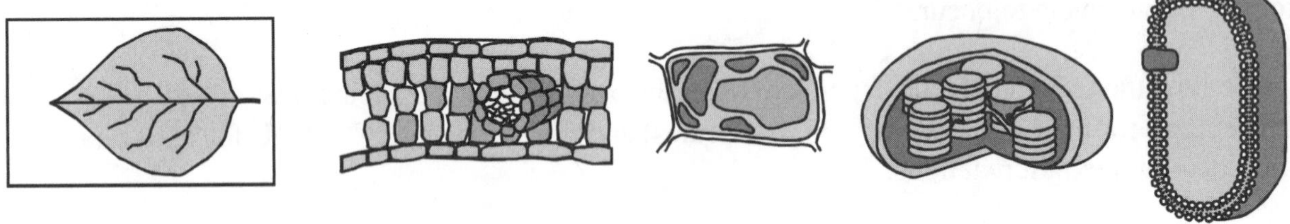

Fig. 1

The reactions of photosynthesis can be divided into two main sets of events called the light and dark reactions. The light reactions occur in the membranes of the thylakoids and send their products to the stroma where the dark reactions take place. The Calvin-Benson cycle, Calvin's cycle, C3 cycle, light independent reactions and carbon fixation cycle are all names used in reference to the dark reactions. The dark reactions, which can occur without the presence of light, occur in the stroma of a plant's chloroplast. See Figure 1.

Fig. 2

The basic purpose of the dark reactions or the Calvin cycle is to convert carbon dioxide and water into two trioses, phosphoglyceraldye (PGAL), and then later glucose using energy from the light reactions.

Figure 2 illustrates the basic processes of the Calvin cycle. Two energy end products from the light reaction, ATP and NADPH, supply the energy needed for the Calvin cycle. In doing so, energy is transferred from solar energy to the light reactions, to the dark reactions and eventually into the chemical bonds of carbohydrate macromolecules.

In the Calvin cycle, 6 carbon dioxide molecules are used to produce two molecules of PGAL and then combing them into a single 6-carbon glucose. As glucose molecules become available, they are chemically combined to create long chains of starch and cellulose. Starch is a common energy storage molecule in plants. These carbohydrates can be used by the plant to provide energy for cellular activities. Heterotrophs obtain this stored energy when they consume the plants as a food.

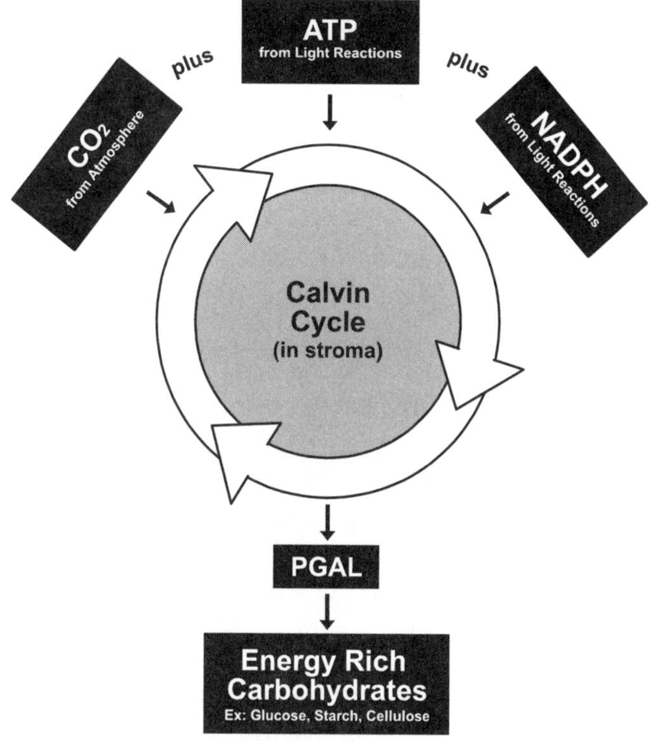

Fig. 3

PURPOSE

In this activity you will use the iodine-starch test to compare the amounts of starch produced in a leaf exposed to light with one that has been light limited.

MATERIALS

- plant that has been in the dark for 48 hours
- 1000 mL beaker
- 150 mL of ethanol in water bath
- Lugol's iodine in dropper bottle
- 4" strip of foil
- scissors
- 250 mL beaker
- hot plates
- access to a plant light or fluorescent light source for 48 consecutive hours.
- 200 mL tap water
- Petri dish bottom
- forceps
- paper clips (2)

Safety Alert
1. Goggles and aprons must be worn during Part II of this activity.
2. Alcohol is flammable, avoid open flame. Heating of the alcohol should be accomplished by using great care and a hot plate.
3. Light sources can produce heat. Avoid touching the bulbs when the lights are plugged in.

PROCEDURE

PART I: PREPARATION

1. At your teacher's instruction, cut out the hierarchy diagrams given to you by your teacher and place them in order from largest to smallest in the space provided on the student answer sheet.

2. Record the photosynthetic structural hierarchy for where the Calvin cycle occurs in your favorite plant in the space provided on the student answer page. Begin with the smallest component and end with your favorite plant's location.

3. Read the introduction section of this activity and answer the pre-lab questions located in the analysis section of your student answer page.

4. In this lab you will test for the presence of starch produced during the Calvin cycle of photosynthesis. Do you think there will be more starch in the area of the leaf exposed to light or the area of the leaf that is not exposed to light? Write your answer in the form of a hypothesis in the space provided on your student answer page.

5. Using scissors cut your initials or a shape out of the piece of foil. The letters of this foil cut-out should be large enough to reach across most of the surface of a leaf of the plant your teacher provided. See Figure 1 below:

Fig. 1

6. Using paperclips and the edges of your foil cut out, gently attach your group's initials to one of the leaves of the plant provided by your teacher.

7. Your plant should be watered and kept in the light for 48 hours.

PART II: TESTING FOR THE PRESENCE OF STARCH

1. Put on goggles and an apron for this portion of the lab.

2. Locate the plant containing your group's initials.

3. Remove your leaf by cutting it at the base of the petiole.

4. Your teacher has set up a water bath in which a smaller beaker containing alcohol is heating. Drop your leaf into the boiling water in the larger beaker or pan of the water bath and boil for 1 minute. See Figure 2. *Caution: Leave the smaller beaker containing alcohol in place as you boil your leaf in the larger beaker.*

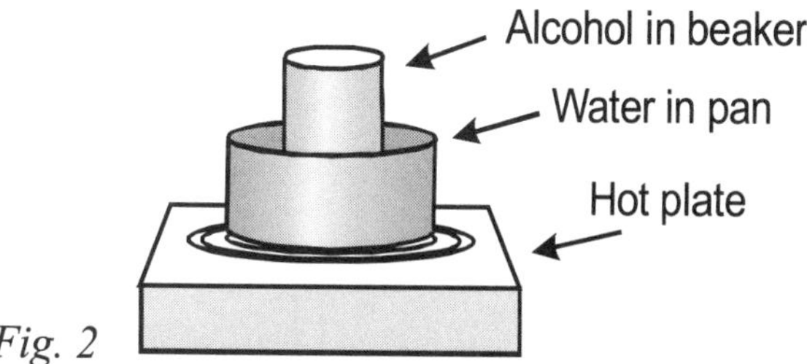

Fig. 2

5. After boiling your leaf in water for 1 minute, use the forceps to move your leaf to the smaller beaker containing alcohol. The alcohol will cause the leaves to lose their color.

6. When most of the color is gone from your leaf, use the forceps to remove it from the alcohol. Rinse the alcohol from the leaf by dipping it in the hot water in the outer beaker a few times.

7. Place the leaf in the Petri dish bottom and cover the surface of the leaf with Lugol's iodine solution.

8. Wait one minute and then pour off the excess Lugol's iodine solution into a designated waste container.

9. Observe your leaf. Draw your observations in the space provided on the student answer page.

10. Remove a second leaf from the plant. Select a leaf that did not have any foil attached to it during the 48-hour light treatment.

11. Repeat steps 11-16 using the second leaf.

12. Clean up your work area and return your supplies to the designated areas.

Name ______________________________

Period ______________________________

Lights Out
Demonstrating Dark Reactions

HYPOTHESIS

DATA AND OBSERVATIONS

PART I
Hierarchy of photosynthesis diagrams:

Hierarchy of photosynthesis structures for my favorite plant:

______________, ______________, ______________, ______________, ______________ of my

favorite plant the ____________________ located ________________________.

PRE-LAB QUESTIONS

1. What are the two main events of photosynthesis?

2. Where, specifically, do the Calvin cycle reactions occur?

3. Name three chemicals that are used by the Calvin cycle.

4. How many carbon dioxides must enter the Calvin cycle in order to form a single glucose molecule? How many molecules of ATP and NADPH are needed to form a single glucose molecule?

5. Give three examples of energy rich end products of the dark reactions of photosynthesis:

PART II

Diagram of leaf with initials after boiling:

Diagram of plain, non-treatment leaf:

ANALYSIS

1. Describe the similarities in the two leaves after they have been boiled and stained with Lugol's iodine solution.

2. Describe the differences in the two leaves after they have been boiled and stained with Lugol's iodine solution.

3. Which portion of the leaf contains the most starch, the part that had been covered with foil or the part that was not covered? Explain your answer using evidence from the lab.

CONCLUSION QUESTIONS

1. What is the purpose of removing, boiling and staining the second leaf in this experiment?

2. Did the Calvin cycle take place in the mesophyll cells located underneath your group's foil cut-out initials? How do you know?

3. Photosynthesis produces glucose. Lugol's iodine solution tests for starch. What is the relationship between starch and glucose?

4. Why is it important to primary consumers, like you, that plants store their energy as starch?

5. What Lugol's iodine test results would have been obtained from a leaf that had been entirely covered with foil?

6. Give an example of how structure is related to function in a chloroplast of your favorite plant.

7. Describe how the Calvin cycle is dependent upon the events of the light reactions.

8. Write a chemical equation that describes the process of photosynthesis.

Write Your Notes and Ideas Here!

Numbers Do Indeed Make a Difference
Investigating the Importance of Sample Size

OBJECTIVE
Students will investigate the importance of using a large sample size in studying genetics. This procedure uses the graphing calculator. In addition, students will statistically analyze the results to determine how well they fit predicted ratios.

LEVEL
Biology I

NATIONAL STANDARDS
UCP.2, UCP.3, UCP.4, C.2, E.1, E.2, G.1, G.2, G.3

TEKS
2(A), 2(B), 2(C), 6

CONNECTIONS TO AP
AP Biology:

II Heredity and Evolution A. Heredity 3. Inheritance patterns

TIME FRAME
45 minutes

MATERIALS
(For a class of 28 working in pairs)

28TI 83 or TI 83+ graphing calculators

TEACHER NOTES
This exercise supplements a unit on genetics.

This lab can be done on other graphing calculators if they have a function that will select random integers and histograms. Consult the manufacturer's manual.

The TI 83 calculator with each random number execution will generate the same random number for a given seed value. The TI 83 calculator is "seeded" to the number zero. If you are starting out with brand-new calculators, you will get the same random numbers and results for each student, unless you seed them with a different nonzero number. This is the optional part of the lab.

Students will be sharing their data with all groups twice during this activity. Groups will report their results outloud. The teacher can record the information on the board or on an overhead so that the entire class can see the results.

POSSIBLE ANSWERS TO THE CONCLUSION QUESTION AND SAMPLE DATA

	Family of 10				Family of 100			
Class Group #	# of females	%	# of males	%	# of females	%	# of males	%
1	7	0.7	3	0.3	45	0.45	55	0.55
2	6	0.6	4	0.4	55	0.55	45	0.45
3	6	0.6	4	0.4	49	0.49	51	0.51
4	5	0.5	5	0.5	57	0.57	43	0.43
5	5	0.5	5	0.5	51	0.51	49	0.49
6	7	0.7	3	0.3	50	0.50	50	0.50
7	6	0.6	4	0.4	51	0.51	49	0.49
8	3	0.3	7	0.7	47	0.47	53	0.53
9	7	0.7	3	0.3	54	0.54	46	0.46
10	8	0.8	2	0.2	53	0.53	47	0.47
11	7	0.7	3	0.3	52	0.52	48	0.48
12	5	0.5	5	0.5	53	0.53	47	0.47
13	4	0.4	6	0.6	56	0.56	44	0.44
14	2	0.2	8	0.8	51	0.51	49	0.49
15	5	0.5	5	0.5	48	0.48	52	0.52

1. Which group in your class had the family of ten with the lowest percentage of females? Males? What is the percentage of males versus females in each of those families?
   - Answers will vary but should cite the family with the lowest number of females and males, respectively.
   - Using the sample data above, Family 14 had the lowest percentage of female with (20%) and males (80%). Family 10 had the lowest percentage of male (20%) and females (80%).

2. Which group in your class had the family of 100 with the lowest percentage of females? Males? What is the percentage of males versus females in each of those families?
   - Answers will vary but should cite the family with the lowest number of females and males, respectively.
   - Using the sample data above, Family 1 had the lowest percentage of female with (45%) and males (55%). Family 4 had the lowest percentage of male (57%) and females (43%).

3. What is the predicted percentage of males versus females in a family of ten? In a family of 100?
   - In both cases the predicted ratio is 1:1 or 50% females and 50% males.

4. Write a conclusion about the effects of sample size on predicted genetic ratios.
   - The larger the sample size, more likely that predicted ratios will be obtained.

5. Select the family from each sample size (10 and 100) that exhibits the greatest deviation from the predicted outcomes and perform a chi-square analysis (χ^2).

$$\chi^2 = \sum \frac{(\text{expected - observed})^2}{\text{expected}}$$

What is the probability that your deviation is due to chance?

- (Using the sample data as an example)
- Family of ten.

  $$\frac{(3^2)}{5} + \frac{(3^2)}{5} = 3.6$$

- Family of 100.

  $$\frac{(7^2)}{50} + \frac{(7^2)}{50} = 1.96$$

- In all cases there is one degree of freedom. Examine the Table of Critical Values for Chi square at the p = .05 level. The critical value is 3.84. Both cases are less than 3.84, which means there is a 1 in 20 probability that the deviation observed is due to random chance. Notice that the larger sample size yields a smaller Chi square value of 1.96 even though the deviation was larger. The larger the sample size, the more likely that predicted ratios will be obtained.

6. Are the results acceptable by meeting the predicted results?
   - Most biologists agree that a deviation that has a chance probability equal to or greater than .05 (5% or 1 in 20) are not statistically significant. It is possible that a family of 10 might have a higher Chi-square value than the family of 100. Increasing the family size would most likely decrease the Chi-square value.

REFERENCES

Combs, Eunice, Editor. *Biological Science Interaction of Experiments and Ideas*. Englewood Cliffs: Prentice Hall, Inc., 1977. pg. 92

Milani, Jean P., Revision Coordinator. *Biological Science, A Molecular Approach*. Dubuque: Kendall Hunt Publishing Company, 1990. pp. 278-281

Ferl, Robert, Gerald P. Sanders, and Robert Wallace. *Biology the Science of Life*. New York: Harper Collins Publishers, 1990. pp. 228-235

Texas Instruments TI-83 plus Graphing Calculator Guide Book. Menasha: Banta Book Group, 1999. pp. 2-20

Numbers Do Indeed Make a Difference
Investigating the Importance of Sample Size

Gregor Johan Mendel (1822-1884) was an Abbot Monk who discovered the fundamental principles of genetic traits. His work was published in 1866 but was not recognized for its brilliance until the turn of the 20th century. While at the monastery, his superiors sent him to the University of Vienna to study math and science. During this time he studied statistics. When he returned to the monastery, his work focused on plant breeding projects and, in particular, the garden pea. At the time, he was able to work with true-breeding strains, with each strain differing from each other in very distinct characteristics. This made it easy to quantify the results of his breeding experiments. Peas were a very appropriate choice because Mendel could obtain large numbers of offspring in a relatively short period of time. As a result of his statistical training, Mendel had an appreciation for the significance that large sample sizes played in a study. Below is the data that Mendel collected on his garden pea. His data included a large number of offspring.

	Dominant form	Number in F2 Generation		Recessive form	Number in F2 Generation	Total examined	Ratio
	Round seeds	5474		Wrinkled seeds	1850	7324	2.96:1
	Yellow seeds	6022		Green seeds	2001	8023	3.01:1
	Gray seed coats	705		White seed coats	224	929	3.15:1
	Green pods	428		Yellow pods	152	580	2.82:1
	Inflated pods	882		Constricted pods	299	1181	2.95:1
	Long stems	787		Short stems	277	1064	2.84:1
	Axial flowers	651		Terminal flowers	207	858	3.14:1

Throughout this exercise you will examine the importance of sample size to the study of genetics.

The human gender ratio in the general population is approximately 50% females and 50% males. Given that ratio, a family of 10 children should have 5 boys and 5 girls. However, there are families of 10 that consist of all males or all females. On a larger scale, in a city of a million people, there should approximately 500,000 females and 500,000 males. Yet we never find a city that is all one gender or the other. The smaller the sample size, the more likely that random chance increases a deviation in the predicted ratios.

PURPOSE

In this activity you will start with the premise that you will create a family of ten offspring. The graphing calculator will create your family by randomly choosing 1's and 2's. Ones will represent females and twos will represent males. In each family there should theoretically be 50% females and 50% males. You will repeat the exercise to make a family of one hundred offspring and compare the results to the family of ten. Then, you will survey the class and compare results.

MATERIALS

TI-83+ graphing calculator

PROCEDURE

1. Write a hypothesis predicting the gender ratio for a family with 10 offspring and a family of 100 offspring.

2. Turn on your calculator [ON] and press [CLEAR] to clear the screen.

3. Clear all lists by pressing [2nd], [+] [mem]. Move cursor to ClrAllLists (by pressing the [↓] key OR press [4]) and then press [ENTER] twice. Done should appear on the screen.

4. * Recommended — If your teacher decides that your calculator needs to be "seeded", then do the following steps.
   a. Key in your birthday (i.e. 100385 for October 3rd 1985).
   b. Press [STO→], then press [MATH] and move the cursor at the top of the screen to PRB (probability) by pressing [→] key (Figure 1).
   c. Then press [ENTER] to store this number to the random number function. Press [ENTER] a second time (Figure 2).

Figure 1

Figure 2

5. Press STAT (Figure 3) and then ENTER. The list screen should appear (Figure 4).

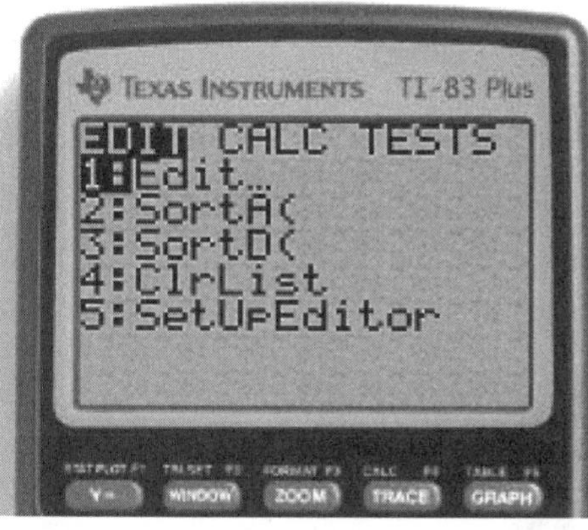

Figure 3

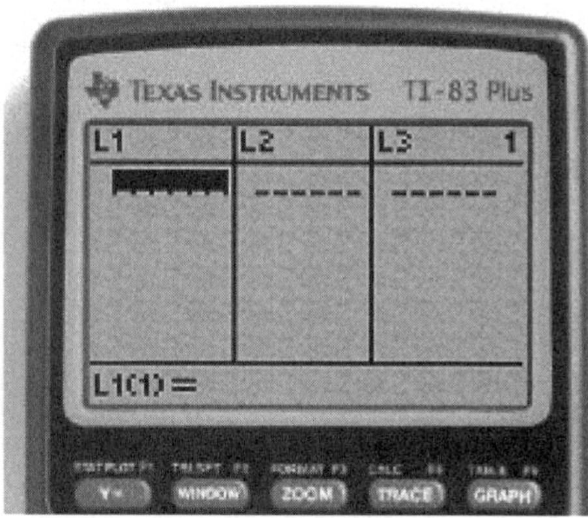

Figure 4

6. Put the cursor at the top of L1 (by pressing ▲) and press ENTER. A blinking black square will appear at the bottom after L1 = (Figure 5).

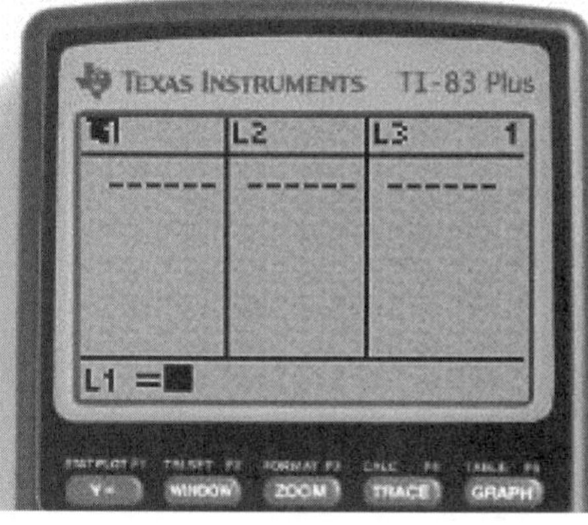

Figure 5

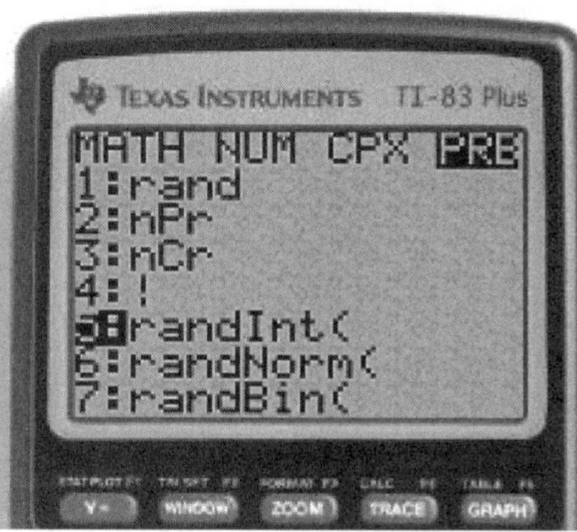

Figure 6

7. Now press MATH and move the cursor at the top of the screen to PRB (probability) with the ➔ key.

8. You want the calculator to randomly choose either a 1 or a 2 ten times. Move the cursor down to randInt (Figure 6) with the ▼ key and press ENTER, OR press 5. This should return you the list screen and at the bottom a blinking black square should appear after L1 =randInt(.

9. At this time you want to direct the calculator to randomly select 1's and 2's ten times. Do this by pressing 1, ",", 2, ",", 1, 0, ")". The screen at the bottom should now look like this L1 =...Int(1,2,10). See Figure 7. Press ENTER and L1 should be filled with 10 entries of either a 1 or a 2 (Figure 8).

Figure 7

Figure 8

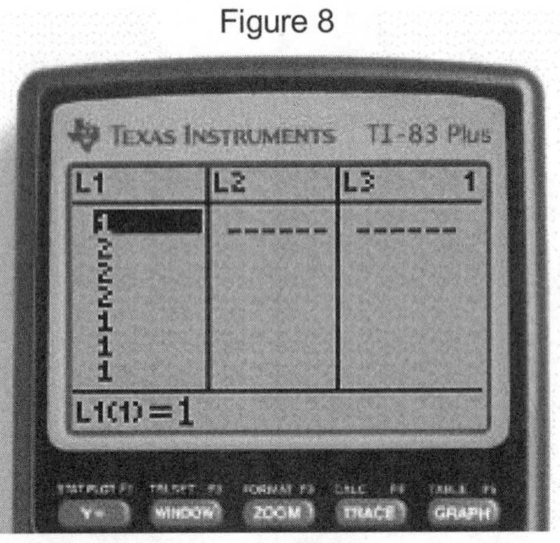

10. To view this graphically, press 2nd, Y= (Figure 9) ENTER. At this time make sure to put your cursor on PLOT 1 and press ENTER. Move the cursor down to ON and press ENTER. Both PLOT 1 and ON should be highlighted. All other plots should be inactivated.

Figure 9

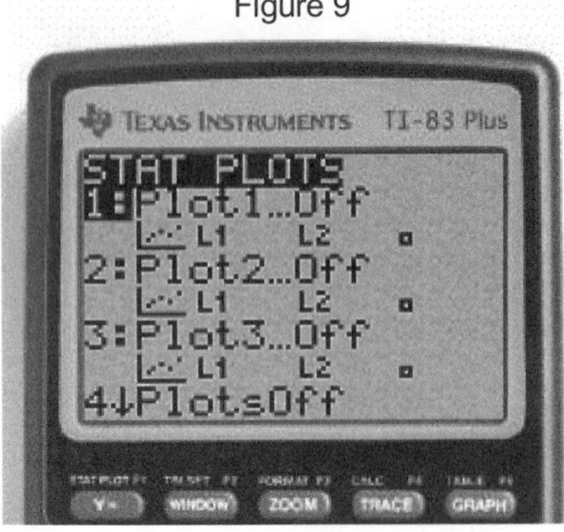

Figure 10

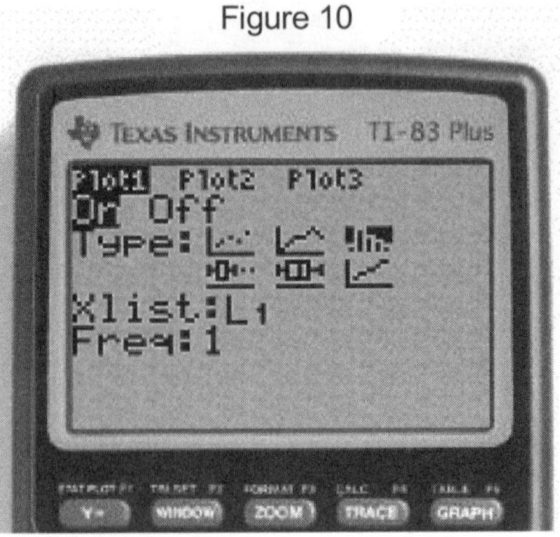

11. Move the cursor down and activate the bar graph or histogram, by putting the cursor on the bar graph (Figure 10) and pressing ENTER.

12. The list that you want to display is L1. Move the cursor down to the Xlist line and press 2nd, 1 [L1] (Figure 10).

13. To view the bar graph, press ZOOM, 9.

14. The bar graph should appear displaying the number of females versus males. To look at this press TRACE. Using the ◄ or ►, place the blinking cursor on the left bar. This represents the females and the bottom screen n= displays the number of females. Use the ► and place the blinking cursor on the right bar. This represents the males and the bottom screen n= displays the number of males. Record the number of male and female offspring in the data table in the space provided for group #1.

15. The teacher will survey each group for their results. Record the results each group reports on your student answer page.

16. The effect of sample size on a population can be emphasized by repeating steps 1-14 changing step 9 to reflect a family of 100. To do this replace the keystrokes with the following 1, ,, 2, ,, 1, 0, 0,). The screen at the bottom should now look like this L1 =...nt(1,2,100). Press ENTER and L1 should be filled with one hundred entries of ones and twos. Record the number of male and female offspring for your group in the data table in the space provided for group #1.

17. Again, the teacher will survey each group for their results. Record the results each group reports on your student answer page.

Name ______________________________

Period ______________________________

Numbers Do Indeed Make a Difference
Investigating the Importance of Sample Size

DATA AND OBSERVATIONS

	Family of 10				Family of 100			
Class Group #	**# of females**	**%**	**# of males**	**%**	**# of females**	**%**	**# of males**	**%**
1								
2								
3								
4								
5								
6								
7								
8								
9								
10								
11								
12								
13								
14								
15								

CONCLUSION QUESTIONS

1. Which group in your class had the family of ten with the lowest percentage of females? The lowest percentage of males? What is the percentage of males versus females in each of those families?

2. Which group in your class had the family of 100 with the lowest percentage of females? The lowest percentage of males? What is the percentage of males versus females in each of those families?

3. What is the predicted percentage of males versus females a family of ten? In a family of 100?

4. Write a conclusion about the effects of sample size on predicted genetic ratios.

5. Select the family from each sample size (10 and 100) that exhibits the greatest deviation from the predicted outcomes and perform a chi-square analysis (χ^2).

$$\chi^2 = \sum \frac{(\text{expected - observed})^2}{\text{expected}}$$

What is the probability that your deviation is due to chance?

6. Are the results acceptable by meeting the predicted results? Most biologists agree that deviations that have a chance probability equal to or greater than p = .05 (5% or 1 in 20) are not statistically significant.

Table of Critical Values of χ^2

p is the probability that the results could be due to chance alone. The numbers in parentheses below each value of p restate p in terms of chance: 9 in 10 likelihood that the results could be due chance alone.

Degrees of freedom	p = 0.9 (9 in 10)	p = 0.5 (1 in 2)	p = 0.2 (1 in 5)	p = 0.05 (1 in 20)	p = 0.01 (1 in 100)	p = 0.001 (1 in 1000)
1	0.158	0.455	1.642	3.841	6.635	10.827
2	0.214	1.386	3.219	5.991	9.210	13.815
3	0.584	2.366	4.642	7.815	11.345	16.268
4	1.064	3.367	5.989	9.488	13.277	18.465
5	1.610	4.351	7.289	11.070	15.086	20.517
6	2.204	5.348	8.558	12.592	16.812	22.457
7	2.333	6.346	9.903	14.067	18.475	24.322
8	3.490	7.344	11.303	15.507	20.090	26.125
9	4.168	8.343	12.242	16.919	21.660	27.877
10	4.865	9.342	13.442	18.307	23.209	29.588

Write Your Notes and Ideas Here!

Mendel and His Peas
Investigating Monhybrid Crosses Using the Graphing Calculator

OBJECTIVE
Students will investigate Mendel's Law of Segregation of Alternate Alleles using the graphing calculator. In addition, students will statistically analyze the results to determine how well they fit predicted ratios.

LEVEL
Biology I

NATIONAL STANDARDS
UCP.2, UCP.3, UCP.4, C.2, E.1, E.2, G.1, G.2, G.3

TEKS
2(A), 2(B), 2(C), 6

CONNECTIONS TO AP
AP Biology:

II. Heredity and Evolution A. Heredity 3. Inheritance Patterns

TIME FRAME
45 minutes

MATERIALS
(For a class of 28 working in pairs)

28 TI-83 or TI-83+ graphing calculators

TEACHER NOTES
This lab activity supplements a unit on Mendelian Genetics.

This lab can be done on other graphing calculators if they have a function that will select random integers and generate histograms. Consult the manufacturer's manual.

The TI 83 calculator with each random number execution will generate the same random number for a given seed value. The TI 83 calculator is "seeded" to number zero. If you are starting out with brand-new calculators, you will get the same random numbers and results, unless you seed them with different nonzero numbers. This is the optional part of the lab.

This exercise is a follow-up to the exercise, "The Importance of Sample Size in Genetics". It demonstrates Mendel's first law of Segregation of Alternate Alleles.

POSSIBLE ANSWERS TO THE CONCLUSION QUESTION AND SAMPLE DATA

	TT (2)	Tt (3)	tt (4)
Predicted Number of Offspring	25	50	25
Calculator Number of Offspring	20	52	28
Difference	5	2	3

1. How do the predicted ratios differ from the calculator ratios?
   - The ratios should approximate 1:2:1 ratio but there will be some variation. There will be very few that will have exactly 25:50:25.

2. How does this demonstrate what can be expected in actual crosses such as those done with real fruit flies?
   - In actual genetic crosses, there will always be some deviation from predicted ratios due to random chance.

3. Survey some of your classmates and determine if their results are similar or different from yours. Explain your findings.
   - Most of the students in the class should approximate the 1:2:1 predicted ratios. For a better fit to the predicted ratios, class data can be pooled.

4. What is the predicted phenotypic ratio for tall versus short offspring? In a sample of 100 offspring how many of each phenotype are expected? How many offspring of each phenotype were predicted by your calculator?
   - The predicted ratio of tall versus short is 3:1.
   - 75 tall versus 25 short.
   - The sample data above has a ratio of 72 tall to 28 short.

5. Based on the data produced by the calculator determine a Chi-square value for both the phenotypes and genotypes produced. Remember the equation for Chi-Square is

$$\chi^2 = \sum \frac{(\text{expected - observed})^2}{\text{expected}}$$

What is the probability that your deviation is due to chance?

$$\frac{(3^2)}{75} + \frac{(3^2)}{25} = .48$$

TEACHER PAGES

- There are two alleles, thus one degree of freedom (recall Foundation Lesson __). The calculated value for Chi-square is greater than 0.455 found in the table yet less than 1.642 thus p = 0.20 which means a 20% probability that the deviation observed is due to random chance. It may be more student friendly to state it as a 1 in 5 probability that the deviation observed is due to random chance.

6. Are the results acceptable and meet the predicted results? Most biologists agree that deviations that have a chance probability greater than or equal to 0.05 (5% or 1 in 20) are not statistically significant.
   - Based on the sampled data, the deviation is not significant.

7. If a person wanted to demonstrate a cross of Tt x tt with the graphing calculator, what changes in the procedure would need to be made?
   - When making the L2 list, the random number generator needs to only choose between 1 and 1 or rnd int = (1,1,100).

REFEREENCES

Combs, Eunice, Editor. *Biological Science Interaction of Experiments and Ideas*. Englewood Cliffs: Prentice Hall Inc., 1977 pg. 92

Milani, Jean P., Revision Coordinator. *Biological Science, A Molecular Approach*. Dubuque: Kendall Hunt Publishing Company, 1990. pp. 278-281

Ferl, Robert, Gerald P. Sanders, and Robert Wallace. *Biology the Science of Life*. New York: Harper Collins Publishers, 1990. pp. 228-235

Texas Instruments TI-83 plus Graphing Calculator Guide Book. Menasha: Banta Book Group, 1999. pp. 2-20

Mendel and His Peas
Investigating Monhybrid Crosses Using the Graphing Calculator

This activity will use the graphing calculator's random number generator to simulate the production of gametes in a monohybrid cross. The height of peas is the trait that can vary in peas. Peas can be tall or peas can be short. There is a gene that is responsible for this trait, and it has two forms or alleles: T for tall and t for short. The graphing calculator will simulate a cross of two peas that are heterozygous for being tall, Tt. This is based on the ability of the graphing calculator to generate 1's and 2's randomly much like flipping a coin to obtain random heads and tails. A 1 represents the T gamete for tall peas and a 2 represents a t gamete for short pea. The genotype for particular individual is found by adding both integers together.

Thus a tall pea that is homozygous dominant, TT, is represented by the number 2.

T T = 2
1 + 1 = 2

Other possible genotypes may be:

Tt = 3
tt = 4

PURPOSE
This exercise uses the graphing calculator to demonstrate genotypic ratios of a classic Mendelian Monohybrid cross.

MATERIALS
TI-83 plus graphing calculator

PROCEDURE
1. Write a hypothesis predicting the phenotypic ratio for the offspring of a cross involving two peas that are both heterozygous for tall, Tt x Tt. Be sure and state your hypothesis in the "If…then…" format.

2. Turn on your calculator [ON] and press [CLEAR] to clear the screen.

3. Clear all list by pressing [2nd], [+] [mem]. Move cursor to ClrAllLists (by pressing the [▼] key OR press [4]) and then press [ENTER] two times. Done should appear on the screen.

4. * Optional — If your teacher decides that your calculator needs to be "seeded", then do the following steps.
   a. Key in your birthday (i.e. 100385 for October 3rd 1985)
   b. Press STO▸, then press MATH and move the cursor at the top of the screen to PRB (probability) by pressing ▸ key (Figure 1).
   c. Then press ENTER to store this number to the random number function. Press ENTER a second time to execute the function (Figure 2).

Figure 1

Figure 2

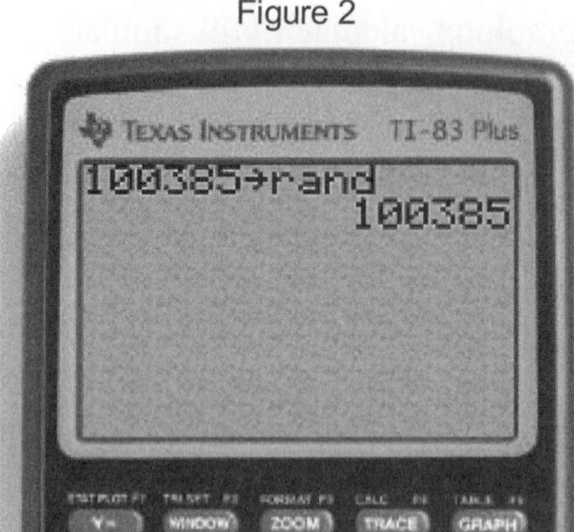

5. Press STAT (Figure 3) and then ENTER. The list screen should appear.

Figure 3

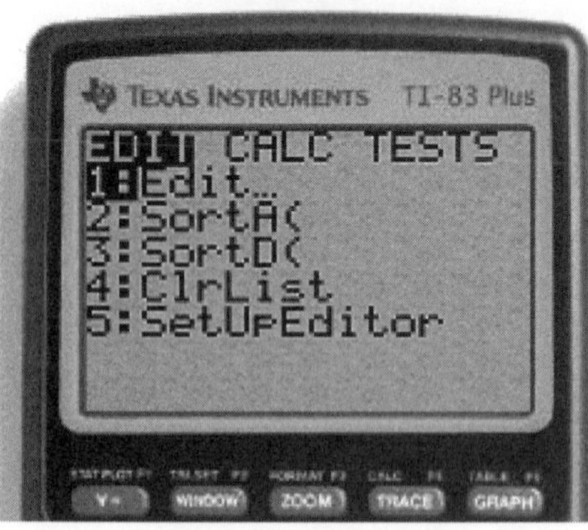

Figure 4

6. Put the cursor at the top of L1 (by pressing ▲) and press ENTER. A blinking black square will appear at the bottom after L1 =.

7. List 1 represents a parental pea plant that is heterozygous or Tt. The pea plant will produce 100 gametes either T or t. The calculator will randomly produce the gametes. This is done by randomly choosing the integer 1 or 2 one hundred times. If the calculator chooses the number 1, the gamete will be a T and if the calculator chooses the number 2, the gamete will be t.

8. With the cursor still blinking at the bottom, press [MATH] and move the cursor at the top of the screen to PRB (probability) with the [→] key.

9. You want the calculator to choose either a 1 or a 2 randomly and to make that random choice 100 times. Move the cursor down to randInt (Figure 4) with the [↓], then press [ENTER], OR press [5]. This should return you to the list screen and at the bottom a blinking black square should appear after L1 =randInt(.

10. At this time you want to direct the calculator to randomly select 1's and 2's one hundred times. Do this by pressing [1], [,], [2], [,], [1], [0], [0], [)]. The screen at the bottom should now look like this L1 =. randInt(1,2,100). See Figure 5. Press [ENTER] and L1 should be filled with 100 entries of either a 1 or a 2.

Figure 5

Figure 6

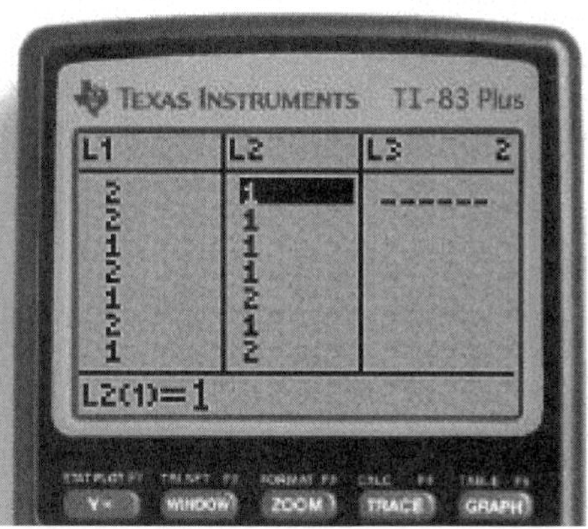

11. List 2 represents the parental pea plant # 2, and it is also heterozygous or Tt. The male is to make 100 gametes either T or t. The calculator will randomly produce the gametes. Put the cursor at the top of L2 and repeat steps 7 - 10 (Figure 6).

12. Now the gametes from the female (L1) need to be fertilized by the gametes from the male (L2). This is done by adding the two lists. Put the cursor on L3 and press [ENTER]. At the bottom of the list screen should appear L3=. Now press [2nd], [1], [L1], [+], [2nd], [2], [L2] (Figure 7). Press [ENTER] and L3 should fill in with the sums of L1 and L2 (Figure 8). List 3 represents the genotypes that result from the fertilization from the various gametes to produce 100 offspring. The following numbers represent the following genotypes:
    a. TT = 2.
    b. tT = 3.
    c. tt = 4.

Figure 7

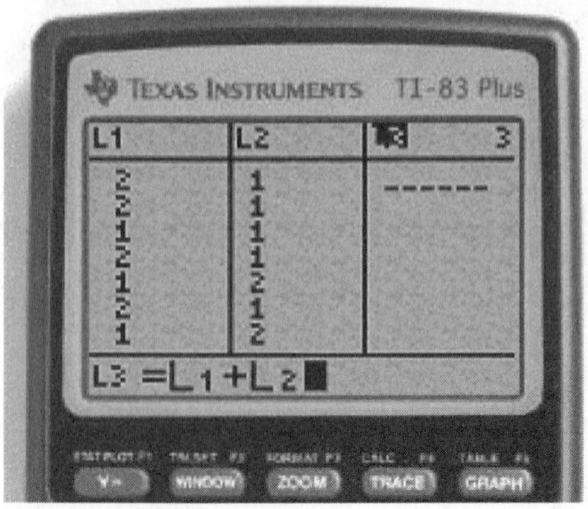

Figure 8

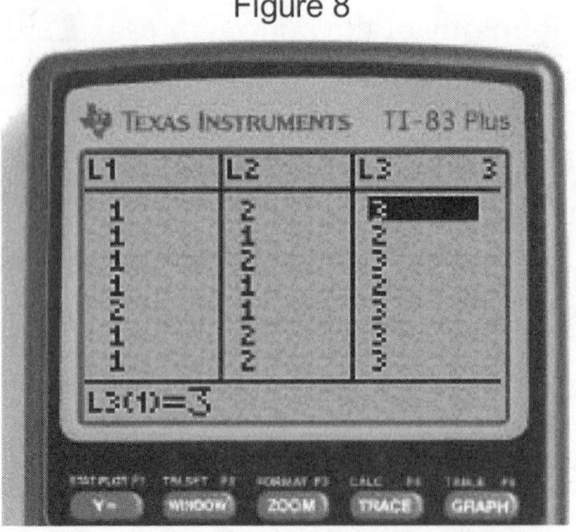

13. To view this graphically, press 2nd , Y= , (Figure 9). At this time, make sure to put your cursor on PLOT 1 and press ENTER and move the cursor down to ON and press ENTER . Both PLOT 1 and ON should be highlighted. All the other plots should be inactivated.

Figure 9

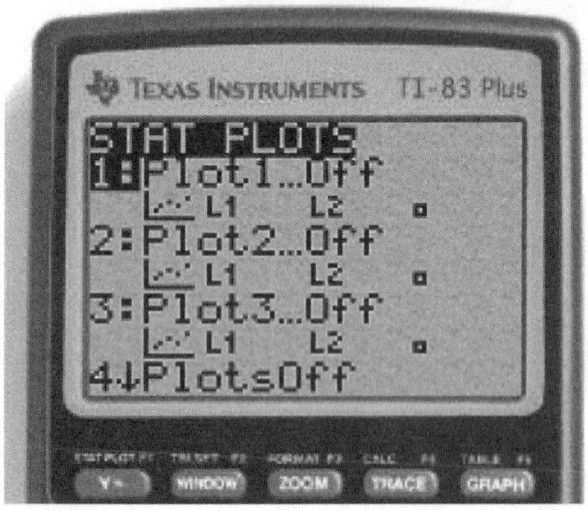

Figure 10

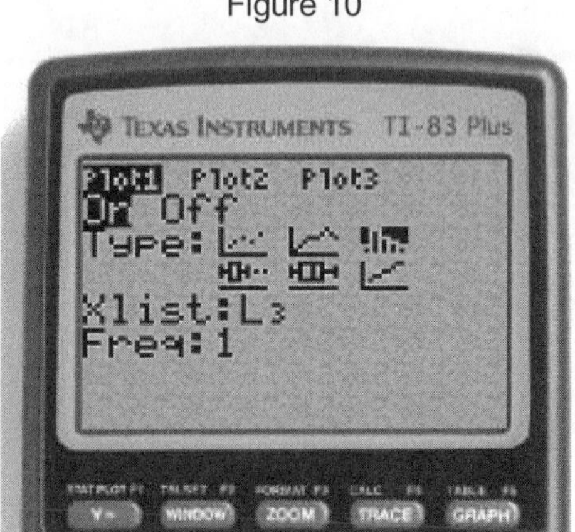

14. Move the cursor down and activate the bar graph, by putting the cursor on the bar graph and pressing ENTER .

15. The list that you want to display is L3. Move the cursor down to the next line and press 2nd , 3 (Figure 10).

16. To view the bar graph, now press ZOOM , 9 .

17. The bar graph should appear displaying the number of TT, Tt, tt genotypes. To look at this, press TRACE. Using the ◄ or ►, place the blinking cursor on the left bar (Figure 11). This represents the TT genotypes and the bottom screen n= displays the number. Use the ► to place the blinking cursor on the middle bar. This represents the heterozytotes, Tt and the bottom screen n= displays the number. Use the ► to place the blinking cursor on the right bar. This represents the homozygotes, tt, and the bottom screen n= displays the number.

18. Record the ratios of TT, Tt, and tt generated in the data table provided on the student answer sheet.

Figure 11

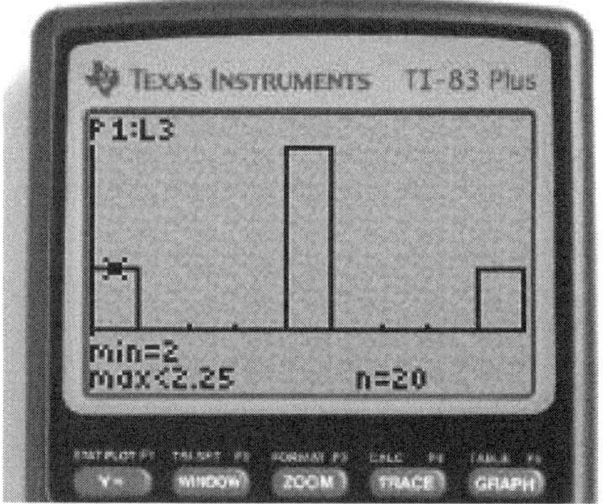

19. Survey three other groups and compare your data. Discuss with your partner possible explanations for the variation found among different groups.

Name ________________________________

Period________________________________

Mendel and His Peas
Investigating Monhybrid Crosses Using the Graphing Calculator

HYPOTHESIS

DATA AND OBSERVATIONS

	TT (4)	Tt (3)	tt (2)
Predicted Number of Offspring			
Calculator Number of Offspring			
Difference			

CONCLUSION QUESTIONS

1. How do the predicted ratios differ from the calculator ratios?

2. How does this demonstrate what can be expected in actual crosses such as fruit flies?

3. Survey some of your classmates and determine if their results are similar or different from yours. Explain your findings.

4. What is the predicted phenotypic ratio for tall versus short offspring? In a sample of 100 offspring how many of each phenotype are expected? How many offspring of each phenotype were predicted by your calculator?

5. Based on the data produced by the calculator, determine a Chi-square value for both the phenotypes and genotypes produced. Remember the equation for Chi-Square is

$$\chi^2 = \sum \frac{(\text{expected - observed})^2}{\text{expected}}$$

What is the probability that your deviation is due to random chance?

6. Are the results acceptable and meet the predicted results? Most biologists agree that deviations that have a chance probability greater than or equal to .05 (5% or 1 in 20) are not statistically significant.

7. If a person wanted to demonstrate a cross of Tt x tt with the graphing calculator, what changes in the procedure would need to be made?

Table of Critical Values of X^2

p is the probability that the results could be due to chance alone. The numbers in parentheses below each value of p restate p in terms of chance: 9 in 10 likelihood that the results could be due chance alone.

Degrees of freedom	p = 0.9 (9 in 10)	p = 0.5 (1 in 2)	p = 0.2 (1 in 5)	p = 0.05 (1 in 20)	p = 0.01 (1 in 100)	p = 0.001 (1 in 1000)
1	0.158	0.455	1.642	3.841	6.635	10.827
2	0.214	1.386	3.219	5.991	9.210	13.815
3	0.584	2.366	4.642	7.815	11.345	16.268
4	1.064	3.367	5.989	9.488	13.277	18.465
5	1.610	4.351	7.289	11.070	15.086	20.517
6	2.204	5.348	8.558	12.592	16.812	22.457
7	2.333	6.346	9.903	14.067	18.475	24.322
8	3.490	7.344	11.303	15.507	20.090	26.125
9	4.168	8.343	12.242	16.919	21.660	27.877
10	4.865	9.342	13.442	18.307	23.209	29.588

Write Your Notes and Ideas Here!

The Amazing Maize
Investigating Dihybrid Crosses

OBJECTIVE
Students will collect and analyze the results of a dihybrid cross in maize. Students will statistically analyze and compare the observed results with the predicted results.

LEVEL
Biology

NATIONAL STANDARDS
UCP.2, UCP.3, UCP.4, C.2, E.1, E.2, G.1, G.2, G.3

TEKS
1(A), 2(B), 2(C), 2(D), 6(A)

CONNECTIONS TO AP
AP Biology:
II Heredity and Evolution A. Heredity 3. Inheritance Patterns

TIME FRAME
50 minutes

MATERIALS
(For a class of 28 working in pairs)

14 ears of corn that exhibit the F2 generation from a parental cross of purple (RR), starchy (SuSu) crossed with yellow (rr), sweet (susu)
7 ears of homozygous purple starchy
7 ears of heterozygous purple starchy
7 ears of homozygous yellow sweet
28 push pins

TEACHER NOTES
This activity can be used to supplement a unit on genetics.

The ears of corn can be purchased from scientific supply companies such as Carolina Biological Supply or Ward's Natural Science Company.

There are other traits that can be examined and purchased from the above companies.

To keep track of the kernels, the students use two different colored push pins. One color is used to mark the first row counted. The second colored push pin is used to mark the row that is currently being counted. As a student finishes one row the pin should be moved to the next row. The pins should be placed at the end of the corn cob and inserted carefully so as to avoid damaging the kernels of corn. The best way to count kernels is to start at the beginning of a row and count the number of kernels with a given phenotype and record that information. Then return to the beginning of that same row and count the number of kernels in a second phenotype. Continue in this manner until all the phenotypes have been counted before moving onto the next row.

POSSIBLE ANSWERS TO THE CONCLUSION QUESTIONS AND SAMPLE DATA

Phenotype	Purple Smooth	Purple Wrinkled	Yellow Smooth	Yellow Wrinkled
	25, 31, 28, 24, 19, 27, 27, 25, 21, 20, 22, 33, 22	11, 10, 4, 9, 9, 5, 5, 5, 11, 7, 6, 2, 11	10, 5, 9, 10, 13, 6, 8, 9, 3, 11, 13, 6, 6	1, 3, 2, 4, 5, 7, 4, 2, 4, 2, 2, 1, 4
Total Number Observed	324	95	109	41
Total Number Expected	320	107	107	36
Deviation	4	12	2	5

1. Describe the P1 generation's phenotype and write out their genotypes.
   - The purple-smooth phenotype has kernels that are deep purple and the kernels appear to be smooth. The genotype is PPSS.
   - The yellow-wrinkled phenotype has kernels that are golden yellow and the kernels are wrinkled. The genotype is ppss.

2. Which phenotypes are dominant? How do you know?
   - The phenotypes of purple and smooth are dominant
   - These are the only phenotypes that appears in the F1 generation.

TEACHER PAGES

- Below write out a summary of the P1, F1 and F2 crosses.

P

Purple Smooth	X	Yellow Wrinkled
PP SS	↓	**pp ss**

	p s
PS	Purple Smooth **Pp Ss**

F1

Purple Smooth	X	Purple Smooth
Pp Ss		**Pp Ss**

F2

	PS	**Ps**	**pS**	**ps**
PS	Purple Smooth **PP SS**	Purple Smooth **PP Ss**	Purple Smooth **Pp SS**	Purple Smooth **Pp Ss**
Ps	Purple Smooth **PP Ss**	Purple Wrinkled **PP ss**	Purple Smooth **Pp Ss**	Purple Wrinkled **Pp ss**
pS	Purple Smooth **Pp SS**	Purple Smooth **Pp Ss**	Yellow Smooth **pp SS**	Yellow Smooth **pp Ss**
ps	Purple Smooth **Pp Ss**	Purple Wrinkled **Pp ss**	Yellow Smooth **pp Ss**	Yellow Wrinkled **pp ss**

3. How do the observed numbers differ from the predicted numbers?
   - Based on sample data, the numbers support the 9:3:3:1 predicted ratio. Class data can be combined to get more accurate results.

4. Based on your data, determine a Chi-square value for the phenotypes produced. Remember the equation for Chi-Square is

$$\chi^2 = \sum \frac{(\text{expected - observed})^2}{\text{expected}}$$

What is the probability that your deviation is due to chance?

$$\frac{(4^2)}{320}+\frac{(12^2)}{107}+\frac{(2^2)}{107}+\frac{(5^2)}{36}=2.13$$

- This is less than 7.8 which means that there is 1 in 5 probability that the deviation observed is due to chance. If the experiment was repeated five times, one could expect the same results that were obtained above at least once. These are acceptable results even though they do not match the predicted results perfectly.

REFERENCES

Combs, Eunice, Editor. *Biological Science Interaction of Experiements and Ideas*. Englewood Cliffs: Prentice Hall Inc., 1977. pg. 92

Keller, Evelyn Fox. *A Feeling for the Organism, The Life and Work of Barbara McClintock*. New York: W.H. Freeman and Company, 1983. pp. 1-14

Phillip McClean. “Transposon Tagging of Plant Genes.” <http://www.cc.ndsu.nodak.edu/instruct/mcclean/plsc731/transposon/tag1.htm> (viewed September 15, 2003).

Milani, Jean P., Revision Coordinator. *Biological Science, A Molecular Approach.* Dubuque: Kendall Hunt Publishing Company, 1990. pp. 278-281

King, Jack, Gerald P. Sanders, and Robert Wallace. *Biology the Science of Life*. Dallas: Scott Foresman, 1981. pp. 265-280

“Biology 216. Genetics and Development. Lab Exercise 2. Endosperm Genetics and Sordaria.” <http://lappel.web.wesleyan.edu/206_16/216lab2.htm> (viewed September 15, 2003).

“HORT410-Vegetable Crops, Sweet Corn-Notes. Department of Horticulture and Landscape Architecture” <http://www.hort.purdue.edu/rhodcv/hort410/sweetc/sw00002.htm> (viewed September 15, 2003).

The Amazing Maize
Investigating Dihybrid Crosses

Gregor Johan Mendel (1822-1884) was an Abbot Monk who discovered the fundamental principles of genetic traits. His work was published in 1866 but was not noticed and recognized for its brilliance until the turn of the 20th century. His work focused on plant breeding projects and, in particular, the garden pea. At the time, he was able to work with true-breeding strains, with each strain differing from each other in very distinct characteristics. This made it easy to identify the results from his experiments. Peas were a very appropriate choice because Mendel could obtain large numbers of results in a relatively short period of time.

After studying and analyzing monohybrid crosses, Gregor Mendel began to study the results of crossing two traits at a time. It is a fortunate coincidence that Mendel selected two traits that happened to be on different chromosomes. He worked with pure-bred peas that were round and yellow and crossed them with pure-bred peas that were wrinkled and green. In the parental cross of round and yellow with that of wrinkled and green, all of the offspring from the parental cross were yellow and round seeds. This meant that yellow and round alleles were dominant. Mendel then allowed these F1 offspring which were heterozygous for both traits to self-pollinate and produce a F2 generation. The F2 generation produced seeds that were yellow and round and seeds that were green and wrinkled.

The surprising point though was that there were new combinations that were not present in either the P generation or the F1. Two new phenotypes were produced — yellow and wrinkled peas and green and round peas. He also found that the peas occurred in specific phenotypic ratios; 9/16 were round and yellow, 3/16 were round and green, 3/16 were wrinkled and yellow and finally 1/16 were wrinkled and green.

He explained the results of the F2 generation by proposing that the traits underwent independent assortment. This means that when the F1 parents made gametes or pollen and eggs, the traits, or genes, for seed coat color and texture segregated independent of one another. This is known as Mendel's law of independent assortment. It states that if an organism is heterozygous for two different genes that are unlinked, then those alleles will assort independently of one another in the formation of gametes.

Mendel's Predicted Ratios and Results				
Phenotype of F2	Ratio Predicted	Number Predicted out of 556	Number Actually Observed	Deviation
Yellow and Round	9/16	313	315	2
Yellow and Wrinkled	3/16	104	101	3
Green and Round	3/16	104	108	4
Green and Wrinkled	1/16	35	32	3

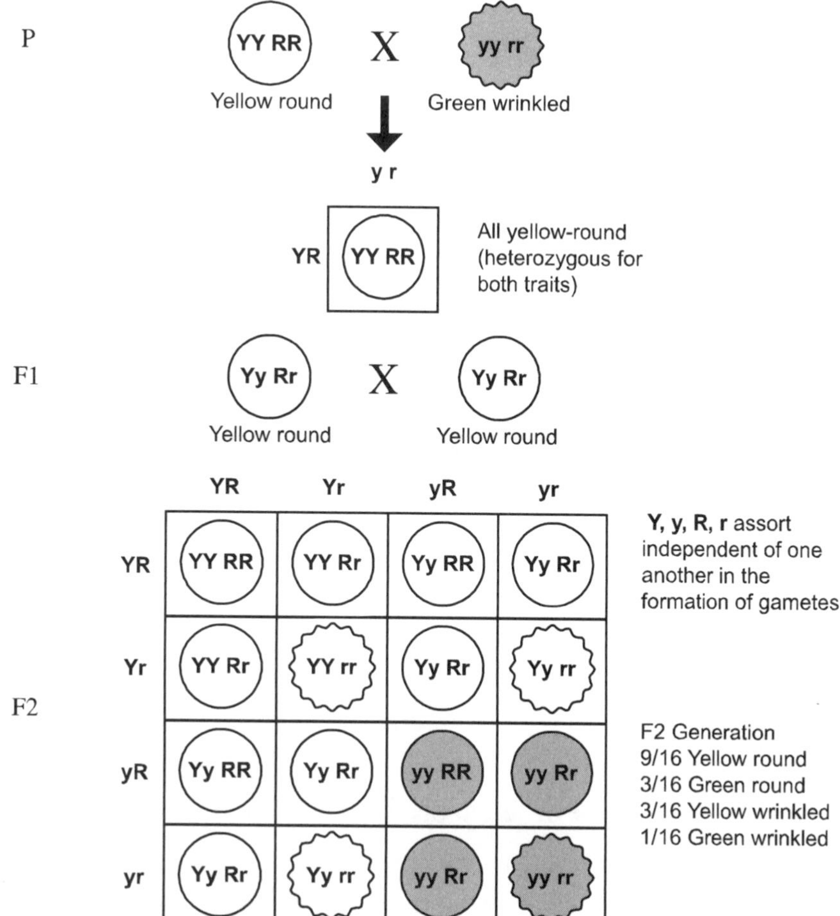

After the rediscovery of Mendel's work in 1900, many biologists began studying genetics. The two organisms of choice were the Drosophila fruit fly and maize or corn. Barbara McClintock and her colleagues studied corn extensively at Cornell University. Maize is an excellent choice for genetic study for the very same reasons that Mendel chose peas. There are a number of very distinct traits for the seed or corn kernel and a large number of offspring are produced in each generation. The large number of offspring in corn makes it even more advantageous than peas. An ear of corn can average 500-600 seeds whereas pea pods contain 4-6 seeds. It is through McClintock's studies that transposons or "jumping genes" were discovered. Barbara McClintock received a belated Nobel Prize in 1983 for her discovery.

In this activity you will use corn to examine two traits. You will study *starchy* kernels versus *sweet* kernels and *purple* kernels versus *yellow* kernels. The *starchy* gene produces kernels of corn that have a high content of starch. When these starchy kernels dry out, they remain full and plump whereas the kernels that contain high sugar content wrinkle upon drying. The second trait to be examined is color. The purple trait found in corn is due to the deposition of anthocyanin (plant pigment) in the outer layer of the endosperm or seed. If the pigment is not made, then the seed will typically have a yellow color.

PURPOSE

The purpose of this activity illustrates Mendel's Law of Independent Assortment through a dihybrid cross using maize.

MATERIALS

2 parental ears of corn
1 F1 ear of corn
1 F2 ear of corn
2 colored push pins

PROCEDURE

1. **DO NOT REMOVE ANY SEED FROM ANY EAR OF CORN**. Obtain two ears of corn that represent the parental generation. One ear should be purple and smooth; the other should be yellow and wrinkled. Observe the two ears of corn and write a description of their phenotypes. Make a hypothesis about the phenotypes and the ratios of those phenotypes resulting from a cross of two corn plants that are both heterozygous for purple and starch. Record this on student answer sheet.

2. Obtain an F1 ear of corn. By looking at the F1 ear of corn, determine what phenotypes are dominant and what phenotypes are recessive.

3. Write out the genotype using R's for purple and yellow and S's for starchy and sugary for the P generation and the F1 generation.

4. Predict the phenotypic ratio in the F2 generation for a cross that is heterozygous for both color of seed coat and texture (RrSs x RrSs). Make a Punnet square to support your prediction. In your Punett square, include genotypes.

5. Obtain an F2 ear of corn. Look at the different phenotypes for the kernels of corn. There should be four distinct phenotypes:
   a. Purple and smooth.
   b. Purple and wrinkled.
   c. Yellow and smooth.
   d. Yellow and wrinkled.

6. Put a colored marker pin in the end of one row of corn kernels. This will be used to mark your starting position. Count all the kernels that are both purple and smooth in that row. Record that number.

7. Repeat, but this time count all the kernels that are purple and wrinkled. Be sure to record the number. Repeat for the last two phenotypes.

8. Using another colored pin to mark your current position, move one row over. Repeat steps 6 and 7. After each row is counted, move the row marker to the next row and continue until you return to your starting place.

9. Total the number of seeds found in each phenotype.

10. Do a Chi-square analysis to see if the phenotypes fit the predicted ratios.

Name ______________________________

Period ______________________________

The Amazing Maize
Investigating Dihybrid Crosses

HYPOTHESIS

DATA AND OBSERVATIONS

Data Table				
Phenotype	Purple Smooth	Purple Wrinkled	Yellow Smooth	Yellow Wrinkled
Total Number Observed				
Total Number Expected				
Deviation				

CONCLUSION QUESTIONS

1. Describe the P1 generation's phenotype and write out their genotypes.

2. Which phenotypes are dominant? How do you know?

- Write out a summary of the P1, F1 and F2 crosses.

P

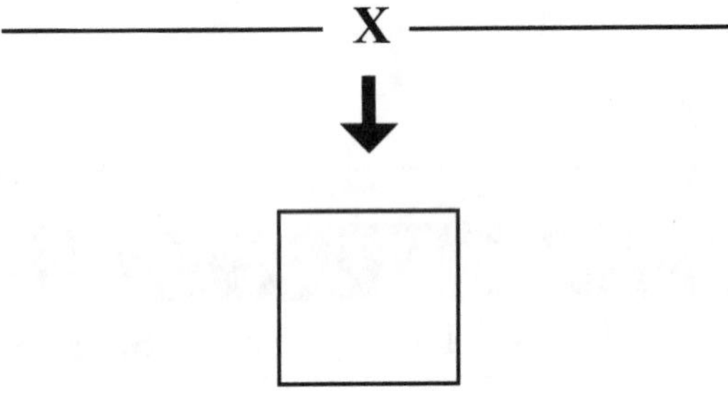

F1

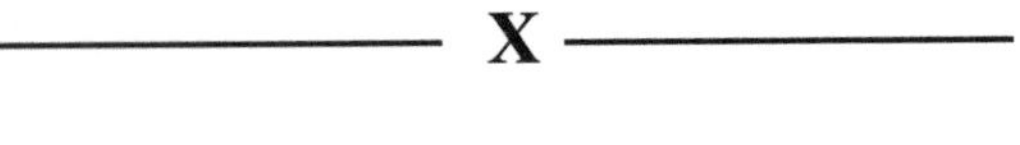

F2

3. How do the observed numbers differ from the predicted numbers?

4. Based on your data determine a Chi-square value for the phenotypes produced. Remember the equation for Chi-Square is

$$\chi^2 = \sum \frac{(\text{expected - observed})^2}{\text{expected}}$$

What is the probability that your deviation is due to chance?

Table of Critical Values of χ^2

p is the probability that the results could be due to chance alone. The numbers in parentheses below each value of p restate p in terms of chance: 9 in 10 likelihood that the results could be due chance alone.

Degrees freedom	p = 0.9 (9 in 10)	p = 0.5 (1 in 2)	p = 0.2 (1 in 5)	p = 0.05 (1 in 20)	p = 0.01 (1 in 100)	p = 0.001 (1 in 1000)
1	0.158	0.455	1.642	3.841	6.635	10.827
2	0.214	1.386	3.219	5.991	9.210	13.815
3	0.584	2.366	4.642	7.815	11.345	16.268
4	1.064	3.367	5.989	9.488	13.277	18.465
5	1.610	4.351	7.289	11.070	15.086	20.517
6	2.204	5.348	8.558	12.592	16.812	22.457
7	2.333	6.346	9.903	14.067	18.475	24.322
8	3.490	7.344	11.303	15.507	20.090	26.125
9	4.168	8.343	12.242	16.919	21.660	27.877
10	4.865	9.342	13.442	18.307	23.209	29.588

Proteins, the Essence of Life
Simulating the Process of Protein Synthesis

OBJECTIVE
Students will simulate the process of protein synthesis using models.

LEVEL
Biology I

NATIONAL STANDARDS
UCP.1, UCP.2, UCP.5, B.2, C.2, G.1, G.2, G.3

TEKS
6 (A), 6 (B)

CONNECTIONS TO AP
AP Biology:

II Heredity and Evolution B. Molecular Genetics 1. RNA and DNA structure and function

TIME FRAME
45 Minutes for transcription
45 Minutes for translation

MATERIALS
(For a class of 28 working in pairs)

14 copies of a portion of a "double helix" DNA molecule (strip of paper with letters)
14 scissors
14 kits to simulate protein synthesis
14 copies of mRNA codons (paper with six rectangles and letters in them)
14 rolls of clear tape

TEACHER NOTES
The lab is a simulation for the process of protein synthesis. This simulation uses models for protein synthesis. The DNA strands and mRNA nucleotides need to be photocopied and distributed to students as homework prior to the classroom activity. Have students cut these models out and bring them back to class.

Assembling the kits:

The simulation models contain both paper components and three-dimensional components. The materials for these items are available at a craft shop or large discount department store.

Paper models

The ribosome, RNA polymerase, spliceosome, release factor, and charging enzyme can be photocopied and laminated. These pieces should then be durable enough to last for many years. Photocopy masters for all of the paper components are included at the end of the Teacher Notes.

Assembly of the tRNA (three-dimensional model)

You will need the following materials:

- Assorted colors of pipe cleaners
- Hot glue gun
- Anti-codon copied from included master

Below are the patterns for the anti-codons. They can be copied, laminated, and cut out for maximum durability.

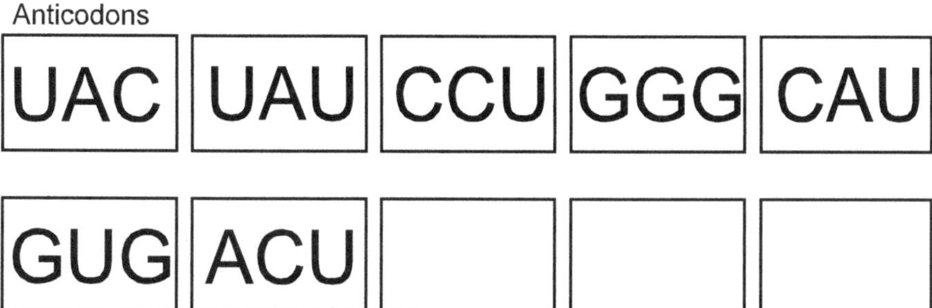

The tRNA is made from colored pipe cleaners. Cut a length of pipe cleaner approximately 25 cm long and fold it into the shape below. Use the hot glue gun to glue the ends together.

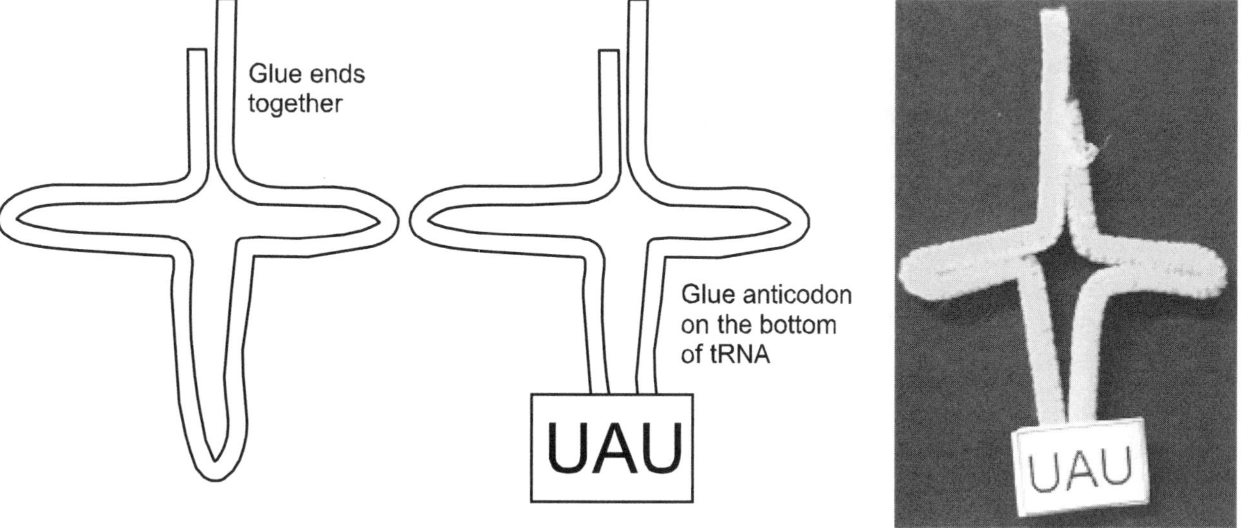

Assembly of the amino acids (three-dimensional model)

You will need the following materials:

- 1 ½ inch Styrofoam® balls.
- Assorted colors of jumbo craft sticks (6 inch long x ¾ inch wide).
- Pipe cleaners
- Assorted colors of permanent markers
- Copied and laminated hydrogen, carboxyl and amine groups from included master
- Hot glue gun
- Tin snips or heavy-duty scissors (to cut the jumbo craft sticks)

Below are the patterns for the amine, carboxyl, and hydrogen groups on the amino acid. They should be copied, laminated and cutout for maximum durability.

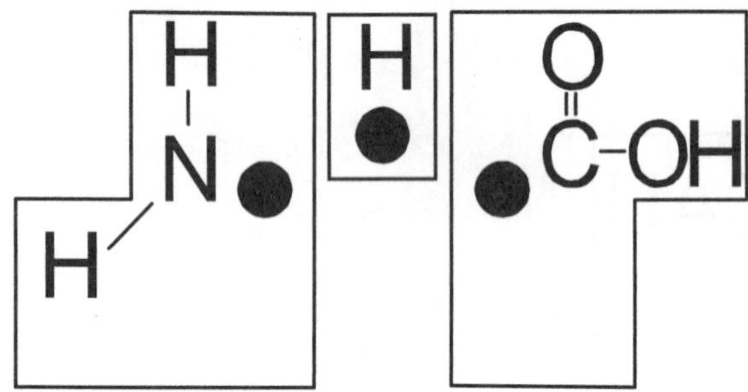

Punch holes in the patterns at the large black dots. They will be inserted into the Styrofoam® ball by using a small loop of pipe cleaner. Insert the pipe cleaner into the punched hole, twist it, and then insert it into the Styrofoam® ball. Use the hot glue to cement the pipe cleaner to the ball and keep the functional groups in place.

Next, cut jumbo sticks to a length of approximately 2 inches long. Try to color coordinate the sticks with their tRNA. For example, if the tRNA has an orange pipe cleaner use an orange jumbo craft stick for its amino acid. Draw the appropriate R groups on the jumbo stick. Insert the stick into the bottom of the Styrofoam® ball and secure with hot glue.

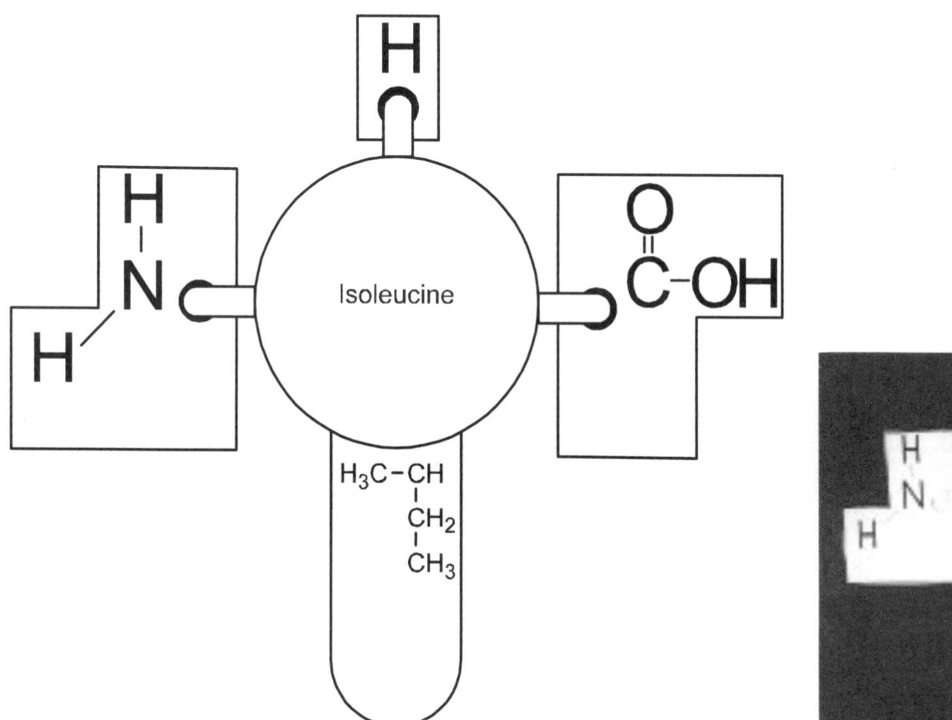

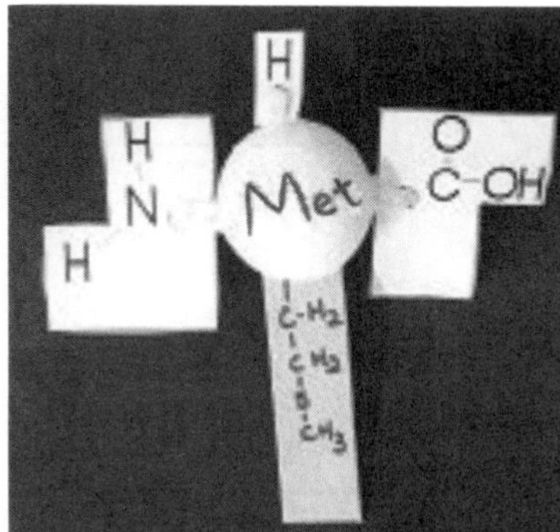

The models once made and collected can be stored in a sealed bag. The first year this is done, you may want to enlist the help of your classes to cut the laminated, paper models. Once they are cut and laminated, they will last for years.

The models for each event described in the activity include only the models needed to make the simulation work.

Suggested teaching procedures:
You may want to walk you students through the identification of model pieces. It may also be beneficial for the students to look at a diagram in their book that depicts protein synthesis. Remind students that as they work through the simulation, they should answer the questions as they do it. As the teacher, you should go around the room and check for understanding while the students are working.

Photocopy Masters

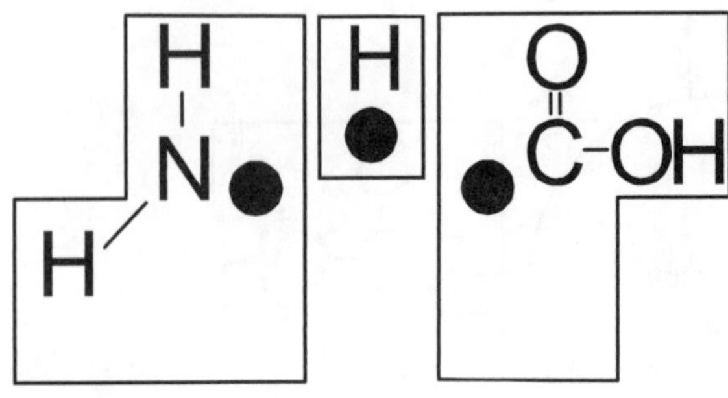

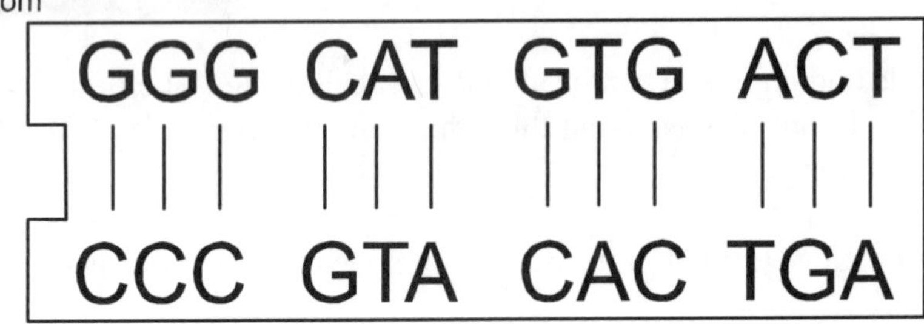

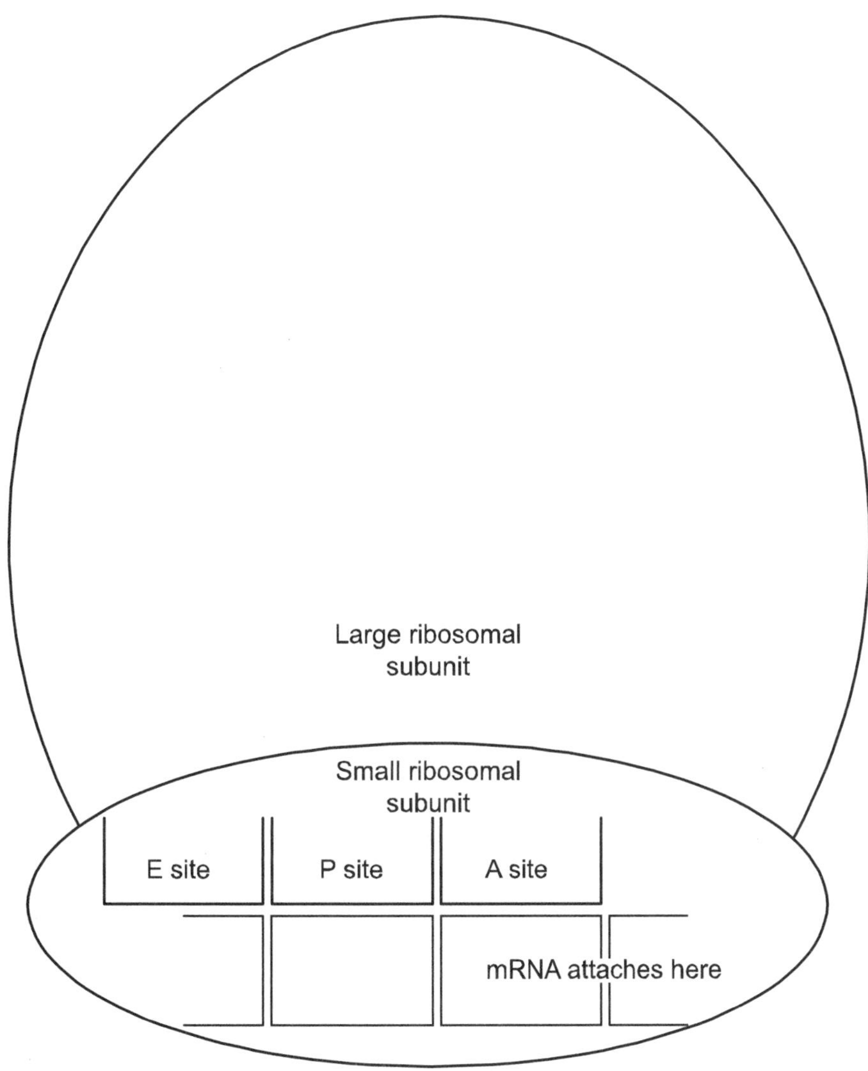
Large ribosomal
subunit
Small ribosomal
subunit
E site
P site
A site
mRNA attaches here

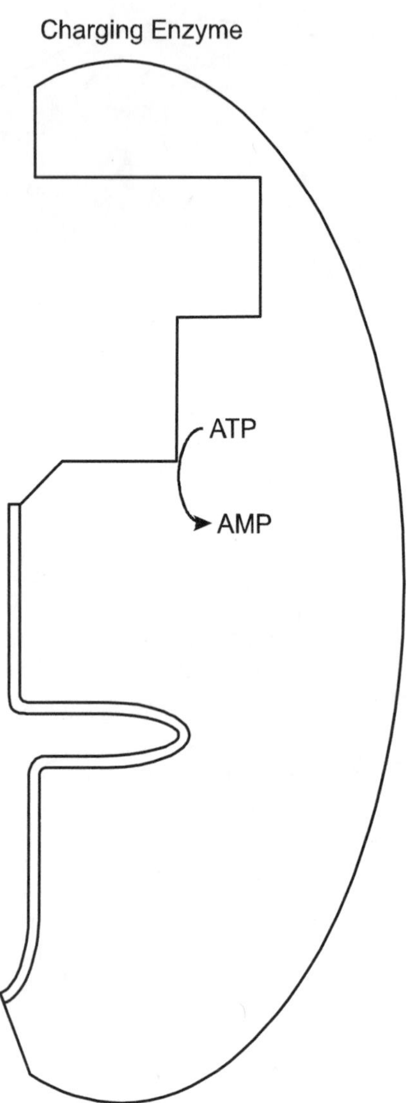
Charging Enzyme
ATP
AMP

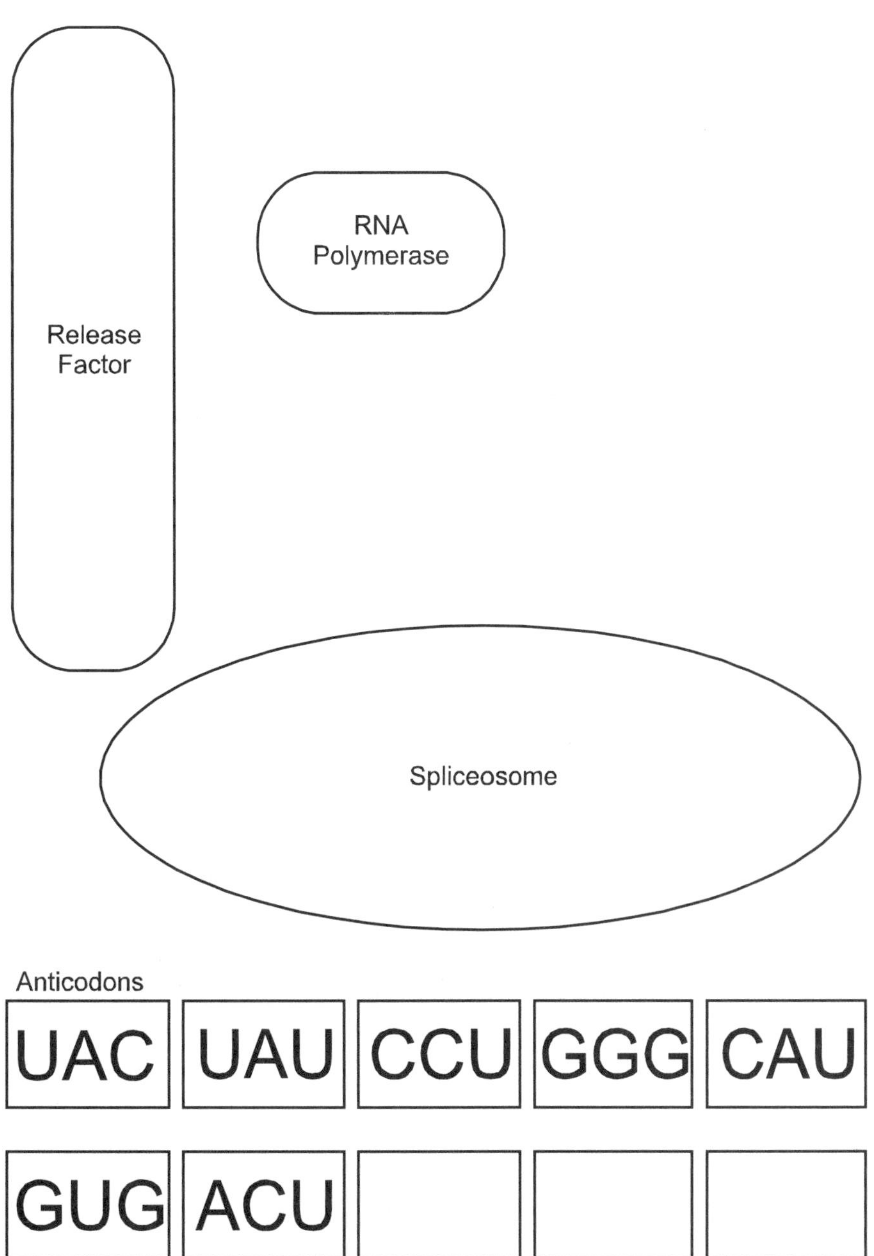
Release
Factor
RNA
Polymerase
Spliceosome
Anticodons
UAC
UAU
CCU
GGG
CAU
GUG
ACU

POSSIBLE ANSWERS TO THE CONCLUSION QUESTIONS AND SAMPLE DATA

1. Where is DNA located in the cell? Describe the structure of the DNA molecule.
   - DNA is found in the nucleus, and it is a part of chromosomes found in eukaryotic cells. A chromosome is made of DNA and a number of proteins.

2. DNA is a long polymer made of many subunits. What are those subunits called and what parts do they have?
   - DNA is polymer made up of subunits called nucleotides.
   - A nucleotide consists of ribose, a nitrogenous base, and a phosphate group.

3. Write out both the top and bottom portion of the DNA molecule in the space below.
   - Top TAC TAT GGCC CCT GGG GTG ACT
   - Bottom ATG ATA CCGG GGA CCC CAC TGA

4. Define the term gene and explain exactly what a gene does.
   - A gene is a sequence of DNA nucleotides that specifies a polypeptide chain.
   - A gene will determine which protein will be made and the order of its amino acids.

5. How many genes are found on a chromosome?
   - There are thousands of genes on a chromosome.

6. What biological molecule do the scissors represent?
   - They represent enzymes that have the ability to break hydrogen bonds on a DNA molecule.

7. What is a DNA codon?
   - A codon is a sequence of three DNA nucleotides that code for a specific amino acid.

8. What enzyme is responsible for base pairing the RNA nucleotides to the DNA gene?
   - RNA polymerase is the enzyme responsible for the base pairing between RNA nucleotides and DNA nucleotides.

9. Fill in the chart below for the base pairing of DNA to RNA nucleotides

DNA	RNA
Adenine	Uracil
Cytosine	Guanine
Thymine	Adenine
Guanine	Cytosine

10. What are introns and exons?
    - Introns are intervening sequences of DNA nucleotides that not expressed or translated. Exons are the DNA nucleotides that are translated and expressed.

11. What molecule is responsible for removing introns and rejoining exons?
    - A spliceosome is responsible for the removal of introns and splicing of exons.

12. Write out the RNA codons that remain after the intron has been removed.
    - RNA Codons: A U G A U A G G A C C C C A C U G A

13. What are two purposes of a 5' cap?
    - The 5' cap functions to protect of the mRNA from degradation and to aid in recognition between the ribosome and mRNA.

14. What are two purposes of poly-A-tail?
    - The poly-A-tail functions to protect the mRNA from degradation and to determine how many times the mRNA can be translated.

15. How is mature mRNA different from immature mRNA? How does mRNA determine the sequence of a polypeptide chain?
    - Mature mRNA has been processed to have its introns removed, exons spliced back together, a 5' cap and poly-A-tail added.
    - The sequence of the nucleotides in the exons will determine the order of the amino acids in a polypeptide chain.

16. What is an mRNA codon?
    - An mRNA codon is a sequence of three RNA nucleotides that code for a specific amino acid and are complementary to the DNA codon.

17. Determine the amino acid sequence using the mRNA codon chart below.
    a. mRNA AUG AUA GGA CCC CAC UGA
    b. amino acid sequence met- ile- gly- pro- his- Stop

	Second letter				
First letter	**U**	**C**	**A**	**G**	**Third letter**
U	UUU } Phe UUC UUA } Leu UUG	UCU } Ser UCC UCA UCG	UAU } Tyr UAC UAA Stop UAG Stop	UGU } Cys UGC UGA Stop UGC Trp	U C A G
C	CUU } Leu CUC CUA CUG	CCU } Pro CCC CCA CCG	CAU } His CAC CAA } Gln CAG	CGU } Arg CGC CGA CGG	U C A G
A	AUU } Ile AUC AUA AUG Met/ Start	ACU } Thr ACC ACA ACG	AAU } Asn AAC AAA } Lys AAG	AGU } Ser AGC AGA } Arg AGG	U C A G
G	GUU } Val GUC GUA GUG	GCU } Ala GCC GCA GCG	GAU } Asp GAC GAA } Glu GAG	GGU } Gly GGC GGA GGG	U C A G

18. List the complementary anticodons that will be found on the tRNA for the mRNA in question 17.
    - tRNA anticodons UAC UAU CCU GGG GUG ACU

19. What is translation and where does it occur? What four items are needed for translation to occur?
    - Translation is the actual synthesis of a polypeptide chain.
    - Translation requires a ribosome, mRNA, tRNA, and amino acids.

20. What is the structure of an amino acid?
    - An amino acid has a central carbon atom with 4 groups bonded to it. Those groups are a hydrogen atom, an amine group, a carboxyl group, and a variable group.

21. What type of bond is made when amino acids are joined?
    - A covalent peptide bond is made when amino acids join.

22. How many water molecules were removed from the polypeptide chain?
    - Since five amino acids were used in the polypeptide chain there were 4 molecules of water removed.

23. Write in the space provided the amino acids that were used to make this protein and what molecule was formed from the atoms removed.

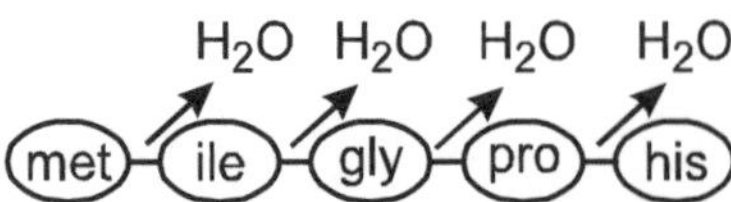

24. Describe the process of termination.
    - When the ribosome comes to the stop codon, a release factor protein binds with the codon instead of a tRNA. This causes the ribosome to disengage releasing the mRNA, tRNA and polypeptide chain.

REFERENCES

Greenberg, Jon, Revision Editor. *Biological Science, A Molecular Approach,* Chicago: Everyday Learning, 2001. pp. 234-254

Proteins, the Essence of Life
Simulating the Process of Protein Synthesis

Proteins are the molecules that carry out the "business of living". Humans can synthesize over 50,000 different proteins. How does a cell synthesize so many different proteins? The blueprint for the synthesis of these proteins is found in molecules of DNA. DNA contains the genetic information needed for protein synthesis. DNA is restricted to the nucleus in eukaryotic cells yet the actual synthesis of proteins occurs on ribosomes found in the cytoplasm of cell. This implies that there must be some sort of intermediate molecule that is responsible for moving the information from the nucleus out to the cytoplasm. That intermediate is RNA.

There are two parts to protein synthesis, transcription and translation. Transcription is the process of converting the information encoded in the DNA molecule into a messenger RNA molecule. This occurs in the nucleus. Translation is the actual synthesis of a protein or polypeptide chain. This occurs in the cytoplasm and requires several components. The ribosome serves as the workbench for this process by bringing together the mRNA instructions with the tRNA carrier of the amino acid.

PURPOSE
In this activity you will simulate the process of transcription and translation. These processes will lead to the formation of a protein from a DNA gene.

MATERIALS
- copy of a portion of a double helix DNA molecule
- scissors
- kits to simulate protein synthesis
- copy of mRNA codons
- clear tape

PROCEDURE
Transcription

1. The following should be cut prior to class: DNA strand and mRNA codons. Tape the two strands of the DNA molecule together to form one long DNA strand. Obtain a kit that contains the models needed for this simulation. Answer questions 1-3 on the student answer sheet.

2. To begin transcription, enzymes break the weak hydrogen bonds between the base pairs of the two DNA strands. To simulate this use scissors to cut the double stranded DNA into two single strands. This demonstrates how the DNA molecule unwinds. Answer questions 4-6 on the student answer page.

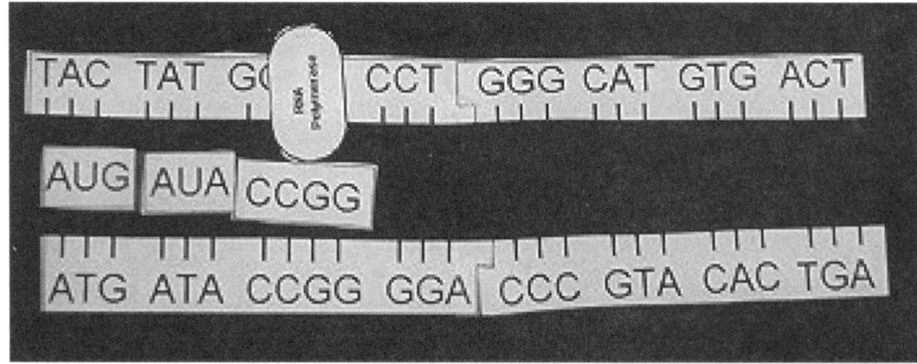

3. Notice that many of the DNA nucleotides are in groups of three nucleotides. This grouping represents a codon. A DNA codon is a group of three nucleotides that will determine which amino acid will be placed in the polypeptide chain. Answer question 7 on the student answer page.

4. Transcription occurs when mRNA nucleotides base pair with DNA nucleotides. The enzyme, RNA polymerase, is responsible for base pairing the correct RNA nucleotides to the correct DNA nucleotides. Only one side of the DNA molecule is transcribed. Transcribe the top side of the DNA molecule by base pairing the appropriate mRNA base pairs using RNA polymerase. Tape the RNA nucleotides together to make one long mRNA strand. Answer questions 8 and 9.

5. Remove the mRNA from the DNA gene and "zip" the DNA gene back together with tape. At this point the mRNA is an immature mRNA molecule and must be processed. In eukaryotic genes, there are nucleotides that are not used or expressed. One might view these DNA nucleotides as "junk DNA". They are called introns because they are intervening sequences. RNA polymerase can not tell the difference between these intron (intervening) and exon (expressed) regions. Therefore these introns are also found on the mRNA. Look at the mRNA. Notice a sequence that is not grouped in three nucleotides. This represents an intron. In reality, a eukaryotic gene has many introns and introns are much longer than four nucleotides. The intron must be removed, and a structure called a spliceosome is responsible for removing the intron. Place the mRNA on the paper spliceosome. Using scissors, remove the intron. The mRNA nucleotides that remain are called exons because they will be expressed. The spliceosome will splice the remaining exons together. Tape the exons together using tape. Answer questions 10-12.

6. The next thing that occurs is the addition of a 5' cap, which is composed of a number of RNA nucleotides. The purpose of the 5' cap is to protect the RNA molecule from being degraded in the cytoplasm and also aids in recognition between the ribosome and mRNA. Cut out the 5' cap and add it to the mRNA. Answer question 13.

7. At the 3' end, a series of adenine nucleotides, called a poly-A-tail, are added. The function of the poly-A-tail seems to also aid in protecting the mRNA from being degraded and plays a role in determining how many times the mRNA can be translated. The tail can average between 100 and 200 adenines long. Answer question 14.

8. After splicing and adding the 5' cap and 3' tail, this mature piece of mRNA is ready for the actual synthesis of a protein. The process of synthesizing a protein is called translation. The sequence of the mRNA nucleotides determines the order of the amino acids in the protein. Notice that the RNA nucleotides are in groups of three nucleotides. This grouping represents a codon. The RNA codon is a group of three nucleotides that will determine what amino acid will be placed in the polypeptide chain. Remember the RNA codon has it sequence determined by the original DNA codon. Below is the genetic code based RNA codons. For example if an mRNA codon is UUU, this is the code for the amino acid, phenylalanine. Answer questions 15 and 16.

First letter	Second letter: U	C	A	G	Third letter
U	UUU Phe UUC Phe UUA Leu UUG Leu	UCU Ser UCC Ser UCA Ser UCG Ser	UAU Tyr UAC Tyr UAA Stop UAG Stop	UGU Cys UGC Cys UGA Stop UGC Trp	U C A G
C	CUU Leu CUC Leu CUA Leu CUG Leu	CCU Pro CCC Pro CCA Pro CCG Pro	CAU His CAC His CAA Gln CAG Gln	CGU Arg CGC Arg CGA Arg CGG Arg	U C A G
A	AUU Ile AUC Ile AUA Ile AUG Met/Start	ACU Thr ACC Thr ACA Thr ACG Thr	AAU Asn AAC Asn AAA Lys AAG Lys	AGU Ser AGC Ser AGA Arg AGG Arg	U C A G
G	GUU Val GUC Val GUA Val GUG Val	GCU Ala GCC Ala GCA Ala GCG Ala	GAU Asp GAC Asp GAA Glu GAG Glu	GGU Gly GGC Gly GGA Gly GGG Gly	U C A G

9. Determine sequence of amino acids encoded in your mRNA and record them on your student answer page under question 17.

Translation

1. Translation is the actual synthesis of a polypeptide chain. Move your mRNA from the hypothetical nucleus to the hypothetical cytoplasm on your desk. There are three necessary components for translation to take place. They are:
   a. MRNA — This will determine the sequence of the amino acids
   b. tRNA charged with an appropriate amino acid — This molecule brings the appropriate amino acid to the correct codon on the mRNA
   c. Ribosome — This is a workbench where the actual synthesis of the polypeptide will occur.

   Answer question 19.

2. Another important RNA molecule used in the process of translation is transfer RNA or tRNA. For each mRNA codon in this model, there is a specific tRNA. tRNA is a single stranded molecule that folds and base pairs with itself to form a clover-leaf shaped structure. At the bottom of the tRNA is series of 3 nucleotides. These nucleotides are complementary to the mRNA codon (A-U and G-C) and are called the anti-codons. For example if an mRNA codon is UUU, then the tRNA anticodon found on the bottom of the tRNA is AAA. Look at the tRNA models in the kit and notice the anticodon found at the bottom. For each mRNA codon you listed in question 17, list the anticodon in question 18.

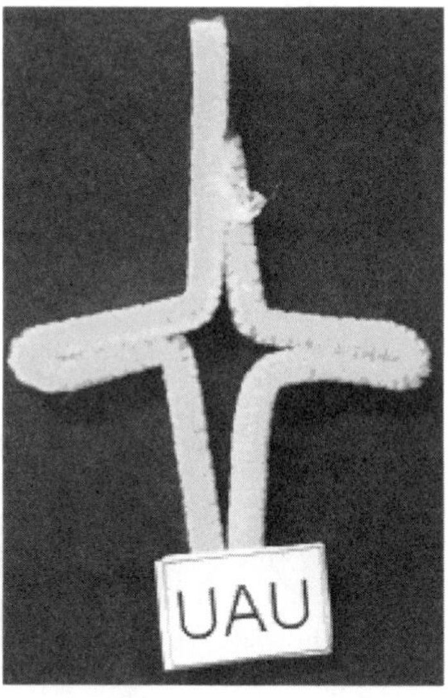

3. The function of the tRNA is to bring the appropriate amino acid to the appropriate mRNA codon. This is works because there is a charging enzyme responsible for bonding the correct tRNA with the correct amino acid. This bonding requires ATP. Find the charging enzyme. Notice that the active site fits a tRNA and an amino acid.

4. Find an amino acid. The Styrofoam® ball represents the central carbon. Notice that hydrogen is attached as are an amine group, and a carboxyl group. Also notice there is a jumbo craft stick representing the variable R group. On the jumbo stick is a drawing of the variable R group. Each amino acid has a different colored stick and a different variable R group. Answer question 20.

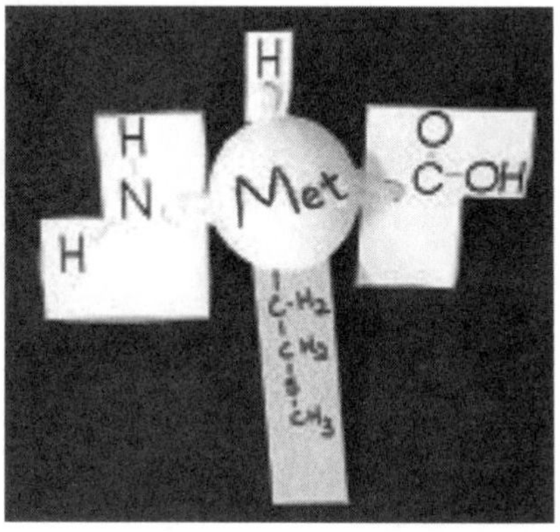

5. Now, using the charging enzyme, combine each tRNA with its correct amino acid. This is done by using a paper clip to attach the amino acid (on the jumbo stick) to the tRNA (at the top end of the pipe cleaner). The correct amino acid is bonded to the correct tRNA by a sequence of nucleotides on the anticodon and the codon of mRNA. The charging enzyme will release the charged tRNA once the amino acid is bonded to it. Look at the answers for questions 17 and 18 to make sure that the correct amino acid is bonded to the correct tRNA. At this point every tRNA should have an amino acid attached to it.

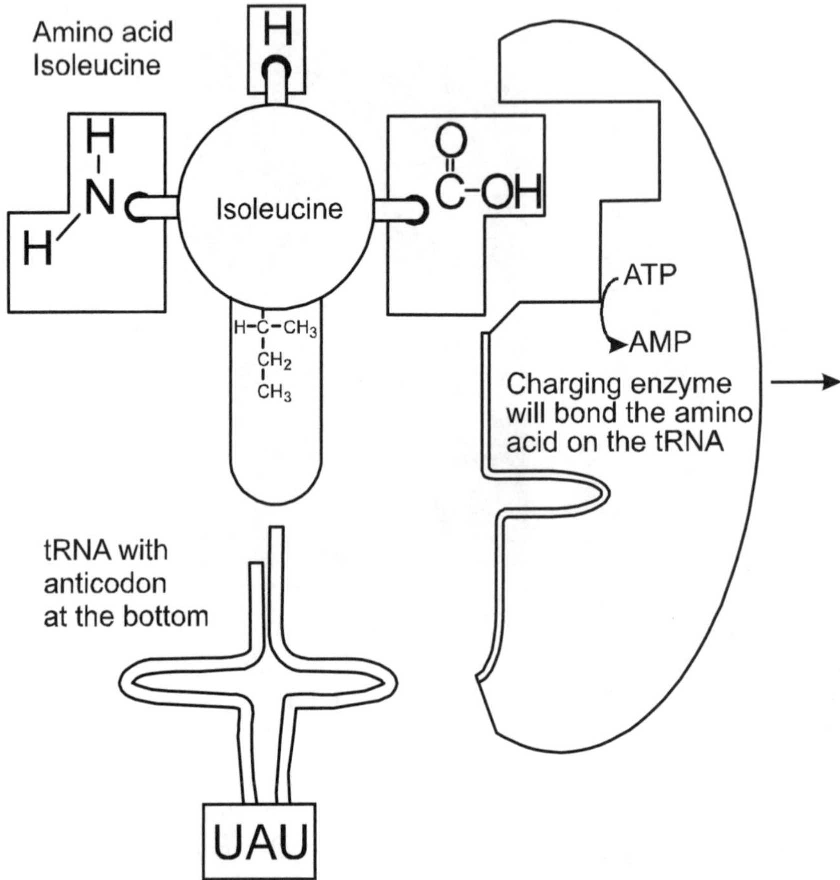

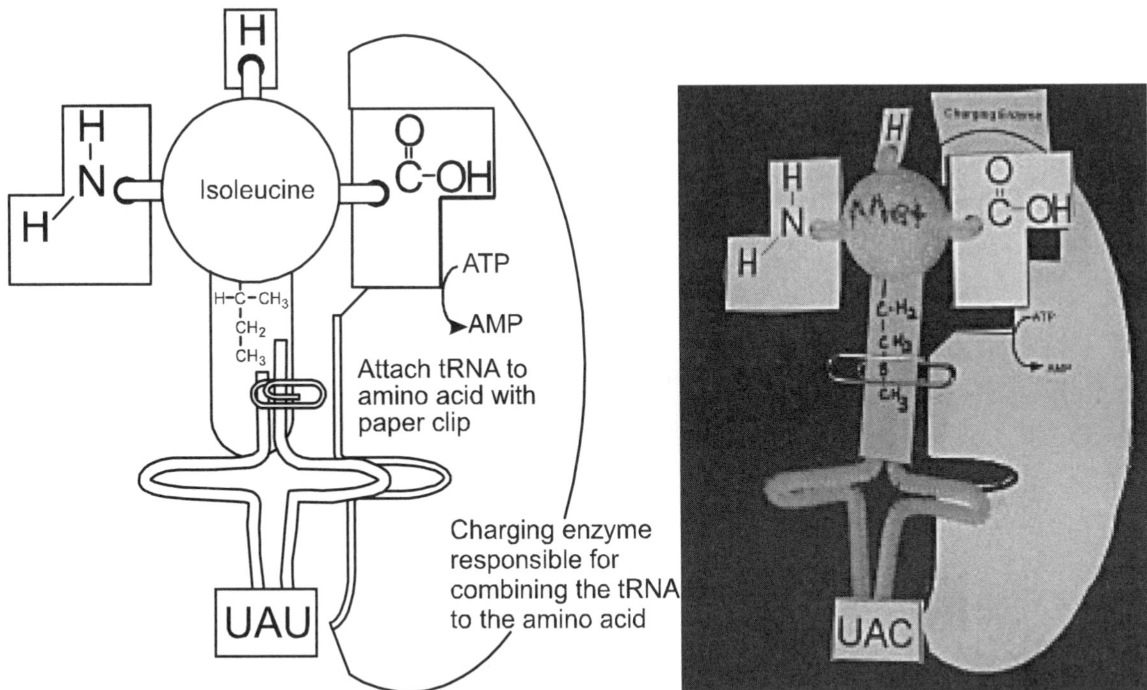

6. Find the ribosome. Notice that it is composed of two subunits, one that is large and one that is small. There are three places for the tRNA's and one place for the mRNA. Now simulate the process of making the polypeptide chain, using your mRNA and your tRNA that have been "charged" with amino acids. Put the start codon (AUG) on the mRNA under the P site. Now find the tRNA with the complementary anticodon and place it on the P site. Once this is done, notice that a second mRNA codon is positioned under the A site. Find the tRNA with the complementary anticodon and place it on the A site. This should bring two amino acids (found at the top of the tRNA) next to one another.

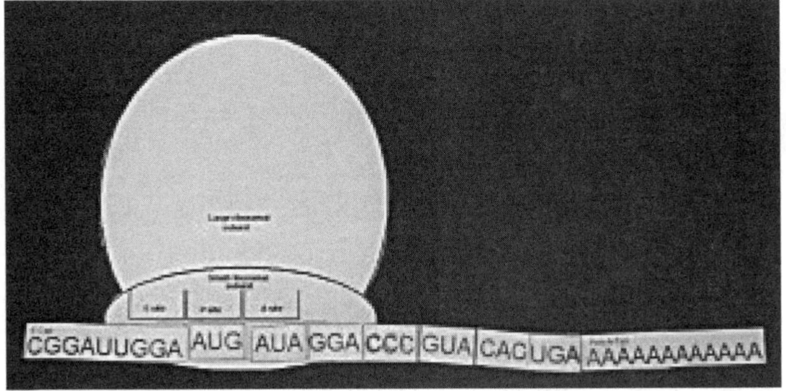

7. Join the two together amino acids together by joining the carboxyl group on the first amino acid to the amine group on the second amino acid. Fasten the two together with a paper clip at their amine and carboxyl sites. The paperclip simulates the covalent bond that will form between these two functional groups. It is called a peptide bond. Notice which atoms are no longer visible. This means that a water molecule has been removed from the chemical reaction.

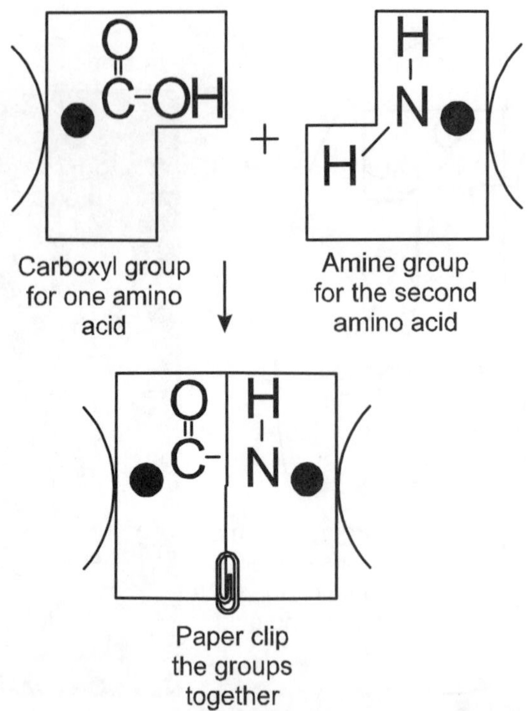

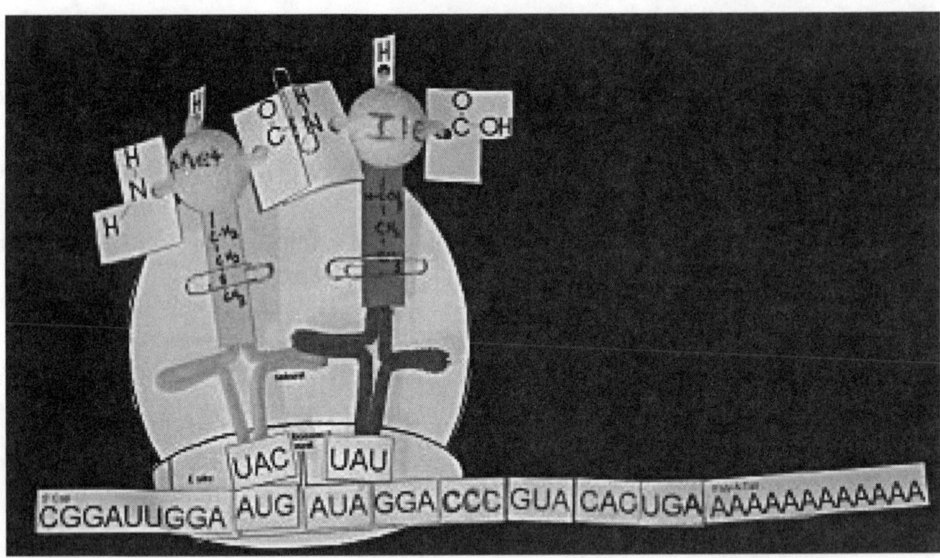

8. Remove the tRNA on the P site over to the E site leaving the amino acid behind. This tRNA then will leave the ribosome altogether. Move the mRNA down one codon and begin the process again. The tRNA at the A site moves over to the P site. The A site is now open to receive the next tRNA that is complementary to the mRNA below. This is called translocation. Continue this process until the stop codon is reached.

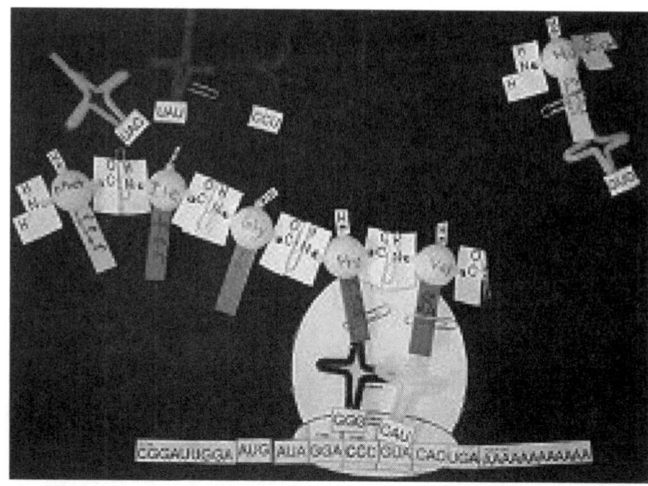

9. When the stop codon is reached, a release factor binds with the mRNA stop codon. This causes the ribosome to disengage, releasing the polypeptide chain and the mRNA. This process is called termination. At this point you should have synthesized a model of a polypeptide chain.

10. Answer the remaining questions on your student answer page.

Name ______________________________

Period______________________________

Proteins, the Essence of Life
Simulating the Process of Protein Synthesis

SIMULATION QUESTIONS

1. Where is DNA located in the cell? Describe the structure of the DNA molecule.

2. DNA is a long polymer made of many subunits. What are those subunits called and what parts do they have?

3. Write out both the top and bottom portion of the DNA molecule in the space below.

4. Define the term gene and explain exactly what a gene does.

5. How many genes are found on a chromosome?

6. What biological molecule do the scissors represent?

7. What is a DNA codon?

8. What enzyme is responsible for base pairing the RNA nucleotides to the DNA gene?

9. Fill in the chart below for the base pairing of DNA to RNA nucleotides

DNA	RNA
Adenine	________
________	Guanine
Thymine	________
________	Cytosine

10. What are introns and exons?

11. What molecule is responsible for removing introns and rejoining exons?

12. Write out the RNA codons that remain after the intron has been removed.

13. What are two purposes of a 5' cap?

14. What are two purposes of poly-A-tail?

15. How is mature mRNA different from immature mRNA? How does mRNA determine the sequence of a polypeptide chain?

16. What is an mRNA codon?

17. Determine the amino acid sequence using the mRNA codon chart below.

First letter	Second letter: U	Second letter: C	Second letter: A	Second letter: G	Third letter
U	UUU Phe UUC Phe UUA Leu UUG Leu	UCU Ser UCC Ser UCA Ser UCG Ser	UAU Tyr UAC Tyr UAA Stop UAG Stop	UGU Cys UGC Cys UGA Stop UGC Trp	U C A G
C	CUU Leu CUC Leu CUA Leu CUG Leu	CCU Pro CCC Pro CCA Pro CCG Pro	CAU His CAC His CAA Gln CAG Gln	CGU Arg CGC Arg CGA Arg CGG Arg	U C A G
A	AUU Ile AUC Ile AUA Ile AUG Met/Start	ACU Thr ACC Thr ACA Thr ACG Thr	AAU Asn AAC Asn AAA Lys AAG Lys	AGU Ser AGC Ser AGA Arg AGG Arg	U C A G
G	GUU Val GUC Val GUA Val GUG Val	GCU Ala GCC Ala GCA Ala GCG Ala	GAU Asp GAC Asp GAA Glu GAG Glu	GGU Gly GGC Gly GGA Gly GGG Gly	U C A G

18. List the complementary anticodons that will be found on the tRNA for the mRNA in question 17.

19. What is translation and where does it occur? What four items are needed for translation to occur?

20. What is the structure of an amino acid?

21. What type of bond is made when amino acids are joined?

22. How many water molecules were removed from the polypeptide chain?

23. Write in the space provided the amino acids were used to make this protein and what molecule was removed.

24. Describe the process of termination.

The *trp* Operon
Modeling Gene Regulation

OBJECTIVE
Students will prepare a model of an operon and use the model to explain the basic components and functioning of an operon. Additionally, students will practice defining terms related to the regulation of genes.

LEVEL
Biology I

NATIONAL STANDARDS
UCP.1, UCP.2, UCP.5, B.2, C.2, G.1, G.2, G.3

TEKS
6 (A), 6 (B)

CONNECTIONS TO AP
AP Biology:

II. Heredity and Evolution B. Molecular Genetics 2. Gene regulation

TIME FRAME
45 minutes

MATERIALS
(For a class of 28 working in pairs)

- colored straws of two different sized diameters
- several rolls of clear tape
- 14 scissors
- 14 paperclips
- 28 sets of terms puzzles pieces
- various colors of pipecleaner (match straw colors if possible)
- 70 pony beads
- 14 operon component labels
- resealable plastic bags sandwich size
- small strip of masking tape or colored tape
- 5 different colors of yarn that match colors of straws
- gene terms transparency
- central dogma transparency

TEACHER NOTES
Students in the first year biology course need an introduction to the concept of an operon and how an operon functions in very general terms. This modeling activity will add a concrete dimension to the very abstract concept of gene regulation. By presenting the concept during the first year course, the students will begin to formulate an understanding of the operon which will be more fully developed in the AP Biology course. This lesson should be used after students have been exposed to the processes of DNA replication and protein synthesis.

You will need to assemble an operon model for yourself to use during the presentation of this lesson (see student procedure pages). Use a waterproof marker to label the operon components on your model.

Additionally, you will need to prepare the 14 student sets of the operon model by placing the following in a resealable sandwich bag or other suitable container.

- 0.5 mm diameter flexible neck straw.
- 5 straw pieces, approximately 3 cm long, of five different colors
- one 3 cm long piece of 0.6 mm diameter straw
- one paper clip
- 5 pieces of yarn approximately 6 cm long with colors to match the straw pieces
- 5 pieces of pipecleaner with each pipecleaner's color matching the straw pieces if possible.
- 5 pony beads (all the same color)
- 1 roll of clear tape
- operon component labels

Alternatively, to save preparation time you may want to place all of the supplies in one central location and have the students pick up their own components.

Colored straws may be purchased at local discount stores. The exact diameter of the straw is not important. What is important about the size is that one type of straw must be large enough to fit inside the other type of straw. If pipecleaners are unavailable you can substitute colored modeling dough, colored twist-ties or colored craft pompoms.

Suggested teaching procedure:

1. In an opening discussion, ask the students the following questions to introduce the topic of operons:
   - Does a cell in your finger contain the same genetic information as a cell in your pancreas? (yes)
   - Why do you suppose your finger cells are not producing insulin as do your pancreas cells? *(Genetic information is not simply inherited and automatically used in every cell all the time. Each cell is only using or expressing a small portion of the genes that it contains. The finger cells are not expressing the gene for insulin production.)*

2. Explain that in this lesson they will explore Jacob-Monod's model of gene expression, the operon. Jacob and Monod devised this model in 1961 to explain how a particular set of genes are expressed in prokaryotes. While operons are not present in eukaryotes, the expression of genes in eukaryotes works in a similar fashion. Eukaryotic gene expression is controlled at multiple levels. Generally speaking, eukaryotic gene expression is more complex because regulation can occur at pre-transcriptional and post-transcriptional levels.

3. Explain/review the central dogma using the central dogma transparency to point out the fundamental flow of genetic information into an expressed product.

4. Using the operon transparency and the gene terms transparency, describe the basic structural components of an operon and the terms used to identify the components.

5. Use the sample student model to identify the parts of a typical operon and to demonstrate how the *trp* operon works. Place the large diameter piece of straw (RNA polymerase) over the smaller straw (operon genes) to show how when the operon is on, the RNA polymerase can move down the operon and transcribe the mRNA segments. Use the pieces of yarn to represent the mRNA that is transcribed. You can place the model on the overhead to make it easier for all students to view.

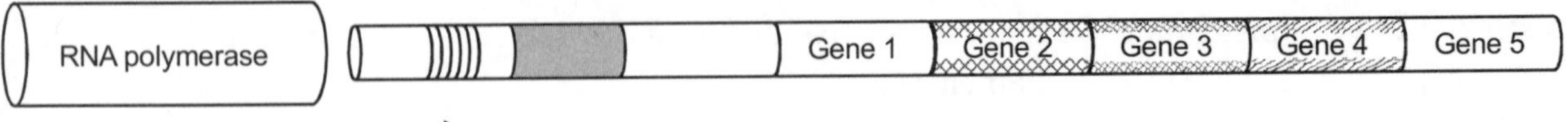

6. The ribbed area of the straw represents the promoter region and the operator is represented by the piece of masking tape on the straw. Place a paperclip in the operator region of your model to show the students how the repressor prevents RNA polymerase from transcribing the genes.

7. Have the students complete the definition/description column of the table on the student answer sheet using the information that you have presented along with the introduction portion of the student handout.

8. Provide each pair of students with the operon model components and have the students complete the modeling the operon portion of the student activity page. The students are to signal you when they have completely assembled their model so that you can initial their student answer page.

9. Give each student a set of the terms puzzle pieces. Explain to them that the purpose of the puzzle is to give them a chance to practice using the definitions of the terms related to gene expression. When the puzzle is completed it will have a rectangular shape. The center piece is the one with the DNA diagram on it. The blackline master to the term puzzle will serve as your answer key. The students are to signal you when they have completed their puzzle so that you can initial their student answer page.

10. Students should then answer the questions found on their student answer sheet.

POSSIBLE ANSWERS TO THE CONCLUSION QUESTIONS AND SAMPLE DATA

Operon component	Definition/Description	Model component
operon	A group of genes operating together in prokaryotic cells	Straw with multi-colored segments
Promoter region of operon	Region of DNA that indicates to an enzyme (RNA polymerase) where to bind to make RNA	Flexible neck of straw
Operator region of operon	A group of genes operating together in prokaryotic cells	Masking tape strip
mRNA coded for by the operon	messenger RNA to be translated	Yarn

TEACHER PAGES

End product/enzyme coded for by mRNA	The enzyme produced when translation is complete.	pipecleaner
Repressor	A protein that suppresses the transcription of a gene.	Paper clip
Ribosome	Site of protein synthesis	Pony bead

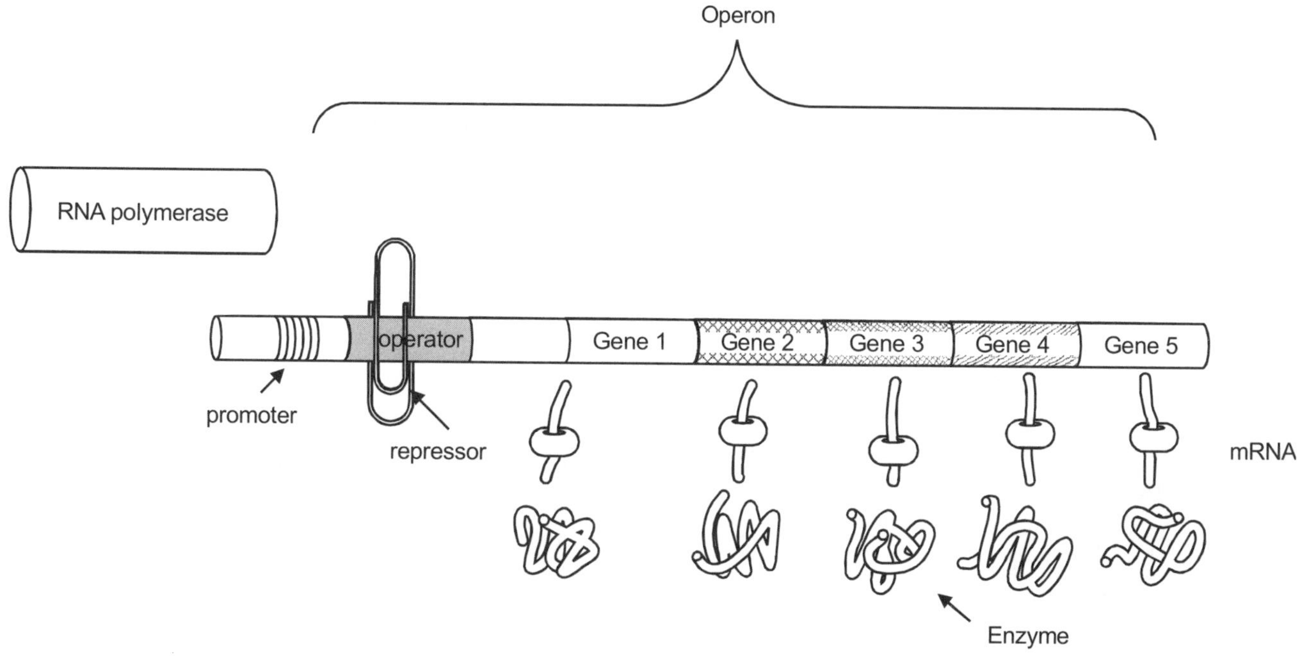

1. According to the central dogma, what is the relationship among DNA, RNA, and proteins?
   - DNA is transcribed into RNA which is translated into proteins.

2. What is the difference in the role of an operator and the role of a promoter?
   - The promoter is the site of RNA polymerase attachment and the operator is region where the repressor binds.

3. How are inducible and repressible operons different?
   - Repressible operons are normally on and can be turned off. Inducible operons are normally off and can be turned on.

4. How are inducible and repressible operons similar?
   - Both types of operons have promoters, operators, and genes.

5. Is the *trp* operon inducible or repressible?
   - The *trp* operon is repressible.

6. What would happen to the amount of tryptophan being produced in an *E.coli* when the repressor is attached to the operator?
   - Tryptophan production will stop when the repressor is attached to the operator.

7. What would happen to the amount of tryptophan being produced in an *E.coli* if the RNA polymerase was destroyed?
   - If the bacteria's RNA polymerase was destroyed tryptophan would not be produced.

8. In your own words, explain how prokaryotic genes are expressed according to the Jacob and Monod operon model.
   - The Jacob and Monod model describes sets of genes that operate together to produce a specific protein (enzymes) as operons. These operons produce protein end products following the central dogma. The DNA is transcribed into RNA which is then translated into specific protein products. Genes that are being expressed are being transcribed into mRNA sequences by RNA polymerase. The expression of some genes is prevented by the presence of a repressor molecule in the operator region.

Blackline master for transparency

Gene Regulation/Expression Terms

Gene expression – **gene activity or transcription**

Gene – **a segment of DNA coding for a specific protein product**

Operon – **A group of genes operating together in prokaryotic cells**

Operator – **Region of a chromosome in an operon to which the repressor binds when the operon is turned off.**

Promoter – **Region of DNA that indicates to an enzyme (RNA polymerase) where to bind to "promote" the synthesis of RNA**

Repressor – **A protein that suppresses the transcription of a gene.**

Inducible operon – **An operon that is normally off, but can turn on in the presence of a specific metabolite**

Repressible operon – **An operon generally on, but that can be turned off in the presence of a specific metabolite**

Homeotic gene (HOX) – **Genes that control the body plan of animals by controlling the development of a group of cells**

Blackline master for transparency

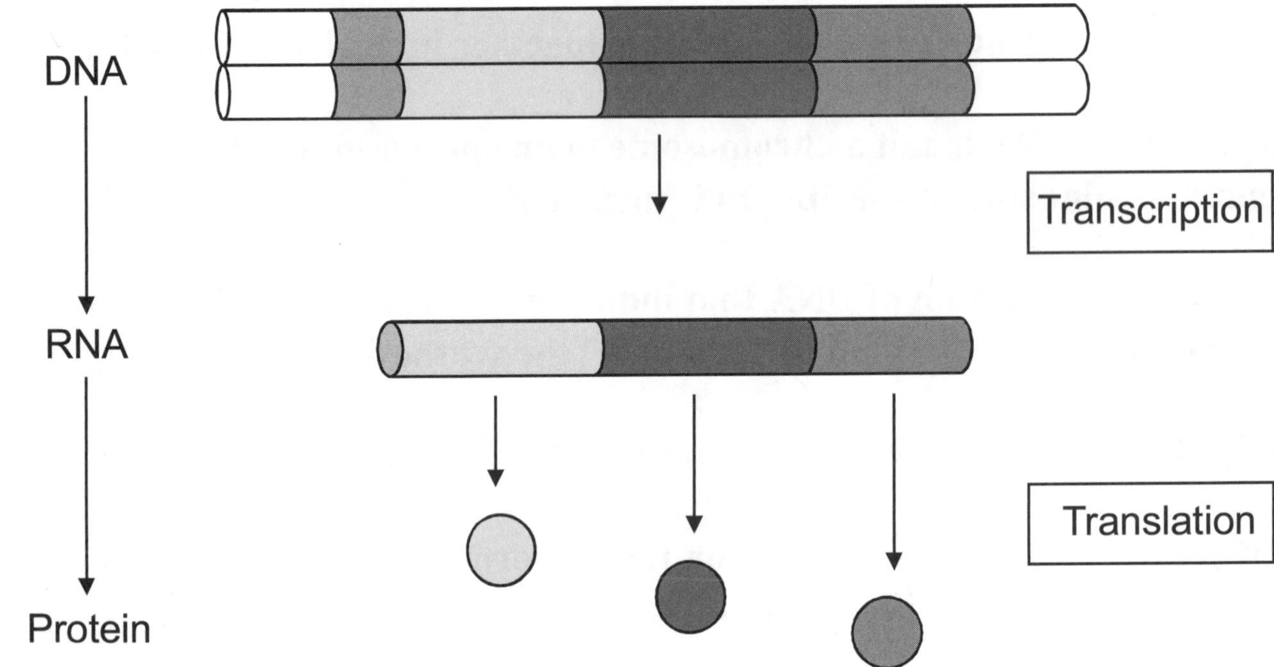

Blackline Master for Terms Puzzle

Operon Genes that control the body plan of animals by controlling the development of a group of cells. Ex. Tryp operon	Homeotic gene An operon generally on, but that can be turned off in the presence of a specific metabolite A group of genes operating together in prokaryotic cells	Repressible Operon Operator Sequence of DNA that codes for a protein & determines a trait
Repressible Operon Operon Region of DNA that indicates to an enzyme where to bind to make RNA An operon that is normally off, but can turn on in the presence of a specific metabolite	Operon Promoter Regulatory site. Operator	Gene Segment on a DNA strand that codes for a protein that controls transcription of another gene group Repressible Operon Gene Expression
Inducible Operon Operon Ex. Lac Operon	Region of a chromosome in an operon to which the repressor binds when the operon is turned off. Inducible Operon Repressor	Gene activity or transcription A protein that suppresses the transcription of a gene Genes that control the body plan of animals by controlling the development of a group of cells.

Blackline master for operon model component label

Operon Ribosome Promoter Operator mRNA end product/enzyme Repressor RNA polymerase	Operon Ribosome Promoter Operator mRNA end product/enzyme Repressor RNA polymerase	Operon Ribosome Promoter Operator mRNA end product/enzyme Repressor RNA polymerase
Operon Ribosome Promoter Operator mRNA end product/enzyme Repressor RNA polymerase	Operon Ribosome Promoter Operator mRNA end product/enzyme Repressor RNA polymerase	Operon Ribosome Promoter Operator mRNA end product/enzyme Repressor RNA polymerase
Operon Ribosome Promoter Operator mRNA end product/enzyme Repressor RNA polymerase	Operon Ribosome Promoter Operator mRNA end product/enzyme Repressor RNA polymerase	Operon Ribosome Promoter Operator mRNA end product/enzyme Repressor RNA polymerase

The *trp* Operon
Modeling Gene Regulation

Cells in the skin on your fingers have the same genetic information as the cells in your pancreas yet your finger cells do not produce insulin. How do pancreatic cells "know" to produce insulin? The basic answer to this question lies in the fact that genetic information is not simply inherited and automatically used in every cell all the time. Each cell is using or expressing only a small portion of the total genes that it contains. The finger cells are not expressing the gene for insulin production.

In 1961, Fracois Jacob and Jacques Monod described the control of gene expression as the operon model. In the operon model, sets of genes operate together to result in the production of a specific protein (enzymes) following the central dogma. As shown in Figure 1 below, the central dogma indicates that the genetic information coded for in the DNA strand directs the production of proteins. The DNA is transcribed into RNA which is then translated into specific protein products. Operons are groups of genes operating together in prokaryotic cells to allow the formation of necessary proteins.

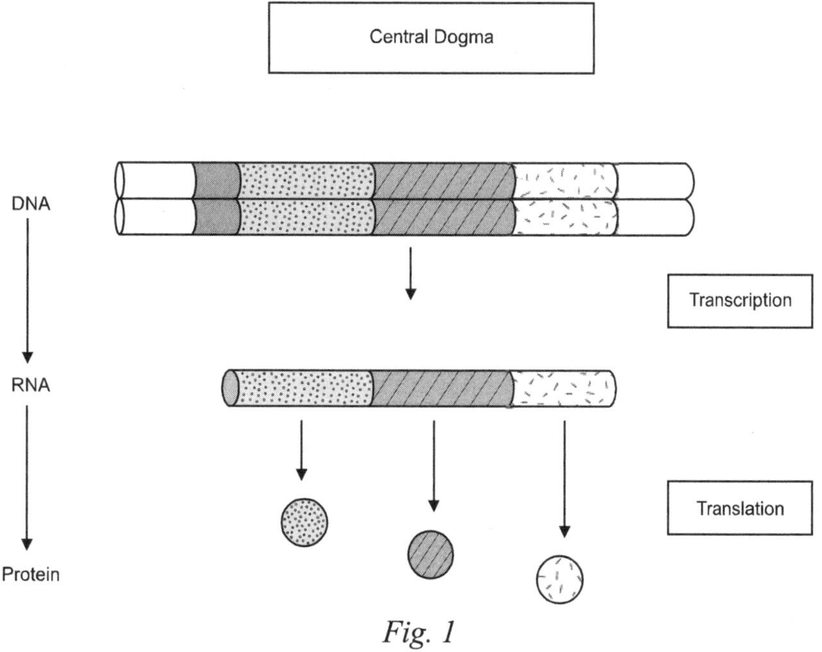

Fig. 1

The basic structure of an operon is shown in Figure 2. The operon contains an operator which is a region of a chromosome or DNA to which the repressor binds when the operon is turned off and not producing a protein product. The area of the operon called the promoter indicates to the enzyme, RNA polymerase, where to bind to make mRNA during the process of transcription. The repressor is a protein that suppresses the transcription of a gene.

promoter	operator	gene 1	gene 2	gene 3

Fig. 2

One of the first operons discovered in *E.coli* was the operon that results in the production of tryptophan. The tryptophan operon or *trp* operon contains a promoter, an operator and five genes that result in the production of the enzymes that cause tryptophan synthesis to occur. See Figure 3. Tryptophan is an essential amino acid used in a variety of metabolic pathways within an *E.coli* cell. As such, tryptophan is frequently needed by the *E.coli* cell so; it is not surprising to find that the *trp* operon is normally activated in the *E.coli* cell. Operons that are typically activated, but can be turned off are referred to as repressible operons. Alternatively, those that are normally off but can be turned on are called inducible operons. The *trp* operon is a repressible operon.

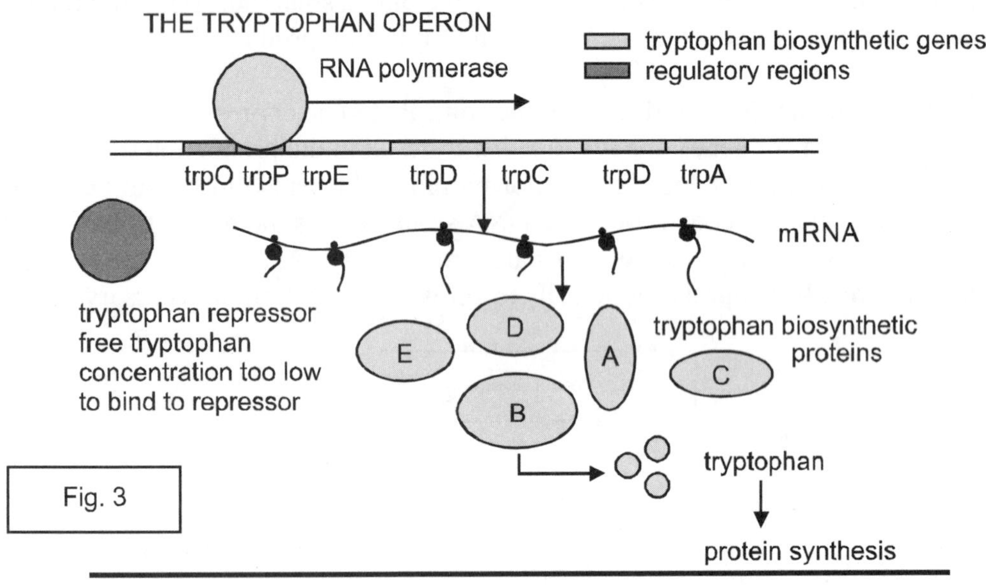

Fig. 3

While operons are not present in eukaryotes, the expression of genes in eukaryotes works in a similar fashion. Eukaryotic gene expression is controlled at multiple levels. Generally speaking, eukaryotic gene expression is more complex because regulation can occur before and after transciption.

PURPOSE

In this activity you will prepare a model of an operon and use that model to explain how an operon functions. Additionally, you will practice defining terms related to the regulation of gene expression.

MATERIALS

1 operon model set
2 sets of terms puzzle pieces
scissors

PROCEDURE

1. Read through the introduction section of this activity and listen as your teacher demonstrates the components of an operon.

2. Write a definition or description for each of the gene expression terms in the table on the student answer page.

3. Obtain the components needed to prepare an operon model from your teacher.

4. Construct a model of an operon by doing the following:
   a. Obtain a flexible neck straw and cut its length in half using scissors. Keep the portion with the flexible neck.
   b. Place your flexible neck straw on the surface of your desk or lab table with the flexible neck portion on your left-hand side. Wrap a piece of masking tape around the straw in the area just to the right of the flexible neck area. The flexible neck area of the straw will represent the promoter area and the masking tape will represent the operator.
   c. Use clear tape to secure the five segments of colored straw end to end onto the right-hand end of the flexible neck straw. Smooth the tape down as much as possible. Each colored straw segment represents a gene. Collectively, the structure formed when the pieces are taped to the longer straw now represents the *trp* operon.
   d. The RNA polymerase is represented by the segment of straw with the larger diameter that can fit over the entire operon model. The work of RNA polymerase will be simulated by sliding this larger diameter segment down the straw. Try sliding your RNA polymerase down the *trp* operon model. Smooth down any tape ridges that block the sliding action. As RNA polymerase "reads" the DNA code, a segment of messenger RNA will be formed. The messenger RNA is represented in the model by the pieces of yarn.
   e. The pony beads represent the ribosomes which are the cell organelles where the synthesis of the enzymes would occur. Simulate the action of the ribosomes (represented by the pony beads) by threading the yarn through the pony bead. Place the colored pieces of yarn below the matching colored gene of the model. Each piece of yarn represents a different segment of mRNA which codes for an enzyme needed in the production of the amino acid tryptophan.
   f. Use the pipecleaner to represent the five enzymes produced by this operon. Coordinate the colors as much as possible. Take the pipecleaner and fold it onto itself. This action represents the folding of the enzyme into its native conformation. Place the folded enzyme below the mRNA pieces in the model.
   g. The repressor of the *trp* operon is represented by the paper clip. The repressor attaches to the operator segment of the operon. When the repressor is in place the RNA polymerase is unable to transcribe the DNA. To simulate this action in your model, attach the paperclip to the operator segment of the straw. Notice that now the RNA polymerase is unable to move down the operon.

5. Cut apart the operon component labels and place them beside the appropriate part of the model. When you have completed this portion, signal your teacher to come view your model and initial the model completed box on your student answer page.

6. Label the diagram of the model on the student answer page using the following terms: gene 1, gene 2, gene 3, gene 4, gene 5, mRNA, operator, operon, repressor, RNA polymerase, enzyme products, promoter and ribosome

7. Practice using the definitions of the components of the operon by completing the terms puzzle. When you have your puzzle completed. Signal your teacher to initial the puzzle complete box on your student answer page.

8. Answer the questions in the conclusion section of the student answer page

Name ______________________________

Period ______________________________

The *trp* Operon

DATA AND OBSERVATIONS

Operon component	Definition/Description	Model component
operon		Straw with multi-colored segments
Promoter region of operon		Flexible neck of straw
Operator region of operon		Masking tape strip
mRNA coded for by the operon		Yarn
End product/enzyme coded for by mRNA		Pipe cleaner
Repressor		Paper clip
Ribosome		Pony bead

Teacher Initials ________
Model completed

Teacher Initials ________
Puzzle completed

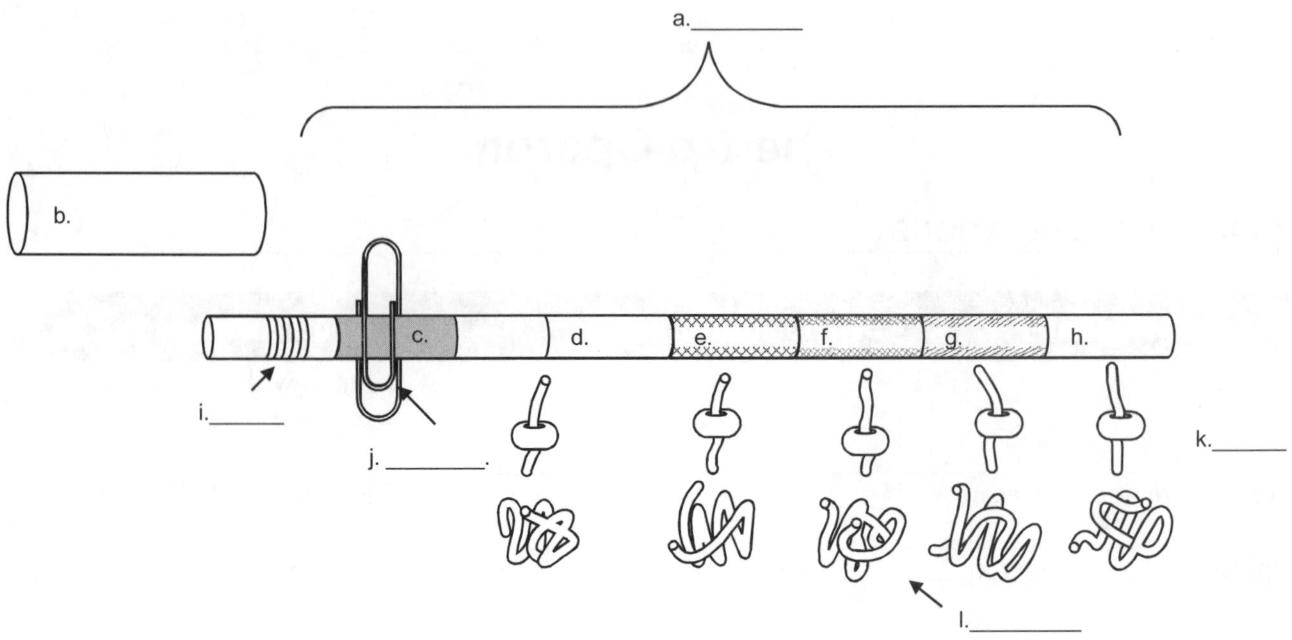

CONCLUSION QUESTIONS

1. According to the central dogma, what is the relationship among DNA, RNA and proteins?

2. What is the difference in the role of an operator and the role of a promoter?

3. How are inducible and repressible operons different?

4. How are inducible and repressible operons similar?

5. Is the *trp* operon inducible or repressible?

6. What would happen to the amount of tryptophan being produced in an *E.coli* cell when the repressor is attached to the operator?

7. What would happen to the amount of tryptophan being produced in an *E.coli* cell if the RNA polymerase was destroyed?

8. In your own words, explain how prokaryotic genes are expressed according to the Jacob and Monod operon model.

Protein Properties
Using Electrophoresis to Determine Net Charge

OBJECTIVE
Students will observe proteins migrating through an agarose gel and determine the net charge of the protein.

LEVEL
Biology I

NATIONAL STANDARDS
UCP.2, UCP.3, UCP.5, B.2, C.2, C.5, G.1, G.2, G.3

TEKS
2 (B), 2(C), 9(A)

CONNECTIONS TO AP
AP Biology:
I. Molecules and cells, A. Chemistry of Life 2. Organic molecules in organisms
II. Heredity and Evolution, B. Molecular Genetic 5. Nucleic acid technology and applications

TIME FRAME
45 minutes

MATERIALS
(For a class of 28 working in pairs)

electrophoresis gel boxes (enough for 14 stations)
1.2 % melted agarose solution (enough for 14 casting trays)
several rolls of masking tape
sufficient buffer for electrophoresis boxes
14 microcentrifuge tubes with myoglobin
14 microcentrifuge tubes with serum albumin
14 rulers
DC power supply (enough for 14 stations)
14 micropipets
14 disposable beral pipets
14 microcentrifuge tubes with cytochrome c
14 microcentrifuge tubes with hemoglobin
14 microcentrifuge tubes with unknown protein

Optional
Coomassie blue stain
14 staining trays
destain

TEACHER NOTES
This laboratory activity is appropriate when studying protein structure, protein synthesis, or biotechnology. Students need to understand the underlying principles of electrophoresis and the effect of the net charge of proteins on their migration through an agarose gel.

If a paper chromatography activity has been done prior to this lab you can use that as an analogy for the mechanism of electrophoresis.

Preparations
Before beginning solution preparations, read the instruction manual that accompanies your electrophoresis equipment to determine the capacity of your chamber and gel plate. Use these values to figure out the total amount of buffer solution and agarose that will be needed for your class(es).

If money is not a consideration, there are molecular kits that can be purchased for a protein separation. The kit will include the proteins and buffer solution. They may or may not include the agarose. The following includes directions for preparing this lab without a kit. Once the lab is prepared, the protein solutions will last for some time.

Electrophoresis buffer should be made first since it is needed make the agarose gels. It will also be the buffer solution used to fill the electrophoresis chamber.

To prepare 1.0 L of buffer:
Mix 2.8 g of glycine and 0.4 g Tris base in 500 mL of distilled water. Bring the volume up to one liter of solution. Make enough for number of boxes that will be used during the lab. Electrophoresis buffer can be used for as many as three runs.

To prepare 1.2% agarose:
Use graduated cylinder and water to determine the volume of melted agarose needed per casting tray. Be sure to tape the ends securely and fill the tray until it reaches half-way up the comb. Multiply the volume required for one tray by the number of trays needed. Add 10% to this value to account for errors and sealing the wells. This volume of buffer solution will be mixed to the powdered agarose to make the agarose solution. Pour the determined amount of buffer solution into a beaker capable of holding at least twice the required volume to avoid boiling over during heating. For example use a 500 mL beaker to hold 200 mL of buffer.

To determine the mass of powdered agarose required for the 1.2% solution, multiply the volume of electrophoresis buffer to be used by .012. Weigh out the appropriate number of grams of agarose and add it to the beaker containing the buffer. To melt the agarose put in a microwave and heat on high until all of the agarose has melted. This may take 2-4 minutes depending on the amount of agarose being melted and the power of the microwave. Check and stir every 30 seconds until the agarose has completely melted.

Sample Preparation Calculation

- One tray holds 30 mL of agarose
- $\left(14\text{ trays}\times\frac{30\text{ mL}}{\text{tray}}\right)+10\%=(420\,\text{mL})+42\,\text{mL}=462\,\text{mL of melted agarose needed}$
- Round to 475 mL of melted agarose needed
- $475\,\text{mL of buffer}\times\frac{0.012\,\text{g agarose}}{\text{mL of buffer}}=5.7\,\text{g of powderd agarose needed}$

- Add 5.7 g of powdered agarose to 475 mL of electrophoresis buffer.
- Put solution in a 1000 mL beaker to avoid boiling over in the microwave.
- Put in a microwave and heat on high until all the agarose has dissolved. Check and stir every 30 seconds until the agarose is completely dissolved.

Protein preparation

The proteins can be purchased from Sigma -Aldrich

Sigma-Aldrich
3050 Spruce Street
St. Louis, Mo 63103
(800)-325-5052
www.sigma-aldrich.com

These proteins can be stored in the freezer for an indefinite time. The amount needed to make the protein solutions is minimal and the purchased protein can last for years.

The proteins used are

Protein	Color	Net charge in buffer 8.6
cytochrome c	Orange	positive
myoglobin	rusty red	negative
hemoglobin	rusty red	negative
serum albumin	* blue	very negative
* Serum albumin is blue because bromophenol blue has been added to the sample and it binds to serum albumin.		

Protein solutions once made, can be stored in the freezer and are good for several years as long as they are kept frozen. It is recommended that you make 10 mL of each protein solution. This is enough to dispense 0.5 mL into14 1 mL microcentrifuge tubes or 1.5 mL microcentrifuge tubes. This should supply 14 groups working in pairs. It will also allow you to make some unknown protein tubes.

To prepare the protein solutions:

1. Make 50 mL of a 50% glycerol solution by adding 25 mL of glycerol to 25 mL of water mix.

2. Protein solution #1: Add 10 mg of cytochrome c to 10 mL of 50% glycerol solution. Dispense 0.5 mL into each of 14 microcentrifuge tubes and label the tubes cytochrome c. Save the rest to make solutions of unknown proteins.

3. Protein solution #2: Add 10 mg of myoglobin to 10 mL of 50% glycerol solution. Dispense 0.5 mL into each of 14 microcentrifuge tubes and label the tubes myoglobin. Save the rest to make solutions of unknown proteins.

4. Protein solution #3: Add 10 mg of hemoglobin to 10 mL of 50% glycerol solution. Dispense 0.5 mL into each of 14 microcentrifuge tubes and label the tubes hemoglobin. Save the rest to make solutions of unknown proteins.

5. Before making this protein solution, take 10 mL of 50% glycerol and add .01 g of bromophenol blue. This will dye the serum albumin. Protein solution #4: Add 10 mg of serum albumin to 10 mL of 50% glycerol/bromophenol blue solution. Dispense 0.5 mL into each of 14 microcentrifuge tubes and label the tubes serum albumin. Save the rest to make solutions of unknown proteins.

6. To make unknown protein solutions, use the left over proteins. You may want to combine proteins so that there are two proteins that will separate out. Be sure you make a key so that you can check your student's answers.

The selected proteins are colored and can be observed without staining, however, you may want to stain them so that students can observe this process. Proteins are stained with Coomassie brilliant blue R stain. The staining and destaining process takes several hours so students will have to view the gels the following day. After the gels are stained, they are then destained to make the protein bands more visible.

To prepare the stain solution:
Combine the following:

440 mL methanol
480 mL distilled water
80 mL glacial acetic acid
2.5 g Coomassie brilliant blue R

To prepare the destaining solution:
Combine the following:

100 mL methanol
100 mL glacial acetic acid
800 mL distilled water

Let the gel stain for approximately 10 minutes, pour off stain and apply destaining solution. The destaining solution should completely cover the gels. You may have to destain several times and the destain may have to be changed after several hours. Destain until the proteins are visible. View the gels on a light box or overhead projector. Use plastic wrap to avoid staining the light source.

Be sure to instruct the students on the proper micropipeting technique. This protocol recommends filling the gels outside of the box and then sealing the wells with some melted agarose. This will save a significant amount of time. If time is not a factor, you may want to demonstrate to the students how to load under buffer.

POSSIBLE ANSWERS TO THE CONCLUSION QUESTIONS AND SAMPLE DATA

Data Table			
Protein	Color of Protein	Distance Migrated Through Gel	Charge of the Protein
cytochrome c	orange	2.8	negative
myoglobin	rusty-orange	0.8	negative
hemoglobin	rusty-orange	0.6	negative
serum albumin	blue	-2.4	positive
unknown protein(s)			

1. What are the building blocks or monomers that make up the proteins? Explain how these molecules are structured and how they are different from one another.
   - Proteins are made from monomers called amino acids.
   - An amino acid has a central carbon and attached to the central carbon are: hydrogen, an amino group, a carboxyl group and a variable R group. There are twenty amino acids and each one has a different variable.

2. Explain what is meant by a protein's primary, secondary, tertiary and quaternary structure.
   - A protein's primary structure is the sequencing of its amino acids. Its secondary structure is hydrogen bonding between one amino acid's amino group and a neighbor amino acid's carboxyl group. This can take on several structures like the alpha helix and the beta pleated sheets. The tertiary structure is how the protein folds on itself to form three-dimensional structure. The quaternary structure involves a protein that has more than one polypeptide chain and how they fit with one another.

3. Explain why the four proteins used in this experiment moved at different rates through the gel?
   - The proteins moved at different rates because they have different charges. The net charge of the protein is due to the R groups. Different proteins have different number of amino acids with different R groups.

4. What can be determined by comparing the unknown proteins with the known proteins in the gel?
   - The charges of the unknown proteins can be determined and compared to the proteins with their known charges.

5. Explain why in most protein separations, the final step is the staining of the gels.
   - Most proteins do not have color and by staining the proteins they can be visualized.

REFERENCES

Anderson, John. *A Laboratory Course in Molecular Biology, Overview of Proteins, Instructors Manual*. Dayton: Modern Biology. pp. 1-5

Campbell, Neil, Lawrence Mitchell, and Jane Reece. *Biology*. Menlo Park: Benjamin/Cummings, 1999. pp. 68-76

Greenberg, Jon, Revision Editor. *Biological Science, A Molecular Approach.* Chicago: Everyday Learning, 2001. pp. 38-40

Gattorzzi, Linda, Earl Hagstrom, Marie Rediess, Mark Salminen, Dr. Clarence Suelter. "Constructing and Electrophoretic Gel Box for Running Miniature Agarose Submarine Gels", *Natural Science*. Fall 1988: 13-14.

Protein Properties
Using Electrophoresis to Determine Net Charge

Proteins are the molecules that carry out the "business of living". Humans can synthesize over 50,000 different proteins. Genes composed of DNA direct the synthesis of protein. The list below gives one an idea of the importance of proteins and how diverse their functions are.

Type of protein	**Function / Examples**
Structural Proteins	(hair, horns, nails, etc.)
Storage Proteins	(albumin, casein)
Transport Proteins	(permeases used for active transport)
Hormonal Proteins	(insulin used to lower sugar in blood)
Contractile Proteins	(found in muscles)
Antibodies	(used to fight off foreign invaders)
Enzymes	(digestive enzymes)

Proteins are relatively large polymers made from chemical building blocks or monomers known as amino acids. Twenty amino acids are used to build proteins. An amino acid is composed of a central carbon and bonded to this central carbon are four groups: hydrogen, an amine group, a carboxyl group, and a variable group (R group). Below are two amino acids, glycine and alanine. Notice that the difference between the two molecules lies in their R groups. There are twenty amino acids and each is different from one another in their R groups. It should be noted that some R groups are non-polar, some are polar and some are charged. The charged R groups are either an acid or a base.

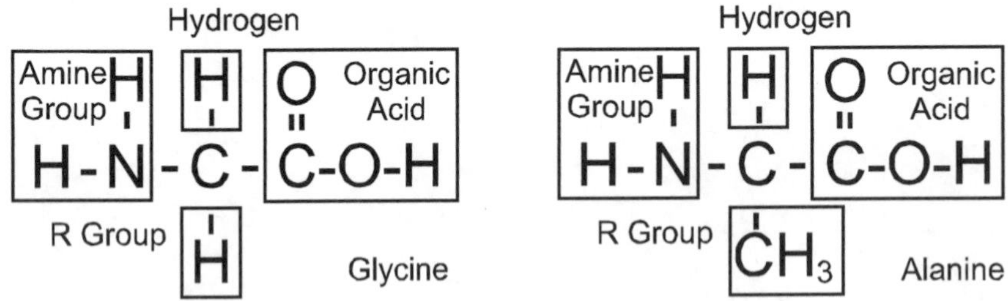

A polypeptide chain is a single chain of amino acids that are bonded together. A protein may contain one or more polypeptide chains. The formation of a polypeptide chain is called protein synthesis and occurs on the ribosome found in the cytoplasm. When two amino acids join together a molecule of water is removed in a dehydration reaction.

```
                                            H2O
  H H O          H H O             H H O  ↑  H H O
  | | ||         | | ||            | | ||    | | ||
H-N-C-C-O-H + H-N-C-C-O-H  →  H-N-C-C——N-C-C-O-H
    |              |                |        |
    R              R                R        R
```

The R groups of a given protein will influence the properties of that protein. Proteins in general usually range from 40-500 amino acids long. The particular sequencing of the amino acids in a polypeptide chain is called the primary structure of that protein. In addition to this sequencing, the primary structure may also include disulfide bonds. These are covalent bonds, which will cause the polypeptide to fold at a certain site and in a certain manner. Disulfide bonds are the result of a condensation reaction between two amino acids of cysteine. Cysteine has an S-H as part of its R Group. Two molecules of cysteine will bond forming an S-S bond and removing H_2. These disulfide bonds are very strong and will hold the shape of the polypeptide chain.

Proteins very seldom remain as linear molecules and generally fold on themselves to form three-dimensional shapes. Hydrogen bonding can occur between the hydrogen on the amine group and the oxygen on a neighboring amino acid's carboxyl group giving the protein secondary structure. This hydrogen bonding can produce a helical structure called an α-helix or a pleated sheet called a β-pleated sheet. These structures can then fold on themselves forming a three-dimensional structure termed the tertiary structure. If a protein has more than one polypeptide chain, then the protein can exhibit quaternary structure.

As a protein folds on itself to obtain its three-dimensional structure, the R groups of the amino acids play an important role. The polar R groups or that have a charge are usually found on the outside of the protein because these R groups are attracted to water. The R groups that are non-polar are buried inside the protein away from the water environment. A protein can be overall positive or negative, depending on whether the protein has more positive R groups or more negative R groups.

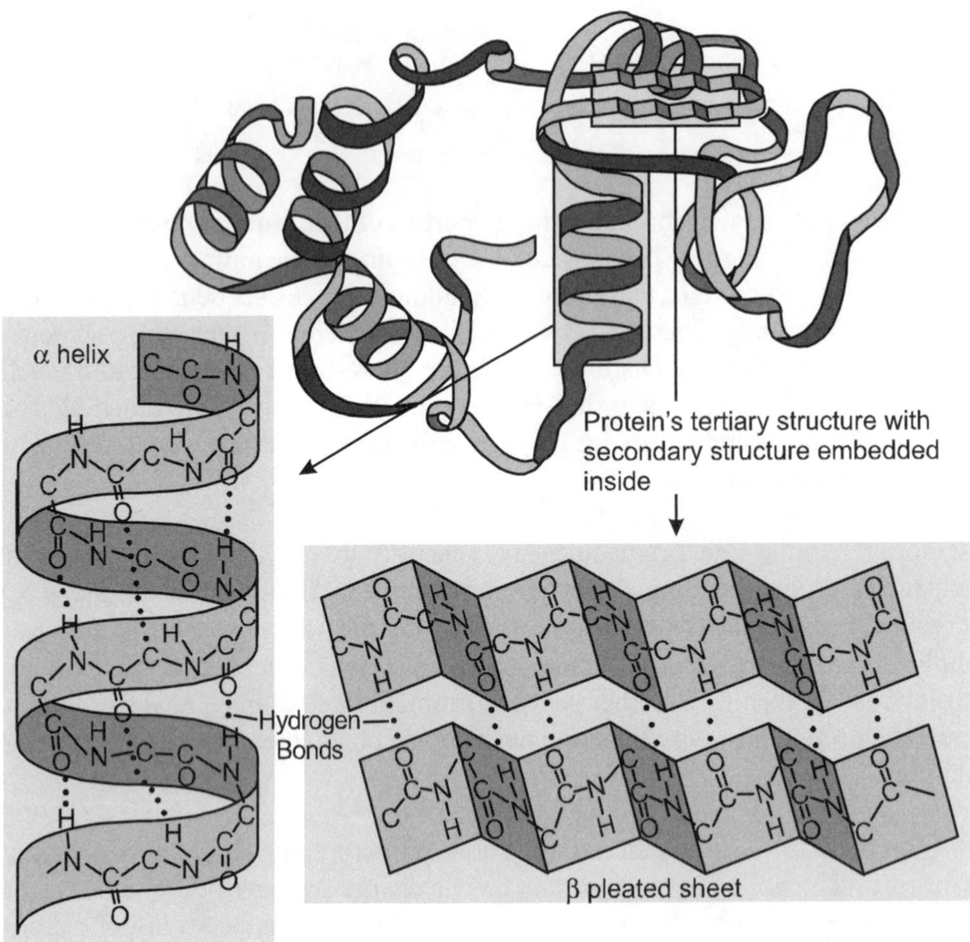

A protein's function is related to its shape. Change the shape of the protein, and the protein will most often lose its function. There are certain physical factors that can also affect the shape of the protein. These include heat and pH. The factors can disrupt the H-bonds and thereby disrupt the protein's three-dimensional shape.

There are times when it is necessary or desirable to separate a mixture of proteins. One method for separating proteins involves electrophoresis. Electrophoresis is the separation of molecules through an agarose gel that is placed in an electric field. The agarose gel has preformed wells that the proteins are loaded into. The gel is porous and serves as a medium allowing the proteins to migrate. This migration is caused by the fact that proteins are positively or negatively charged. The rate that the proteins migrate depends on their relative charges and not their size as the pores are large compared to the proteins. Positive proteins will migrate to the negative pole and negative proteins will migrate to the positive pole. Proteins that have a greater charge will migrate faster than those proteins that have a lesser charge. Two proteins that have the same charge will migrate at the same rate.

Some proteins are colored and can be observed migrating through an agarose gel. Most proteins are colorless, however, and after the migration is complete the proteins must be dyed to determine their positions on the gel. A tracking dye is also used to make sure that the proteins do not migrate too far and run off the gel.

The proteins that will be used in this activity are equine cytochrome c, bovine myoglobin, bovine albumin, and rabbit hemoglobin.

Cytochrome c is protein found in the mitochondrion. It is a part of the electron transport chain during the production of ATP. This is a single polypeptide chain that has a heme group as a side group. The heme group contains iron, which gives this protein its characteristic orange color.

Myoglobin is a protein found in muscles and hemoglobin is the protein found in red blood cells. Myoglobin is closely related to hemoglobin. Both of these molecules can combine with oxygen and cells use these molecules for oxygen storage and transport. Both of these molecules contain an iron-based heme group. Because of the iron atoms, the proteins are rust colored. Myoglobin is found in muscle cells and stores oxygen. This oxygen is released to the muscle when the muscle demands an increase in oxygen. Hemoglobin is a much larger, complicated protein with four polypeptide chains and four heme groups. This protein is found in red blood cells and transports oxygen from the lungs to other cells in the body.

Serum albumin is the major protein found in blood plasma. It is used to transport a number of smaller molecules in the blood. Serum albumin is a colorless protein so it will need to be dyed with bromophenol blue in order to be visible on the gel.

PURPOSE

In this activity you will investigate the separation of proteins using electrophoresis. This method will determine whether a given protein has a net negative or positive charge.

MATERIALS

electrophoresis gel box
1.2 % melted agarose solution
masking tape
buffer
myoglobin
serum albumin
ruler
DC power supply
micropipets
disposable beral
cytochrome c
hemoglobin
unknown protein
250 mL beaker

Optional - If the gels are to be stained.

Coomasie blue stain
staining tray
destain

Safety Alert

1. **Caution:** Coomassie blue stain may stain clothing and skin. Wear gloves when handling the gels and stain.
2. **Caution:** Follow the safety instructions on the proper use of eletrophoresis equipment to minimize electrical shock.

PROCEDURE

1. Make argarose gels by following the directions below:
   a. Obtain a casting tray, eletrophoresis box, and masking tape.
   b. Seal both ends of the gel casting tray with masking tape.
   c. Press the tape firm to get a tight seal.
      - This is to insure that the melted agarose will not leak out of the tray.
      - Note some trays have their own dams, and do not need to be taped.
      - If this is the case, follow your teacher's instructions on the handling of the casting trays.

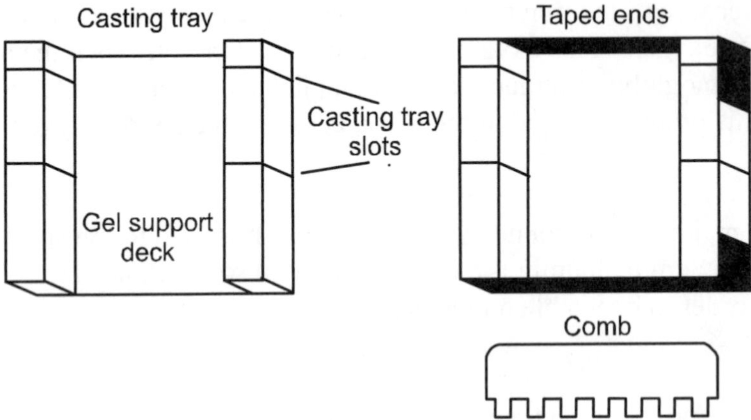

Fig. 1

2. Insert the comb at the midway point. Most casting trays are made so that the comb may be inserted either at the end or in the middle of the tray (Figure 1). If the tray does not allow you to insert the comb in the middle of the tray, you will have to watch and time your electrophoresis more carefully so that the positive proteins do not run off the short end of the tray.

3. Pour enough melted agarose in the casting tray so that the agarose reaches about half-way up the teeth of the comb.

4. Allow the agarose to solidify.
   - The agarose changes appearance from clear to cloudy.
   - It should take about 10-15 minutes to solidify.

5. Once the gel has solidified, carefully remove the comb by pulling straight up. Remove the tape from the ends of the casting tray.

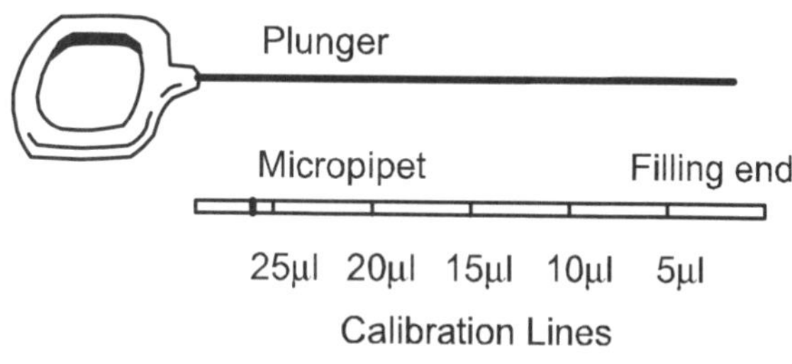

Fig. 2

6. Figure 2 shows an example of a micropipet. Above is an example of a micropipet. Insert the plunger into the glass micropipet at the end with the thick white line. There are other types of micropipets. If the pipet you are using is different from the one above. If this is the case, follow your teachers' instructions on the handling of the use of the micropipet.

7. Put the micropipet between the thumb and middle finger. The plunger can be pulled up with the index finger. Place the filling end of the micropipet into the solution to be measured. Measure out 20 mL of solution.

8. Load 10-20 mL of each of the four colored proteins and your unknown into the sample wells as indicated below.

Sample Well Number	Protein Sample
1	cytochrome c
2	myoglobin
3	hemoglobin
4	serum albumin
5	unknown protein

9. Rinse the pipet out between measurements by drawing up and expelling water three times by the pipet.

10. Seal your wells with some of the left over melted agarose using a disposable plastic pipet.

11. Transfer your gel to the electrophoretic box making sure you note the position of your gel in the electrophoresis chamber. Pour the Tris-buffer into the electrophoresis box until is just covers the gel.

12. Put of lid onto the electrophoresis box. Connect the box to the DC power supply. Turn the power to the voltage as directed by your teacher. Different boxes will require different voltage settings. Let protein move through the gel for 8 minutes. After 8 minutes, turn off and disconnect the power supply. Observe the color of the various proteins and record this information in the data table on the student answer page.

13. Remove the lid of the electrophoresis unit and record the relative position of the four proteins as compared to their starting point in the sample wells. Determine which proteins are positive and which are negative.

14. Resume electrophoresis until the bromophenol blue in the serum albumin sample has migrated to within 1 cm of the positive electrode end of the gel. Remove the gel from the casting tray unit and measure the distance of each protein (in cm) from the sample well.

Optional - If the gels are to be stained follow the directions below.

1. Carefully remove the casting tray from the electrophoresis box.

2. Slide the gel into a staining tray or weigh boat.

3. Add enough stain to cover the gel and allow it to sit undisturbed 1-24 hours.

4. When staining is complete, pour off the stain into the designated container.

5. Add about 100 mL of destaining solution. After several hours decant the destaining solution and replace with 100 mL of new destaining solution. Continue destaining until the proteins are visible when the gel is placed on a light source such as an overhead projector.

6. Measure the distance of each protein (in cm) from the sample well. Record this information on the student answer page.

Name ________________________________

Period ________________________________

Protein Properties
Using Electrophoresis to Determine Net Charge

HYPOTHESIS

DATA AND OBSERVATIONS

Data Table			
Protein	Color of Protein	Distance Migrated Through Gel	Charge of the Protein
cytochrome c			
myoglobin			
hemoglobin			
serum albumin			
unknown protein(s)			

CONCLUSION QUESTIONS

1. What are the building blocks or monomers that make up the proteins? Explain how these molecules are structured and how they are different from one another.

2. Explain what is meant by a protein's primary, secondary, tertiary and quaternary structure.

3. Explain why the four proteins used in this experiment moved at different rates through the gel?

4. What can be determined by comparing the unknown proteins with the known proteins in the gel?

5. Explain why in most protein separations, the final step is the staining of the gels.

Write Your Notes and Ideas Here!

Bacterial Transformation
Simulating the Production of Recombinant DNA

OBJECTIVE
Students will sequence the steps of bacterial transformation and design an imaginary recombinant DNA organism.

LEVEL
Biology I

NATIONAL STANDARDS
UCP.1, UCP.2, UCP.5, B.2, C.2, G.1, G.2, G.3

TEKS
6(A)

CONNECTIONS TO AP
AP Biology – Heredity and Evolution-Molecular Genetics-nucleic acid technology and applications

TIME FRAME
Two 45 minute periods

MATERIALS
(For a class of 28 working in pairs)

14 scissors
14 sets of map colors
tape
28 paper strands of DNA
28 chromosome and plasmid patterns
bacterial transformation transparency

TEACHER NOTES
This activity is designed to be an introduction to the process of bacterial transformation.

Suggested Teaching Procedure:

1. Explain the action of restriction enzymes and then have students complete Part I of this activity.
   - Before they tape their fragments onto their papers, have them to hold up two sections of DNA that have sticky ends (they could show you any of the cut ends of the chromosome or plasmid)
   - Ask: "What observations can you make about these ends of the desired chromosome and the cut ends of the plasmid?" (they will recognize that the ends could match back up)
   - Explain that these ends are called sticky ends.

2. Using the transformation transparency, describe the basic steps used in the process of bacterial transformation using the insulin gene as the example. Emphasize the following:
   a. The plasmids are naturally occurring, small, circular pieces of DNA that can be exchanged naturally between bacteria through conjugation and transformation. Plasmids can be used as molecular carriers or vectors to transport new genes into bacteria cells.
   b. Plasmid vectors can be engineered to have particular genes, such as antibiotic resistance. This antibiotic resistance can be used as a selection factor in the transformation process.
   c. The donor DNA and the plasmid DNA must be cut with the same restriction enzymes so that the ends will bond appropriately. In this example the donor DNA is a human chromosome and the desired gene is the insulin production gene.
   d. The desired DNA (insulin gene) and plasmid DNA can be joined using DNA ligase. The newly formed DNA is called recombinant DNA. The plasmid now contains the genetic instructions on how to produce the protein insulin.
   e. By placing bacteria in an appropriate environment, they can be artificially induced to take up the recombinant DNA plasmids and be transformed.
   f. Not all of the bacteria will take up the plasmids, but the ones that do can be identified by using culture plates that contain antibiotics. If the bacterium was successfully transformed,it will have the desired insulin gene as well as the antibiotic resistance gene. The antibiotic resistance gene will allow the transformed cells containing the plasmid to grow in a culture plate that contains the antibiotic while the non-transformed bacteria will not be able to grow. This allows the transformed cells to be easily recognized.
   g. The bacteria that contain the insulin gene can be isolated and grown. As these transformed bacteria grow and metabolize, they will produce the insulin proteins coded for by the recombinant DNA. The insulin can then be harvested.

3. Give each student a chromosome pattern, a plasmid pattern, and the rest of the supplies needed to complete Part II of the activity. Ask them what chemical is represented by the action of their scissors? *(the restriction enzyme EcoR1)*

4. Stop the students after step six and have them practice explaining the transformation process to their partner using their transformed plasmid. Call on some of the students to explain the process aloud.

5. The students should then tape their recombinant DNA in the appropriate space on the diagram of the transformation process on the student answer page and label the diagram.

6. Briefly discuss the complexity of changing the DNA in eukaryotes. Clarify the task required in Part III and indicate to the students whether or not they can come up with their own gene in their design. Encourage their creativity in their design. Ask some of the students to describe their organisms to the class. You may want to post some of their creations.

This activity is designed to be used in conjunction with a bacterial transformation lab. Several scientific supply companies offer bacterial transformation kits with transformant traits that are easily recognized by the students. For example, some kits will produce transformants that are blue, other kits produce green bacterial colonies and some will produce colonies that glow in the dark. You should find out what type of transformant is being used in your AP Biology course and then select a kit that will produce different colonies.

As an extension to this activity you could have the students discuss the ethics of gene manipulation and/or cloning.

POSSIBLE ANSWERS TO THE CONCLUSION QUESTION AND SAMPLE DATA

PART I

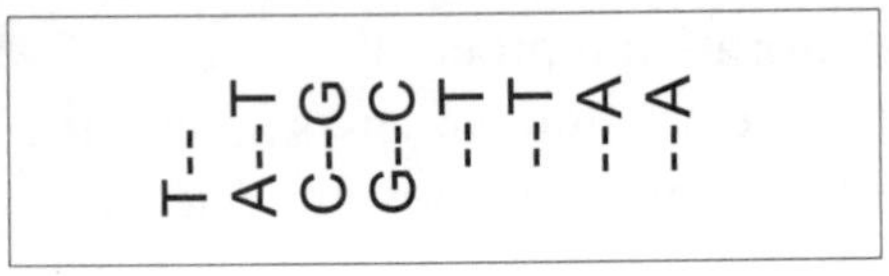

T--
A--T
C--G
G--C
--T
--T
--A
--A

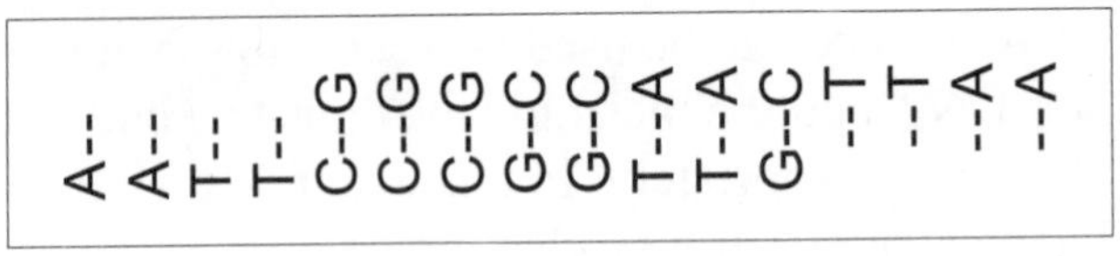

A--
A--
T--
T--
C--G
C--G
C--G
G--C
G--C
T--A
T--A
G--C
--T
--T
--A
--A

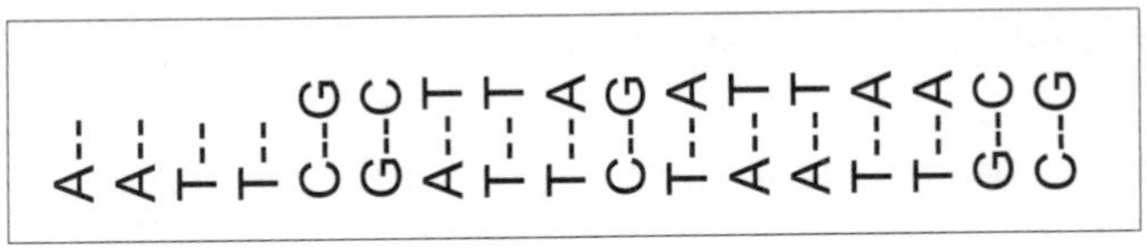

A--
A--
T--
T--
C--G
G--C
A--T
T--T
T--A
C--G
T--A
A--T
A--T
T--A
T--A
G--C
C--G

TEACHER PAGES

PART II

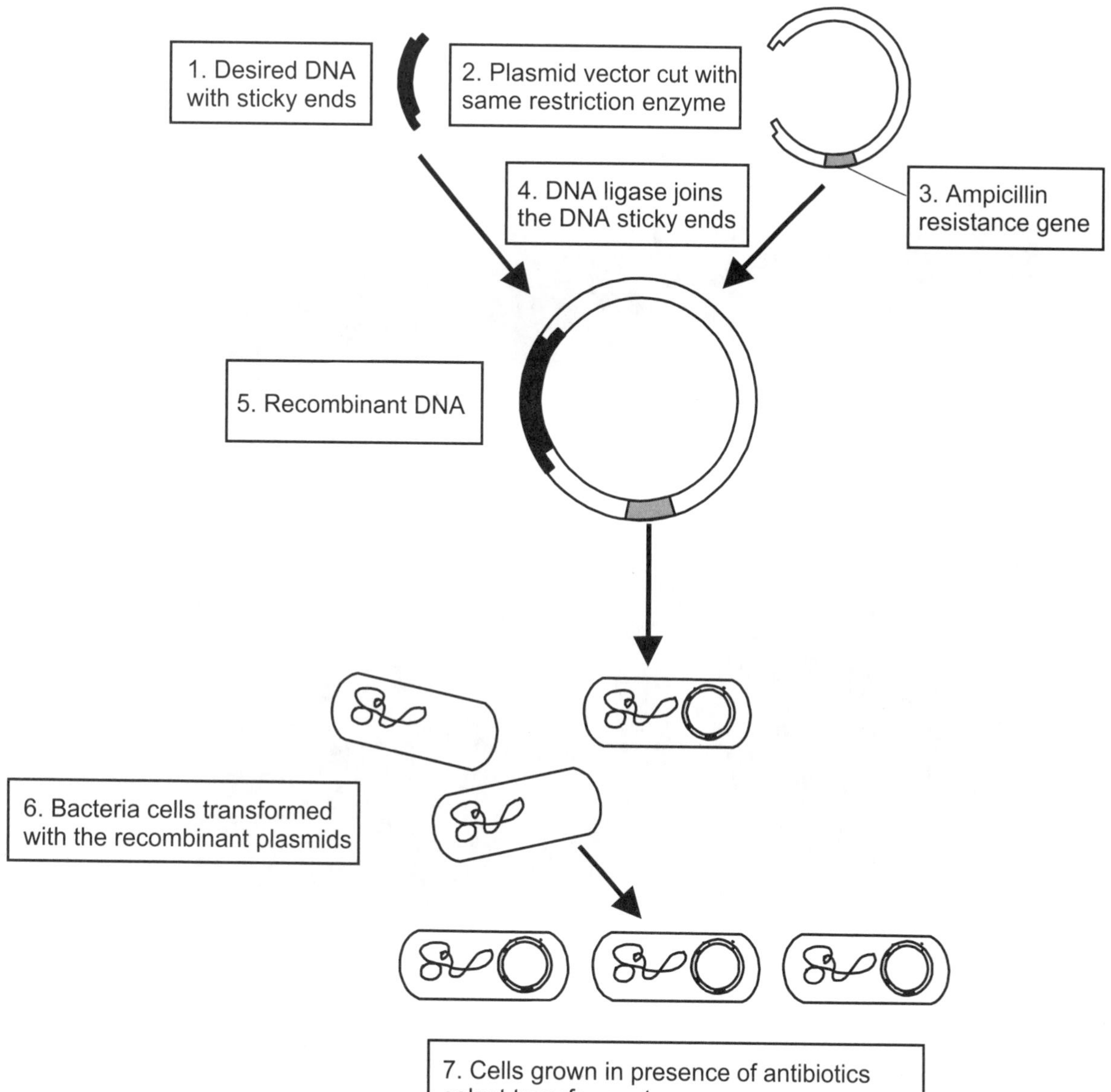
1. Desired DNA with sticky ends
2. Plasmid vector cut with same restriction enzyme
3. Ampicillin resistance gene
4. DNA ligase joins the DNA sticky ends
5. Recombinant DNA
6. Bacteria cells transformed with the recombinant plasmids
7. Cells grown in presence of antibiotics select transformant

PART III: IMAGINARY TRANSFORMANT
Gene insert: glow in the dark gene
Organism transformed: chihuahua
Name of Recombinant Organism: Chihuaglowa
Sketch of Recombinant Organism:

CONCLUSION QUESTIONS

1. Describe the role of restriction enzymes in the process of transformation.
   - restriction enzymes are used to cut the DNA at specific sites

2. In the process of transformation explain what is a sticky end and how is it useful in the process of transformation?
   - sticky ends are the ends of the cut DNA that are open to new bonding. This is useful because the sticky ends from two different pieces of DNA will match, and can be joined using DNA ligase.

3. The restriction enzyme BamH1 cuts DNA between the two G's when it encounters the base sequence GGATCC / CCTAGG. How many recognition site are found the following segment of DNA for the restriction enzyme BamH1? __3__ Mark them on the strand.

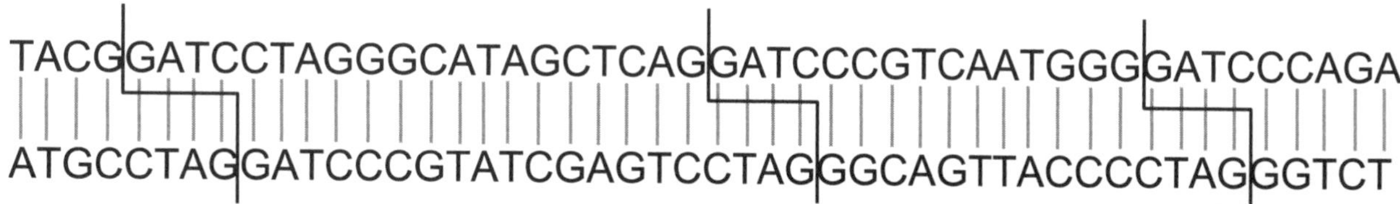

4. Describe how bacteria can be made to produce human insulin.
   - The human insulin gene is isolated and cut from its location on the chromosome using a restriction enzyme. A plasmid is cut using the same restriction enzyme. The desired DNA (insulin gene) and plasmid DNA can be joined using DNA ligase. The bacteria are placed in an appropriate environment, to be artificially induced to take up the recombinant DNA plasmids and be transformed. The transformed bacteria can be isolated using antibiotic plates. The transformed bacteria containing the insulin gene can be isolated and grown.

5. Why must the donor DNA containing the desired gene and the plasmid DNA be cut with the same restriction enzyme?
   - so they will have matching or complementary sticky ends

6. What is the purpose of using a plasmid containing an antibiotic resistance gene in the transformation process?
   - The antibiotic resistance gene allows the transformed cells to be identified because they will grow in the presence of the antibiotic.

7. What trait does your imaginary recombinant organism possess? What advantage or disadvantage does your organism have as a result of the recombinant DNA?
   - (answers will vary)
   - My recombinant organism contains a gene for glowing in the dark. This gene would make my dog easier to see at night. That way if I let the dog outside at night, I could find it.

8. Why are eukaryotes more difficult to transform than prokaryotes? What methods can be used to transform eukaryotes?
   - Eukaryotes have many cells. Eukaryotic cells can by stimulated to take up DNA using electrical shock, bombarding the cells with DNA coated projectiles, injecting the DNA into the zygote cell and by modified viruses.

Transformation Transparency

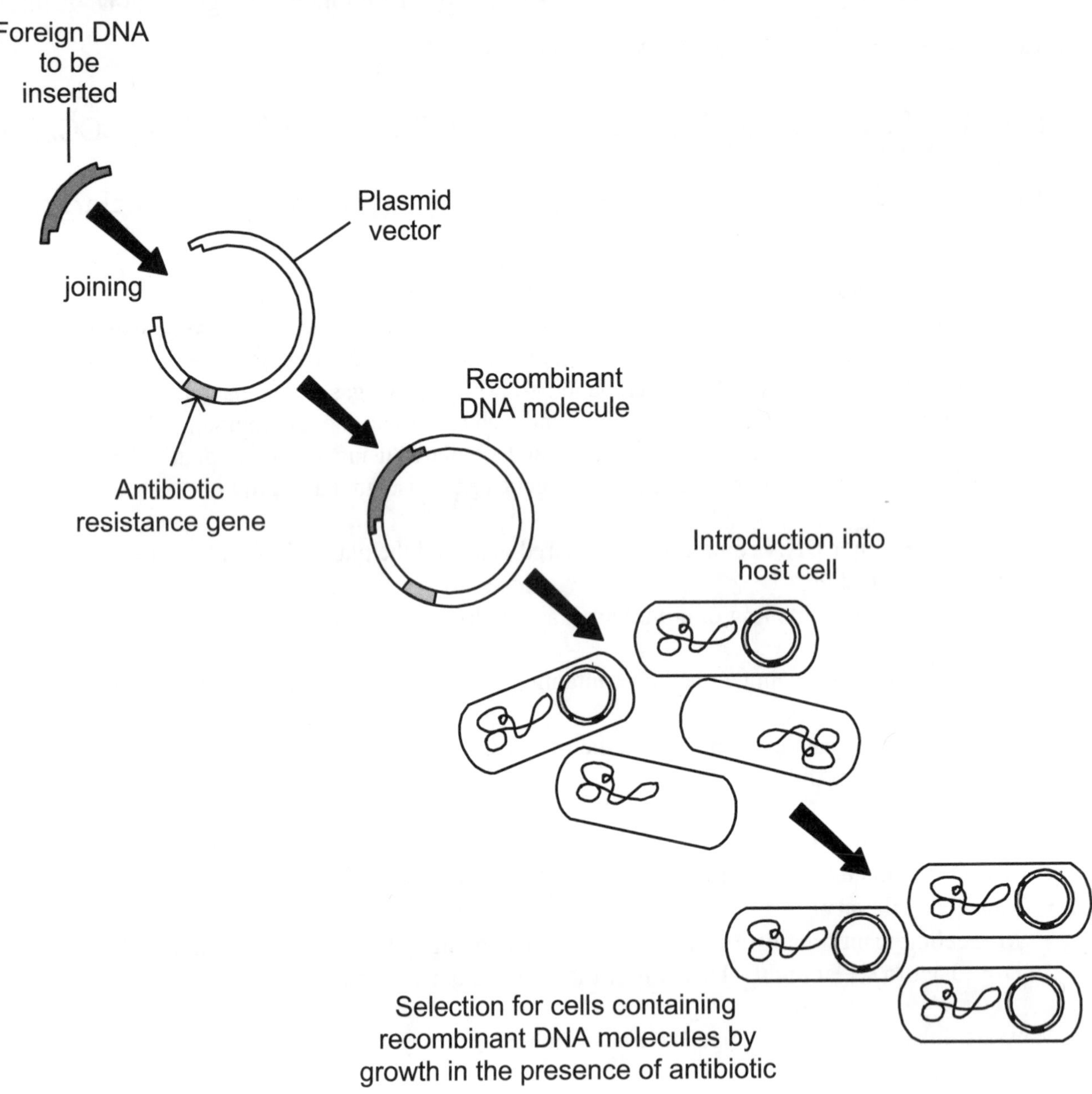

Black line master for chromosome and plasmid:

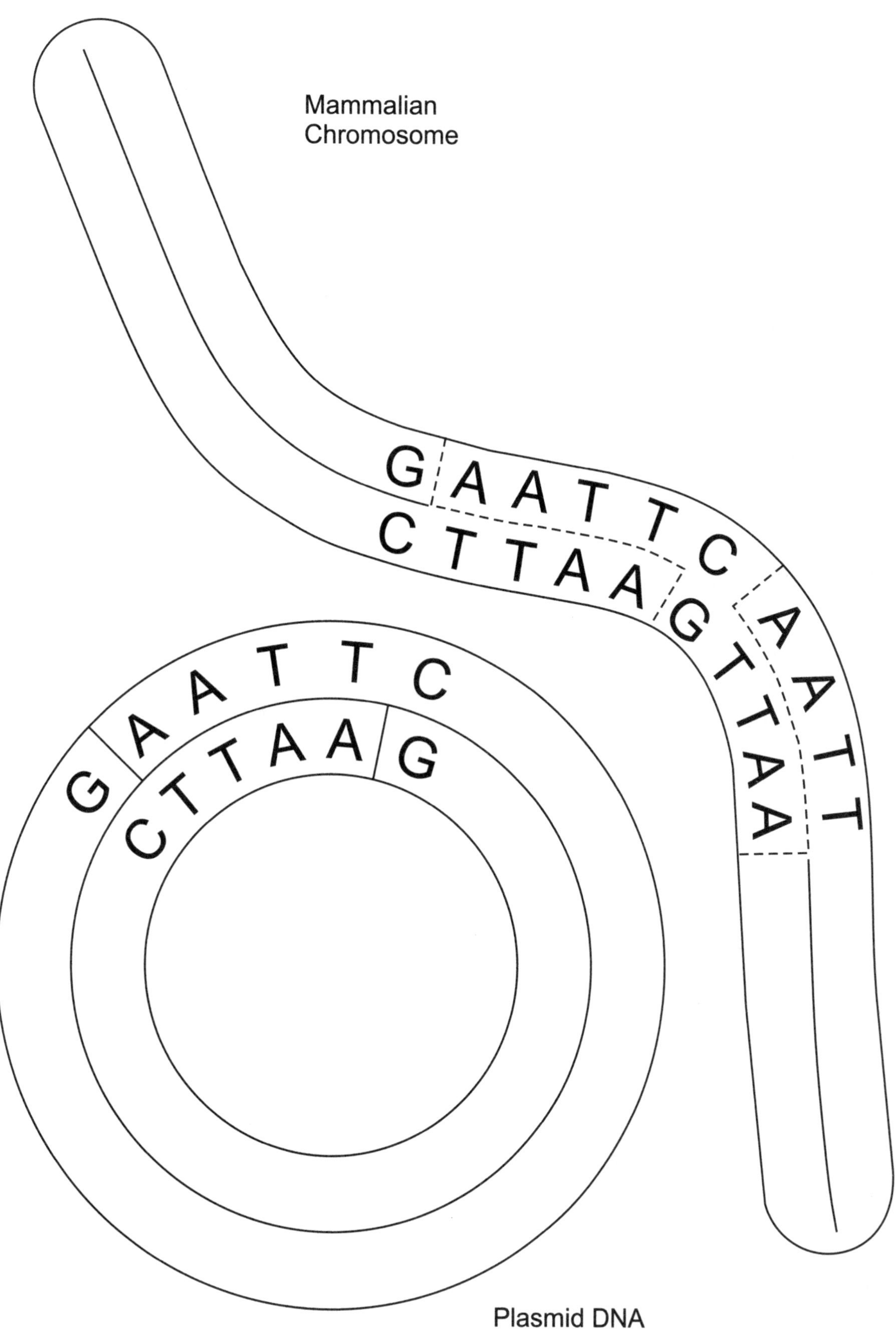

Black line master for Part I DNA strands

T--A
A--T
C--G
G--C
A--T
A--T
T--A
T--A
C--G
C--G
C--G
G--C
G--C
T--A
T--A
G--C
A--T
A--T
T--A
T--A
C--G
G--C
A--T
T--T
T--A
C--G
T--A
A--T
A--T
T--A
T--A
G--C
C--G

T--A
A--T
C--G
G--C
A--T
A--T
T--A
T--A
C--G
C--G
C--G
G--C
G--C
T--A
T--A
G--C
A--T
A--T
T--A
T--A
C--G
G--C
A--T
T--T
T--A
C--G
T--A
A--T
A--T
T--A
T--A
G--C
C--G

T--A
A--T
C--G
G--C
A--T
A--T
T--A
T--A
C--G
C--G
C--G
G--C
G--C
T--A
T--A
G--C
A--T
A--T
T--A
T--A
C--G
G--C
A--T
T--T
T--A
C--G
T--A
A--T
A--T
T--A
T--A
G--C
C--G

T--A
A--T
C--G
G--C
A--T
A--T
T--A
T--A
C--G
C--G
C--G
G--C
G--C
T--A
T--A
G--C
A--T
A--T
T--A
T--A
C--G
G--C
A--T
T--T
T--A
C--G
T--A
A--T
A--T
T--A
T--A
G--C
C--G

T--A
A--T
C--G
G--C
A--T
A--T
T--A
T--A
C--G
C--G
C--G
G--C
G--C
T--A
T--A
G--C
A--T
A--T
T--A
T--A
C--G
G--C
A--T
T--T
T--A
C--G
T--A
A--T
A--T
T--A
T--A
G--C
C--G

REFERENCES

Strauss Eric and Marylin Lisowski. *Biology, The Web of Life*. Menlo Park: Scott Foresman Addison Wesley. 1998. pp. 209-214

Campbell, Neil and Jane Reece. *Biology*. San Francisco: Benjamin Cummings 2002. pp. 344-345

Bacterial Transformation
Simulating the Production of Recombinant DNA

One of the ways that bacteria remain genetically diverse is through the naturally occurring process of *transformation*. During transformation bacteria take up plasmid DNA from their environment. *Plasmids* are small, circular pieces of DNA that can be exchanged naturally between bacteria. Plasmids provide bacteria with special traits such as antibiotic resistance.

Molecular biologists have developed procedures to take advantage of the naturally occurring transformation process to produce cells that contain desired segments of DNA. Genetic engineering refers to manipulation techniques used by scientists to change the genetic makeup of an organism. The basic transformation process is to select the desired gene to be inserted into the organism, cut the two DNA molecules into fragments using special enzymes called *restriction enzymes*, splice the two DNA fragments together, and then introduce the new DNA into a living cell for replication and expression of the inserted gene.

Enzymes play an important role in the formation of recombinant DNA. To excise the desired gene from the donor DNA, restriction enzymes are used to cut DNA bonds in specific locations called recognition sites. There are many different restriction enzymes and each recognizes and cuts at a different short sequence of DNA. For example, the restriction enzyme EcoR1 will recognize and cleave DNA at any section of DNA that reads GAATTC. This cut results in the production of "sticky ends" that are open to new bonds. See Figures 1 and 2. By cutting the donor DNA containing the desired gene and the plasmid DNA with the same restriction enzyme, matching sticky ends will be produced. The two types of DNA with sticky ends can be joined using another enzyme, DNA ligase. The newly formed DNA is called *recombinant DNA*

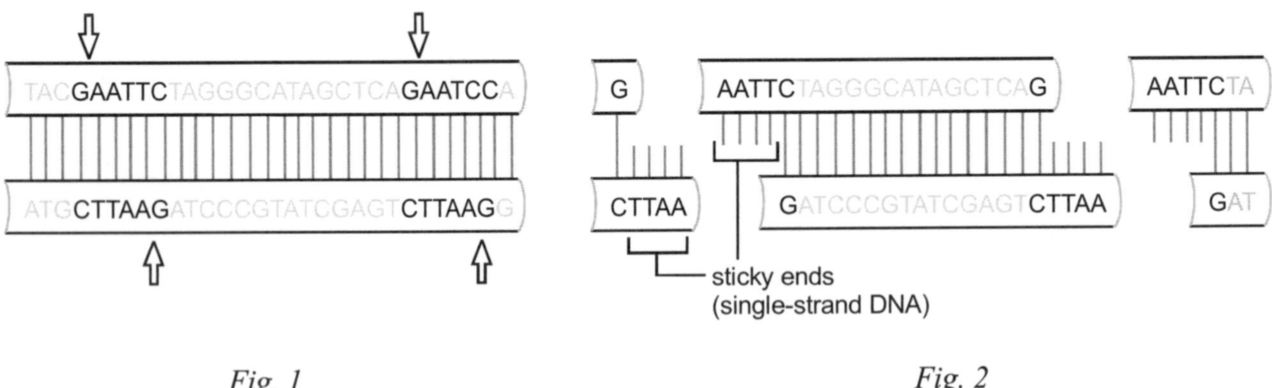

Fig. 1 *Fig. 2*

Scientists have developed transformation methods based on the naturally occurring plasmid DNA. They construct plasmids to be molecular carriers or **vectors** to move specific segments of DNA into bacteria cells. The bacterial cells will then treat this new DNA as their own and produce the proteins coded for by the newly introduced segment of DNA. Plasmid vectors can be engineered to have particular genes, such as antibiotic resistance in addition to the specific inserted DNA. This antibiotic resistance can be used as a selection factor in the transformation process.

One of the best examples of transformation success is the production of insulin. The human insulin gene is isolated and cut from its location on the human chromosome using a restriction enzyme. A plasmid is cut using the same restriction enzyme. The desired DNA (insulin gene) and plasmid DNA can be joined using DNA ligase. The plasmid now contains the genetic instructions on how to produce the protein insulin. By placing bacteria in an appropriate environment, they can be artificially induced to take up the recombinant DNA plasmids and be transformed.

Not all of the bacteria will take up the plasmids, but the ones that do can be identified by using culture plates that contain antibiotics. The successfully transformed bacteria will contain the desired insulin gene as well as the antibiotic resistance gene. The antibiotic resistance gene will allow the plasmid to grow in a culture plate that contains the antibiotic. The non-transformed bacteria will not be able to grow in the presence of the antibiotic. The transformants, therefore are easily recognized because they are the survivors.

The transformed bacteria containing the insulin gene can be isolated and grown. As these transformed bacteria grow and metabolize, they will produce the insulin proteins coded for by the recombinant DNA. The insulin can then be harvested and used to treat diabetes.

Eukaryotic cells can also be transformed; however, the process is not quite as simple since these organisms are frequently multicellular. Simply stated, eukaryotic cells can by stimulated to take up DNA using electrical shock, by bombarding the cells with DNA coated projectiles, or by injecting the DNA into the zygote cell. Additionally, viruses can be modified and used to carry desired DNA into a eukaryotic cell.

PURPOSE

In this activity you will simulate the action of restriction enzymes and the process of producing recombinant DNA. You will also design an imaginary organism made from recombinant DNA.

MATERIALS

- scissors
- pattern for chromosome and plasmid
- paper strand of DNA
- set of map colors
- tape
- student answer pages

PROCEDURE

PART I: SIMULATING THE STEPS OF BACTERIAL TRANSFORMATION

1. Your teacher will provide you with a paper strand of DNA. Use scissors to cut the strand of DNA at every EcoR1 recognition site found within the strand. (Refer to the introduction for the base pattern found in this site.)

2. Tape the DNA fragments into the boxes provided on the student answer page. Label all of the sticky ends.

3. Answer conclusion questions 1-3 on the student answer page.

PART II: SIMULATING THE PRODUCTION OF RECOMBINANT DNA

1. Obtain a chromosome pattern and a plasmid pattern. Locate the ampicillin resistance gene on the plasmid. Color this segment of the plasmid green and all remaining plasmid DNA red. Color the chromosome DNA blue.

2. Cut out both colored DNA patterns.

3. The recognition site for the restriction enzyme EcoR1 is G▼GATCC / CCTAG▲G. Simulate the action of EcoR1 by cutting the plasmid and the donor DNA at the EcoR1 recognition site.

4. Prepare your recombinant DNA model by matching the ends of the desired chromosomal DNA to the plasmid DNA ends and taping them together.

5. Use your recombinant DNA model to practice explaining the steps of the bacterial transformation process with your partner.

6. Tape your recombinant DNA in the appropriate space on the transformation diagram on the student answer page. Complete the diagram by labeling each step of the process using the following labels: ampicillin resistance gene, DNA ligase joins the DNA sticky ends, plasmid vector cut with same restriction enzyme, recombinant DNA, desired DNA with sticky ends, cells grown in presence of antibiotics to select transformed, bacteria cells containing the recombinant plasmids.

7. Answer conclusion questions 4 through 6 on the student answer page.

PART III: DESIGNING A RECOMBINANT ORGANISM

1. Work with a partner to design an imaginary recombinant organism. Select one of the desired genes below to use to create your organism (with your teacher's permission you may use a gene not included in this list). Your organism can be prokaryotic or eukaryotic. Record you choice in the space on the student answer page.
   a. A gene that causes cells to glow in the dark.
   b. A gene that codes for the production of a growth hormone.
   c. A gene that causes cells to stop dividing.
   d. A gene that causes the production of glycerol in the cell resulting in freeze resistant cells.
   e. A gene that increases the production of muscle proteins.
   f. A gene that increases intelligence.

2. Identify an organism into which you would like to insert the gene. Place the name of your organism in the space provided on the student answer page.

3. In the space provided on the student answer page make a drawing of your transformed organism expressing the newly inserted gene. Give your transformed organism a unique name and use that as the title of your diagram. Write a paragraph describing your transformant and be ready to share your description with the class.

4. Answer conclusion questions 7 and 8.

Name ______________________________

Period______________________________

Bacterial Transformation
Simulating the Production of Recombinant DNA

DATA AND OBSERVATIONS

PART I

PART II
Tape Recombinant Model here:

PART II

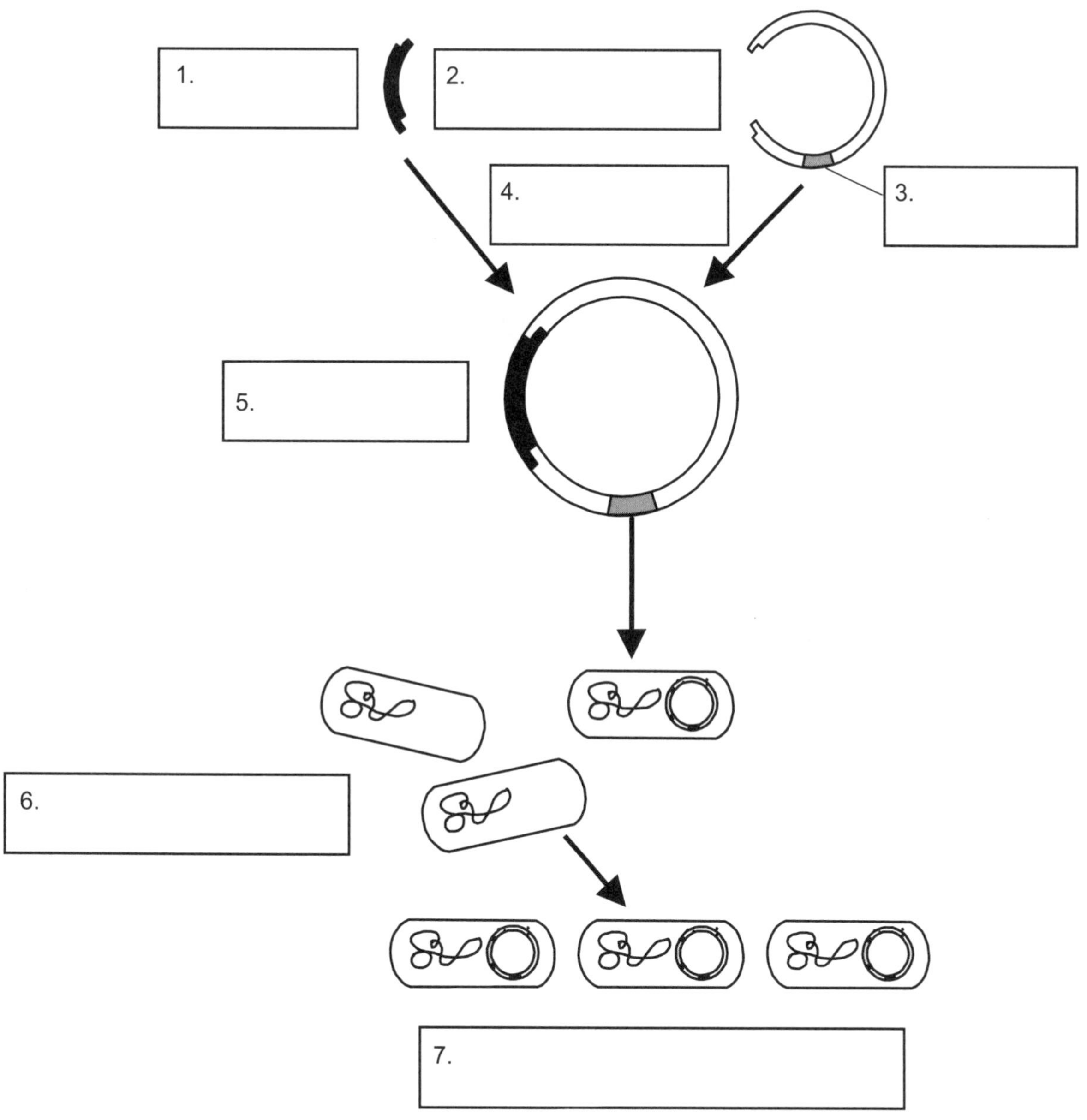

PART III: IMAGINARY TRANSFORMANT

Gene insert:_______________________________

Organism transformed:_____________________

Name of Recombinant Organism: ____

Sketch of Recombinant Organism:

CONCLUSION QUESTIONS

1. Describe the role of restriction enzymes in the process of transformation.

2. In the process of transformation explain what is a sticky end and how is it useful in the process of transformation?

3. The restriction enzyme BamH1 cuts DNA between the two G's when it encounters the base sequence GAATTC / CTTAGG. How many recognition site are found the following segment of DNA for the restriction enzyme BamH1? ______ Mark them on the strand.

TACGGATCCTAGGGCATAGCTCAGGATCCCGTCAATGGGGATCCCAGA

ATGCCTAGGATCCCGTATCGAGTCCTAGGGCAGTTACCCCTAGGGTCT

4. Describe how bacteria can be made to produce human insulin.

5. Why must the donor DNA containing the desired gene and the plasmid DNA be cut with the same restriction enzyme?

6. What is the purpose of using a plasmid containing an antibiotic resistance gene in the transformation process?

7. What trait does your imaginary recombinant organism possess? What advantage or disadvantage does your organism have as a result of the recombinant DNA?

8. Why are eukaryotes more difficult to transform than prokaryotes? What methods can be used to transform eukaryotes?

Quackers
Simulating Natural Selection

OBJECTIVE
Students will simulate the impact of natural selection on a population of ducks (quackers) which are represented by two different colors of snack crackers.

LEVEL
Biology I

NATIONAL STANDARDS
UCP.1, UCP.2, UCP.3, UCP.4, C.3, C.4, G.1, G.2, G.3

TEKS
7(B)

CONNECTIONS TO AP
AP Biology:
    II. Heredity and Evolution C. Evolutionary Biology 3. Mechanisms of evolution

TIME FRAME
45 minutes

MATERIALS
(For a class of 28 working in pairs)

14 resealable bags
14 paper plates
transparency of class data table
1 box of light colored snack crackers
1 box of dark colored snack crackers

TEACHER NOTES
This activity is designed to introduce the concept of natural selection. One of the main points of this activity is to help students see that an organism cannot adapt to it's environment, but that it will survive if it possesses a successful adaptation. Make it clear to the students that an organism cannot willingly adapt itself. The data collected in this activity can be used as a reference point for terms used during presentations on microevolution and speciation.

The students pretend to be predators of the "quacker" population. The quackers are represented in this activity by two different flavors of the same type snack cracker. You can find relatively inexpensive store brand white cheddar snack crackers to represent the light feathered ducks. The dark feathered ducks can be represented by inexpensive store brand yellow cheddar snack crackers. You could substitute two colors of M&M's or other candies if you have difficulty finding affordable crackers. The type of food is not significant. You just need to versions of the same type of item.

Prior to the activity, you will need to prepare 14 resealable bags containing 20 dark and 20 light colored snack crackers (or suitable substitute).

This activity should be conducted in a classroom setting rather than a laboratory setting since the students will be simulating predation by eating the prey. Be sure to check for food allergies before conducting this activity. As an alternative, you may choose to use a non-food item for this simulation. For example, you could use two different colored poker chips as the prey.

Use the class data transparency to collect data on all five generations from each lab group. The students will then total the numbers for each generation and write the averages in Data Table 2.

POSSIBLE ANSWERS TO THE CONCLUSION QUESTIONS AND SAMPLE DATA

HYPOTHESIS

If light organisms are preferred then there will be more dark organisms than light at the end of 5 generations.

DATA AND OBSERVATIONS

Data Table 1: Light and Dark Quackers Each Generation		
Generation	Light Quackers	Dark Quackers
1	3	7
2	2	8
3	3	7
4	0	10
5	1	9

ANALYSIS

Data Table 2: Class Averages Light and Dark Quackers Each Generation		
Generation	Average Light Quackers	Average Dark Quackers
1	4.3	5.7
2	3	7
3	2.3	7.7
4	1.6	8.4
5	1.4	8.6

Graph 1:

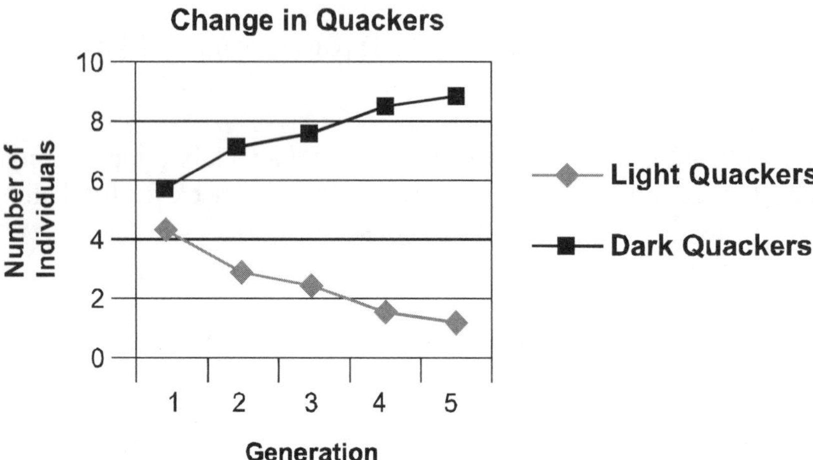

CONCLUSION QUESTIONS

1. Write a statement describing how the number of light and dark quackers changed over the period of 5 generations.
   - The number of light quackers decreases while the number of dark quackers increases from generation 1 to generation 5.

2. What do you predict would happen to the number of light quackers if you had continued predation for a total of 10 generations? Explain your prediction.
   - The number of light colored quackers would continue to decline.
   - The light quackers are being preyed upon in higher numbers which reduces their presence in the gene pool. With fewer light quackers mating and producing light offspring, the light numbers decline.

3. Which type of quacker would Darwin consider "most fit" in this predation situation, the light quacker or the dark quacker? Why?
   - The dark colored quackers would be considered most fit because they have survived predation and will live to be the parents of the next generation.

4. What adaptation do these quackers possess that allows them to survive?
   - The adaptation for dark colored feathers.

5. Explain why it is incorrect to say that an organism adapts to its environment.
   - A single organism cannot willingly become adapted to the environment. The organism either possesses the favorable adaptation and survives or does not possess it and dies.

6. What changes in the population would occur if the predation changed and began to prefer the dark quackers? Explain why these changes would occur.
   - The numbers of dark quackers would decline. The light quacker numbers would increase since they are less likely to be eaten, more likely to survive. The quackers that survive are the parents of the next generation.

REFERENCES

Strauss Eric and Marylin Lisowski. *Biology, The Web of Life*. Menlo Park: Scott Foresman Addison Wesley, 1998.

Campbell, Neil and Jane Reece. *Biology*. San Francisco: Benjamin Cummings, 2002.

Class Data Transparency:

Class Results: Generations 1-5										
	Light					Dark				
Group #	Gen.1	Gen.2	Gen.3	Gen.4	Gen.5	Gen.1	Gen.2	Gen.3	Gen.4	Gen.5
1										
2										
3										
4										
5										
6										
7										
8										
9										
10										
11										
12										
13										
14										
TOTAL										
AVERAGE										

Quackers
Investigating Natural Selection

Charles Darwin published *The Origin of Species* in 1859. In his book Darwin presented two main concepts, descent with modification and natural selection. Descent with modification was the phrase Darwin used to describe how modern species arose from a series of ancestors through accumulated changes over time. The second concept, natural selection, is the process in which the organisms that are best adapted to a set of environmental conditions will survive long enough to reproduce. By reproducing, these organisms will pass the successful genetic information to the next generation. Those organisms that are not as well adapted are more likely to die. The overall composition of the population will change as the survivors with the more beneficial genes or adaptations produce more offspring.

Natural selection is sometimes referred to as 'survival of the fittest'. The organisms that are best adapted will be the parents of the subsequent generation. It is important to note that the organisms do not adapt to their environment. For example, in a desert setting, narrow leafed plants survive at a higher rate than a broad leafed, tropical plant would survive. The narrow leafed plant is better adapted and will survive to reproduce. The broad leafed plant would lose too much water and die before reproducing. The broad leafed plant can't adapt to the desert environment. The narrow leafed plants "become adapted", rather they possess adaptations that make them better suited for survival. An adaptation then is an inherited trait that gives an organism possessing that trait a reproductive advantage. When natural selection is occurring, those organisms that possess the adaptation survive at a higher rate than those that do not possess the adaptation.

PURPOSE

In this activity you will simulate the events of natural selection. The population experiencing natural selection in this simulation is a flock of ducks with light feathers and dark feathers. The light feathered ducks are more easily spotted by the predator than the dark ducks. The duck or "quacker" population is represented by light and dark colored crackers.

MATERIALS

clean paper plate
light colored snack crackers
dark colored snack crackers

PROCEDURE

1. In this activity you will begin with a population that has equal numbers of light and dark "organisms" that will be fed on by you, the predator. As the predator, you prefer to eat the light organisms rather than the dark ones. Formulate a hypothesis regarding what will happen to the ratio of light to dark colored organisms if the predator more easily preys upon the light colored organisms. Record your hypothesis in the space provided on the student answer page.

2. The organisms in this activity will be ducks or "quackers" and will be represented by light and dark colored snack crackers. Obtain a pond (or bag) of quackers from your teacher. This bag will contain equal numbers of light and dark snack crackers.

3. Establish your generation 1 flock of quackers by having one partner reach in the bag, without looking, and randomly select 10 quackers (crackers).

4. Place the 10 quackers on a clean paper plate or napkin. Count how many light and how many dark quackers are present. Record your numbers for generation 1 on Data Table 1 of the student answer page.

5. Simulate predation by choosing three light feathered quackers from the flock of 10 and eating them. If you only have one or two light quackers, eat them first and then consume enough dark quackers to meet your quota. For example if you have only one light quacker, eat it and then two dark ones. If you have two light quackers, eat both of them and one dark one. But remember, as the predator, you prefer the light quackers.

6. To simulate reproduction in the population, close your eyes, reach into the bag, and choose three quackers to add to your plate. This should bring the total number of quackers back to 10.

7. Record the number of light and dark quackers that are now present in the flock in the space for generation 2 on Data Table 1.

8. The other partner should now take a turn at being a predator. The predator should eat three light quackers from the flock. If there are not three light quackers in the flock, follow the procedure described in step 5.

9. Simulate reproduction in the population by repeating step 6. Count the numbers of each type of quacker in the replenished flock and record the data in space for generation 3 on Data Table 1.

10. Repeat steps 8 and 9 two more times for a total of 5 generations of data.

11. As instructed by your teacher, combine your individual data with the class data for each of the five generations. Calculate the class average for each color quacker for each generation.

12. In the space provided on the student answer page, prepare a graph of the class averages of light and dark quackers for each generation. Be sure to include axes labels, units, and a title on your graph.

13. Answer the conclusion questions.

Name ______________________

Period ______________________

Quackers
Investigating Natural Selection

HYPOTHESIS

DATA AND OBSERVATIONS

Data Table 1: Light and Dark Quackers Each Generation		
Generation	Light Quackers	Dark Quackers
1		
2		
3		
4		
5		

ANALYSIS

Data Table 2: Class Averages Light and Dark Quackers Each Generation		
Generation	Average Light Quackers	Average Dark Quackers
1		
2		
3		
4		
5		

Graph 1:

CONCLUSION QUESTIONS

1. Write a statement describing how the number of light and dark quackers changed over the period of 5 generations.

2. What do you predict would happen to the number of light quackers if you had continued predation for a total of 10 generations? Explain your prediction.

3. Which type of quacker would Darwin consider "most fit" in this predation situation, the light quacker or the dark quacker? Why?

4. What adaptation do these quackers possess that allows them to survive?

5. Explain why it is incorrect to say that an organism adapts to its environment.

6. What changes in the population would occur if the predation changed and began to prefer the dark quackers? Explain why these changes would occur.

Life in the Cold
Investigating Survival Strategies and Adaptations

OBJECTIVE
Students will investigate how various adaptations and habitats allow animals to survive in the cold.

LEVEL
Biology I

NATIONAL STANDARDS
UCP.2, UCP.5, C.3, C.4, E.1, E.2, G.1, G.2

TEKS
2(A), 2(B), 2(C), 2(D), 7(B)

CONNECTIONS TO AP
AP Biology:

II. Heredity and Evolution C. Evolutionary Biology 3. Mechanism of evolution

TIME FRAME
45 minutes for Part I
45 minutes for Part II

MATERIALS
(For a class of 28 working in pairs)

14 TI-83 or TI-83 + graphing calculators
(used for graphing calculator lab)
14 computers
(used for computer lab)
14 temperature probes
14 lids to fit the cups
14 swaths of fur approximately 30 cm x 30 cm
14 1 lb coffee cans or 1 gallon resealable bags
hay, leaves, grass or wood chips
14 rubber bands
14 Lab Pro's or CBL's
(used for graphing calculator protocol)
14 Lab Pro's or Serial Interface Device
(used for computer protocol)
14 8 oz paper cups for hot liquids
(can use yogurt containers)
14 100 mL graduated cylinders
14 knee-high stockings stuffed with feathers
sand
water bath with 37° C water

TEACHER NOTES

Water can be kept warm by using a polystyrene container. If you do not have a coffee can for part II, resealable one gallon bags will work. For time considerations, you may want the students to work in groups of 4. Two students can do part I and two students can do part II and then share the information.

The cups can be the paper type used to hold hot liquids or yogurt containers work well. The cups should be marked to hold 200 mL of water by marking them with a permanent marker. The feather filled stocking can be made by using feathers from a feather pillow and nylon knee-high stockings. You should fill them with feathers prior to class. The fur cover can be made by purchasing fake fur at a store that sells yard goods.

Sand can be purchased at any discount department store with a garden center or a garden shop. You will find that when the sand is used, the cup will actually cool down faster than the control due to the heat capacity of sand and the fact that there are very few pockets of air in the sand.

1. Calculator Information

The lab protocol is based on using a LabPro® or CBL 2 (Calculator-Based Laboratory System). Students will need a TI 83+ or the TI 83, 85, 86, 89 or 92 can be easily used. Be aware that this lab can be adapted for a number of interface systems and calculators. Check with the individual manuals when making adaptations. The standard pressure probe that is needed for this lab comes from Vernier. These probes, calculators and interfaces can also be purchased from Vernier. The address is:

Vernier Software Company
13979 SW Millikan Way
Beaverton, OR 97005-2886
(503)-277-2299
www.vernier.com

2. Calculator Software Information

This activity uses DATAMATE as the data collection program. This program must be installed on the graphing calculators and can be downloaded free from Vernier. A TI-GraphLink cable is necessary for connecting the CBL2 or LabPro to a computer for download or upload processes. It is a good idea to check the Vernier site periodically for updates and update both the DATAMATE program and the operating system of your data collection devices.

3. Computer Hardware Information

Macintosh System Requirements

Power Macintosh or newer computer
At least 32 MB of RAM
System 7.5 or newer

Windows System Requirements

Windows 98/NT/ME/2000/XP
At least 32 MB of RAM
Pentium processor-base or compatible, PC

4. Computer Software Information

The computer equipment that is needed to make this lab work comes from Vernier, you need a serial box (SBI), or LabPro and a pressure sensor or the gas pressure sensor (the standard pressure probe is sensitive enough) and Logger Pro Software. These can be purchased from Vernier. The address is:

13979 SW Millikan Way
Beaverton, OR 97005-2886
(503)-277-2299

The software that is used in conjunction with the pressure probe is **Logger Pro Software**. It can be purchased for the PC or Mac. Start the program.

One nice feature of Logger Pro Software is that there are templates for the probes already installed. They can be modified to fit your own experiment and then saved under your own title for the students. This lab is based on version 2.1.1. The following directions may have to be modified for other versions of this software. The following steps work nicely for this experiment:

- It is important that you try this lab and software before working with students so that you can modify the templates or instructions to meet the particular needs of your own experiment.
- Be sure you have the experimental apparatus set up for this experiment by connecting the interface to the computer through the modem port, the temperature probe is connected to Port 1 or Ch 1 on the interface.
- Pull down the File menu and click on Open. A menu with Experiments will appear.
- Open the file Probes & Sensors.
- Open the file Temperature Probes and select the type of temperature probe. Note select the probe without any units as this is the default for Celsius.
- Pull down the Set-up Menu and click on Data Collect, a dialog box should appear. Select Sampling Tab. Now type in the length of time you wish to run the experiment. Usually 10 minutes per run will be sufficient. Select minutes for the unit of time. Type in 10 to run the experiment for 10 minutes for experiment length.
- Now change the sampling speed. It should be set at 10 pts. per minute. Close this window by clicking OK.
- Pull down the Data Menu and open the Column Options, Temperature. Go to Displayed Precision and check the decimal place and change the numeric display to 3 decimal places. Press OK
- Pull down the View Menu. Select Graph Options and select the Axis option tab. Change the scaling of the temperature or Y Axis to 30 for the Min and 45 for the Max. Press Apply and press OK to close the window.

- The temperature of the water only cools down 0.5 to 2o C. The range above will allow this change to be illustrated.
- Once the parameters are set, you can name and save this template to your computer be used by your students

ANSWERS TO PRE-LAB QUESTIONS

1. List three characteristics of the tundra.
   a. There is a permanent layer of soil that remains frozen called the permafrost.
   b. The annual precipitation is 25-30 cm per year.
   c. Above the artic circle, there are nearly three months of darkness.

2. What is an adaptation?
   - An adaptation is a genetically inherited trait that will give an organism a slight reproductive advantage in a given environment.

3. What types of animals are found in the tundra?
   - The following animals are found in the tundra: mush-oxen, lemmings, migratory birds, caribou, and foxes. Others answers may also be correct.

4. What types of plant life are found in the tundra?
   - Small plants adapted to dry, cold environments. There are few woody plants or trees.

POSSIBLE ANSWERS TO THE CONCLUSION QUESTIONS AND SAMPLE DATA

Data Table				
	Experimental Set-up	Minimum Temperature (°C)	Maximum Temperature (°C)	Total Temperature Change (°C)
Part I	Control	35.1	37.7	2.6
	Feathers	37.6	38.6	1.0
	Fur	36.1	37.7	1.6
Part II	Control	32.0	34.0	2.0
	Sand	30.9	33.1	2.2
	Natural Materials	33.5	34.2	0.7

PART I

1. Which set up or adaptation stayed the warmest by showing the least amount of change in temperature?
   - According to the data, the container with the fur wrapped around it stayed the warmest or had the least amount of cooling. This result may vary and the container with the feathers may have the least amount of cooling.

2. Which set up or adaptation cooled the fasted by showing the greatest amount of temperature change?
   - The container without any insulation lost the greatest amount of heat.

3. Compare and contrast the results produced when feathers and fur served as insulation for the animal. What do these materials have in common?
   - Both of these materials kept the water warmer.
   - These materials are both able to trap air and keep it warm.

4. What are some other adaptations that animals have evolved to aid their survival in the tundra?
   - Answers will vary, but the students may answer that in addition to fur and feathers animals that live in this area may have layers of fat to keep warm.

PART II

1. Which set up or shelter stayed the warmest by showing the least amount of change in temperature?
   - The container that had natural materials showed the least amount of cooling.

2. Which set up cooled the fasted by showing the greatest amount of temperature change?
   - The sand had the greatest amount of cooling.

3. Compare and contrast the results obtained when sand and natural materials simulated a shelter to protect animals in the cold? Explain any differences that were observed.
   - The sand crystals actually cooled more than the container that did not have any sort of wrapping. This is because the crystals are packed close to one another and there are no pockets of trapped air to the keep the water warm.

Life in the Cold
Investigating Survival Strategies and Adaptations Using a Graphing Calculator and Data Collection Device

An adaptation is an inherited trait or characteristic an individual organism possesses that will help it to survive and ultimately reproduce. These favorable genes or characteristics will then be passed on to the next generation. This exercise will investigate adaptations that aid in survival in cold climates.

Biomes are ecosystems that are characterized by the predominant vegetation found in that biome. The tundra is a biome located in northern most latitudes. The climate of the tundra is very cold and with very little rainfall. It covers approximately 20% of the Earth's land. There is very little sunshine received for any given time as the sun is always low in the sky. The sun rays are not directly above the land as they are at the equator. In the winter, the days are very short, lasting only a few hours but in the summer the days are very long, lasting up to 24 hours in the latitudes of the Arctic Circle. Because of this increase in day length, the total amount of radiant energy is great. The tundra's top layer of soil only thaws during the summer but the soil layer underneath remains frozen and is called the permafrost. The presence of permafrost causes water to collect on the top of soil, forming small pools of water rather than draining into the soil below. Soils are poorly developed and contain very little nitrogen. This coupled with a short growing season limits the size of plants. As a result, grasses and sedges are the dominant plant life. Any woody plants that are found in the tundra are only a few centimeters tall. In the summer flowers and their seeds appear quickly. The animals in the tundra are a reflection of the plant life found there. During the summers there is a migration of many birds and mammals to the region. These animals feed on the plentiful plant life. Migratory water birds come to the tundra to raise their young in an environment that allows around-the-clock food gathering. Arctic foxes and showshoe hares are present in their brown summer coats which turn white when winter arrives.

The fall season is extremely short and the transition to winter occurs quickly. Lakes and ponds freeze. Snowfall is surprisingly little, only 25-30 cm per year. Winds across the region forms snow drifts. Above the Arctic Circle after the winter solstice, there are three months of near darkness. The plants become dormant and many animals migrate south as food resources are reduced. Only a few, well-adapted, animals remain behind. For example, lemmings survive in the tundra by burrowing under the snow. The musk-oxen are one of the few animals that possess the adaptations necessary to survive the winter's full force. These warm-blooded large animals have the ability to survive the Arctic's extreme winter due to their adaptations of thick hide and two coats of fur.

PURPOSE

The purpose of this investigation is to compare the effectiveness of insulating adaptations such as fur and feathers. A cup of warm water will represent the animal. The temperature of the water inside the cup will be monitored under three conditions: no insulation (the control), fur insulation, and feather insulation. The second purpose of this investigation is to investigate the effects of different shelters in stabilizing temperatures. A cup will once again represent the animal. The temperature of the water in the cup will be monitored under three sheltering conditions: air (the control), sand, and natural plant materials such as leaves, hay, or wood chips.

MATERIALS

temperature probe
interface
lids to fit the cup
swath of fur approximately 30 cm x 30 cm
sand
water bath with 37° C water
graphing calculator
8 oz paper cup for hot liquids or yogurt containers
100 mL graduated cylinder
1 lb coffee can or 1 gallon resealable bag
hay, leaves, grass or wood chips
rubber bands
knee-high stocking with feathers

Safety Alert
1. CAUTION: Take care when working with liquids near calculators and computers.
2. CAUTION: The water is warm. Avoid spilling.

PROCEDURE

PART I

1. Answer the pre-lab questions.

2. In the space marked HYPOTHESIS on your student answer page write a hypothesis concerning which set-up will lose the least amount of heat.

3. Slide the calculator and CBL or LabPro Interface in the bottom part of the cradle and it will click into place. Snap the calculator into the top portion of the cradle.

4. Plug the short black link cable into the link port on the bottom of the TI Graphing Calculator and the interface.

5. Plug the temperature probe into channel 1 of the LabPro interface or channel 1 of a CBL 2. Turn on the calculator and press APPS for a TI 83+ or PRGM for the TI 83 then press the number key that precedes the DATAMATE program. At this time the interface should have automatically identified your temperature probe. It will display the correct temperature in the upper right hand corner. If the correct temperature is not displayed do the following:
   - Select SETUP from the MENU by pressing 1.

6. Turn on the calculator and press APPS for a TI 83+ or PRGM for the TI 83 then press the number key that precedes the DATAMATE program. At this time the interface should have automatically identified your pressure sensor. It will display the correct pressure in the upper right hand corner. If the correct pressure is not displayed do the following:
   - Select SETUP from the MENU by pressing 1.
   - Select "CH1" from the MENU and press ENTER.

- Press [1] for temperature.
- Select the correct type of temperature probe and unit (Celsius) being used by pressing the number next to that probe.
- Press [1] to indicate OK.

7. Select SETUP from the MENU by pressing [1].
   - Select "MODE" by pressing the [▲] key and then [ENTER].
   - Select "TIME GRAPH" by pressing [2] and then [2] again to change the time settings.

8. Select SETUP from the MENU by pressing [1].
   - Select "MODE" by pressing the [▲] key and then [ENTER].
   - Select "TIME GRAPH" by pressing [2] and then [2] again to change the time settings.
   - Enter "10" as the time between samples, in seconds, press [ENTER].
   - Enter "60" as the number of sample (the interface will collect data for 10 minutes). Press [ENTER].

9. Another window will appear with the summary of the probes and the length of the experiment. Press [1] to indicate OK. Press [1] again to return to the main menu.

10. A new window will appear and the calculator is now ready to start the experiment. **DO NOT** press [2] until you are ready to run the experiment.

11. Pour 200 mL of warm water from water bath into your cup. Your cup should be marked with a line indicating the correct water level. Put the lid on the cup of warm water.

12. Put the temperature probe into the hole of the top of the cup.

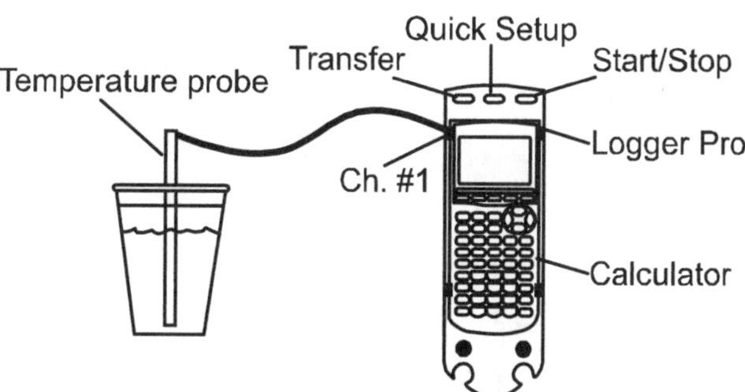

13. After about 15 seconds, the temperature should stabilize. Press [2] to begin data collection. The experiment will run for 10 minutes. There should be 4 short beeps and the quick setup light will flash. You should notice that the temperature is being graphed as the data is being collected. It will continue taking data for ten minutes.

14. When the experiment is complete, 4 short beeps will sound and the quick setup light will flash. Now a labeled, fitted graph will be displayed.

15. Use the [◄] and [►] keys to move the cursor. View the data points displayed at the bottom of the graph. Use these keys to determine the initial or maximum temperature and the final or minimum temperature. Record this data in the data table on the student answer page.

16. Press [ENTER] on the calculator and return to the main menu. The parameters you set for this experiment are still in the calculator. Another run of the experiment can be done without resetting the calculator.

17. Pour out the water and get another 200 mL of warm water. Before starting the data collection, insert your covered cup into a feather filled nylon stocking. Take care not to spill the water and try to cover the container with as many feathers as possible

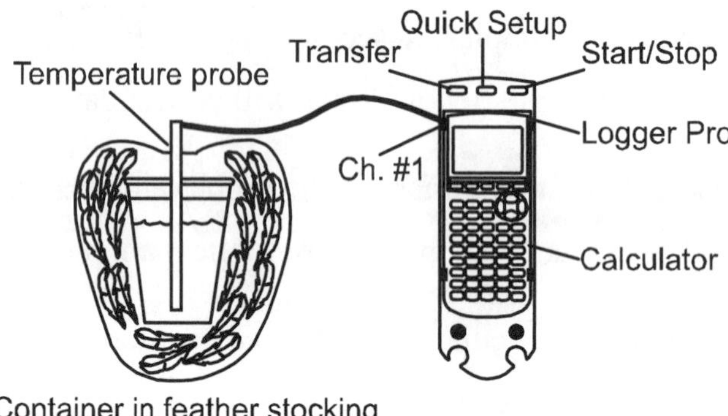

18. When your cup is secure, press [2] to start the data collection again. Be sure to record the initial and final temperatures on your student answer page.

19. Pour out the water and get another 200 mL of warm water. Before starting your data collection, carefully wrap your cup with fur. Take care not to spill the water and try to cover the container with as much fur as possible. Keep this in place by using rubber bands.

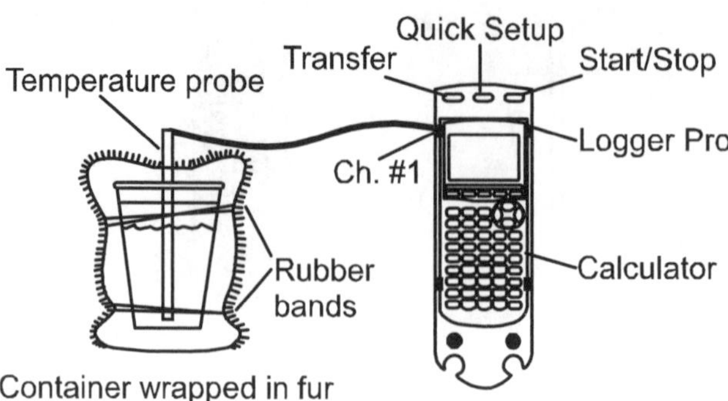

20. When your cup is secure, press [2] to start the data collection again. Be sure to record the initial and final temperatures on your student answer page.

21. When you have completed all three trials, return the equipment to its original condition and clean your lab area.

22. Use the initial and final temperature values to calculate the change in temperature for the water. Record these values in your data table. Complete the Part I conclusion questions.

PART II

1. Answer the pre-lab questions.

2. In the space marked HYPOTHESIS on your student answer page write a hypothesis concerning which set-up will lose the least amount of heat.

3. Slide the calculator and CBL or LabPro Interface in the bottom part of the cradle and it will click into place. Snap the calculator into the top portion of the cradle.

4. Plug the short black link cable into the link port on the bottom of the TI Graphing Calculator and the interface.

5. Plug the temperature probe into channel 1 of the LabPro interface or channel 1 of a CBL 2. Turn on the calculator and press APPS for a TI 83+ or PRGM for the TI 83 then press the number key that precedes the DATAMATE program. At this time the interface should have automatically identified your temperature probe. It will display the correct temperature in the upper right hand corner. If the correct temperature is not displayed do the following:
   - Select SETUP from the MENU by pressing 1.

6. Turn on the calculator and press APPS for a TI 83+ or PRGM for the TI 83 then press the number key that precedes the DATAMATE program. At this time the interface should have automatically identified your pressure sensor. It will display the correct pressure in the upper right hand corner. If the correct pressure is not displayed do the following:
   - Select SETUP from the MENU by pressing 1.
   - Select "CH1" from the MENU and press ENTER.
   - Press 1 for temperature.
   - Select the correct type of temperature probe and unit (Celsius) being used by pressing the number next to that probe.
   - Press 1 to indicate OK.

7. Select SETUP from the MENU by pressing 1.
   - Select "MODE" by pressing the ▲ key and then ENTER.
   - Select "TIME GRAPH" by pressing 2 and then 2 again to change the time settings.

8. Select SETUP from the MENU by pressing 1.
   - Select "MODE" by pressing the ▲ key and then ENTER.
   - Select "TIME GRAPH" by pressing 2 and then 2 again to change the time settings.
   - Enter "10" as the time between samples, in seconds, press ENTER.
   - Enter "60" as the number of sample (the interface will collect data for 10 minutes). Press ENTER.

9. Another window will appear with the summary of the probes and the length of the experiment. Press 1 to indicate OK. Press 1 again to return to the main menu.

10. A new window will appear and the calculator is now ready to start the experiment. **DO NOT** press 2 until you are ready to run the experiment.

11. Pour 200 mL of warm water from water bath into your cup. Your cup should be marked with a line indicating the correct water level. Put the lid on the cup of warm water.

12. Put the temperature probe into the hole of the top of the cup.

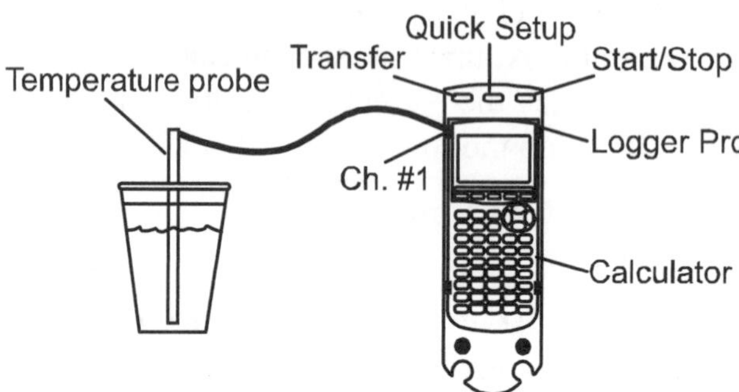

13. After about 15 seconds, the temperature should stabilize. Press 2 to begin data collection. The experiment will run for 10 minutes. There should be 4 short beeps and the quick setup light will flash. You should notice that the temperature is being graphed as the data is being collected. It will continue taking data for ten minutes.

14. When the experiment is complete, 4 short beeps will sound and the quick setup light will flash. Now a labeled, fitted graph will be displayed.

15. Use the ◄ and ► keys to move the cursor. View the data points displayed at the bottom of the graph. Use these keys to determine the initial or maximum temperature and the final or minimum temperature. Record this data in the data table on the student answer page.

16. Press ENTER on the calculator and return to the main menu. The parameters you set for this experiment are still in the calculator. Another run of the experiment can be done without resetting the calculator.

17. Pour out the water from the first run and refill the cup with fresh warm water from the water bath. Put the lid onto the water container. When closing the coffee can insert the temperature probe through the hole in the coffee can lid, through the lid on the water cup and into the warm water.

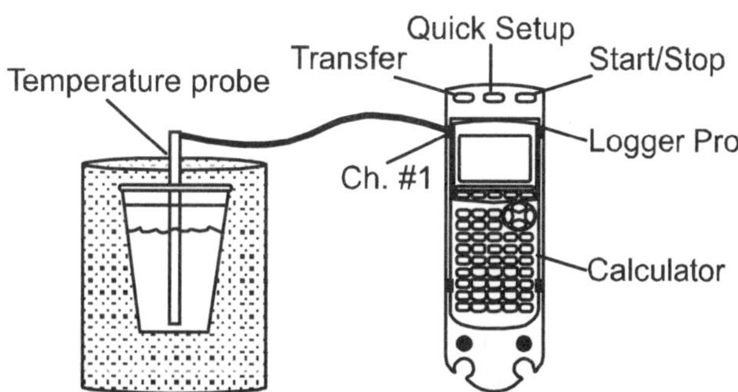

Container in coffee can with sand

18. Pour about 1 inch of sand into the bottom of a coffee can and set the empty cup into the can. Arrange the cup so that it is in the center of the can and the top of the cup is below the rim of the can. Now, using a funnel, pour sand between the cup and the wall of the can until the can is full.

19. Press [2] to start the data collection again. Be sure to record the initial and final temperatures on your student answer page.

20. Disassemble the sand-filled coffee can and pour out the water from the sand trial. For this trial you are to fill the coffee can with grass and leaf cuttings instead of the sand. When your cup is secure, add 200 mL of warm water and prepare the lids for data collection.

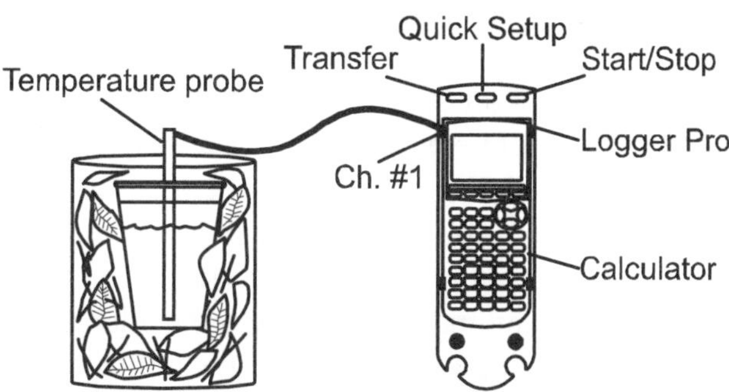

Container in coffee can with grass and leaves

21. Press [2] to start the data collection again. Be sure to record the initial and final temperatures on your student answer page.

22. When you have completed all three trials, return the equipment to its original condition and clean your lab area.

23. Use the initial and final temperature values to calculate the change in temperature for the water. Record these values in your data table. Complete the Part II conclusion questions.

Life in the Cold
Investigating Survival Strategies and Adaptations Using a Computer and a Data Collection Device

An adaptation is an inherited trait or characteristic an individual organism possesses that will help it to survive and ultimately reproduce. These favorable genes or characteristics will then be passed on to the next generation. This exercise will investigate adaptations that aid in survival in cold climates.

Biomes are ecosystems that are characterized by the predominant vegetation found in that biome. The tundra is a biome located in northern most latitudes. The climate of the tundra is very cold and with very little rainfall. It covers approximately 20% of the Earth's land. There is very little sunshine received for any given time as the sun is always low in the sky. The sun rays are not directly above the land as they are at the equator. In the winter, the days are very short, lasting only a few hours but in the summer the days are very long, lasting up to 24 hours in the latitudes of the Arctic Circle. Because of this increase in day length, the total amount of radiant energy is great. The tundra's top layer of soil only thaws during the summer but the soil layer underneath remains frozen and is called the permafrost. The presence of permafrost causes water to collect on the top of soil, forming small pools of water rather than draining into the soil below. Soils are poorly developed and contain very little nitrogen. This coupled with a short growing season limits the size of plants. As a result, grasses and sedges are the dominant plant life. Any woody plants that are found in the tundra are only a few centimeters tall. In the summer flowers and their seeds appear quickly. The animals in the tundra are a reflection of the plant life found there. During the summers there is a migration of many birds and mammals to the region. These animals feed on the plentiful plant life. Migratory water birds come to the tundra to raise their young in an environment that allows around-the-clock food gathering. Arctic foxes and showshoe hares are present in their brown summer coats which turn white when winter arrives.

The fall season is extremely short and the transition to winter occurs quickly. Lakes and ponds freeze. Snowfall is surprisingly little, only 25-30 cm per year. Winds across the region forms snow drifts. Above the Arctic Circle after the winter solstice, there are three months of near darkness. The plants become dormant and many animals migrate south as food resources are reduced. Only a few, well-adapted, animals remain behind. For example, lemmings survive in the tundra by burrowing under the snow. The musk-oxen are one of the few animals that possess the adaptations necessary to survive the winter's full force. These warm-blooded large animals have the ability to survive the Arctic's extreme winter due to their adaptations of thick hide and two coats of fur.

PURPOSE

The purpose of this investigation is to compare the effectiveness of insulating adaptations such as fur and feathers. A cup of warm water will represent the animal. The temperature of the water inside the cup will be monitored under three conditions : no insulation (the control), fur insulation, and feather insulation. The second purpose of this investigation is to investigate the effects of different shelters in stabilizing temperatures. A cup will once again represent the animal. The temperature of the water in the cup will be monitored under three sheltering conditions: air (the control), sand, and natural plant materials such as leaves, hay, or wood chips.

MATERIALS

temperature probe
lids to fit the cup
swath of fur approximately 30 cm x 30 cm
1 lb coffee can or 1 gallon resealable bag
hay, leaves grass or wood chips
rubber bands
computer with Logger Pro installed
8 oz paper cup for hot liquids or yogurt containers
100 mL graduated cylinder
knee-high nylon stocking with feathers
sand
water bath with 37° C water
Lab Pro interface box

Safety Alert
1. CAUTION: Take care when working with liquids near calculators and computers.
2. CAUTION: Water is warm. Avoid spilling.

PROCEDURE

PART I

1. Answer the pre-lab questions.

2. In the space marked HYPOTHESIS on your student answer page write a hypothesis concerning which set-up will lose the least amount of heat.

3. Plug the temperature probe into Port 1 of the serial interface box.

4. Turn on the computer. Click on the folder called **Experiment Templates**, and then open up **Adaptation Lab**. Logger Pro should open.
   - CAUTION: Electricity is being used; take care not to spill any liquids on any of the computer equipment or electrical outlets.

5. The temperature reading of the air should be around 20° C. If it does not register a similar temperature, let your teacher know.

6. Pour 200 mL of warm water from water bath into your cup. Your cup should be marked with a line indicating the correct water level. Put the lid on the cup of warm water.

7. Put the temperature probe into the hole of the top of the cup.

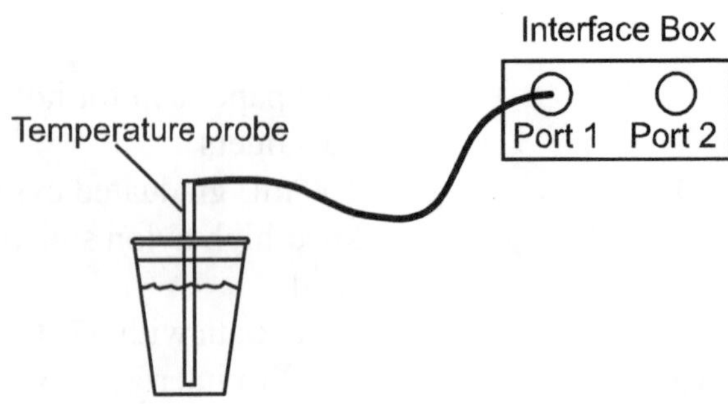

8. After about 15 seconds, the temperature should stabilize. When the temperature is stable, click on the **Collect** button. You should notice that the temperature is being graphed as the data is being collected. It should continue taking data for ten minutes. After ten minutes the **Stop** button will turn into a **Collect** button.

9. When the experiment is complete, pull down the **Analyze menu** and highlight **Statistics**. This will display the maximum or initial temperature and the minimum or final temperature. Record this information in your data table on the student answer page.

10. Pull down the **Data Menu** and click on **Store Latest Run**. This will allow you to compare this run to the subsequent runs of the experiment. The red line should become a thinner red line. This should allow you to compare your next two runs to this control run.

11. Pour out the water and get another 200 mL of warm water. Before starting your data collection, carefully insert your cup into a feather filled nylon stocking. Take care not to spill the water and try to cover the container with as many feathers as possible.

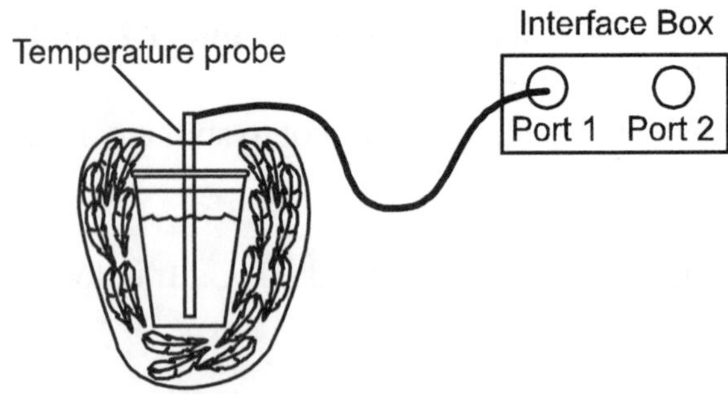

Container in feather stocking

12. Repeat steps 7-10. Be sure to record the minimum and maximum temperatures in your data table on your student answer page.

13. Pour out the water and get another 200 mL of warm water. Before starting your data collection carefully wrap your cup with fur. Take care not to spill the water and try to cover the container with as much fur as possible. Keep this in place by using rubber bands.

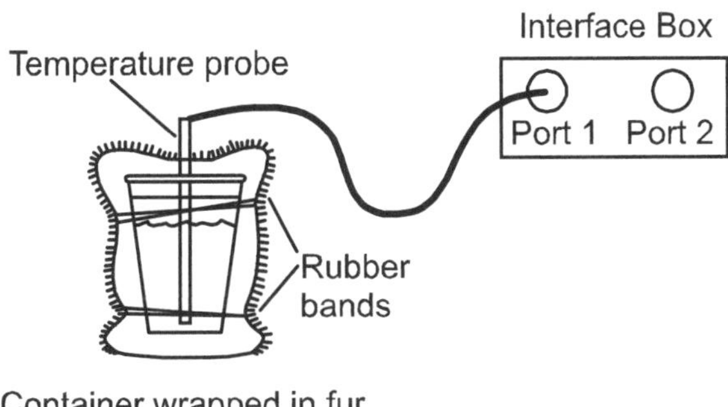

Container wrapped in fur

14. Repeat steps 7-10. Be sure to record the minimum and maximum temperatures in your data table on your student answer page.

15. When you have completed all three trials, return the equipment to its original condition and clean your lab area.

16. Use the maximum and minimum temperatures to calculate the change in temperature for the water. Record these values in your data table. Complete Part I conclusion questions.

PART II

1. Answer the pre-lab questions.

2. In the space marked HYPOTHESIS on your student answer page write a hypothesis concerning which set-up will lose the least amount of heat.

3. Plug the temperature probe into Port 1 of the serial interface box.

4. Turn on the computer. Click on the folder called **Experiment Templates**, and then open up **Adaptation Lab**. Logger Pro should open.
    - CAUTION: Electricity is being used; take care not to spill any liquids on any of the computer equipment or electrical outlets.

5. The temperature reading of the air should be around 20° C. If it does not register a similar temperature, let your teacher know.

6. Pour 200 mL of warm water from water bath into your cup. Your cup should be marked with a line indicating the correct water level. Put the lid on the cup of warm water.

7. Put the temperature probe into the hole of the top of the cup.

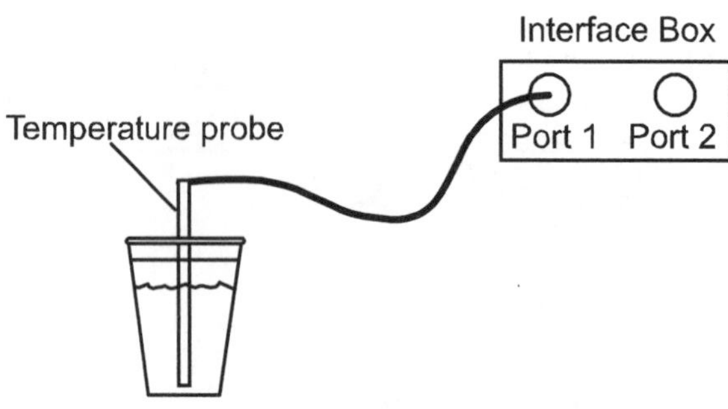

8. After about 15 seconds, the temperature should stabilize. When the temperature is stable, click on the **Collect** button. You should notice that the temperature is being graphed as the data is being collected. It should continue taking data for ten minutes. After ten minutes the **Stop** button will turn into a **Collect** button.

9. When the experiment is complete, pull down the **Analyze menu** and highlight **Statistics**. This will display the maximum or initial temperature and the minimum or final temperature. Record this information in your data table on the student answer page.

10. Pull down the **Data Menu** and click on **Store Latest Run**. This will allow you to compare this run to the subsequent runs of the experiment. The red line should become a thinner red line. This should allow you to compare your next two runs to this control run.

11. Pour out the water from the first run and refill the cup with fresh warm water from the water bath. Put the lid onto the water container. When closing the coffee can insert the temperature probe through the hole in the coffee can lid, through the lid on the water cup and into the warm water.

12. Pour about 1 inch of sand into the bottom of a coffee can and set the empty cup into the can. Arrange the cup so that it is in the center of the can and the top of the cup is below the rim of the can. Now, using a funnel, pour sand between the cup and the wall of the can until the can is full.

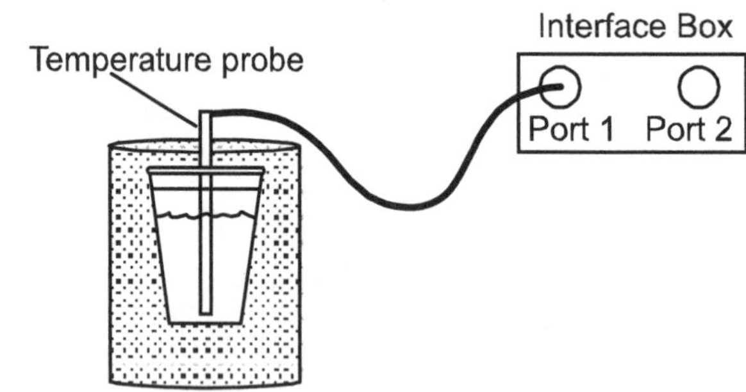

Container in coffee can with sand

13. Repeat steps 7-10. Be sure to record the minimum and maximum temperatures in your data table on the student answer page.

14. Disassemble the sand-filled coffee can and pour out the water from the sand trial. For this trial you are to fill the coffee can with grass and leaf cuttings instead of the sand. When your cup is secure, add 200 mL of warm water and prepare the lids for data collection.

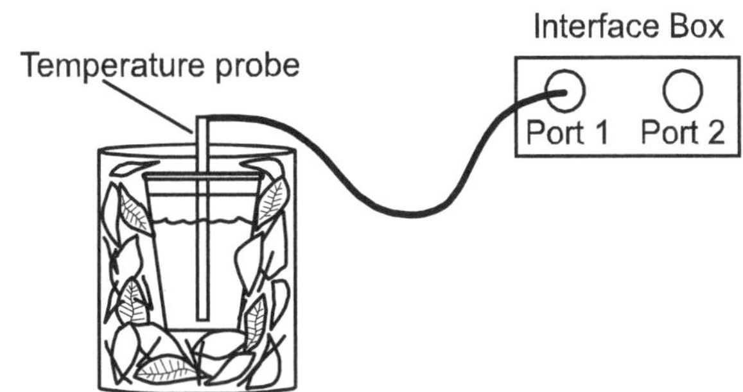

Container in coffee can with grass and leaves

15. Repeat steps 7-10. Be sure to record the minimum and maximum temperatures in your data table on your student answer page.

16. When you have completed all three trials, return the equipment to its original condition and clean your lab area.

17. Use the initial and final temperature values to calculate the change in temperature for the water. Record these values in your data table. Complete the Part II conclusion questions.

Name ______________________

Period ______________________

Life in the Cold
Investigating Survival Strategies and Adaptations

HYPOTHESIS

DATA AND OBSERVATIONS

Data Table				
	Experimental Set-up	Minimum Temperature (°C)	Maximum Temperature (°C)	Total Temperature Change (°C)
Part I	Control			
	Feathers			
	Fur			
Part II	Control			
	Sand			
	Natural Materials			

PRE-LAB QUESTIONS

1. List three characteristics of the tundra.

2. What is an adaptation?

3. What types of animals are found in the tundra?

4. What types of plant life are found in the tundra?

CONCLUSION QUESTIONS

PART I

1. Which set up or adaptation stayed the warmest by showing the least amount of change in temperature?

2. Which set up or adaptation cooled the fasted by showing the greatest amount of temperature change?

3. Compare and contrast the results produced when feathers and fur served as insulation for the animal. What do these materials have in common?

4. What are some other adaptations that animals have evolved to aid in their survival in the tundra?

PART II

1. Which set up or shelter stayed the warmest by showing the least amount of change in temperature?

2. Which set up cooled the fasted by showing the greatest amount of temperature change?

3. Compare and contrast the results obtained when sand and natural materials simulated a shelter to protect animals in the cold? Explain any differences that were observed.

Write Your Notes and Ideas Here!

Classification Webquest
Surveying Animalia Attributes

OBJECTIVE
Students will conduct a webquest survey of the attributes of each of the six kingdoms and phyla of kingdom Animalia. Students will share the information gathered by labeling lab specimen to be viewed by the class.

LEVEL
Biology I

NATIONAL STANDARDS
UCP.1, UCP.5, C.3, E.1, E.2, G.1, G.2, G.3

TEKS
8(A), 8(B), 8(C)

CONNECTIONS TO AP
AP Biology:

III. Organisms and Populations A. Diversity of Organisms 2. Survey of the diversity of life

TIME FRAME
two 45 minute periods

MATERIALS
(For a class of 28 working in groups of three on day 1, working alone on day 2)

14 computers with internet access
14 data disks
preserved specimen: sponge, jellyfish, tapeworm, roundworm, leech, slug, beetle, starfish, mouse
copies of blank summary charts
copies identification cards

TEACHER NOTES
This activity can be completed in two class periods as follows:

Day 1 – Describe the project and have students complete parts I, II and III. This information can be found in textbooks or in the library if computers are unavailable. Depending upon the length of your class periods, the students may need to complete the identification card as homework and bring it in for your approval.

Day 2 – Approve each group's identification card and supply them with a preserved specimen of their assigned organism. Instruct them to place the specimen along with the approved information card in an accessible area of your lab or classroom. The students should then rotate through each of the stations using the information provided on the identification cards to complete the summary chart.

Prior to conducting the webquest, verify that each web address is valid. Update the URL's as needed.

In preparation for this activity, students will need to know the definitions of autotrophic, heterotrophic, ingestive, absorptive, coelom, multicellular, and unicellular.

To make the webquest portion of this activity go more smoothly, provide each group with a floppy disk containing a digital version of the lab handout which includes the URL's. Using Explorer, students can go directly to the website from the Word document. Even if that function is not available due to network settings, the students will be able to copy and paste the URL's as they conduct their searches. This capability will lessen the chance for error in entering the addresses. Additionally, the floppy disk will provide students with a digital version of the identification card that can be filled in using the computer, eliminating penmanship issues.

A sample list of organisms to be researched is included in the summary chart. You will need to edit the chart to reflect the preserved specimen you have available. When substituting organisms on the summary chart be sure to include members of the major phyla.

POSSIBLE ANSWERS TO THE CONCLUSION QUESTIONS AND SAMPLE DATA

PART I

1. Why are classification systems useful?
   - Systems of classification used in the biological sciences describe and categorize all living things allowing for clarity in communication regarding living organisms. Classification is essentially an effort by scientists to discover, reconstruct, and clarify the phylogeny, or evolutionary history, of an organism or group of organisms.

2. What is ***Systema Naturae***? Who wrote it and when?
   - *Systema Naturae* was an influential book on classification written by Linnaeus in 1735.

3. What is binomial nomenclature and what two categories are used in a binomen?
   - Binomial nomenclature is classification based on the use of two Latin name categories, genus and species, to designate each type of organism.

4. What is your binomen?
   - *Homo sapiens*

5. Complete the chart below:

Kingdom	Characteristics
Animalia	Eukaryotic, multicelluar, sexual/asexual, heterotrophic, ingestive
Plantae	Eukaryotic, multicellular, sexual/asexual, autotrophic, photosynthetic
Fungi	Eukaryotic, multicellular/unicellular, sexual/asexual, heterotrophic, absorptive
Protista	Eukaryotic, multicellular/unicellular/colonial, sexual/asexual, photoautotrophic/ingestive/absorptive
Eubacteria/Archaebacteria (Monera)	Prokaryotic, unicellular, binary fission, autotrophic/heterotrophic

6. How are kingdoms of the six kingdom system different from those of the five kingdom system?
   - In the five kingdom system, bacteria are included in the kingdom Monera. In the six kingdom system, bacteria are divided into the two kingdoms Eubacteria and Archaebacteria.

PART II/III

Data Table 1: Classification of Tapeworm	
Kingdom	Animalia
Phylum	Platyhelminthes
Class	Cestoidea
Order	Cyclophyllidea
Family	Taeniidae
Genus	*Taenia*
Species	*solium*

Kingdom Animalia Summary Chart					
Common Name	Sketch of organism	Phylum	Phylum Traits	Habitat/info	2 Other phyla members
Sponge		Porifera	Lack true tissues, sessile, choanocyte cells	aquatic	glass sponge calcareous sponge
Jellyfish		Cnidaria	Gastrovascular cavity, Radial symmetry	Aquatic	hydra anemone
Tapeworm		Platyhelminthes	Acoelomate, gastro-vascular cavity	Vertebrate host	planaria fluke
Roundworm		Nematoda	Psuedocoelomate, parasitic	Host	Hookworm pinworm
Leech		Annelida	True coelom, segmented body	Terrestrial, aquatic, and parasitic	earthworm clamworm
Slug		Mollusca	Muscular foot, visceral mass, mantle	Terrestrial and aquatic	snail octopus
Beetle		Arthropoda	Segmented, true coelom, jointed appendages, exoskeleton	Terrestrial (some arthropods aquatic)	lobster pill bug
Starfish		Echinodermata	Water vascular system, spiny outer covering	Aquatic	sea urchin brittle star
Mouse		Chordata	Notochord, dorsal hollow nerve cord, pharyngeal slits, postanal tail	Terrestrial, some members aquatic	human dog

CONCLUSION QUESTIONS

1. To which kingdom would an organism belong if it is
   a. Prokaryotic, unicellular, and has a cell wall?
      - Monera
   b. Photosynthetic, aquatic, unicellular?
      - Protista
   c. Photosynthetic, multicellular and terrestrial?
      - Plantae
   d. Heterotrophic, multicellular, and ingestive?
      - Animalia

2. Based on the binomial classification system, the mosquito, *Anopheles punctulatus*, is most closely related in structure to ….
   a. *Culex pipiens* b. *Anopheles quadrimaculatus* c. *Ades aeqypti* d. *Aedes sollicitans*
      - (b) is the correct choice

3. Jellyfish, earthworms, grasshoppers and humans are all classified in the same
   a. Kingdom b. phylum c. class d. species
      - (a) is the correct choice

4. Which of the classification groups would contain the most similar members? Explain your answer.
   - The classification group species contains organisms that are most similar because this category is the most exclusive grouping.

5. How are all of the organisms observed in Part IV of this activity similar?
   - all of the organisms are eukaryotic, multicellular, and heterotrophic because they are all classified as animals.

6. What similarities are found among segmented worms, like the leech, and flatworms, such as the tapeworm? What differences are found among these two groups?
   - The worms are similar in that they are eukaryotic, multicellular and heterotrophic.
   - They are different in that the leech contains a true coelom where the flatworms are psuedocoelomates.

7. To what phylum would an organism belong if it has tissues, a coelom and a vertebral column?
   - Chordata

Blackline master for identification cards

Organism	
Phylum name	
Phylum traits	
Habitat	
Two additional examples	

Organism	
Phylum name	
Phylum traits	
Habitat	
Two additional examples	

Organism	
Phylum name	
Phylum traits	
Habitat	
Two additional examples	

Classification Webquest
Surveying Animalia Attributes

What makes a worm a worm? Why isn't a ringworm a worm? Is a sponge an animal? All of these questions can be answered through taxonomy, the science of naming and classifying organisms. Taxonomy arranges organisms into groups based on similarities. The most inclusive level in the taxonomic hierarchy is a kingdom which can be subdivided into phyla. The phyla can in turn be separated into smaller groups called classes. A class can be subdivided into families and a family into genuses. A genus can be split into smaller groups called species.

PURPOSE

In this webquest you will explore the classification system currently used to sort and categorize living organisms. You will focus on the kingdom Animalia and its diverse set of members as you explore the various levels at which organisms can be classified. You will be assigned a specific organism to investigate as you explore the classification system.

MATERIALS

- computer with internet access and power point capabilities
- data disk
- preserved sample of your assigned organism
- blank summary chart
- blank identification card

> **Safety Alert**
> 1. Parental approval for internet access must be on file in order to use the internet.
> 2. School policy for internet use must be followed at all times during this activity.

PROCEDURE

PART 1: UNDERSTANDING CLASSIFICATION

1. Visit the following websites to answer the questions 1-4 on Part 1 of your student answer page:
   a. http://anthro.palomar.edu/animal/animal_1.htm
   b. http://www.seaworld.org/just-for-teachers/guides/diversity-of-life/animalia.html
   c. http://www.sidwell.edu/us/science/vlb5/Labs/Classification_Lab/classification_lab.html
   d. http://www.hrw.com/science/onlinese/modbio/pdfs/hm2ne1092.pdf
   e. http://jrscience.wcp.muohio.edu/lab/TaxonomyLab.html
   f. http://web.bio.utk.edu/guffey/Biodiversitysite/Taxonomy/Taxonomy.html
   g. http://en.wikipedia.org/wiki/Suborder

2. Research sites such as these to determine the traits used to separate organisms into kingdoms. Use the information to complete item 5 on the student answer page.

   http://www.sidwell.edu/us/science/vlb5/Labs/Classification_Lab/classification_lab.html#background

   http://www.microscopy-uk.org.uk/mag/indexmag.html?http://www.microscopy-uk.org.uk/mag/artmay98/classif.html

PART II: CLASSIFYING A SPECIFIC ORGANISM

1. Obtain the name of an organism to classify from your teacher.

2. Use the following websites to locate the information needed to fill out Data Table 1 based on your assigned organism. In addition to these sites, it may be necessary to perform a keyword search in order to locate the class, order, family, genus and species names.
   a. http://www.sidwell.edu/us/science/vlb5/Labs/Classification_Lab/Eukarya/Animalia/
   b. http://bioweb.uwlax.edu/zoolab/Table_of_Contents/table_of_contents.htm
   c. http://cas.bellarmine.edu/tietjen/images/general_overview_of_animal_phyla.htm

PART III: PREPARING AN IDENTIFICATION CARD

1. Fill out an identification card on your organism. Write clearly so that others may read your writing.

2. Submit your card to your teacher for approval.

PART IV: SURVEY LAB

1. Once the information on your card is approved, place the card by the corresponding preserved specimen.

2. Rotate through the labeled specimens as directed by your teacher.

3. Use the information provided on the information cards completed by the other groups in the class to complete the summary chart.

4. Complete the conclusion questions on the student answer page.

Name ______________________________

Period______________________________

Classification Webquest
Surveying Animalia Attributes

PART I

1. Why are classification systems useful?

2. What is ***Systema Naturae***? Who wrote it and when?

3. What is binomial nomenclature and what two categories are used in a binomen?

4. What is your binomen or scientific name?

5. Complete the chart below:

Kingdom	Characteristics

6. How are kingdoms of the six kingdom system different from those of the five kingdom system?

PART II/III

Data Table 1 Classification of ________	
Kingdom	
Phylum	
Class	
Order	
Family	
Genus	
Species	

PART IV

Kingdom Animalia Summary Chart					
Common Name	Sketch of organism	Phylum	Phylum Traits	Habitat/info	2 Other phyla members
Sponge					
Jellyfish					
Tapeworm					
Roundworm					
Leech					
Slug					
Beetle					
Starfish					
Mouse					

CONCLUSION QUESTIONS

1. To which kingdom would an organism belong if it is

   a. Prokaryotic, unicellular, and has a cell wall? ____________________

   b. Photosynthetic, aquatic, unicellular? __________________________

   c. Photosynthetic, multicellular and terrestrial? ____________________

   d. Heterotrophic, multicellular, and ingestive? ________________

2. Based on the binomial classification system, the mosquito, *Anopheles punctulatus*, is most closely related in structure to

   a. *Culex pipiens* b. *Anopheles quadrimaculatus* c. *Ades aeqypti* d. *Aedes sollicitans*

3. Jellyfish, earthworms, grasshoppers and humans are all classified in the same

   a. Kingdom b. phylum c. class d. species

4. Which of the classification groups would contain the most similar members? Explain your answer.

5. How are all of the organisms observed in Part IV of this activity similar?

6. What similarities are found among segmented worms, like the leech, and flatworms, such as the tapeworm? What differences are found among these two groups?

7. To what phylum would an organism belong if it has tissues, a coelom and a vertebral column?

"Killer" Defects
Exploring the Impact of Bacteria on Integrated Circuits

OBJECTIVE
Students will learn how tiny bacteria can cause "killer" defects in integrated circuits. Students will learn about deionized water and its importance to semiconductor integrated circuit fabrication. Finally students will observe bacteria cultures and determine whether or not the observed bacteria would be "killer" defects in today's semiconductor fabrication facilities.

LEVEL
Biology

NATIONAL STANDARDS
UCP.2, UCP.3, C.1, E.1, E.2, F.4

TEKS
8C

CONNECTIONS TO AP
III Organisms and Populations A. Diversity of Organisms 2. Survey of diversity of life

TIME FRAME
45 minutes

MATERIALS
(For a class of 28 working in groups of 4)

2 prepared bacteria samples from city water
2 prepared bacteria samples from distilled or deionized water
6 memory chips if available
2 prepared samples from pond water
6 microscopes with 100X power capability

TEACHER NOTES
To prepare bacteria samples:

The following is a suggested way to prepare the samples, but if there is already an accepted method for doing so, it is highly recommended that method be used. The objective is to give the students grids with bacteria colonies from several different water sources to compare qualitatively. Quantitative results may be added at your preference. Preparation of the samples might be assigned to more advanced students.

- Materials:
  - vacuum pump
  - membrane filter assemblies (sterile)
  - side-arm flask, 1000 mL size, and rubber hose
  - 3 sterile 250 mL graduated cylinders

  - o 6 sterile plastic Petri dishes, 50 mm diameter, with culture medium in them (suggest *m* Endo MF broth)
  - o 6 sterile membrane filter disks
  - o 6 sterile absorbent disks (usually packed with filters)
  - o sterile water
  - o at least 500 mL of pond or lake water
  - o at least 500 mL of city water
  - o at least 500 mL of deionized or distilled water

  Note: Millipore is a good source of the filters, Petri dishes, etc.
- Assemble a membrane filtering unit:
  1. Aseptically insert the filter holder base into the neck of a 1-Liter side-arm flask.
  2. With a sterile forceps, place a sterile membrane filter disk, grid side up, on the filter holder base.
  3. Place the filter funnel on top of the membrane filter disk and secure it to the base with the clamp.
- Attach the rubber hose to the vacuum pump and pour 250 mL of the distilled or deionized water into the funnel using one of the sterile graduates.
- Rinse the inner sides of the funnel with 20 mL of sterile water.
- Carefully transfer the filter disk with sterile forceps to the Petri dish containing the culture medium. Keep the grid side up.
- Label the sample "D-H_2O-1" and incubate for 22-24 hours at 35°C. Do not invert.
- Prepare another filter disk with the distilled or deionized water by repeating the assembly through transfer steps above.
- Label the sample "D-H_2O-2" and incubate it for 22-24 hours at 35°C. Do not invert.
- Repeat the assembly process with another sterile membrane filter disk.
- Attach the rubber hose to the vacuum pump and pour 250 mL of the city water into the funnel using a different sterile graduate.
- Rinse with 20 mL of sterile water.
- Carefully transfer the filter disk to a Petri dish containing the culture medium. Keep the grid side up.
- Label the sample "C-H_2O-1" and incubate it for 22-24 hours at 35°C. Do not invert.
- Repeat the process to generate "C-H_2O-2" and incubate it using the same conditions. Do not invert.
- Repeat the assembly process with another sterile membrane filter disk.
- Attach the rubber hose to the vacuum pump and pour 250 mL of the pond water into the funnel using the last sterile graduate. Rinse with 20 mL of sterile water.
- Carefully transfer the filer disk to a Petri dish containing the culture medium. Keep the grid side up.
- Label the sample "P-H_2O-1" and incubate it with the other samples. Do not invert.
- Repeat the process to generate "P-H_2O-2" and incubate it with the other samples. Do not invert.
- After the incubation period, remove the filters from the Petri dishes and dry for 1 hour on absorbent paper. Be sure to maintain the filter identifications.
- Verify that colonies did form on the samples. The distilled or deionized water will usually have at least 1 but may not if it has not been open long and was handled very well.

Note: The filter may clog for the pond water before 250 mL can be filtered. If so, record the number of mL processed and have the students note this on their worksheets so that they are aware that the comparisons will be for different amounts of water.

Suggested teaching procedures:

1. Before breaking into smaller groups ask students the following questions:

   Q: What is an integrated circuit? Where are integrated circuits used?
   A: An *integrated circuit* is an electronic circuit in which many elements are fabricated and interconnected on a single chip of semiconductor material. (A "nonintegrated" circuit is one in which the transistors, diodes, resistors, capacitors, etc., are fabricated separately and then assembled.) Integrated circuits are in almost everything we use today—computers, calculators, automobiles, coffee makers, televisions, VCRs, copy machines, electronic games, musical greeting cards, etc.

   Q: What are bacteria?
   A: *Bacteria* are small living, reproducing organisms. The typical sizes of bacteria that thrive in water are 1-10 microns in diameter.

   Q: What is a micron?
   A: A *micron* is one-millionth of a meter (10^{-6} m). To put this in perspective, a human hair is about 100 microns in diameter.

   Q: What are typical dimensions for elements in today's integrated circuits?
   A: The critical dimensions in today's integrated circuits are as small as 0.3-0.5 micron.

   Q: What are "killer" defects?
   A: In semiconductor integrated circuit fabrication areas, potential "killer" defects are any contaminants 10% or more of the minimum critical dimension (>/=0.03 micron). Actual *"killer" defects* are contaminants that are 10% or more of the minimum critical dimension and that have become incorporated into one or more of the layers in the integrated circuit.

   Q: What kind of facility is needed to enable the fabrication of such small dimensions with virtually no contaminants greater than 0.02 micron?
   A: Semiconductor integrated circuit fabrication is performed in clean rooms. Extensive contamination control of the facility, the equipment, the chemicals, the gases, the incoming material, and the people must be defined, incorporated, and maintained.

   Q: What is deionized water?
   A: *Deionized water* is the most widely used solvent in most semiconductor fabrication facilities. It is water that has been treated to remove, or to significantly reduce, unacceptable contaminants: dissolved ions, organic materials, particles, bacteria, silica and dissolved O_2.

   Q: Where can information be found about the semiconductor industry and its potential career paths?
   A: Check the web site: www.DestinationDigital.org.

2. Instruct the students to divide into six groups.

3. Tell the students that they will view at least one sample from each of the three water sources using low magnification (100X) microscopy. The most effective way to do this is to have a microscope available for each group.

4. Give the students the following directions:

5. When all groups have finished, bring the students back into a large group and complete the concluding questions.

POSSIBLE ANSWERS TO THE CONCLUSION QUESTIONS AND SAMPLE DATA

Data Table 1: Memory Chip	
Test Performed	**Qualitative Results**
Locate maker or other ID on chip	Could be Intel, TI, Micron, etc.
Human hair on memory chip	Fine hair covers many elements Coarse hair covers 2X as many elements
Optional memory chip observations	Human hair would cover many elements in any of the chips the hair crosses.

Data Table 2: Bacteria Samples	
Test Performed	**Qualitative Results**
Sample P________ checked for colony formation	Colonies cover entire filter or colonies are all over filter grid
Sample P________ colonies compared to human hair	Human hair covers a lot of the colonies.
Sample C _____ checked for colony formation	1-several colonies on grid
Sample C______ colonies compared to human hair	Human hair covers all of the colonies.
Sample D _____ checked for colony formation	No colonies found or 1-2 colonies found
Sample D _____ colonies compared to human hair	Human hair covers all of the colonies.

CONCLUSION QUESTIONS

1. How can bacteria that are only 1-10 microns in diameter either ruin or degrade the performance of an integrated circuit?

   The internal elements of the integrated circuit are less than 1 micron. If 1-10 micron contaminants, like bacteria, deposit on a chip, they can completely block the much smaller internal elements or they can degrade the integrity of any layer deposited on top of them.

2. Why does the semiconductor industry have to use deionized water rather than city water?

   City water contains many contaminants that can cause major yield problems in the fabrication of integrated circuits. Bacteria are one category of these contaminants. The main reason deionized water is required rather than other pure water is because the ions in it have been removed. These ions also cause significant yield problems and must not be allowed to come in integrated circuits in-process.

3. Would the bacteria samples observed today be considered potential "killer" defects in semiconductor fabrication facilities?

   Yes, the individual bacteria that make up the colonies observed today are at least twice as large as many of the elements in each integrated circuit and, therefore, 20 times larger than allowable defects. The fact that any bacteria are in the water indicates a source of "killer" defects.

REFERENCES

H. Benson, *Microbiological Applications, Laboratory Manual in General Microbiology*, Seventh Edition, WCB McGraw-Hill Publishing, 1998, pp. 178-179

Destination Digital Brochure and www.destinationdigital.org

M. Quirk & J. Serda, *Semiconductor Manufacturing Technology*, Prentice-Hall Publishing, 2001, pp. 127, 129

P. Van Zant, *Microchip Fabrication*, Fourth Edition, McGraw Hill Publishing, 2000, pp. 90-91, 108-110, glossary

"Killer" Defects
Exploring the Impact of Bacteria on Integrated Circuits

Semiconductor fabrication is one of the names for the mass production of integrated circuits. Fabrication includes all of the processes that can be done in wafer form. Many integrated circuits now have internal dimensions that are sub-micron in width. To put this in perspective, the human hair is about 100 microns in diameter. In order to produce integrated circuits with predictable yields, everything that comes near the integrated circuits prior to top-surface protective coating must essentially be free of particles and other contaminants.

Deionized water (DI H_2O) is a widely used solvent in semiconductor fabrication. This water has had all of the conductive ions removed from it. With a pH of 7, which is neutral, DI water is neither an acid nor a base. To manufacture today's integrated circuits with internal dimensions that are 0.3-0.5 micron in width, ultra pure DI water is required in large quantities. DI water is the most used chemical in semiconductor fabrication, primarily in the chemical wafer cleaning solutions and as a post-clean rinse. City water has too many contaminants to be acceptable for the production of semiconductor integrated circuits. These unacceptable contaminants consist of dissolved ions, organic materials, particles, bacteria, silica and dissolved oxygen.

Bacteria are unacceptable contaminants for two major regions: (1) They are 1-10 microns in diameter and, therefore, are potential "killer" defects if they deposit on the surface of in-process semiconductor wafers. (2) They may contribute unwanted metallic ions to the surface of the integrated circuits. Bacteria thrive in untreated water. They also thrive in very pure water unless the water system is sterilized to kill the bacteria and filtered to remove the dead bacteria. Ultrapure water systems use ultraviolet (UV) lamps for sterilization. UV systems are simple and reliable and can reduce bacteria to low levels. Biological control of an ultrapure semiconductor-grade water system is also done by ozonating the water. Ozone (O_3) is created by discharging an electric current through dry air. The resulting ozone mixture is purified and then injected into the ultrapure water to kill the bacteria. Point-of-use filtration removes any dead bacteria that get into the water lines.

GLOSSARY

Bacteria: plural of bacterium; live, reproducing organisms that live in water

Chip (or microchip): An individual integrated circuit built in a tiny, layered rectangle or square on a silicon wafer. There may be hundreds of these chips on a single wafer.

Clean Room: A manufacturing facility where integrated circuits are fabricated. The air inside these rooms is cleaner than a typical surgical operating room.

Contaminant: A general term used to describe unwanted material that adversely affects the physical or electrical characteristics of a semiconductor product

Deionized Water (DI H_2O): Process water in semiconductor fabrication that is free of dissolved ions. Specifications are usually 15-18 ohms of resistance.

Discrete Devices: Individual electronic elements, such as transistors, capacitors, resistors, *etc.*, that have a single electrical function

Integrated Circuit: An electronic circuit containing as many as millions of microscopic transistors that work together to perform specific functions. All elements of the circuit are fabricated and interconnected in and on a single chip of semiconducting material.

Killer Defect: A flaw that causes the failure of an integrated circuit

Micron (or micrometer): One-millionth of a meter (10^{-6} meter); symbol is μ or μm.

Semiconductor: A material that can be an electrical conductor or insulator. Silicon is the most common semiconductor used to manufacture integrated circuits.

Silicon: A basic element in the periodic table. Sand is the primary source of silicon (Si).

Wafer: A thin slice of silicon, or other semiconductor material, in which multiple integrated circuits of the same design are fabricated

PURPOSE

In this activity you will learn how tiny bacteria can cause "killer" defects in integrated circuits. You will learn about deionized water and its importance to semiconductor integrated circuit fabrication. Finally you will observe bacteria cultures from several types of water and determine whether or not the observed bacteria would be "killer" defects in today's semiconductor fabrication facilities.

MATERIALS

- 2 prepared bacteria samples from city water
- 2 prepared bacteria samples from distilled or deionized water
- 6 memory chips if available
- 2 prepared samples from pond water
- 6 microscopes with 100X power capability

PROCEDURE

1. Place a memory chip on the microscope stage and focus the microscope, at 100X, such that the identification of the chip or the chip maker is legible. Follow your teacher's instructions as to the use of the microscope.

2. Place a human hair on the stage and across the surface of the memory chip. (If one of the students has fine hair and another has very coarse hair, use a sample from each.)

3. Allow each student in the group to observe the hair and memory chip.

4. Record the extent that the hair covers elements on the chip; e.g., "covers many elements" or "covers one large section" or other description. (The intent is for the students to be able to visualize how tiny defects can destroy integrated circuits.)

5. Remove the memory chip from the microscope stage. Save the hair for the rest of the observations or allow others in the group to contribute hair for the next steps.

6. Obtain a bacteria sample in a Petri dish and record its identification on the worksheet.

7. Allow each student in the group to look at the grid and determine whether or not colony formation is noticeable. (It may not be noticeable for the purified water.)

8. Place the Petri dish on the microscope stage and focus the microscope, at 100X, so that the grid on the filter is in focus.

9. Observe the bacteria colonies using the microscope. Record a qualitative amount for the number, such as "1 per square" "1 large one in middle square" or "many per square" or "too many to count."

10. Optional: count the number of colonies on the filter disk.

11. Place a human hair on the stage and across the filter disk.

12. Focus the microscope such that the hair can be seen and compare it to the size(s) of several colonies on the disk.

13. Record the comparison, such as "hair much bigger than colony" or "hair about the same size" or other.

14. Repeat steps (6) through (13) for the 2 other types of water.

15. Optional: If time permits, place the memory chip back on the microscope stage and look at its small internal elements using the highest magnification possible. The students should be able to visualize how defects the sizes of bacteria (1-10 microns in diameter) could easily interfere with the performance of the tiny internal elements that are much less than 1 micron in width.

16. When all groups have finished, bring the students back into a large group and complete the concluding questions.

Name ______________________________

Period ______________________________

"Killer" Defects
Exploring the Impact of Bacteria on Integrated Circuits

DATA AND OBSERVATIONS

Data Table 1: Memory Chip	
Test Performed	**Qualitative Results**
Locate maker or other ID on chip	
Human hair on memory chip	
Optional memory chip observations	

Data Table 2: Bacteria Samples	
Test Performed	**Qualitative Results**
Sample P________ checked for colony formation	
Sample P________ colonies compared to human hair	
Sample C _____ checked for colony formation	
Sample C______ colonies compared to human hair	
Sample D _____ checked for colony formation	
Sample D _____ colonies compared to human hair	

CONCLUSION QUESTIONS

1. How can bacteria that are only 1-10 microns in diameter either ruin or degrade the performance of an integrated circuit?

2. Why does the semiconductor industry have to use deionized water rather than city water?

3. Would the bacteria samples observed today be considered potential "killer" defects in semiconductor fabrication facilities?

Monocots and Dicots, Two Plants with Differences
Examining Stem Structure

OBJECTIVE
Students will compare and contrast monocot and dicot stem structures. They will identify the parts of the stem and relate those parts to stem structure and function. In addition, students will explain why different types of stains are used in histology.

LEVEL
Biology I

NATIONAL STANDARDS
UCP.1, UCP.2, UCP.5, C.1, E.1, E.2, G.1, G.2

TEKS
Biology 1(A), 2(B), 2(C), 2(D), 13(A), 13(B)

CONNECTIONS TO AP
AP Biology:

III Organisms and populations C. Structure and function of plants and animals 2. Structural, physiological and behavioral adaptations

TIME FRAME
50 minutes

MATERIALS
(For a class of 28 working in pairs)

- 28 Petri dishes
- 14 syringes (10 cc)
- 28 cover slips
- 28 pairs of goggles
- 28 pairs of latex gloves
- 28 dissecting microscopes
- several new razor blades
- airplane plant (*Chlorophytum comosom*)
- 14 dropper bottles with IKI solution
- 28 slides
- 14 tweezers
- 28 lab aprons
- paper towels
- 300 mL toluidine blue O solution (20 mL / team)
- Hawaiian schefflera (*Brassaia arbricola*)

Teacher Safety Alert

1. You must wear goggles, aprons and gloves.
2. Razor blades are sharp; handle with care.
3. Handle solid I_2 under the hood and do not breathe the vapors or allow it to contact your skin.
4. The solutions should be labeled as:

CAUTION: Irritant
CAUTION: Will stain clothing

5. Be sure to warn the students of the following:

CAUTION: The toluidine blue O contains an acid. This solution is an irritant and can damage clothing. Avoid skin/eye contact; do not ingest. Should any of the solutions come in contact with your skin, flush with copious amounts of water immediately. Continue flushing the affected skin for 10 minutes and notify your teacher.

CAUTION: The toluidine blue O and IKI solution will stain clothing and skin.

TEACHER NOTES

The two plants can be obtained at most nurseries. They can be sectioned into very thin slices that are appropriate for staining. The petiole of the Hawaiian schefflera and the white aerial stem of the airplane plant are the parts of each plant, respectively, that should be sectioned. These parts are stiff enough that thin sectioning can occur. The stem of the airplane plant is well suited for this investigation since it does not contain chloroplasts.

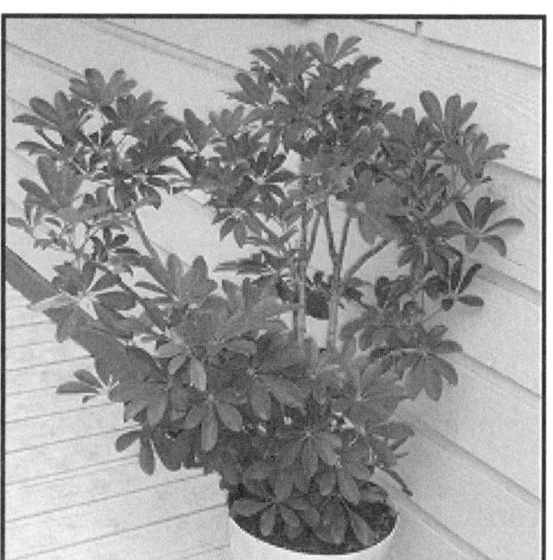

The teacher should thin section these stems for the student. Use a new razor or scalpel blade to cut the stem. A new blade should used after each 4-5 sections have been made. Double-edged razor blades are better suited for this task than single-edge razor blades because they are sharper. If you use a double-edged razor blade, tape one side of the blade to avoid cuts. Plastic safety razor blade holders are also available at most hardware stores.

To cut the stem, hold it firmly about 1 cm from the end you wish to cut between the index finger and thumb while placing it on a hard surface. Cut at a 90° angle straight down toward the surface. Try to avoid oblique cuts. Dissecting microscopes are adequate to view the structures of the stem. Try to make the cuts as thin as possible

The stain toluidine blue O will stain different parts of the stem different colors. It will interact with the ligin found on xylem and sclerenchyma cells and turn blue-green. It will interact with phloem to turn pink or slightly pink. The phloem is usually sandwiched between these two tissues in the vascular bundles.

Mix the following to make the toluidine blue O solution:

1. Prepare 400 mL benzoate buffer with a pH 4.4 by using 0.50 g of benzoic acid (C_6H_5COOH) with 0.58 g of sodium benzoate (C_6H_5COONa).

2. Add enough deionized or distilled water to dissolve the solids and then dilute the solution to a total volume of 400 mL.

3. To make a 0.1% solution of toluidine blue O solution by mass, add 400 mL of the 0.1 M benzoate buffer to 0.4 g of toluidine blue O.

The iodine potassium iodide stain (IKI) will test for starch. The stain accumulates in the center of the helical starch molecule causing it to change color. The more monomers present in the starch molecule, the more intense the color change. Long starch polymers give an intense purple.

To make the iodine potassium iodide solution:

1. Add 6.0 g of potassium iodide, KI, to 300 mL of distilled water.

2. Add 0.6 g of iodine, I_2, to the potassium iodide solution. Be careful NOT to inhale the vapors or allow the crystals to come in contact with your skin — perform this step under a fume hood. The iodine will take some time to dissolve since it is nonpolar.

3. Dispense 15 mL into the 14 brown dropper bottles. Alternately, if brown bottles are not available, you can wrap aluminum foil around clear ones to block the light.

4. Store the bottles tightly capped and in the dark.

POSSIBLE ANSWERS TO THE CONCLUSION QUESTIONS AND SAMPLE DATA

The students should find that the airplane plant is the monocot and the Hawaiian schefflera is the dicot.

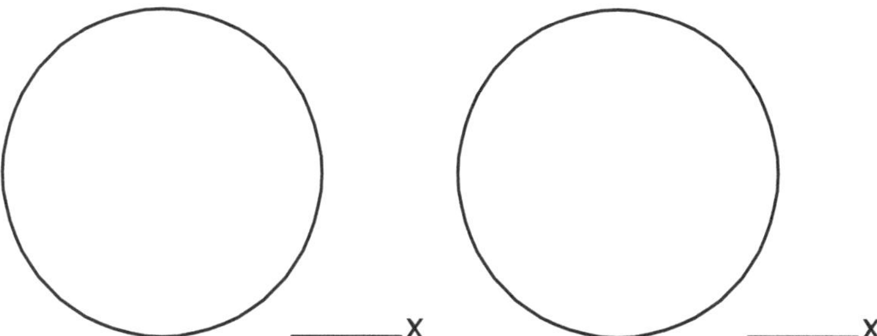

1. Classify each plant as either a monocot or a dicot. Describe their structures.
   - The airplane plant is the monocot and the Hawaiian schefflera is the dicot.
   - The vascular bundles in the monocot are scattered while the vascular bundles in the dicot are arranged in a ring with the xylem to the interior of the phloem which is found on the periphery.
   - The cortex is between the vascular bundles and the epidermis.

2. Explain how each stem structure seen under the dissecting microscope relates to its function.
   - The phloem and xylem both form long tubes which are important in the movement of materials. The fibers found outside the vascular bundle are used to aid the xylem in support. The cortex layer is thicker and stores starch.

3. The ligin present in the cell walls of both the sclerenchyma and xylem cells caused these tissues to dye the same color when exposed to the toluidine blue O stain. Speculate on the function of ligin.
   - Both of these tissues are used for support. Ligin strengthens the cell walls and increases support.

4. Which had a larger diameter, the phloem tubes or the xylem tubes? Speculate why this might be so.
   - Xylem vessels are larger than phloem. Xylem is used to move water from the roots throughout the plant. Phloem is used to move material within the plant. There is a greater demand for water from the roots.

5. Where in the stem was the starch located? What test did you perform? What constitutes a positive test for starch?
   - The starch is located in the cortex.
   - This should be obvious because that is the part of the stem that turned purple when using IKI to test for the presence of starch.

6. What function does a tissue found to contain starch most likely perform?
   - The starch is used for the storage of energy.

TEACHER PAGES

7. Why might a botanist use different types of stains when performing histological stains of plants?
   - Various plant tissues perform different functions and thus contain different molecules. Different stains interact with those molecules. You can infer the function of various cells and tissues based on the presence of certain molecules. For example, idodine stains starch. If the tissue stains purple, then the stem has starch. That also implies that one of the functions of that tissue is to store energy. Stains can also enhance the viewing of plant cells.

REFERENCES

Campbell, Neil, Lawrence Mitchell, and Jane Reece. *Biology*. New York: Addison Wesley Longman, 1999. pp. 672-675

"Chapter 9: A Beginner's Guide to the Study of Plant Structure." Edward C. Yeung. June 2002. ABLE. August 2003. <http://www.zoo.utoronto.ca/able/volumte/vol-19-09-yeung.htm>.

Monocots and Dicots, Two Plants with Differences
Examining Stem Structure

Both plants and animals are intricate organisms containing specialized tissues. Recall that tissue is composed of a group of cells working together to perform a specialized function. The ability of a tissue to perform its specialized function properly is directly linked to its location within an organism. The stem of a plant, appearing quite plain and simple, belies its true structure. Stems first evolved to perform two functions for the plant organism, structural support and transportation of materials. Over time, natural selection has produced stems with additional, enhanced functions. For example, the white potato is a stem that is modified for starch storage while the stem of a cactus is modified for water storage.

The basic structure of a herbaceous stem includes the epidermis, the cortex and the vascular tissue. The epidermis is the outer covering of the stem and consists of epidermal cells. Epidermal cells produce a waxy covering for the stem. This waxy covering is one cell thick, its function is to reduce water lost through evaporation. The vascular tissue of the stem can be found in either discrete vascular bundles or in rings. There are two main types of conducting tissue, the xylem and the phloem.

Xylem is composed of tracheid cells and vessel cells. Tracheids are elongated cells that join together to form a long tube. There are large pits at the adjoining cell walls. Vessels are squatty cells that also join together to form tubes. The adjoining vessel walls disintegrate eventually forming one continuous tube. As xylem cells mature and become functional, they die. Their cell walls remain intact and xylem serves to transport water and dissolved minerals up from the root system to the stems and leaves. A process we will study later called transpiration, greatly aids in the transport of water and minerals up the plant against the constant pull of gravity.

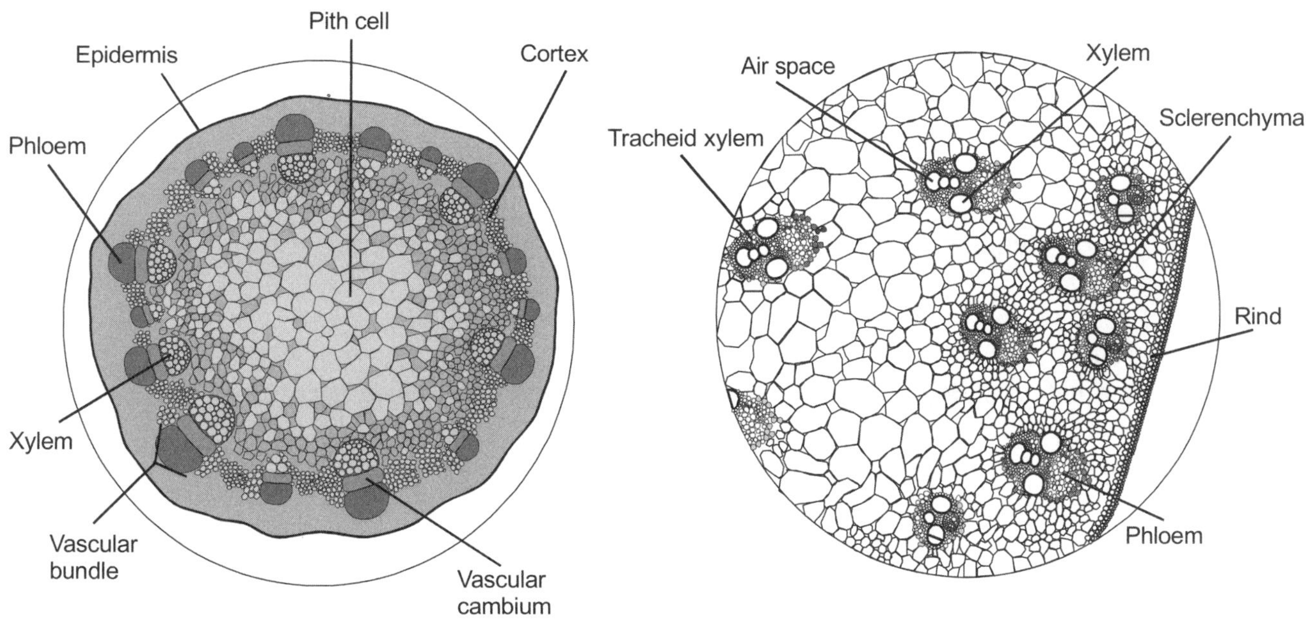

Phloem tissue is constructed of sieve cells and companion cells. This tissue, unlike xylem tissue, is still alive when it reaches maturity. The sieve cells are unusual because they lack a nucleus. Attached to the sieve cells are companion cells. These cells have a nucleus and seem to aid in directing the metabolic activities of the sieve cell. Sieve cells join together and form tubes. The adjoining cells walls are pitted with pores that allow the movement of material from one cell to another. Phloem moves organic material like glucose and sucrose in both the up and down direction in a plant. In general, phloem sieve tubes are smaller in diameter than xylem vessel tubes. Phloem tissue will lie to the outside of the xylem tissue, closer to the periphery of the stem.

The cortex of a plant is the tissue that lies between the vascular tissue and the epidermis. It is often used for storage or support. The most common type of cells found here are parenchyma cells. These cells are unspecialized and have only a primary cell wall. Other cells that may be found in the stem are sclerenchyma and collenchyma. Both of these cells are used in support and have thick primary cell walls or an additional secondary cell wall.

Flowering plants are divided into two large classes, monocots and dicots. Monocots have parallel veins in their leaves, floral parts in threes or multiples of threes, and a fibrous root system. Dicots have branched veins in their leaves, floral parts in fours or fives and multiples thereof, and a tap root system. In addition, the seed of a monocot has only one cotyledon whereas the seed of a dicot has two cotyledons. Cotyledons are seed leaves used to store food for the seed embryo. The structure of the stem for these two classes of plants also differs.

This investigation allows you to compare and contrast the stem structures of monocots and dicots. The stems will be stained with toluidine blue O. Toluidine blue O is a differential stain, meaning different tissues will stain different colors. Xylem and sclerenchyma cells will stain a blue-green because of the ligin found in their cell walls. The phloem may stain pink or not at all. The phloem can be found between the xylem and sclerenchyma tissue.

PURPOSE

In this activity you will perform stains to identify the general stem structures of herbaceous plants and compare and contrast the stem structure of monocots versus dicots.

MATERIALS

- razor blades
- 0.1 % buffered toluidine blue O solution
- water
- cover slips
- syringe 10 cc (mL)
- Hawaiian schefflera (*Brassaia arbricola*)
- apron
- latex gloves
- dissecting microscope
- IKI solution in dropper bottle
- microscope slides
- two small Petri dishes (60 x 15)
- tweezers
- airplane plant (*Chlorophytum comosom*)
- goggles

Safety Alert

1. You must wear goggles, aprons and gloves.
2. The toluidine blue O contains an acid. This solution is an irritant and can damage clothing. Avoid skin/eye contact; do not ingest. Should any of the solutions come in contact with your skin, flush with copious amounts of water immediately. Continue flushing the affected skin for 10 minutes and notify your teacher.

PROCEDURE

PART I

1. Examine the Hawaiian schefflera and the airplane plant and predict which plant is a monocot and which plant is a dicot.

2. Obtain a clean microscope slide so that your teacher can place several cross-sections of both plants on your slide.

3. Dispense approximately 10 mL (cc) of toluidine blue O stain into one of your petri dishes and dispense approximately 10 mL of distilled water into the second petri dish.

4. Use your tweezers to place the cross sections of Hawaiian schefflera into the petri dish containing the toluidine blue O stain for one minute.

5. Remove the cross-sections from the stain and place them in the petri dish of distilled water for one minute.

6. Next, place the cross-sections on your slide and view them under the dissecting microscope. Look for vascular bundles. Draw and label the stem structures correctly.

7. Rinse and dry your slide and cover slip.

PART II

1. Place a cross section of Hawaiian schefflera on the microscope slide and test for the location of starch in your stem. Add a drop of iodine potassium iodide solution to the cross-section and wait two minutes.

2. Apply a cover slip and view using the dissecting microscope. Rinse and dry your microscope slide and cover slip.

3. Repeat steps 2-9 for the airplane plant.

4. When you are through with this investigation clean your area as directed by your teacher.

Name ________________________________

Period ________________________________

Monocots and Dicots, Two Plants with Differences
Examining Stem Structure

ANALYSIS

Draw and label the stems as they were viewed under the microscope.

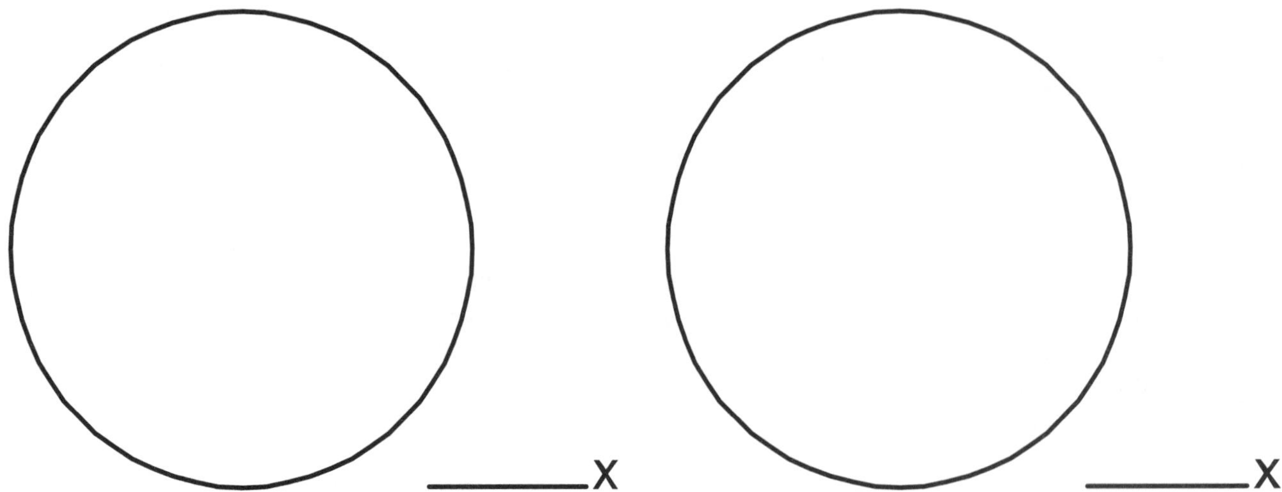

CONCLUSION QUESTIONS

1. Classify each plant as either a monocot or a dicot. Describe their structures.

2. Explain how each stem structure seen under the dissecting microscope relates to its function.

3. The ligin present in the cell walls of both the sclerenchyma and xylem cells caused these tissues to dye the same color when exposed to the toluidine blue O stain. Speculate on the function of ligin.

4. Which had a larger diameter, the phloem tubes or the xylem tubes? Speculate why this might be so.

5. Where in the stem was the starch located? What test did you perform? What constitutes a positive test for starch?

6. What function does a tissue found to contain starch most likely perform?

7. Why might a botanist use different types of stains when performing histological stains of plants?

"Hole-y" Moley
Examining Stomates

OBJECTIVE
Students will compare and contrast the structure and location of stomates on a monocot versus a dicot. They will identify the structure and function of the stomate. Students will determine the number of stomates per mm^2 found on the surface of monocot and dicot using a microscope.

LEVEL
Biology

NATIONAL STANDARDS
UCP.1, UCP.2, UCP.3, UCP.5, C.1, E.1, E.2, G.1, G.2

TEKS
Biology 1(A), 2(B), 2(C), 2(D), 13(A), 13(B)

CONNECTIONS TO AP
AP Biology:

III Organisms and Populations A. Structure and Function of Plants and Animals 2. Structural, physiological and behavioral adaptations

TIME FRAME
45 minutes

MATERIALS
(For a class of 28 working in pairs)

- 14 light microscopes
- 28 coverslips
- 14 clear metric rulers 10 cm long
- airplane plant (*Chlorophytum comosom*)
- 28 microscope slides
- 14 bottles of clear nail polish
- Hawaiian schefflera (*Brassaia arbricola*)
- 14 TI-83 Graphing calculators (optional)

TEACHER NOTES
The best results occur when the nail polish is allowed to dry completely. This takes about 10 minutes. It is easiest to remove the nail polish if the leaf is torn through the nail polish area. There are too many stomates to count when viewing the stomates under 100x, however the student can count the stomates under 430x in a reasonable amount of time. The students should find stomates on the bottom of the plant and few if any on the top of the plant. The stomates on the Hawaiian schefflera are typical of what is shown in most textbooks. Under the microscope, they look like a pair of lips. The stomates on the airplane plant are very different. The epidermal cells are diamond shaped. The stomates are found in the corners of the diamond. There are rows of diamonds with the stomates and rows without stomates. Have the students count the field of view where the stomates are found. The interesting point is that the pattern of stomates is not related to the variegation of the plant.

Both the airplane plant and the Hawaiian schefflera make excellent specimens for the biology classroom. These same plants can be used in monocot/dicot stem comparison activities. The Hawaiian schefflera (*Schefflera arbricola* or *Brassaia arbricola*) is sometimes sold under the common name, umbrella tree or umbrella bush. It is also sold in a variegated version (*Schefflera actinophylla*) in local nurseries.

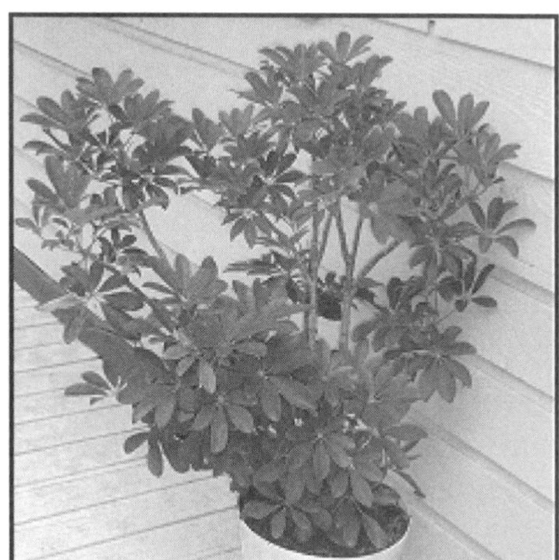

POSSIBLE ANSWERS TO THE CONCLUSION QUESTIONS AND SAMPLE DATA

Airplane Plant Lower Surface (430x)	
Field of View	**# of Stomates**
# 1	13
# 2	14
# 3	10
# 4	15
# 5	14
Average	13

Airplane Plant Upper Surface (430x)	
Field of View	**# of Stomates**
# 1	0
# 2	0
# 3	0
# 4	0
# 5	0
Average	0

Hawaiian Schefflera Lower Surface (430x)	
Field of View	**# of Stomates**
# 1	22
# 2	20
# 3	20
# 4	19
# 5	19
Average	20

Hawaiian Schefflera Upper Surface (430x)	
Field of View	**# of Stomates**
# 1	0
# 2	0
# 3	0
# 4	0
# 5	0
Average	0

Below are photographs taken with a light microscope. The upper and lower epidermis of both plants are shown. Stomates will be found only on the lower surface. Magnification of both 100X and 430X for the lower epidermis of both plants are shown below.

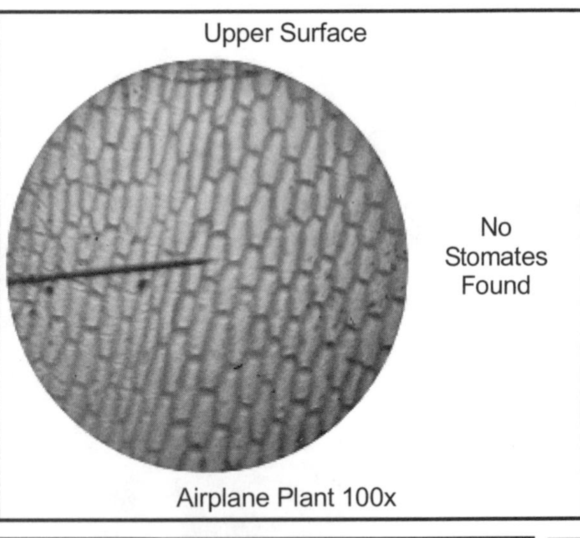

Airplane Plant 100x

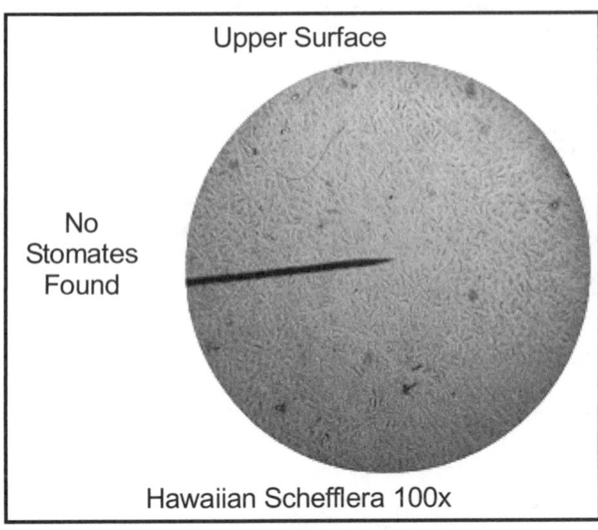

Hawaiian Schefflera 100x

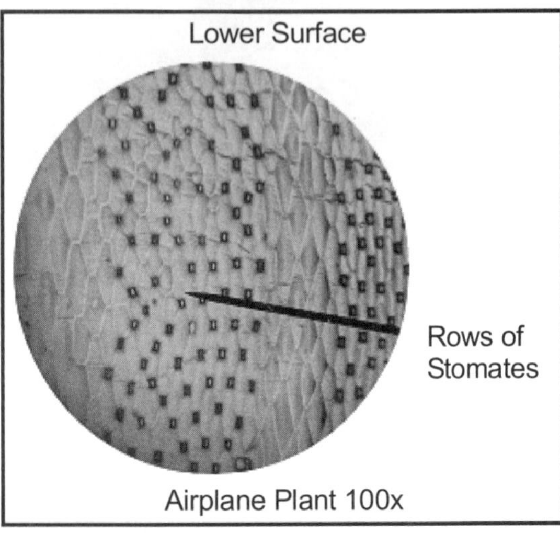

Airplane Plant 100x

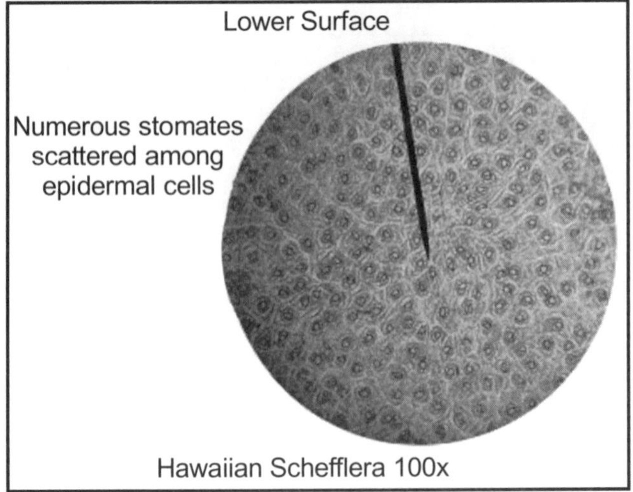

Hawaiian Schefflera 100x

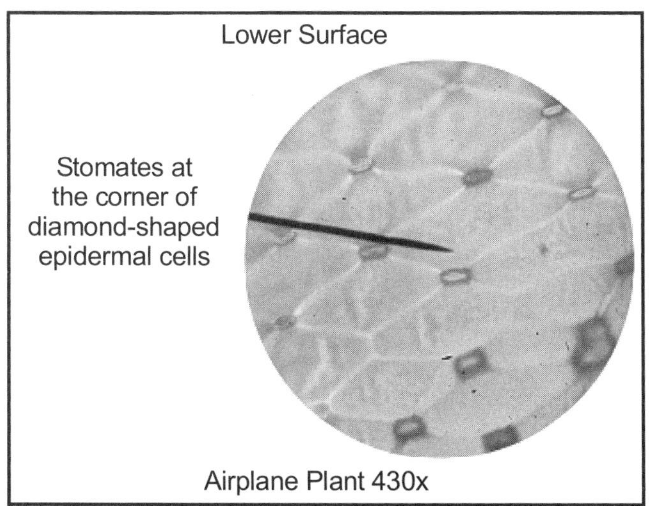

Airplane Plant 430x

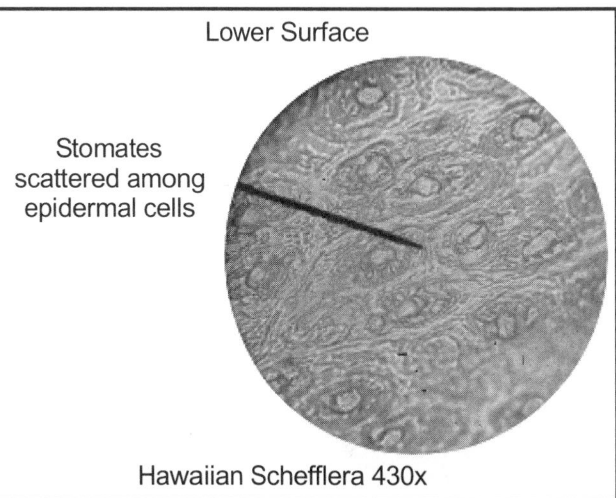

Hawaiian Schefflera 430x

1. Compare and contrast the structure of the stomates found on the airplane plant, a monocot, with that of the Hawaiian schefflera, a dicot.
   - The Hawaiian schefflera has more stomates than the airplane plant. The stomates on the Hawaiian schefflera are evenly distributed among the entire lower epidermis. The epidermal cells on the airplane plants are diamond-shaped. The stomates are found in the corners of the epidermal cells. There are some rows of epidermal cells that do not contain stomates on the airplane plant. The stomates on the Hawaiian schefflera are kidney shaped and the shape of the stomates on the airplane plant are dumbbell shaped.

2. Compare and contrast the number of stomates found on the upper surface of the leaf with that found on the lower surface of the leaf and speculate as to why there might be a difference.
   - The stomates were found only on the bottom of the leaf to minimize water loss. The upper epidermis also has a waxy cuticle, which could clog the stomates and defeat their purpose.

3. Explain what the relationship is between the magnification of a field of view and the diameter of the field of view.
   - An increase in magnification will decrease the diameter of the field of view.

4. Determine the number of stomates per mm^2 on both the upper and lower field of view of both plants. Show your work.
   - On low power, the diameter of the field of view should be between 1.5 and 1.75 mm depending on how it is measured. This assumes 1.5 for this answer and uses the averages above.
   - Diameter on low (100x) = 1.5 mm
   - Ratio of high to low

   $$\frac{430}{100} = 4.3 \rightarrow \frac{1.5\text{mm}}{4.3} = .349 \text{ or about } .350 \text{ mm}$$

   - The radius of the circle is .175 mm
   - The area of a circle is = πr^2

- The area of the field of view = π (.175)2 = .096 mm2
- The number of stomates per mm^2 in the Hawaiian schefflera is

$$\frac{20}{.096\,mm^2} \text{ or about } 208 \text{ stomates}/mm^2$$

- The number of stomates per mm^2 in the airplane plant is

$$\frac{13}{.096\,mm^2} \text{ or about } 135 \text{ stomates}/mm^2$$

5. Draw a square with sides 1 mm long. With a sharp pencil, try to pencil in the number of stomates you would find on a Hawaiian schefflera.
   - The purpose of this is for the student to gain an appreciation of the size of a stomate and how many would be found in a mm^2.

6. Draw a square with sides 1 cm long. Using conversion factors, determine the number of stomates that would be found in a one-centimeter square leaf.

$$\text{Conversion} = .175\,mm * \frac{1\,cm}{10\,mm} = .0175\,cm$$

- The area of the field of view = π (.0175 cm)2 = .00096 cm2
- The number of stomates per cm^2 in the Hawaiian schefflera is

$$\frac{20}{.00096\,cm^2} \text{ or about } 20833 \text{ stomates}/cm^2$$

- The number of stomates per cm^2 in the airplane plant is

$$\frac{13}{.00096\,cm^2} \text{ or about } 14583 \text{ stomates}/cm^2$$

7. Make a conclusion about the observed distribution of the stomates on the upper versus the lower surface of a leaf.
   - There are no stomates found on the upper surface of the leaf. The stomates on these two plants are found on the lower surface of the leaf.

8. Some plants like coleus have hairs found on the lower surface of the leaf. Speculate on their function.
   - The purpose of the hairs is to decrease wind or circulation of the air and therefore decrease transpiration.

REFERENCES

Alexander Joseph, and Paul Brandwein, and Evelyn Morhort. *A Sourcebook for the Biological Sciences*. New York: Harcourt, Brace & World, Inc., 1958. pg. 175

Campbell, Neil. *Biology*. New York: Addison Wesley Longman, 1999. pp. 672-675

Milani, Jean P., Revision Coordinator. *Biological Science, A Molecular Approach*. Dubuque: Kendall Hunt Publishing Company, 1990. pp. 617, 645

"Hole-y" Moley
Examining Stomates

As plants colonized the land, there was a selection pressure for plants to grow and increase in size. This required the development of supportive tissue. An increase in height also meant that some plant parts were away from sources of water. The problem of support and need for water was solved by the development of vascular tissue. Plants also evolved a waxy cuticle as a way to reduce water loss. This waxy cuticle can be found on leaves and herbaceous stems. While this wonderful adaptation prevents water loss, it also prevents the gas exchange in the leaves. Evolution and natural selection has an astonishing way of working. With the need for gas exchange, came the development of stomates. *Stomates* are tiny pores found on leaves. While these pores will allow for gas exchange to occur, some water will also exit the stomates. This process is known as transpiration.

The plant regulates the opening and closing of these stomates with two cells that surround the stomate known as *guard cells*. These cells may be either kidney shaped or dumb-bell shaped. When these cells experience turgor pressure, they swell up and open the stomate. The guard cells, in general, close at night when the plant experiences water stress, or when the leaf has low levels of CO_2.

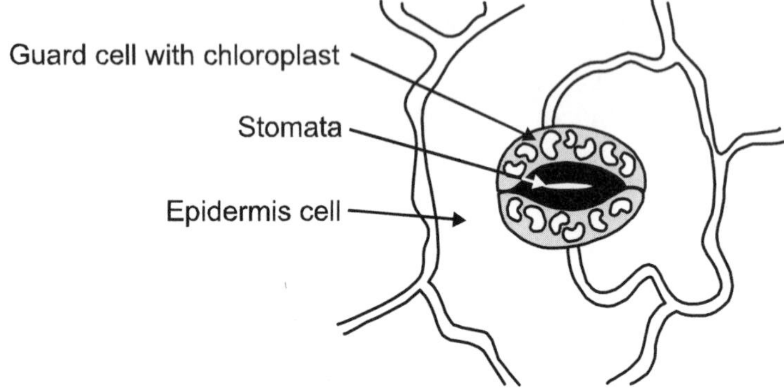

The number of stomates a leaf has varies with the plant species. For some species, the stomates are found on both the upper and lower leaf surfaces while on others they are just found on the lower surface. Below is a list of selected plant species with the number of stomates per mm^2:

Leaves with no stomates on upper surface		
Plant	**# stomates per mm^2 on lower surface**	**# stomates per mm^2 on upper surface**
Norway Maple	400	0
Rubber Plant	145	0
Lily	62	0

Leaves with few stomates on upper surface		
Pumpkin	269	28
Tomato	130	12
Bean	281	40

Leaves with stomates nearly equal on both surfaces		
Oats	23	25
Corn	158	94
Garden Pea	216	101

In this investigation, you will count the number of stomates found on dicot and monocot leaves on both the upper and lower surfaces in a field of view. You will determine the relationship between magnification and the size of the field of view when you look into a microscope. Using this mathematical relationship, you can then determine the number of stomates in a square millimeter of leaf surface.

PURPOSE

The purpose of this investigation is to compare and contrast the stomates found on a monocot versus a dicot. You will also determine the number of stomates per mm^2 on both the upper and lower surfaces of a leaf.

MATERIALS

- light microscope
- coverslips
- Hawaiian schefflera (*Brassaia arbricola*)
- leaves of several plant species
- TI-83 graphing calculator (optional)
- microscope slides
- clear nail polish
- airplane plant (*Chlorophytum comosom*)
- clear metric ruler 10 cm long

> **Safety Alert**
> CAUTION: Fingernail polish can be an irritant if it comes in contact with sensitive tissue. Avoid eye contact; do not ingest. Immediately run water in an eye wash for 10 minutes if fingernail polish comes in contact with your eye.

PROCEDURE

1. Write a hypothesis concerning the number of stomates that will be found on the upper surface of a leaf versus the bottom surface of a leaf. Keep in mind the structure and function of stomates.

2. Obtain a leaf from both plants above. Apply a coat of clear nail polish approximately 1 cm x 1 cm to the upper and lower sides of each leaf. Be sure to do this on different areas of the leaf. Do not make the layer of polish extremely thick. On the airplane plant, coat the green area of the leaf. Make the area approximately 1 cm^2.

3. While the polish is drying, determine the area of the field of view. Lay a clear metric ruler on the stage of the microscope. Using the low power objective (10x), estimate the diameter of the field of view to the nearest .25 mm.
   a. Diameter ________________ mm

4. Determine the diameter of the field of view on high objective (43X) by doing the following calculations.

$$\frac{\text{magnification number of high-power objective}}{\text{magnification number of low-power objective}} = X$$

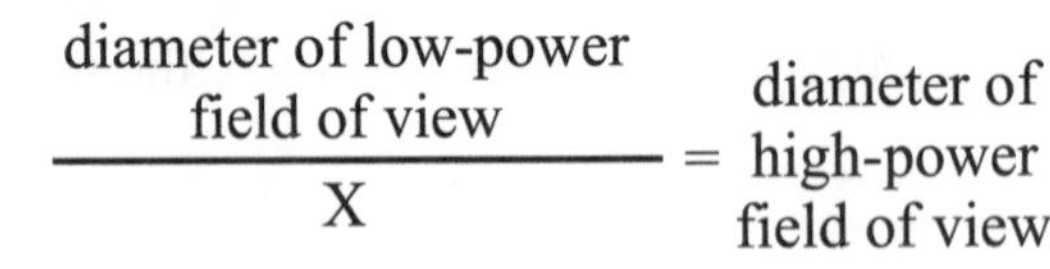

$$\frac{\text{diameter of low-power field of view}}{X} = \text{diameter of high-power field of view}$$

5. Determine the radius of your field of view on high power.
   a. ________________ radius mm

6. Determine the area of a circle for your field of view. Remember the area of a circle = πr^2.

7. Peel off the nail polish from the back of the airplane plant leaf. Be sure you make note of which plant you are using and whether it is the upper surface or the lower surface. Place the peeled nail polish on a microscope slide, cover with a cover slip, and examine it under low power.

8. Observe the slide under the (43x) objective or (430x) for the total magnification. On your student answer page draw the stomates as they appear in the field of view. Count the number of stomates observed. Do this for 5 different areas of the slide. Record in the data table.

9. Repeat steps 7 and 8 for the upper surface of the airplane plant and both the lower and upper surfaces of the Hawaiian schefflera.

10. For each surface examined, calculate the average number stomates per field of view, then determine the average number of stomates per mm^2 of leaf surface area. Show your work on the student answer sheet.

11. Write a conclusion for this experiment. It should include information about the location of stomates, the number of stomates found in a certain area, and comparison of dicot stomates with monocot stomates.

** Optional – These calculations can be done on a TI-83 graphing calculator by doing the following:

12. To enter the number of stomates in a list on the calculator. Turn on your calculator ON and press CLEAR to clear the screen.

13. Clear all lists by pressing 2nd , + [mem]. Move cursor to ClrAllLists (by pressing the ▼ key OR press 4) and then press ENTER twice. Done should appear on the screen.

14. Press STAT , then select EDIT and press ENTER .

15. Now enter the data (number of stomates) collected for lower surface of the airplane plant in L1, the data for the upper surface of the airplane plant in L2, the data for the lower surface of the Hawaiian schefflera in L3 and the data for its upper surface in L4 (Figure 1).

Figure 1

Figure 2

16. Return to the home screen by pressing 2nd , MODE [quit].

17. The following will allow you to determine the average number of stomates per mm^2 for L1 or the lower surface of the airplane plane by doing the following:
    a. Press 2nd , STAT [list].
    b. Move to cursor to the right to highlight MATH (this allows to manipulate lists).
    c. Move the cursor down to highlight MEAN (Figure 2).
    d. Press ENTER (the calculator is ready to average a list).
    e. Press 2nd , 1 [L1].
    f. Press) to close parenthesis.

g. Now you want to divide by the equation for the area of a circle.

Press .

Input your value for the radius to the closest mm.

Press), x^2,), ENTER (Figure 3).

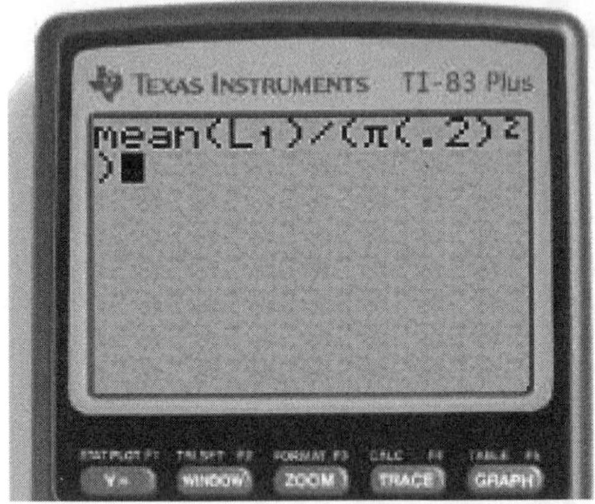

18. Now you have the average number of stomates/mm^2 on the lower surface of the airplane plant. Repeat the above steps for L2, L3, and L4. This will give the average number of stomates/mm^2 of the upper surface of the airplane plane and the lower and upper surfaces of the Hawaiian schefflera, respectively.

Name ______________________________

Period ______________________________

"Hole-y" Moley
Examining Stomates

HYPOTHESIS

DATA AND OBSERVATIONS

Airplane plant

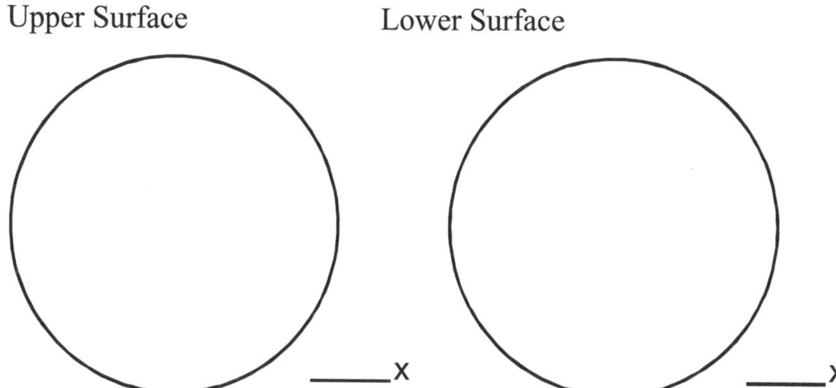

Hawaiian schefflera

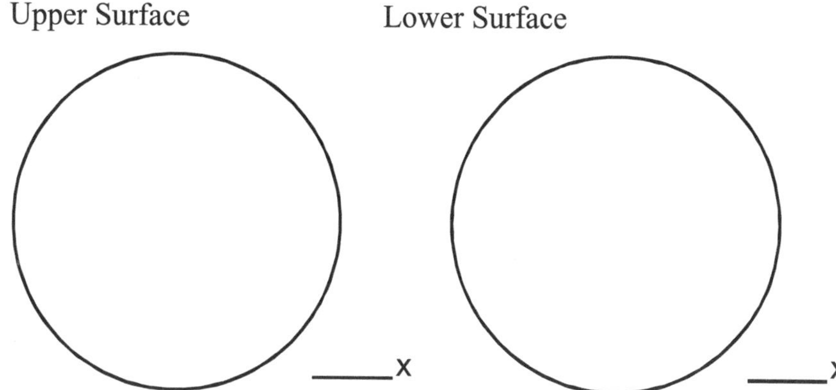

Airplane Plant Upper Surface	
Field of View	**# of Stomates**
# 1	13
# 2	14
# 3	10
# 4	15
# 5	14
Average	13

Airplane Plant Lower Surface	
Field of View	**# of Stomates**
# 1	0
# 2	0
# 3	0
# 4	0
# 5	0
Average	0

Hawaiian Schefflera Upper Surface	
Field of View	**# of Stomates**
# 1	
# 2	
# 3	
# 4	
# 5	
Average	

Hawaiian Schefflera Lower Surface	
Field of View	**# of Stomates**
# 1	
# 2	
# 3	
# 4	
# 5	
Average	

ANALYSIS

This area is provided for your conclusion.

CONCLUSION QUESTIONS

1. Compare and contrast the structure of the stomates found on a monocot or the airplane plant, with that of the dicot or the Hawaiian schefflera.

2. Compare and contrast the number of stomates found on the upper surface of the leaf with that found on the lower surface of the leaf and speculate as to why there might be a difference.

3. Explain what the relationship is between the magnification of a field of view and the diameter of the field of view.

4. Determine the number of stomates per mm^2 on both the upper and lower field of view of both plants. Show your work.

5. Draw a square with sides 1 mm long. With a sharp pencil, try to pencil in the number of stomates you would find on a Hawaiian schefflera.

6. Draw a square with sides 1 cm long. Using conversion factors, determine the number of stomates that would be found in a one-centimeter square of leaf.

7. Make a conclusion about the observed distribution of the stomates on the upper versus the lower surface of a leaf.

8. Some plants like coleus have hairs found on the lower surface of the leaf. Speculate on their function.

Write Your Notes and Ideas Here!

Transpiration
Investigating Water Movement and Evaporation in Monocot and Dicot Plants

OBJECTIVE
Students will investigate the process of transpiration by observing the movement of water through xylem tissues, comparing the presence of water vapor on plant surfaces, and measuring the rate of transpiration.

LEVEL
Biology I

NATIONAL STANDARDS
UCP.1, UCP.2, UCP.3, UCP.5, B.2, B.6, C.1, C.5, G.1, G.2

TEKS
2 (B), 2(C), 2(D), 13(A)

CONNECTIONS TO AP
AP Biology:

III. Organisms and Populations B. Structure and Function of Plants and Animals 2. Structural, physiological, and behavioral adaptations 3. Response to the environment

TIME FRAME
45 minutes on day 1, 20 minutes on day 2

MATERIALS
(For a class of 28 working in pairs)

- 14 stalks of celery
- 14 200 mL beakers or similar containers
- 1 bottle red food coloring
- 14 metric rulers
- 1 bottles mineral oil
- 14 dicot plant specimens (or one large specimen)
- 14 shallow pans or containers of water
- drying oven or hair dryer
- 42 cobalt chloride test strips
- several balances (day 2 only)
- 14 scalpels or razor blades
- 14 10 mL disposable syringes
- 14 disposable dropper pipets
- 7 monocot plant specimens (or one large specimen)
- 76 paper clips (to attach test strips to plants)

TEACHER NOTES

This lab ties a very familiar demonstration of the uptake of food coloring by celery with the process of transpiration. The celery needs to be fresh in order to work properly. The coloration of the xylem tissue is easily missed by the untrained eye so caution your students to look closely for the pinkish-red pigment. To avoid unnecessary stains, you could mix the food coloring and water ahead of time. The colored water can be reused by different classes.

The cobalt chloride test paper can be purchased from a science supplier. The paper should be blue prior to using. High relative humidity during storage can turn the paper pink. If your paper has turned pink, you should put it in a drying oven until the blue color returns. If you do not have access to a drying oven, you can dry the paper using a hair dryer. This portion of the lab asks the students to design their own set of procedures. Remind students that procedures need to be written clearly enough that another person could follow them and obtain the same results. Instruct them to look at the data table to make sure their procedure will allow them to collect the data required. The sample data provided was collected on a *Coleus*. If the relative humidity is high on the day that you do this portion of the lab, the students will need to take readings in much shorter time intervals. The materials list includes 7 dicot plants to be shared among 14 groups for this portion of the lab.

A variety of plants can be used for Part III which measures the rate of transpiration. You can grow your own specimen from bean and corn seeds provided you have an adequate source of lighting in your classroom. Cucumber plants and tomato plants can be purchased at a local garden center in season. These garden specimen work well for this lab. The results included in the answer section were obtained using pansies. Lawn, garden, and house plants that require frequent watering make good specimen for this activity. Airplane plants can be used as the monocot specimen. The amount of transpiration from an airplane plant leaf will be very small (typically less than .2 mL/24hrs.). One airplane plant can provide enough leaves for several classes and be maintained in the classroom. Bamboo plants have notably high rates of transpiration and are nice specimen for this lab if you find them locally accessible. If you are using one large plant and having students remove sections, monitor their cutting to conserve the specimen.

This protocol uses the barrels of 10 mL disposable syringes placed in test tube racks. The protective covering tips that come on the disposable syringes should be firmly attached and checked for leaks. Another choice would be to use regular test tubes by marking the initial and final levels with a waterproof pen. You could also do this activity in 10 mL graduated cylinders.

Students should not remove their plant specimen once they have applied the mineral oil. If it becomes necessary to remove the plant, the apparatus should be emptied, washed out and refilled with water before inserting the plant. This precaution will prevent the open end of the stem from being coated with oil which would inhibit transpiration.

Prepare a transparency of Data Table 3b for the students to record their group's data to be shared with the class.

Students should set up Parts I, II, and III respectively. By the time they finish setting up all three, it will be time to take readings on Part I followed by Part II. Students will get the final reading for Part III on the second day.

POSSIBLE ANSWERS TO THE CONCLUSION QUESTIONS AND SAMPLE DATA

Data Table 1	
Initial Observations of cut end of celery	soft green tissue, occasional darker green circles
Final Observations of cut end of celery	Soft tissue is still green, the occasional circles appear red
Length before cutting sections	27 cm
Length after cutting sections	24 cm
Rate of water movement (cm/min)	0.89 cm/minute

PART II
Experimental Design:

Hypothesis: If the underside of the leaf has a higher rate of transpiration then the cobalt chloride test paper attached to the underside will be a darker blue than the paper attached in other areas.

Materials: four cobalt chloride test strips, three paper clips

Procedure:

1. Obtain three strips of cobalt chloride test paper.
2. Attach the test strips to the upper side of a leaf, the underside of a second leaf and to an open stem area using paper clips.
3. Place one test strip on a paper towel on the lab bench to serve as a control.
4. Note the color of the strip and record the color in the data table.
5. Leave the plant undisturbed for 15 minutes.
6. Observe the test strips and record any color change in the data table.

Data Table 2: Cobalt Chloride Test				
	Control	Upper Leaf Surface	Lower Leaf Surface	Stem
Beginning test strip color	Blue	Blue	Blue	Blue
Description at minute 1	Blue	Blue	Lighter in spots	Blue
Description at minute 5	Blue	Lighter around attachment sites	Faint pink areas	Light Blue
Description at minute 10	Light blue	Pink	Pale whitish pink	Whitish, light blue
Description at minute 15	Pink	Pink	Pink	Pink
Ranking in order of water vapor released	4	2	1	3

Data Table 3a: Transpiration	
Type of plant	Dicot
Initial water level	10 mL
Final water level	5.6 mL
mL of water consumed	4.4 mL
Transpiration mL/g/ hr	.05 mL/g/hr

Data Table 3b: Class Data Monocot & Dicot Transpiration Rates (mL/g/hr)								
	Group 1	Group 2	Group 3	Group 4	Group 5	Group 6	Group 7	Average
Monocot					.005	.003	.006	.005
Dicot	.044	.052	.03	.057				.046

CONCLUSION QUESTIONS

1. Explain why water moved up the celery stalk. What forces were involved in the movement of the colored water?
   - The polar water molecules form hydrogen bonds with each other in cohesion and with other substances in adhesion. This hydrogen bonding, adhesion and cohesion cause water to move up the xylem tissues through capillary action.

2. How would the rate of water movement have changed if the leaves had been removed from the stalk of celery prior to placing it in the colored water?
   - The rate would have been lower since the leaves help to draw water upward as they go through transpiration.

3. If you had left the celery in the colored water for another 20 minutes how far would it have traveled?
   - It would have move to the top of the stalk which was 27 cm long.

4. Calculate how long would it take for the colored water to reach the top of the stalk of celery? Show your work in the space below.
   - The colored water would have reached the top of the example stalk in 23.37 minutes.
   - 3 cm more to travel/0.89 cm/min = 3.37 minutes 20 minutes + 3.37 minutes = 23.37 minutes

5. Which part of the plant you tested had the highest rate of transpiration? Which part had the lowest rate of transpiration?
   - Most plant specimen will show the highest transpiration rates on the underside of the leaf.

6. What is transpiration and why is it important in plants?
   - Transpiration is the evaporation of water from the leaves of plants. It helps cool the leaf tissues through evaporation and helps with the uptake of nutrients from the soil.

7. What is capillary action and why is it important in plants?
   - Capillary action is tendency of water to rise within a thin, narrow tube and is the result of the hydrogen bonding of water molecules. It is important to plants because it is involved in the movement of water from the roots to the leaves.

8. How are adhesion and cohesion different?
   - Adhesion is the hydrogen bonding of water molecules to other substances while cohesion is the hydrogen bonding of water molecules to water molecules.

9. Which type of plant used in Part III had the highest rate of transpiration? Support your answer with data from the lab.
   - Dicot plants have a higher transpiration rate. The dicot transpiration rate in this lab was .046 mL/g/hr while the monocot rate was .005 mL/g/hr.

10. Based on the data you collected in Part I and Part III of this activity, what would happen to the rate of transpiration if the underside of the leaf had been covered with a thin coat of Vaseline? Explain your answer.
    - The plant's transpiration rate would be greatly reduced or stopped completely.

11. In the space below, describe an experiment that could test the following hypothesis:

    Hypothesis: If a dicot plant is placed in an environment with high humidity, then its transpiration rate will be lowered.

Procedures to be followed: *(sample)*

1. Fill a 10 mL syringe with water and insert the plant. Using a disposable pipet, raise or lower the water level until it rests at the 10 mL graduation mark.

2. Place a thin layer of mineral oil on top of the water to prevent evaporation.

3. Place a plastic bag over the top of the plant.

4. Spray a fine mist of water into the bag and seal the bag around the stem of the plant using a twist tie.

5. After a two minute equilibration period, record the level of the water in the graduated cylinder.

6. Allow the plant to transpire for 24 hours.

7. At the end of 24 hours, remove the plant from the syringe. Determine the mass of the leaves after removing the stems from the specimen. Record the mass of the leaves on the student answer page.

8. Determine the amount of water consumed during 24 hours by subtracting the initial reading from the final reading.

   How and when data will be collected: The water level will be read and recorded on the first day and then again 24 hours later.

   Expected results: There should be no change or very little change in the water level at the end of 24 hours.

Transpiration
Investigating Water Movement and Evaporation in Monocot and Dicot Plants

Transpiration is a necessary plant process in which water evaporates from the leaves of plants. The process of transpiration uses approximately 90% of the water that enters a plant's roots. During transpiration, water moves from the tissues inside the leaf to the external environment by passing through the stoma. As water evaporates from the leaves of a plant, replacement water is drawn up by osmosis and capillary action from the tissues below. *Capillary action* is the tendency of water to rise within a thin, narrow tube and is the result of the hydrogen bonding of water molecules. The hydrogen atoms of a water molecule are slightly positive while the oxygen atom is slightly negative. In the property of cohesion, water molecules cling to one another as the positive hydrogen of one water molecule forms a hydrogen bond with the negatively charged oxygen of a second water molecule. When enclosed in a narrow tube, such as the transport vessels, or xylem vessels, of a plant, water molecules will adhere to the walls of the tube. This property of water is called adhesion. Collectively, hydrogen bonding, adhesion, and cohesion produce the capillary action of water that allows it to move up the narrow xylem cells to replace the water evaporated at the surface of the leaf.

Transpiration plays important roles in plant processes. One role transpiration serves in the plant is to cool the leaf tissues through the process of evaporation. This evaporative cooling can reduce heat damage to leaf tissues. A second role of transpiration is to aid in the uptake of nutrients from the soil. Transpiration of water at the leaves helps establish a concentration gradient that drives the movement of water from the soil into the roots. As the water moves into the roots, some nutrients will be carried into the roots. From the roots, water will continue in an upward movement through the xylem tissues of the stem eventually reaching the leaf tissues.

Transpiration rates vary from plant species to plant species. Broad leaf, tropical plants tend to have higher rates of transpiration than narrow leaf plants that survive well in dry environments. Additionally, the rate of transpiration will vary depending upon environmental factors such as temperature, humidity and air movement. Since water vapor moves from areas of high concentration to areas of lower concentration, transpiration rates tend to be higher in hot, dry environments. Many plants have adaptations that allow them to conserve water through lower rates of transpiration. Thin, narrow leaves, recessed stoma, and reduced stoma numbers are adaptations that reduce the rate of transpiration.

PURPOSE

In this set of activities you will explore the process of transpiration by observing the movement of water through xylem tissues, comparing the presence of water vapor on plant surfaces, and measuring the rate of transpiration.

MATERIALS

- 1 stalk of celery
- 200 mL beaker
- 10 drops red food coloring
- metric ruler
- mineral oil
- monocot or dicot specimen
- 4 cobalt chloride test strips
- balance
- scalpel or razor blade
- 10 mL graduated cylinder
- disposable dropper pipet
- 4 paper clips

Safety Alert

1. Handle scalpel and razors carefully, taking care to avoid contact with the sharp edges. Cut away from yourself.
2. Food colorings can stain clothes. Wear an apron during this activity.

PROCEDURE

PART I: THE ROLE OF XYLEM IN TRANSPIRATION

1. Place 100 mL of distilled water in a 200 mL beaker or similar container. Add 10 drops of red food coloring and stir with stirring rod.

2. Obtain a leafy stalk of celery.

3. Use a scalpel to cut off the bottom 2 cm of the celery stalk.

4. Observe the cut end of the stalk, noting its color. Write your observations in Data Table I.

5. Allow the celery to remain in the dye for 20 minutes. During this 20 minute time period, proceed to Part II.

6. At the end of 20 minutes remove the celery from the beaker of food coloring. Rinse and dry the bottom end of the stalk. Measure the length of your celery stalk. Record its length in Data Table 1.

7. Observe the end of the stalk and note the coloration of the xylem tissue. Record your observations in Data Table 1.

8. During the 20 minute wait time, the red colored water will have begun to travel up the stem of the celery through the xylem tissue. In order to determine how far the colored water has moved, begin cutting away 1cm sections from the bottom of the stalk. After each cut, check the color of the xylem tissue in the stalk, if the tissue is still colored, remove another 1cm section. Repeat until you reach the uncolored portion of the stalk.

9. Determine the length of the remaining celery stalk. Record this final length in Data Table 1.

10. Determine the rate of movement of the colored water through the xylem tissue by subtracting the final length from the initial length of the celery stalk and then dividing by 20 minutes. Record the rate of water movement per minute in Data Table 1.

PART II: DETERMINING AREAS OF PLANT WITH HIGHEST TRANSPIRATION LEVELS

1. Anhydrous cobalt chloride paper is an indicator of the presence of water vapor. When dry, this humidity indicator paper is blue. As the paper becomes damp from water vapor it will turn pink. Which part of a plant, the stem, upper surface of a plant's leaf, or underside of a plant leaf would release the most water vapor through transpiration during a 15 minute time interval? Formulate a testable hypothesis for this problem. Record your hypothesis in the space provided on the student answer page.

2. Design and conduct a simple experiment to test your hypothesis. Be sure to include a control in your design. Record your hypothesis, the steps of your procedure, and the data you collect in the space provided on the student answer page.

3. Once you have your experiment set up, you should set up Part III. When the 15 minute wait time has passed, record your final observations in Data Table 2.

4. In Data Table 2, rank the areas of the plant tested based on the amount of water vapor produced.

PART III: COMPARING TRANSPIRATION RATES IN MONOCOT AND DICOT LEAVES

1. Remove the plunger from a disposable 10 mL syringe and place the plastic protective tip securely on the bottom of the syringe barrel.

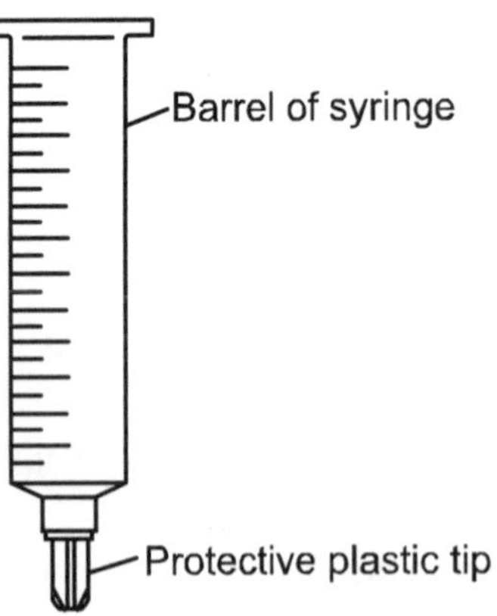

2. Fill the barrel of the syringe with water up to the 8 mL graduation mark.

3. You will be assigned a monocot or dicot specimen to test. Locate the plant specimen your teacher has assigned to your group. Record which type of plant you have been assigned in Data Table 3a on the student answer page.

4. If using a small plant, cut the stem near the soil line. If the plant specimen is to be used by several lab groups, your teacher will assist you as you remove an appropriately sized section of the plant.

5. Insert the stem of the plant into the water filled barrel of the syringe. Using a disposable pipet raise or lower the water level until it rests at the 10 mL graduation mark.

6. Place a thin layer of mineral oil on top of the water to prevent evaporation. Once you have applied the mineral oil you should not remove and reinsert the stem.

7. After a two minute equilibration period, record the level of the water in the syringe barrel. Record your reading in Data Table 3a.

8. Allow the plant to transpire for 24 hours. Once you have set up Part III, it should be time to take readings in Parts I and II.

9. Day 2: Read the water level in the syringe barrel and record the reading in Data Table 3a.

10. Remove the plant from the syringe. Determine the mass of the leaves after removing the stems from the specimen. Record the mass of the leaves in Data Table 3a.

11. Determine the amount of water consumed during 24 hours by subtracting the initial reading from the final reading.

12. Calculate the rate of transpiration per gram of leaf tissue using the following formula:

    Rate in mL/g/hour = mL water consumed/mass of leaves/24 hours

13. Share your data with the class as instructed by your teacher to complete Data Table 3b.

Name ______________________________

Period ______________________________

Transpiration
Investigating Water Movement and Evaporation in Monocot and Dicot Plants

DATA AND OBSERVATIONS

PART I: THE ROLE OF XYLEM IN TRANSPIRATION

Data Table 1	
Initial Observations of cut end of celery	
Final Observations of cut end of celery	
Length before cutting sections	
Length after cutting sections	
Rate of water movement (cm/min)	

PART II: EXPERIMENTAL DESIGN:

Hypothesis:

Materials:

Procedure:

Data Table 2: Cobalt Chloride Test				
	Control	Upper Leaf Surface	Lower Leaf Surface	Stem
Beginning test strip color				
Description at minute 1				
Description at minute 5				
Description at minute 10				
Description at minute 15				
Ranking in order of water vapor released				

PART III: COMPARING TRANSPIRATION RATES IN MONOCOT AND DICOT LEAVES

Data Table 3a: Transpiration	
Type of plant	
Initial water level	
Final water level	
mL of water consumed	
Mass of leaves without stems	
Transpiration mL/g/hr	

Data Table 3b: Class Data Monocot & Dicot Transpiration Rates (mL/g/hr)								
	Group 1	Group 2	Group 3	Group 4	Group 5	Group 6	Group 7	Average
Monocot								
Dicot								

CONCLUSION QUESTIONS

1. Explain why water moved up the celery stalk. What forces were involved in the movement of the colored water?

2. How would the rate of water movement have changed if the leaves had been removed from the stalk of celery prior to placing it in the colored water?

3. If you had left the celery in the colored water for another 15 minutes how far would it have traveled?

4. Calculate how long would it take for the colored water to reach the top of the stalk of celery? Show your work in the space below.

5. Which part of the plant you tested in Part II had the highest rate of transpiration? Which part had the lowest rate of transpiration?

6. What is transpiration and why is it important in plants?

7. What is capillary action and why is it important in plants?

8. How are adhesion and cohesion different?

9. Which type of plant used in Part III had the highest rate of transpiration? Support your answer with data from the lab.

10. Based on the data you collected in Part I and Part III of this activity, what would happen to the rate of transpiration if the underside of the leaf had been covered with a thin coat of Vaseline? Explain your answer.

11. In the space below, describe an experiment that could test the following hypothesis:

    Hypothesis: If a dicot plant is placed in an environment with high humidity, then its transpiration rate will be lowered.

    Procedures to be followed:

    How and when data will be collected:

    Expected results:

Those "Foolish" Plant Hormones
Investigating the Effects of Gibberellin and Auxin

OBJECTIVE
Students will investigate how plant hormones affect plant growth and development.

LEVEL
Biology I

NATIONAL STANDARDS
UCP.1, UCP.2, UCP.3, UCP.5, A.1, A.2, C.6, G.1, G.2

TEKS
2 (B) (C) (D), 13 (A)

CONNECTIONS TO AP
AP Biology:

II. Organisms and Populations B. Structure and Function of Plants and Animals 2. Structural, physiological, and behavioral adaptations

TIME FRAME
30 minutes day 1
10 minutes for an additional 4 days

MATERIALS

Part I

28 Petri dishes
modeling clay
non-absorbent cotton
14 scalpels
250 corn seeds that have been soaked in water for at least 8 hours
transparent tape
paper towels
14 scissors

Part I

28 Erlenmeyer flasks 250 mL
28 bean plants
water
2.5 L gibberellic acid solution
cotton
14 metric rulers

TEACHER NOTES
This investigation can supplement a unit on plant physiology and specifically plant hormones.

Bean plants need to be planted 10-14 days before the investigation begins. The beans, potting soil, and pots can be purchased from a local garden center. Any type of bean (kidney, pinto, or green) with the exception of lima bean can be used. The lab is done over a five-day period. It is best if this lab is started on a Monday.

Crystalline gibberellic acid may be purchased from a scientific supply company.

The gibberellic acid solution can be made by combining 0.1 g of gibberellic acid in 1 L of water.

POSSIBLE ANSWERS TO THE CONCLUSION QUESTIONS AND SAMPLE DATA

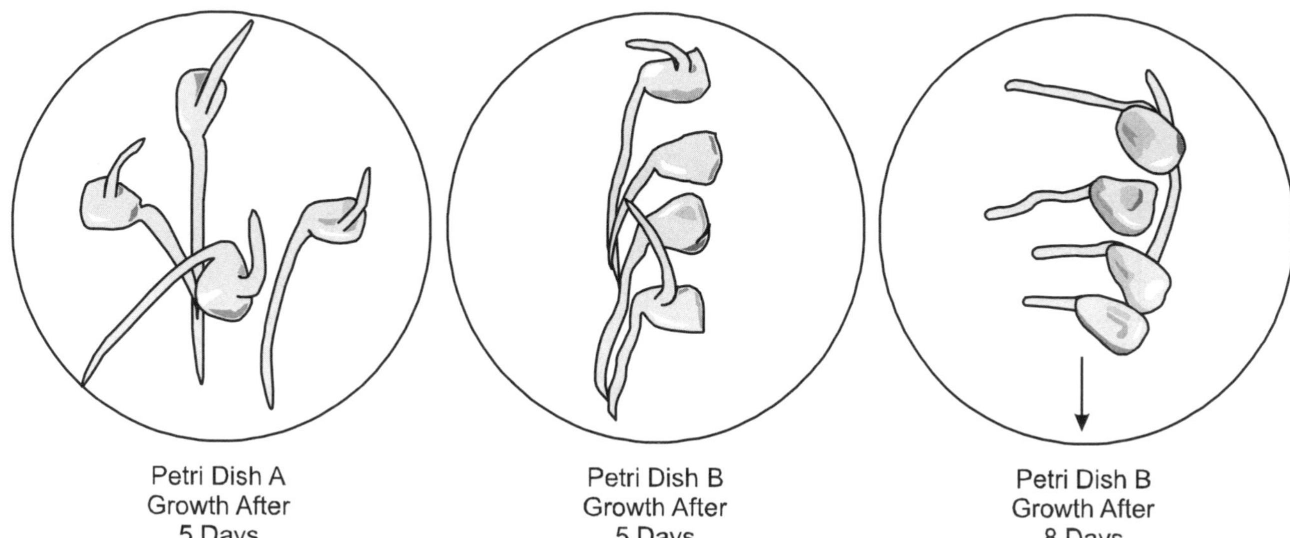

Petri Dish A Growth After 5 Days

Petri Dish B Growth After 5 Days

Petri Dish B Growth After 8 Days

Control Plant - No Treatment			
Day	**Distance from cotyledons to first true leaves (cm)**	**Distance from first leaves to tip (cm)**	**Distance from cotyledons to tip (cm)**
1	9	2	7
2	9	2	7
3	9.5	2.5	7
4	9.75	2.75	7
5	10	3	7

Experimental Plant - Gibberellic Acid			
Day	**Distance from cotyledons to first true leaves (cm)**	**Distance from first leaves to tip (cm)**	**Distance from cotyledons to tip (cm)**
1	8	2	6
2	9.5	3	6.5
3	12.5	6	6.5
4	13.5	7	6.5
5	14.5	8	6.5

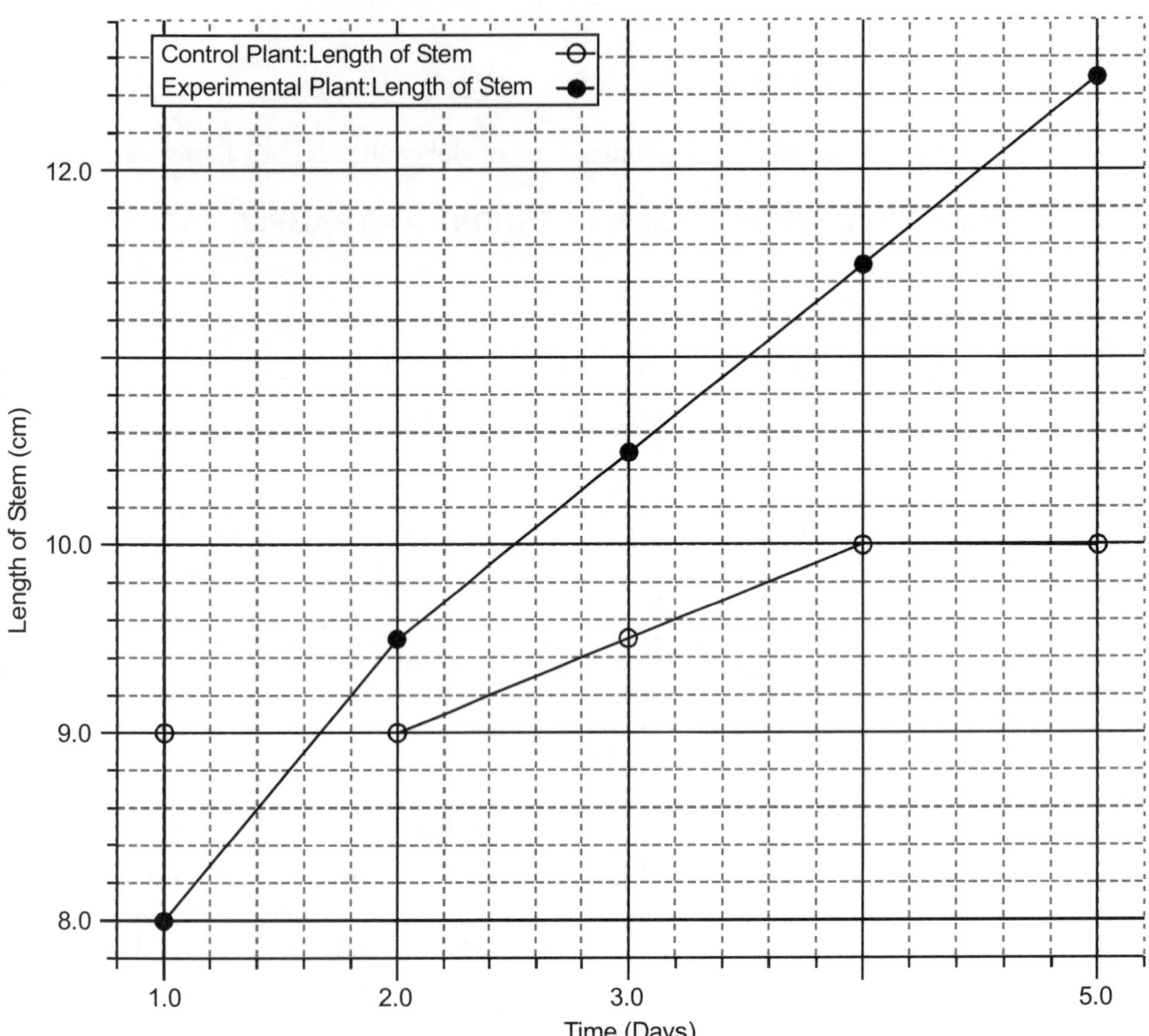
Effects of Gibberellic Acid on Plant Growth
Control Plant:Length of Stem
Experimental Plant:Length of Stem
Length of Stem (cm)
12.0
10.0
9.0
8.0
1.0
2.0
3.0
5.0
Time (Days)

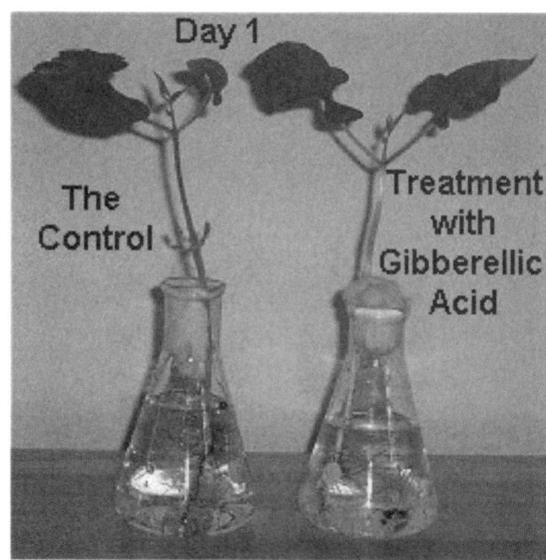

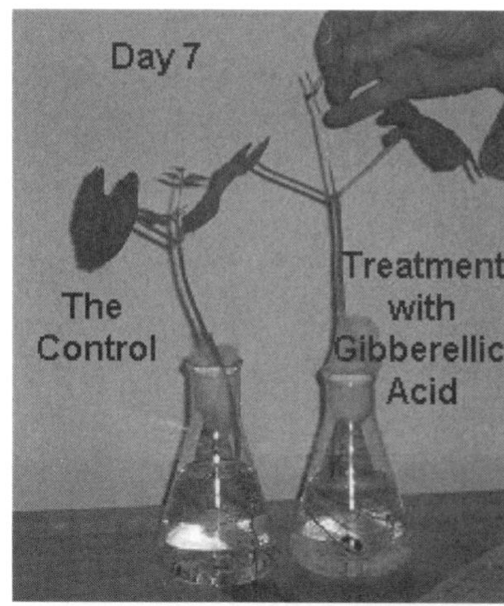

PART I

1. Which direction did the root grow in dish A? Which direction did the shoot grow in dish A? Propose an explanation for the observed response to gravity that the roots and shoots exhibited.
   - The roots grew toward the gravitational pull and the shoots grew away from the gravitational pull. This is because the tissues in these two parts of the plant have different tolerances for auxin concentration. In the root, the auxin inhibits cell elongation on the lower part of the root. This allows the cells on the upper part of the root to elongate and thus the root grows toward the gravitational pull. The shoot accumulates auxin in the lower part of the stem but this level of hormone causes the cells on the lower part of the stem to elongate. This causes the stem to grow away from the gravitational pull.

2. How could you alter this experiment to ensure that the presence of light is not responsible for the shoot growth in this investigation?
   - To ensure that light is not a factor, one could cover the dishes with aluminum foil or put the dishes in an area that does not receive light.

3. Classify the root and the shoot as positively or negatively geotropic.
   - The roots are positively geotropic and the shoots are negatively geotropic.

4. What can you conclude about the location of the auxin in the corn from Petri dish B?
   - It seems that the location of the auxin must be found in the tips of the root because when the tips were removed, the root continued to grow straight instead of downward.

PART II

1. What is the purpose of the bean plant in plain water?
   - The bean plant in plain water is the control.

2. Examine the three different measurements recorded in your data table. What section of the stem is most responsible for increasing the length of the plant?
   - The section of stem between the first true leaves and the top of the plant showed the most elongation. The stem did not elongate from the cotyledon scar to the first true leaves.

3. Propose an explanation for the mechanism by which gibberellic acid increases plant growth. Does it seem that the hormone works by elongating cells or by increasing cell reproduction? Use the data from the lab to support your explanation.
   - It appears that this hormone promotes cell reproduction to increase stem length rather than cell elongation because only the top part of the plant increased in length and not the bottom half.

4. Design an experiment that would investigate the effect of various concentrations of gibberellic acid solutions on plant growth.
   - A similar lab protocol could be used but instead of using 2 plants, there could be 5 plants.. The first plant should be in a flask of 100% of the gibberellic acid solution. This is made as prescribed in the laboratory protocol. The second, third, and four bean plant will be in a gibberellic acid solution that is diluted to 75%, 50%, and 25% respectively. The fifth bean plant is the control and is placed only in water.

REFERENCE

Hummer, Paul I., Albert Kaskel, James Kennedy, Raymond Oram. *Probing Level of Life*. Columbus: Charles E. Merrill Publishing Co., 1976. pp. 165-167

Those "Foolish" Plant Hormones
Investigating the Effects of Gibberellin and Auxin

Plants produce a number of hormones that affect their growth. Some hormones promote plant growth and some hormones inhibit plant growth. They may also affect other attributes of plant life such as the abscission of various plant parts or an increase in fruit ripening.

Gibberellins are a group of organic compounds that promote shoot growth by encouraging both cell reproduction and cell elongation. Gibberellic acid has been isolated from plants and can be used in experiments with dramatic results. Dwarf plants, such as cabbage, will bolt to a height of over 10 feet when treated with gibberellic acid.

Another class of plant hormones, auxins, are like gibberellins in that they cause stems to elongate. Auxins are curious plant hormones because they move toward gravity in a plant, and lack horizontal component of movement. In the stem tissues, auxins promote plant growth, and in the root tissues, auxins inhibit plant growth. Auxins are interesting in that they seem to be the cause of many of the tropisms that plants exhibit which is a plant's response to an environmental factor or stimulus. Tropisms can be positive or negative. If a plant grows toward the stimulus then that tropism it is said to be positive, but if growth is away from the environmental factor, the tropism is said to be negative. The effect of light on plant growth is called phototropism, and the effect of gravity on plant growth is called geotropism. Both of these tropic responses are caused by auxins. For example, roots grow toward gravity and shoots grow away from gravity. Plants exhibit positive geotropism in their roots and negative geotropism in their shoots. When a plant is laid on its side, auxins accumulate in the cells on the lower side of the plant causing them to elongate. This elongation of the bottom edge of cells causes the shoot to turn upward away from gravity. In the roots, the effect is just the opposite of that of the stems. The cells on the lower side accumulate auxin. This tissue is more sensitive to higher auxin concentrations. Therefore, the cells on the lower side are actually inhibited from elongating. The cells on the upper side of the root have a decrease in auxin concentration; this will cause those cells to elongate. This elongation causes the roots to turn toward gravity.

In the following investigation, you will observe the response of plants to gibberillins and auxins and explore how these hormones affect plant growth and development. After reading the introduction and observing the responses, you are to propose possible explanations for the observed responses.

PURPOSE
The purpose of this laboratory investigation is to examine geotropism which are caused by auxins. Part II of this lab is to examine the effect of gibberellic acid on plant growth.

MATERIALS

Part I

2 Petri dishes
modeling clay
scalpel for cutting roots
non-absorbent cotton
8 corn seeds that have been soaked in water for at least 8 hours
transparent tape
scissors
paper towels

Part II

2 Erlenmeyer flasks 250 mL
2 bean plants
water
gibberellic acid solution
cotton
metric ruler

> **Safety Alert**
> 1. Take care when cutting the roots of the corn plant, scalpel blades are sharp.

PROCEDURE

PART I

1. In the space marked HYPOTHESIS on your student answer page, propose a hypothesis examining the effects of gravity and auxins on corn seeds.

2. Mark two Petri dishes A and B. Arrange the corn seeds as shown in Figures 1 and 2. Make sure that the corn seeds are embryo side down on the bottom of the Petri dish. The embryo side is the side with the white inset.

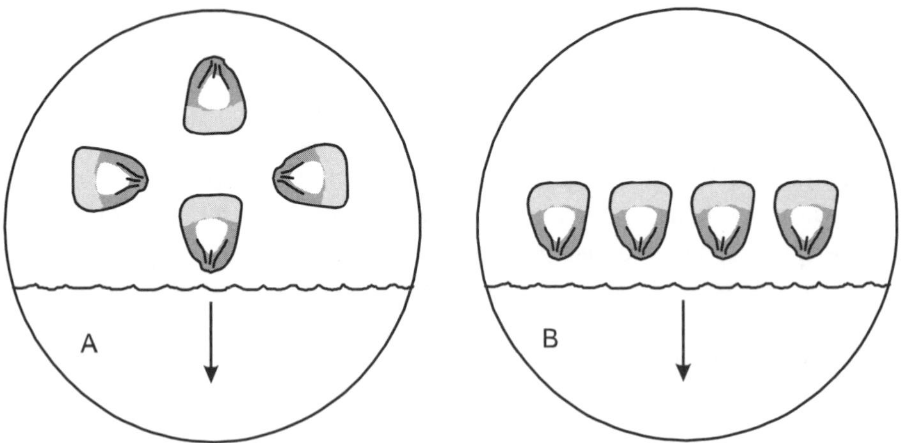

3. Cut pieces of paper towel into circles the size of the Petri dish. The paper towels should fits tightly into the Petri dish.

4. Cover the corn seeds with several layers of paper towel and saturate the towel with water.

5. Pack nonabsorbent cotton on top of the paper towel, so that when the lid of the Petri dish is put on, the corn seeds will not move.

6. Seal the Petri dishes with transparent tape. Use modeling clay to make a base for the dishes that will allow them to stand upright on their edge.

7. With the Petri dishes on their edge, mark both Petri dishes with an arrow to indicate the direction of the gravitational pull.

8. Observe the seeds in Petri dish A daily for five days. Watch the direction of both the root and shoot growth. Make diagrams of the growth in the space provided on your student answer page.

9. Observe the seeds in Petri dish B daily for five days and allow roots to grow until they are approximately 8 mm long. When the roots are 8 mm long, cut a 2.5 mm piece of root from each root tip.

10. After cutting, replace seeds in their original position in the Petri dish and re-seal the dish.

11. Rotate the dish and stand the dish on edge so that the arrow now points perpendicular to the gravitational pull. See figure 3. Observe the roots daily for the next two or three days.

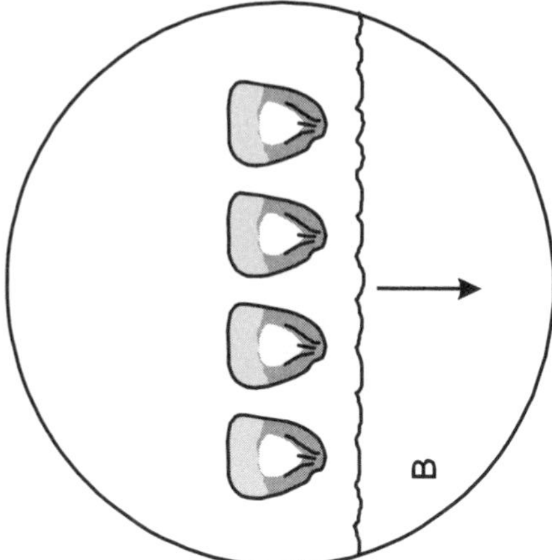

PART II

1. In the space marked HYPOTHESIS on the student answer page, propose a hypothesis examining the effects of giberrillins on corn seeds.

2. Very carefully remove two bean plants from their pots so as not to rip or tear the roots. Rinse off the surrounding soil.

3. Obtain two 250 mL Erlenmeyer flasks. Fill one flask with 150 mL distilled water and fill the other with 150 mL of gibberellic acid solution.

4. Remove the cotyledons from the bean plants.

5. Place one bean plant in the flask with the water, and the other plant in the flask with gibberellic acid solution.

6. Keep the plants in place by putting cotton in the neck of the flask.

7. Measure and record three measurements: the distance from the cotyledons scar to the top of the plant, the distance from the where the cotyledons were to the first true leaves, the distance from the first true leaves to the top of the plant. Record these measurements in your data table on your student answer page.

8. Store the plants in a place where they will receive plenty of light.

9. Take measurements for five consecutive days. If needed, replace any water or gibberellic acid solution that evaporates. Every day measure and record these three measurements:
   - the distance from the where the cotyledons were to the top of the plant
   - the distance from the where the cotyledons were to the first true leaves
   - the distance from the first true leaves to the top of the plant.

10. At the end of 5 days make a graph of the change in height for both plants verses time. Decide which of the three measurements would be most appropriate to graph. It is acceptable to graph more than one measurement

Name ______________________________

Period ______________________________

Those "Foolish" Plant Hormones
Investigating the Effects of Gibberellin and Auxin

HYPOTHESIS

DATA AND OBSERVATIONS

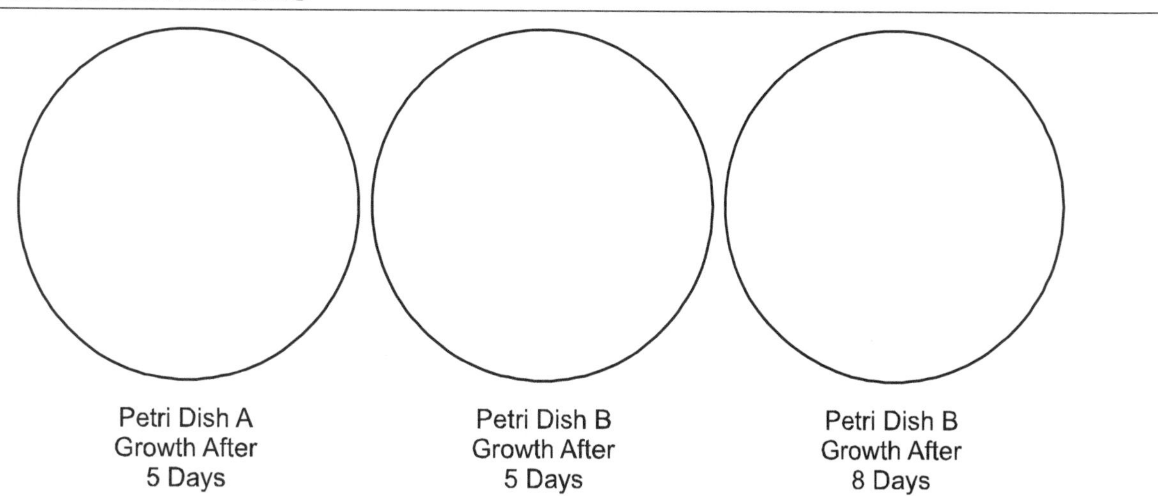

Petri Dish A Growth After 5 Days

Petri Dish B Growth After 5 Days

Petri Dish B Growth After 8 Days

Control Plant - No Treatment			
Day	**Distance from cotyledons to first true leaves (cm)**	**Distance from first leaves to tip (cm)**	**Distance from cotyledons to tip (cm)**
1			
2			
3			
4			
5			

Control Plant - Gibberellic Acid			
Day	**Distance from cotyledons to first true leaves (cm)**	**Distance from first leaves to tip (cm)**	**Distance from cotyledons to tip (cm)**
1			
2			
3			
4			
5			

CONCLUSION QUESTIONS

PART I

1. Which direction did the root grow in dish A? Which direction did the shoot grow in dish A? Propose an explanation for the observed response to gravity that the roots and shoots exhibited.

2. How could you alter this experiment to ensure that the presence of light is not responsible for the shoot growth in this investigation?

3. Classify the root and the shoot as positively or negatively geotropic.

4. What can you conclude about the location of the auxin in the corn from Petri dish B?

PART II

1. What is the purpose of the bean plant in plain water?

2. Examine the three different measurements recorded in your data table. What section of the stem is most responsible for increasing the length of the plant?

3. Propose an explanation for the mechanism by which gibberellic acid increases plant growth. Does it seem that the hormone works by elongating cells or by increasing cell reproduction? Use the data from the lab to support your explanation.

4. Design an experiment that would investigate the effect of various concentrations of gibberellic acid solutions on plant growth.

Plant Wars
Investigating Allelopathic Interactions

OBJECTIVE
Students will investigate the allelopathic interactions between various plant species. They will determine the percent of germination and the average root and shoot lengths of seed samples exposed to a known allelopathic agent and compare the results to a control sample.

LEVEL
Biology

NATIONAL STANDARDS
UCP.2, UCP.3, B.3, C.4, C.6, F.3, G.1, G.2, G.3

TEKS
2 (B) (C) (D), 7(B), 11 (B), 13 (A)

CONNECTIONS TO AP
AP Biology:

III. Organisms and Populations B. Structure and Function of Plants 2. Physiological and behavioral adaptations of plants 3. Response to the environment

TIME FRAME
90 minutes on Day 1; 15 minutes on subsequent days

MATERIALS
(For a class of 28 working in pairs)

28 metric rulers
56 Petri dishes with lids, 4 per group
56 filter paper disks that fit the bottom of the Petri dishes
14 gloves, one per group
28 thin stem plastic Beral pipets, 2 per group
masking tape or 56 zipper sandwich bags
plant extract, about 25 - 50 mL
280 seeds of one type
280 seeds of additional types of seeds
14 permanent markers or grease pencils

TEACHER NOTES

This activity can be done during a unit on plants, evolution or ecology. This activity centers on the biochemical competition between plant species and requires an allelopathic plant extract. The choice of the allelopathic plant for this activity is usually dictated by the climate in which you live. If you survey your surroundings and see shrubs and trees that have virtually nothing growing in their root zone it is likely that they are allelopathic and you can easily make extracts from their leaves, roots, bark, fruit or nut hulls. Also look for plants that are very evenly spaced in the wild. Not all parts of the plant contain the same concentration of the allelopathic agent, so using extracts from various parts of a native plant can introduce an additional variable for this experiment. Some classic examples of allelopathic plants include black walnut, Tree-of-Heaven, chickpea, sagebrush and other shrubs in the genus *Artemisia*, as well as plants from the genera, *Salvia, Eucalyptus*, and *Helianthus*. Your local nursery or landscaping company personnel may also serve as a resource for allelopathic plants.

The extract used in the sample data that follows was purchased in the form of an herbal dietary supplement made from the hulls and leaves of the black walnut tree. It is readily available at Viable Herbal Solutions, 800-505-9475 or www.viable-herbal.com for $8 at the time of this printing. Black walnut extract is also available at GNC and other health & vitamin stores. Dissolve the contents of one capsule in 20 mL of distilled water.

PREPARING YOUR OWN EXTRACT

Since allelopathic plants may produce dermatitis in a few sensitive individuals, wear latex gloves when handling the plant material. Weigh out about 25 g of leaves or roots or other plant parts. Cut them into small pieces and put the pieces into a blender. Add 100 mL of distilled water, and blend until a fairly uniform homogenate is obtained. Filter the homogenate through a few layers of cheesecloth, and collect the extract in an Erlenmeyer flask. Rinse the blender thoroughly when you are done.

CHOOSING SEEDS

It is important to choose seeds that are appropriate for the allelopathic extract that you have chosen. If you selected a native plant based on the observation that it inhibits the growth of native grasses, then use native grass seed. Since these seeds are so small, you may have students use more than 10 seeds per dish. If you select black walnut, some intolerant seeds include: tomato, peppers, eggplant, asparagus, blackberry, honeysuckle, and apple. You can experiment with others, but seeds such as beets, carrot, cabbage, corn, cherry, squash, cucumber or black raspberry are known to be tolerant to black walnut and would be unsuitable since there will be no difference between the experimental and control groups. You may have the entire class use the same two types of seeds or you may provide a variety of seeds for student use.

The seeds used to generate the sample data were Burpee Super Beefsteak tomato and California Wonder pepper. Both were purchased in bulk (about 1,000 seeds) for about $5 each at the time of this printing. Seeds were purchased from Seeds of the South at www.vegetableseedwarehouse.com or FAX 803-232-1119.

POSSIBLE ANSWERS TO THE CONCLUSION QUESTIONS AND SAMPLE DATA

Type of Allelopathic Extract Used: black walnut from Viable Herbal Solutions (1 capsule dissolved in 20 mL of distilled water)

*Note sample data was taken for 8 consecutive days — your students will skip data collection over the weekend.

Data Table

Seed type: Tomato

Control Seed Number										
Day	1	2	3	4	5	6	7	8	9	10
2										
3	*		*	*	*	*			*	*
4	2/1		1/2	2/3	2/1	3/2			2/3	3/2
5	3/2		3/3	5/4	3/2	3/2	3/2	*	3/3	3/2
6	5/3		5/4	6/4	5/3	4/3	4/3	2/2	5/4	5/3
7	7/4		6/4	7/5	7/4	6/4	5/3	3/3	6/5	5/4
8	7/4		7/5	9/6	7/4	6/4	7/4	4/4	8/5	6/4

Extract Seed Number										
Day	1	2	3	4	5	6	7	8	9	10
2										
3							*			
4		*					1/1			*
5		1/1					2/2	*		2/2
6	*	2/1	*				3/2	2/1		3/2
7	2/2	3/2	1/1		*		3/3	2/2		4/3
8	3/2	4/3	2/2		2/3		4/3	3/2	*	5/3

Seed type: Pepper

Control Seed Number										
Day	1	2	3	4	5	6	7	8	9	10
2	*									
3	3/2	*		*			*		*	
4	7/5	3/2		3/2	*	*	3/2		3/2	*
5	10/7	7/4		6/4	2/3	2/4	5/4	*	6/4	2/3
6	16/10	12/7	*	11/6	4/5	5/6	8/5	2/2	8/7	4/5
7	20/12	16/9	3/3	15/8	7/9	7/10	11/7	5/6	11/9	6/7
8	22/14	20/11	5/5	18/9	9/12	12/14	14/9	9/8	14/10	8/9

Extract Seed Number										
Day	1	2	3	4	5	6	7	8	9	10
2										
3										
4										
5										
6	*	*				*			*	
7	2/2	1/2		*		2/2	*		2/2	
8	4/3	3/2		2/2		3/2	2/1		3/2	

Complete the following table after analyzing your data at the conclusion of the experiment:

Rate is always equal to the change in some measurable quantity divided by time. Simply divide each average length by the number of days that data was collected.

Analysis of Data				
	Seed Type: Tomato		Seed Type: Pepper	
	Control	**Extract**	**Control**	**Extract**
Average first day of germination	3	5	3	6
Average final root length (mm)	6.8	3.3	13.1	2.8
Average final shoot length (mm)	4.4	2.6	10.1	2.0
Overall average rate of root growth (mm/day)	.9 mm/day	.4 mm/day	1.6 mm/day	.4 mm/day
Overall average rate of shoot growth (mm/day)	.6 mm/day	.3 mm/day	1.3 mm/day	.3 mm/day

Use your data and outside resources such as your text or the library or the Internet to answer the following questions.

1. Explain one way that animals use chemical signals to communicate and give a specific example.
   - sex attractant—pheromones are especially important in the insect world, the first was discovered in female silkworm moths
   - trail markers—fire ants are famous for this, they employ between 10 and 20 different chemical signals to mark trails and other roles vital to establishing their insect society; mammals often use urine to mark their territory
   - alarm calls—skunks certainly notify us of their alarming presence
   - many other answers are possible

2. Explain one way that plants use chemical signals to communicate and give a specific example.
   - sex attractant—flowering plants use scent to attract insects for pollination
   - alarm calls—plants give off aromas to discourage other organisms; corn and tobacco plants under attack from worms give off a chemical signal that attracts a small black wasp that feeds on the attacking worms
   - defense against bacteria—plants can distinguish between harmful and beneficial bacteria and mimic the bacteria's signals. Bacteria send out chemical signals and do not launch an attack until they have achieved sufficient numbers to have a chance at success. Plants can trick a small group of their enemy into thinking they have the numbers, so they strike prematurely.
   - many other answers are possible

3. Describe a negative consequence of allelopathy.
   - a hearty and prolific allelopathic plant can devastate native vegetation and upset the ecosystem and perhaps even lead to the extinction of the native plants.

4. Describe a positive consequence of allelopathy?
   - if an allelopathic agent can be isolated, it can provide a safer alternative to chemical herbicides.

5. Explain the evolutionary advantage a plant exhibiting allelopathy has over one that does not.
   - An allelopathic plant limits the competition for available resources between itself and other plants (often of its own species—an established plant can inhibit the germination of fellow competitors).
   - An allelopathic plant controls its competitors ensuring that more natural resources are available for its continued survival.

6. List the controlled variables in this experiment and explain why each was necessary.
   - the amount of moisture (drops of liquid) in each dish—seeds need a moist environment in order to germinate. If a seed sample was too dry it would lower the germination percentage and could then have been misinterpreted as an allelopathic event.
   - the number of seeds for each Petri dish—not only did using 10 seeds make figuring the percentage easy, it kept the moisture per seed ratio controlled.
   - temperature—fluctuations in temperature affects germination percentage and growth rate
   - amount of light—fluctuations in the amount of light will affect shoot growth
   - amount of allelotoxin—seeds are exposed to an even distribution or concentration of the chemical toxin per seed.

Plant Wars
Investigating Allelopathic Interactions

Chemical signals are very common in many organisms. Both plants and animals use odors and scents as communication mechanisms. For example, in the animal kingdom insects use chemical signals as sex attractants, trail markers, and alarm calls. Among plants, many of the angiosperms (flowering plants) use strong floral scents to attract potential pollinators. And some organisms (both plants and animals) use airborne chemical compounds to discourage the presence of other organisms. Scientists use the term *allelopathy* to refer to biochemical interactions between different plants. The term usually implies that one plant produces one or more chemicals that have an inhibitory effect on nearby plants, but allelopathy may include stimulatory effects as well.

One of the most famous allelopathic plants is the black walnut (Juglans nigra). The chemical responsible for the toxicity in black walnut is juglone and is a respiration inhibitor. Plants, when exposed to the allelotoxin, exhibit symptoms such as wilting, chlorosis (yellowing of the leaves), and eventually death. Other plants may also exhibit varying degrees of susceptibility and still others have no noticeable effects at all. Juglone is present in all parts of the black walnut, but especially concentrated in the buds, nut hulls, and roots. It is not very soluble in water and thus, does not move very rapidly in the soil. Toxicity has been observed in all soil with black walnut roots growing in it (roots can grow 3 times the spread of the canopy), but is especially concentrated closest to the tree, under the drip line. This is believed to be due to greater root density and the accumulation of decaying leaves and hulls in this area.

Not all plants have allelopathic tendencies. Some, though they exhibit these tendencies, may actually be displaying aggressive competition of a non-chemical form. Much of the controversy surrounding allelopathy is in trying to distinguish the type of competition being displayed. In general, if it is of a chemical nature, then the plant is considered allelopathic.

When organisms compete with one another, they create the potential for resource limitations and possible extinctions. Allelopathic plants prevent other plants from using the available resources and thus have an influence on the evolution and distribution of other species. It might even be said that allelopathic plants control the competitive species within their immediate environment.

PURPOSE

In this activity you will investigate the allelopathic interactions between various plant species. You will determine the percent of germination and the average root and shoot lengths of seed samples exposed to a known allelopathic agent and compare the results to a control sample.

MATERIALS

- metric ruler
- 4 Petri dishes with lids
- 4 filter paper disks
- gloves
- 2 thin stem plastic Beral pipets
- masking tape or plastic zipper sandwich bags
- plant extract
- 20 seeds of each of the two types assigned by your teacher (40 total seeds)
- permanent marker or grease pencil

Safety Alert

1. Do not allow the plant extract to come into contact with your skin.

PROCEDURE

1. All labeling should be done with a permanent marker or grease pencil on the *bottom* of the Petri dish. Label the bottom pan of each of the 4 Petri dishes with your group name and period number.

2. Label your Petri dishes with the types of seeds they will contain. There should be two dishes for each type of seed you will study; one will be labeled "control" and the other labeled "extract".

3. Use the metric ruler as a straight edge and use a pencil to draw the following grid on all four of your filter paper disks. Space the squares evenly and number each square on the grid exactly as you see in Figure 1.

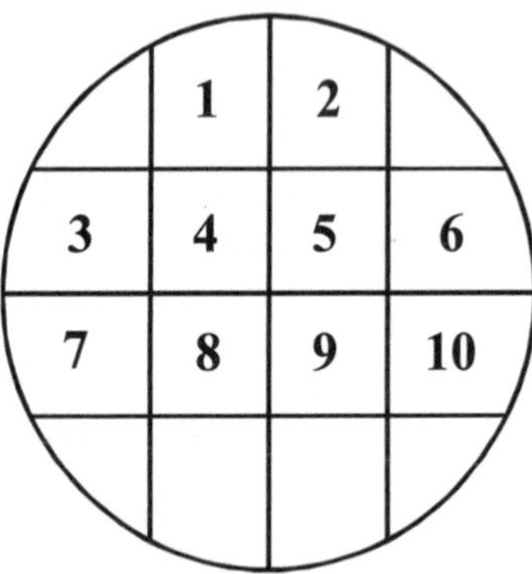

4. Place a filter paper disk grid in the bottom of each of the "control" dishes and use a pipet to place 1 drop of tap water on each number of the grid.

5. Place filter paper disk grids in the bottom of each of the "extract" dishes and use the other pipet to place 1 drop of allelopathic extract on each number of the grid. Discard this pipet, so it does not get confused with the water pipet. It is important that only the water pipet be used from this point forward so as to not contaminate the control dishes during step 6.

6. It is critical that each dish receive exactly the same amount of moisture. Each dish needs to have its filter paper disk grid saturated but not puddled with water. There should be no standing water in the dish. Choose one of your control dishes and using the water pipet, count the number of drops required to saturate the filter paper.

7. Repeat the saturation process for the remaining three dishes using exactly the same number of drops that you used to saturate the control dish. For the "extract" dishes, place the water drops on the areas of the filter paper that do NOT contain the numbers. The water will be absorbed and diffuse throughout the entire disk without washing away the extract.

8. Place a seed of each assigned type on each number of the grid in the properly labeled dish. Place the lid on each dish. Seal and store each dish as instructed by your teacher. Take care not to disturb the seed positions as you store your dishes.

9. Clean your lab station.

10. You will collect data about the seeds for the next 7-10 days. Today is Day Zero. The dishes should be checked at least every two days. Pay careful attention to the following when recording your data in the data table on your student answer page:
    a. All of the root and shoot lengths should be measured to the nearest millimeter. Record the lengths of the roots (usually white) and shoots in the same block for each seed measured on a given day using this format: root/shoot.
    b. The numbered grid will assist you in keeping track of each seed; take care to keep each seed in the same position in each dish throughout the entire experiment.
    c. Make note of the first day of germination for each seed by putting an asterisk (*) in that seed's block on the data table. Germination is evidenced by a splitting of the seed coat or the more obvious emergence of a root or shoot. It is not likely you can measure the shoot or root on the first day of germination.
    d. DO NOT let your filter paper dry out. Use a pipet to re-wet the filter paper, noting the number of drops you added to the dry dish. Add the same number of drops to the other dishes on that same day.

Name ______________________________

Period ______________________________

Plant Wars
Investigating Allelopathic Interactions

DATA AND OBSERVATIONS

Type of Allelopathic Extract Used:______________________________

Data Table

Seed type:											**Seed type:**										
Control Seed Number											**Control Seed Number**										
Day	1	2	3	4	5	6	7	8	9	10	Day	1	2	3	4	5	6	7	8	9	10
Extract Seed Number											**Extract Seed Number**										
Day	1	2	3	4	5	6	7	8	9	10	Day	1	2	3	4	5	6	7	8	9	10

ANALYSIS

Complete the following table after analyzing your data at the conclusion of the experiment:

Analysis of Data				
	Seed Type:		Seed Type:	
	Control	**Extract**	**Control**	**Extract**
Average first day of germination				
Average final root length (mm)				
Average final shoot length (mm)				
Overall average rate of root growth (mm/day)				
Overall average rate of shoot growth (mm/day)				

CONCLUSION QUESTIONS

Use your data and outside resources such as the library or the Internet to answer the following questions.

1. Explain one way that animals use chemical signals to communicate and give a specific example.

2. Explain one way that plants use chemical signals to communicate and give a specific example.

3. Describe a negative consequence of allelopathy.

4. Describe a positive consequence of allelopathy.

5. Explain the evolutionary advantage a plant exhibiting allelopathy has over one that does not.

6. List the controlled variables in this experiment and explain why each was necessary.

Yeast Cells and Digestion of Nutrients
Examining Enzyme Specificity

OBJECTIVE
Students will investigate the nature of enzyme-substrate specificity during the process of carbohydrate digestion in yeast cells.

LEVEL
Biology I

NATIONAL STANDARDS
UCP.1, UCP.2, UCP.3, UCP.5, B.3, C.1, C.5, E.1, E.2, G.1, G.2

TEKS
2(B), 2(C), 2(D)

CONNECTIONS TO AP
AP Biology:

III Organisms and Population B. Structure and Function of Plants and Animals 2. Structural, physiological, and behavioral adaptations

TIME FRAME
30 minutes

MATERIALS
(For a class of 28 working in pairs)

14 TI-83 or TI-83 + graphing calculators (used for graphing calculator protocol)
14 computers (used for computer protocol)
14 10 cc syringes
14 polystyrene cups
14 support stands
28 small cups or 50 mL beakers
yeast solution
sugar solutions (5% lactose, 5% glucose, 5% glucose)

14 Lab Pro's or CBL's (used for graphing calculator protocol)
14 Lab Pro's or Serial Interface Device (used for computer protocol)
14 # 2 one hole stoppers with inserted eye dropper
14 test tube racks
14 Burette clamps
28 test tubes, 35 mL (20 mm x 150)
warm water bath
Lactaid drops
14 linking cords

TEACHER NOTES

This lab is used to supplement the curriculum when studying digestion. Students should have gained knowledge about enzymes and the mechanism by which they work. They should also be familiar with cellular respiration. Discussing the topic of lactose intolerance will help students better understand the lactose/Lactaid portion of this activity.

The yeast and sucrose can be purchased at grocery stores. Other carbohydrates can be purchased from any scientific supply company. Yeast cells can use glucose and sucrose as energy sources but not lactose, as they do not have the enzyme lactase.

The reaction chamber for this experiment is a 35 mL (20mm X 150mm) test tube. The stopper is made using a one-holed, #2 stopper and inserting the glass tubing of an eyedropper through it. Be sure to use glycerin to lubricate the glass and paper towels or other hand protection during the glass insertion. The glass tube should be inserted so that the tapered end points out of the top of the stopper.

The carbohydrates can be purchased from any scientific supply house.

- A 5% solution for each carbohydrate can be made by adding 10 g of the desired carbohydrate to a graduated cylinder or flask and bringing the solution to 200 mL by adding water. For larger quantities, use 50 g in 1000 mL of water.
- A 7% yeast solution must be made fresh prior to every class. This is done by adding 7 g of yeast to 100 mL of water. You may want to keep the cells in a warm water bath of 37o C for better results.
- Lactaid drops can be used as a source of lactase for part II of the experiment. Lactaid drops can be purchased at a grocery or drug store. You may want to add the lactase ahead of time and give the enzyme more time to react.

2. Calculator Information

The lab protocol is based on using a LabPro® or CBL 2 (Calculator-Based Laboratory System). Students will need a TI 83+ or the TI 83, 85, 86, 89 or 92 can be easily used. Be aware that this lab can be adapted for a number of interface systems and calculators. Check with the individual manuals when making adaptations. The standard pressure probe that is needed for this lab comes from Vernier. These probes, calculators and interfaces can also be purchased from Vernier. The address is:

Vernier Software Company
13979 SW Millikan Way
Beaverton, OR 97005-2886
(503)-277-2299
www.vernier.com

3. **Calculator Software Information**
   This activity uses DATAMATE as the data collection program. This program must be installed on the graphing calculators and can be downloaded free from Vernier. A TI-GraphLink cable is necessary for connecting the CBL2 or LabPro to a computer for download or upload processes. It is a good idea to check the Vernier site periodically for updates and update both the DATAMATE program and the operating system of your data collection devices.

4. **Computer Hardware Information**

   Macintosh System Requirements

   Power Macintosh or newer computer
   At least 32 MB of RAM
   System 7.5 or newer

   Windows System Requirements

   Windows 98/NT/ME/2000/XP
   At least 32 MB of RAM
   Pentium processor-base or compatible, PC

5. **Computer Software Information**
   The software that is used in conjunction with the pressure probe is **Logger Pro Software**. It can be purchased for the PC, or Mac.

   One nice feature of Logger Pro Software is that there are templates for the probes already installed. They can be modified to fit your own experiment and then saved under your own title for the students. This lab is based on version 2.1.1. The following directions may have to be modified for other versions of this software. The following steps work nicely for this experiment:

   - It is important that you try this lab and software before working with students so that you can modify the templates or instructions to meet the particular needs of your own experiment.
   - Be sure you have the experimental apparatus set up for this experiment by connecting the interface to the computer through the modem port, the pressure probe is connected to Port 1 or Ch 1 on the interface.
   - Pull down the File menu and click on Open. A menu with Experiments will appear
   - Open the file Probes & Sensors.
   - Open the file Pressure Sensors and select the type of pressure sensor being used, either Bio-gas, Gas Pressure, or Pressure sensor
   - Open the file that indicates units of (mm Hg).
   - A graph will appear. At the bottom of the graph is the pressure as being measured by the pressure sensor.
   - Pull down the Set-up Menu and click on Data Collect, a dialog box should appear. Select Sampling Tab. Now type in the length of time you wish to run the experiment. Usually 10 minutes per run will be sufficient. Select minutes for the unit of time. Type in 10 to run the experiment for 10 minutes for experiment length.

- Now change the sampling speed. It should be set at 10 pts. per minute. Close this window by clicking OK.
- Pull down the Data Menu and open the Column Options, Pressure. Go to Displayed Precision and check the decimal places is check and change the numeric display to 3 decimal places. Press OK.
- At this time your pressure probe should be reading around 760 mm Hg. To be more accurate you could compare it to a barometric reading. The probe should not have to be calibrated. If you feel that this reading is off, you can calibrate the probe by following the directions that accompanying the pressure probe.
- Once the parameters are set, you can name and save this template to your computer be used by your students.

ANSWERS TO PRE-LAB QUESTIONS

1. List four characteristics of enzymes.
   - Enzymes are proteins.
   - Enzymes are biological catalysts.
   - Enzymes can be used over and over again.
   - Enzymes react with specific reactants or substrates.

2. What is cellular respiration?
   - Cellular respiration is the process of cells using nutrients or high energy compounds to make cellular energy or ATP.

3. Explain what must occur in order to use a disaccharide for cell respiration.
   - Cells must digest, or break, disaccharides into monosaccharides.

4. What is the molecular formula for sucrose and lactose?
   - The formula for lactose and sucrose is $C_{12}H_{22}O_{11}$

5. How are sucrose and lactose alike and how are they different?
   - They are both disaccharides and have the same molecular formula, $C_{12}H_{22}O_{11}$. They are isomers of one another and are therefore different because they have different structural formulas.

POSSIBLE ANSWERS TO THE CONCLUSION QUESTION AND SAMPLE DATA

	Experiment	Minimum Pressure, mm Hg	Maximum Pressure, mm Hg	Total Pressure Change, mm Hg	Type of Saccharide
Part I	Glucose	745	1269	524	Monosaccharide
	Sucrose	745	1163	418	Disaccharide
Part II	Lactose	745	783	38	Disaccharide
	Lactose/Enzyme	745	1201	456	Monosaccharide

1. How did you know that respiration was occurring?
   - There was a change in the pressure caused by the production of carbon dioxide gas. Carbon dioxide gas is a by-product of cellular respiration.

2. Which was the best energy source for respiration?
   - Glucose was the best energy source for respiration.

3. Which disaccharide could the yeast cells respire and how is it that they were able to respire that disaccharide if yeast cells can only respire monosaccharides?
   - Yeast cells respired the disaccharide sucrose because they contain the enzyme sucrase. This allowed the yeast cells to breakdown the sucrose.

4. It is said that enzymes have specificity, meaning that enzymes only interact with one substrate. What evidence from this activity can justify this statement?
   - Yeast cells could respire sucrose because they contain the enzyme sucrase. Yet this enzyme was not able to break down the molecule lactose even though it is very similar in structure.

5. What is the role of the lactase in this experiment?
   - Lactase breaks lactose down to monosaccharides. Yeast can then use the monosaccharides for respiration.

6. When most children are born, they make the enzyme lactase. What would be the advantage of children having the enzyme lactase?
   - Milk, which contains lactose, is the main food source for infants. Children that produce the lactase enzyme will be able to digest lactose.

7. As adults some people lose the ability to make lactase. How would this affect their diet and why does this not seem to effect their health?
   - People who cannot digest lactose must modify their diets by avoiding diary products or adding lactase to their dairy foods.

REFERENCE

Greenberg, Jon P., Revision Editor. *Biological Science, A Molecular Approach.* Chicago: Everyday Learning Publishing Company, 2001. pp. 704-707

Yeast Cells and Digestion of Nutrients
Examining Enzyme Specificity

Using a Graphing Calculator and Data Collection Device

The nutrients that heterotrophs consume are very rarely simple compounds. Usually they are large molecules or polymers. For instance, when a heterotroph consumes eggs, the egg white contains large concentrations of the complex protein albumin. Albumin is a large protein made of many smaller monomer subunits called amino acids. In order to be beneficial to the organism, the proteins must be digested or broken down into amino acids before they can be used. In humans there are a number of enzymes our body uses to break down proteins into amino acids. This includes enzymes like pepsin, tryspsin and chemotrypsin to name a few. Remember, an enzyme is a biological catalyst that speeds up a chemical reaction without being used up in the chemical reaction. Enzymes are proteins that can be used many times.

In addition to having enzymes to break down proteins like albumin, it should not be surprising, that additional enzymes are used to breakdown other large molecules like polysaccharides. Polysaccharides are broken down into a number of glucose rings by the enzyme, amylase, and lipids are broken down to glycerol and three fatty acids by the enzyme lipase. Even smaller molecules like the disaccharides sucrose and lactose are broken down before they can be used. Each of these molecules has a different enzyme responsible for their decomposition.

Digestive enzymes are large complex proteins made by the organism to aid in breaking down the consumed nutrients. Digestive enzymes are very specific and only work on their target molecules. The specific reaction catalyzed by an enzyme depends on the molecular structure and shape of a small area called the active site. The active site can attract and hold only the specific molecules. The target molecule that the enzyme attracts and acts upon is called the substrate. The substrate and the active site of the molecule must fit together very closely. Sometimes the enzyme itself changes shape slightly to bring about the necessary fit.

In a decomposition reaction, the substrate joins with the enzyme and is then split into two or more smaller molecules.

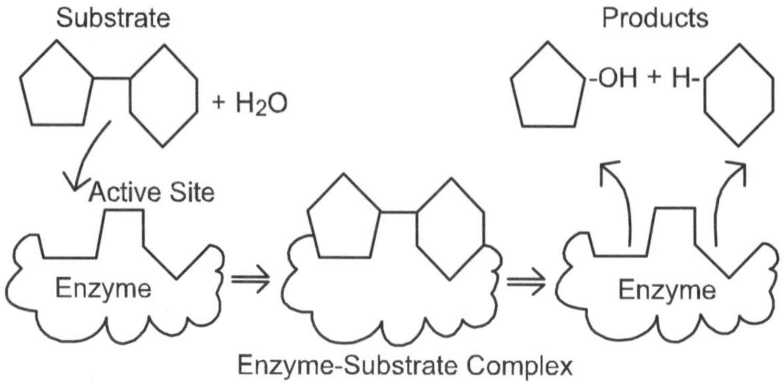

Decomposition Reaction

All cells need energy to survive. Most often carbohydrates supply this necessary energy. Most of the food sources for heterotrophs contain carbohydrates in the form of polysaccharides and disaccharides. Therefore, organisms must break down these carbohydrates to the monosaccharide level before they can be used as an energy source. The energy released as organisms break down carbohydrates is used to make ATP. This energy releasing process is known as cellular respiration produces carbon dioxide as a by-product. This is why, as heterotrophs, we exhale carbon dioxide gas when we breathe. This process of making cellular energy is known as cellular respiration. Yeast cells, like humans, use carbohydrates to make energy and also produce carbon dioxide gas as a by-product.

To produce this energy, yeast cells use carbohydrates but they must use simple sugars or monosaccharides. One of the most common monosaccharides used in cellular respiration is glucose. Below is drawing of glucose.

Two monosaccharides may bond together to form a double sugar, or disaccharide. Sucrose or table sugar is a disaccharide made from the two monosacharides glucose and fructose. Below is a drawing of sucrose.

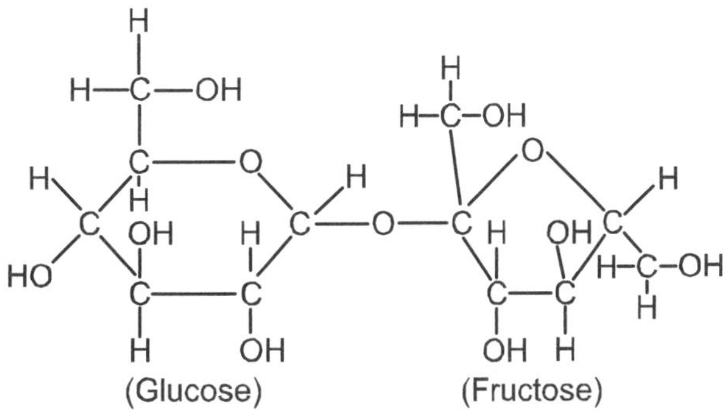

(Glucose) (Fructose)

Sucrose $C_{12}H_{22}O_{11}$

The disaccharide found in milk is lactose, which is made of the monosaccharides glucose and galactose. Below is a drawing of lactose.

If yeast cells are given disaccharides as a nutrient source, they must digest or break down the disaccharides to the monosaccharide level.

The yeast cells must posses an enzyme to break the disaccharide down to two monosaccharides. If the yeast cells do not posses the enzyme necessary to break down the disaccharide, then they cannot use the sugar for energy and no respiration will occur. Disaccharides such as sucrose and lactose are very similar. Do yeast cells have the enzymes needed to digest both of these disaccharides? If they do not, will the enzyme that works on one of the disaccharides also work on the other disaccharide?

A pressure probe connected to a data collection device will measure the change in pressure as carbon dioxide is produced. The more carbon dioxide gas produced, the greater the increase in pressure and therefore the greater the amount of cellular respiration occurring.

PURPOSE

The purpose of this experiment is to determine which carbohydrates can be used by yeast cells for respiration with the assistance of digestive enzymes.

MATERIALS

pressure probe
interface
10 cc syringe
2 test tubes 35 mL
1 polystyrene cup
support stands
Lactaid drops
graphing calculator
sugars (5% lactose, 5% glucose, 5% glucose)
2 small cups or 50 mL beakers
2 one hole stopper with inserted eye dropper
test tube rack
Burette clamp
yeast solution

> **Safety Alert**
> 1. CAUTION: Take care not to spill any liquids on the interface or graphing calculator.

PROCEDURE

Note: You will either do Part I or Part II of this experiment and then share your results with another group.

PART I

1. Answer the pre-lab questions.

2. In the space marked HYPOTHESIS on your student answer page formulate a hypothesis about the effect of enzyme specificity on the process of digestion. …..

3. Slide the calculator and CBL or LabPro Interface in the bottom part of the cradle and it will click into place. Snap the calculator into the top portion of the cradle.

4. Plug the short black link cable into the link port on the bottom of the TI Graphing Calculator and the interface.

5. Plug the gas pressure probe into channel 1 of the interface. There should piece of plastic tubing from the pressure probe. Some versions of certain pressure probes have valves for opening and closing the sensor. If the pressure probe has such a valve, ensure that it is open in accordance to the directions accompanying the probe.

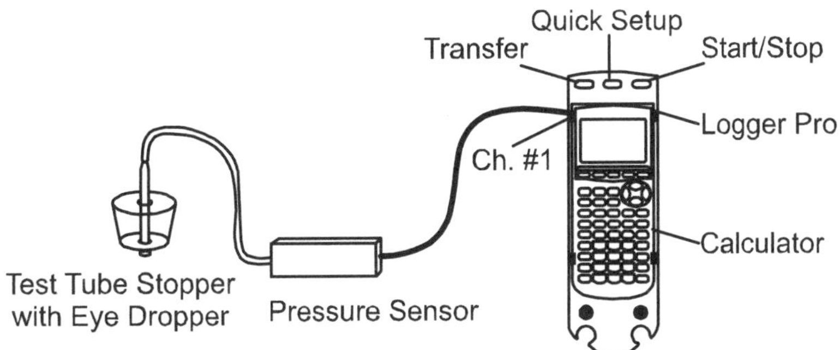

6. Turn on the calculator and press APPS for a TI 83+ or PRGM for the TI 83 then press the number key that precedes the DATAMATE program. At this time the interface should have automatically identified your pressure sensor. It will display the correct pressure in the upper right hand corner. If the correct pressure is not displayed do the following:
   - Select SETUP from the MENU by pressing 1.
   - Select "CH1" from the MENU and press ENTER.
   - Press 4 for more, press 4 again for pressure.
   - Select the correct type of probe
   - Select "MMHG" by pressing 2.
   - Press 1 to indicate OK.

7. Select SETUP from the MENU by pressing 1.
   - Select "MODE" by pressing the ▲ key and then ENTER.
   - Select "TIME GRAPH" by pressing 2 and then 2 again to change the time settings.
   - Enter "10" as the time between samples, in seconds, press ENTER.
   - Enter "90" as the number of sample (the interface will collect data for 15 minutes). Press ENTER.

8. Another window will appear with the summary of the probes and the length of the experiment. Press 1 to indicate OK. Press 1 again to return to the main menu.

9. A new window will appear and the calculator is now ready to start the experiment. **DO NOT** press 2 until you are ready to run the experiment.

10. Using the syringe put 10 cc of glucose solution into one of the test tubes.

11. Using the syringe put 10 cc of yeast solution into the same test tube. Secure the test tube in a clamp connected to a ring stand.

12. Lower test tube and clamp into a polystyrene cup filled with warm water to stabilize the temperature. Let it sit for a few minutes to allow the system to come to equilibrium.

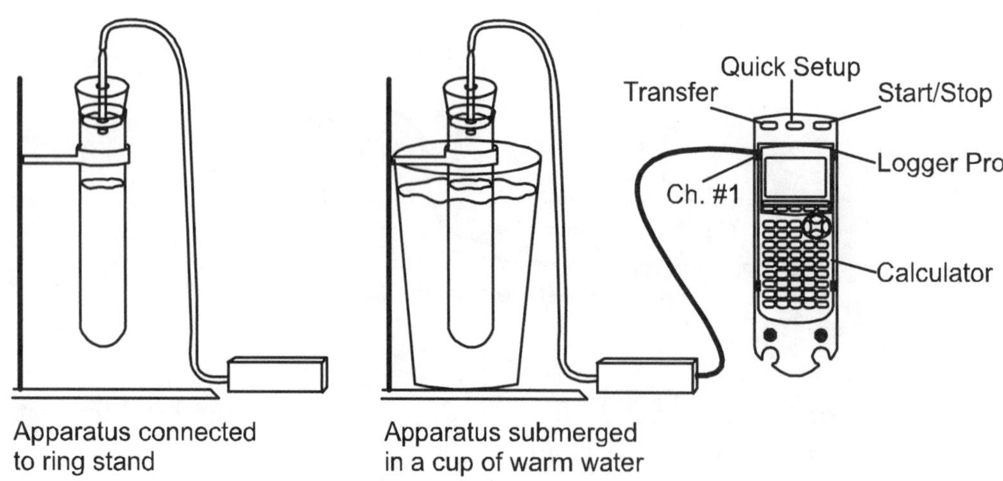

13. Now put the stopper that is connected to the pressure probe into the test tube. Open and close the valve. The pressure reading at this time should be around 760 mm Hg.

14. Press [2]. The experiment will run for 15 minutes. There should be 4 short beeps and the quick setup light will flash. You should notice that the pressure is being graphed as the data is being collected.

15. When the experiment is complete, 4 short beeps will sound and the quick setup light will flash. Now a labeled, fitted graph will be displayed.

16. Use the [◄] and [►] keys to move the cursor. View the data points displayed at the bottom of the graph. Use these keys to determine the initial or minimum pressure and the final or maximum pressure. Record this data in the data table on the student answer page.

17. Press [ENTER] on the calculator and return to the main menu. The parameters you set for this experiment are still in the calculator. Another run of the experiment can be done without resetting the calculator.

18. Repeat the experiment, but this time use sucrose in place of the glucose. Be sure to add your yeast cells. Repeat steps 9-15. When starting DATAMATE do not press [CLEAR]. This will retain your previous experiment parameters so that you do not have to reset the program. Be sure to record the initial/minimum and final/maximum pressure values in your data table on the student answer page.

19. Clean up your area and return your equipment to its original condition.

20. Complete the remaining blanks in your data table and answer the conclusion questions.

PART II

1. Answer the pre-lab questions.

2. In the space marked HYPOTHESIS on your student answer page formulate a hypothesis about the effect of enzyme specificity on the process of digestion.

3. Slide the calculator and CBL or LabPro Interface in the bottom part of the cradle and it will click into place. Snap the calculator into the top portion of the cradle.

4. Plug the short black link cable into the link port on the bottom of the TI Graphing Calculator and the interface.

5. Plug the gas pressure probe into channel 1 of the interface. There should piece of plastic tubing from the pressure probe. Some versions of certain pressure probes have valves for opening and closing the sensor. If the pressure probe has such a valve, ensure that it is open in accordance to the directions accompanying the probe.

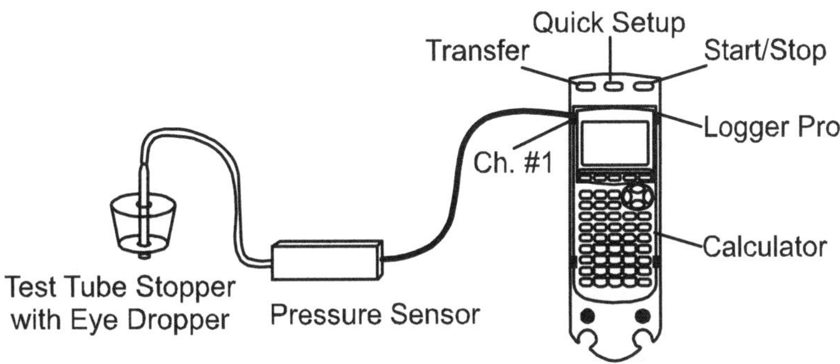

6. Turn on the calculator and press APPS for a TI 83+ or PRGM for the TI 83 then press the number key that precedes the DATAMATE program. At this time the interface should have automatically identified your pressure sensor. It will display the correct pressure in the upper right hand corner. If the correct pressure is not displayed do the following:
   - Select SETUP from the MENU by pressing 1.
   - Select “CH1” from the MENU and press ENTER.
   - Press 4 for more, press 4 again for pressure.
   - Select the correct type of probe
   - Select “MMHG” by pressing 2.
   - Press 1 to indicate OK.

7. Select SETUP from the MENU by pressing 1.
   - Select “MODE” by pressing the ▲ key and then ENTER.
   - Select “TIME GRAPH” by pressing 2 and then 2 again to change the time settings.
   - Enter “10” as the time between samples, in seconds, press ENTER.
   - Enter “90” as the number of sample (the interface will collect data for 15 minutes). Press ENTER.

8. Another window will appear with the summary of the probes and the length of the experiment. Press [1] to indicate OK. Press [1] again to return to the main menu.

9. A new window will appear and the calculator is now ready to start the experiment. **DO NOT** press [2] until you are ready to run the experiment.

10. Using the syringe put 10 cc of lactose solution into one of the test tubes.

11. Using the syringe put 10 cc of yeast solution into the same test tube. Secure the test tube in a clamp connected to a ring stand.

12. Lower test tube and clamp into a polystyrene cup filled with warm water to stabilize the temperature. Let it sit for a few minutes to allow the system to come to equilibrium.

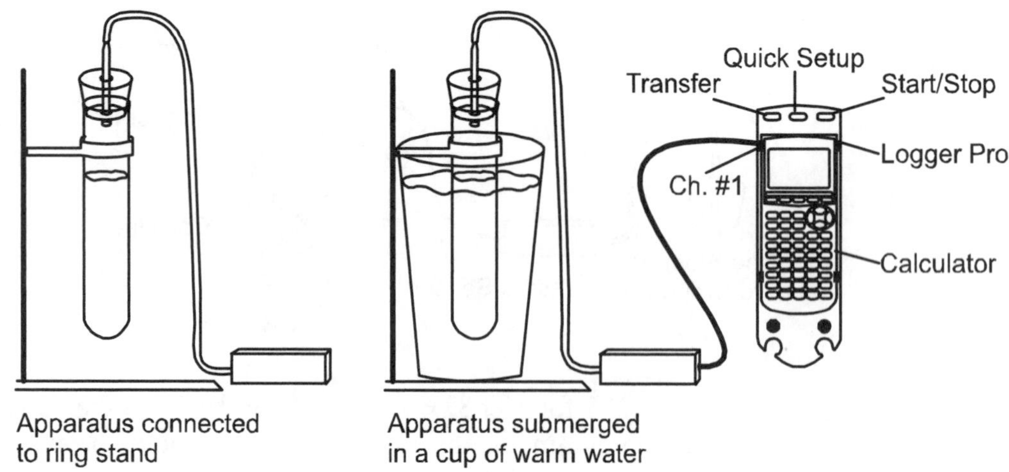

Apparatus connected to ring stand

Apparatus submerged in a cup of warm water

13. Now put the stopper that is connected to the pressure probe into the test tube. Open and close the valve. The pressure reading at this time should be around 760 mm Hg.

14. Press [2]. The experiment will run for 15 minutes. There should be 4 short beeps and the quick setup light will flash. You should notice that the pressure is being graphed as the data is being collected.

15. When the experiment is complete, 4 short beeps will sound and the quick setup light will flash. Now a labeled, fitted graph will be displayed.

16. Use the [◄] and [►] keys to move the cursor. View the data points displayed at the bottom of the graph. Use these keys to determine the initial or minimum pressure and the final or maximum pressure. Record this data in the data table on the student answer page.

17. Press [ENTER] and the screen will tell you which Lists contain your data. Press [ENTER] again and the program is done.

18. Repeat the experiment, but this time use test tube #2 that contains the lactose + Lactaid mixture. Be sure to add your yeast cells. Repeat steps 10-17. When starting DATAMATE do not press CLEAR. This will retain your previous experiment parameters so that you do not have to reset the program. Be sure to record the initial and final pressure values in your data table on the student answer page.

19. Clean up your area and return your equipment to its original condition.

20. Complete the remaining blanks in your data table and answer the conclusion questions.

Yeast Cells and Digestion of Nutrients
Examining Enzyme Specificity

Using a Computer and Data Collection Device

The nutrients that heterotrophs consume are very rarely simple compounds. Usually they are large molecules or polymers. For instance, when a heterotroph consumes eggs, the egg white contains large concentrations of the complex protein albumin. Albumin is a large protein made of many smaller monomer subunits called amino acids. In order to be beneficial to the organism, the proteins must be digested or broken down into amino acids before they can be used. In humans there are a number of enzymes our body uses to break down proteins into amino acids. This includes enzymes like pepsin, tryspsin and chemotrypsin to name a few. Remember, an enzyme is a biological catalyst that speeds up a chemical reaction without being used up in the chemical reaction. Enzymes are proteins that can be used many times.

In addition to having enzymes to break down proteins like albumin, it should not be surprising, that additional enzymes are used to breakdown other large molecules like polysaccharides. Polysaccharides are broken down into a number of glucose rings by the enzyme,amylase, and lipids are broken down to glycerol and three fatty acids by the enzyme lipase. Even smaller molecules like the disaccharides sucrose and lactose are broken down before they can be used. Each of these molecules has a different enzyme responsible for their decomposition.

Digestive enzymes are large complex proteins made by the organism to aid in breaking down the consumed nutrients. Digestive enzymes are very specific and only work on their target molecules. The specific reaction catalyzed by an enzyme depends on the molecular structure and shape of a small area called the active site. The active site can attract and hold only the specific molecules. The target molecule that the enzyme attracts and acts upon is called the substrate. The substrate and the active site of the molecule must fit together very closely. Sometimes the enzyme itself changes shape slightly to bring about the necessary fit.

In a decomposition reaction, the substrate joins with the enzyme and is then split into two or more smaller molecules.

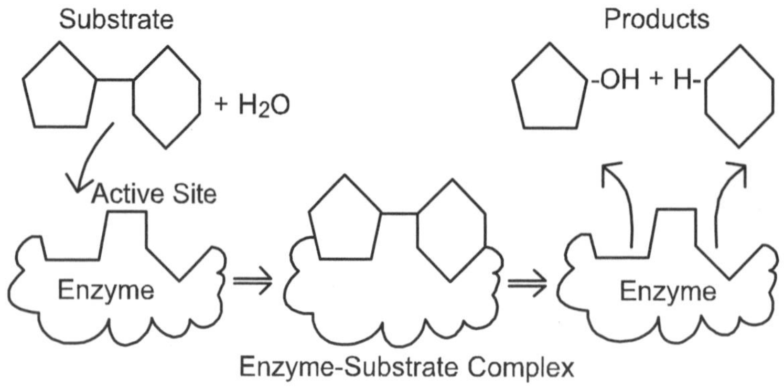

Substrate

$+ H_2O$

Products

-OH + H-

Active Site

Enzyme ⇒ ⇒ Enzyme

Enzyme-Substrate Complex

Decomposition Reaction

All cells need energy to survive. Most often carbohydrates supply this necessary energy.. Most of the food sources for heterotrophs contain carbohydrates in the form of polysaccharides and disaccharides. Therefore, organisms must break down these carbohydrates to the monosaccharide level before they can be used as an energy source. The energy released as organisms break down carbohydrates is used to make ATP. This energy releasing process is known as cellular respiration produces carbon dioxide as a by-product. This is why, as heterotrophs, we exhale carbon dioxide gas when we breathe. This process of making cellular energy is known as cellular respiration. Yeast cells, like humans, use carbohydrates to make energy and also produce carbon dioxide gas as a by-product.

To produce this energy, yeast cells use carbohydrates but they must use simple sugars or monosaccharides. One of the most common monosaccharides used in cellular respiration is glucose. Below is drawing of glucose.

Two monosaccharides may bond together to form a double sugar, or disaccharide. Sucrose or table sugar is a disaccharide made from the two monosacharides glucose and fructose. Below is a drawing of sucrose.

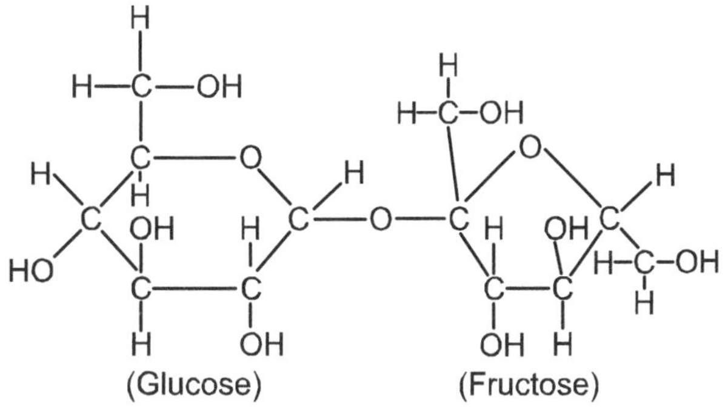

(Glucose) (Fructose)

Sucrose $C_{12}H_{22}O_{11}$

The disaccharide found in milk is lactose, which is made of the monosaccharides glucose and galactose. Below is a drawing of lactose.

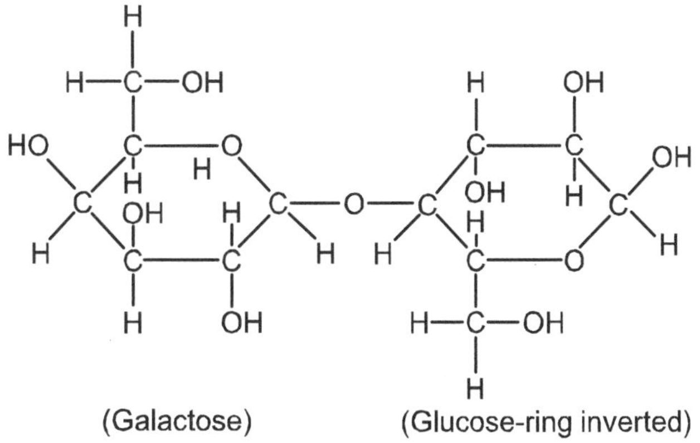

(Galactose) (Glucose-ring inverted)

Lactose $C_{12}H_{22}O_{11}$

If yeast cells are given disaccharides as a nutrient source, they must digest or break down the disaccharides to the monosaccharide level.

The yeast cells must posses an enzyme to break the disaccharide down to two monosaccharides. If the yeast cells do not posses the enzyme necessary to break down the disaccharide, then they cannot use the sugar for energy and no respiration will occur. Disaccharides such as sucrose and lactose are very similar. Do yeast cells have the enzymes needed to digest both of these disaccharides? If they do not, will the enzyme that works on one of the disaccharides also work on the other disaccharide?

A pressure probe connected to a data collection device will measure the change in pressure as carbon dioxide is produced. The more carbon dioxide gas produced, the greater the increase in pressure and therefore the greater the amount of cellular respiration occurring.

PURPOSE

The purpose of this experiment is to determine which carbohydrates can be used by yeast cells for respiration with the assistance of digestive enzymes.

MATERIALS

- pressure probe
- 10 cc syringe
- 2 test tubes 35 mL
- 2 polystyrene cups
- support stands
- Lactaid drops
- computer with Logger Pro installed
- sugars (5% lactose, 5% glucose, 5% glucose)
- 2 small cups or 50 mL beakers
- # 2 one hole stopper with inserted eye dropper
- test tube rack
- Burette clamp
- Lab Pro interface box
- yeast solution

Safety Alert
1. CAUTION: Electricity is being used; take care not to spill any liquids on any of the computer equipment or electrical outlets.

PROCEDURE

Note: You will either do Part I or Part II of this experiment and then share your results with another group.

PART I

1. Answer the pre-lab questions.

2. In the space marked HYPOTHESIS on your student answer page formulate a hypothesis about the effect of enzyme specificity on the process of digestion.

3. Plug the pressure sensor into Port 1 of the serial box or Ch 1 of the LabPro interface box. Plug the gas pressure probe into channel 1 of the interface. There should piece of plastic tubing from the pressure probe. Some versions of certain pressure probes have valves for opening and closing the sensor. If the pressure probe has such a valve, ensure that it is open in accordance to the directions accompanying the probe.

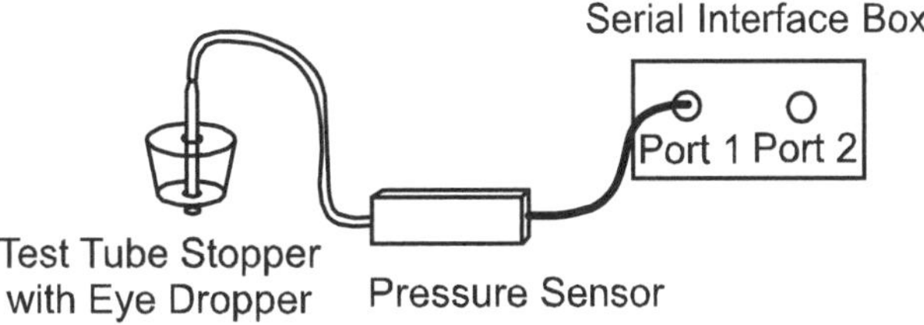

4. Turn on the computer. Click on the folder called **Experiment Templates**, and then open up **Enzyme Lab**. Logger Pro should open.
   - **CAUTION: Electricity is being used; take care not to spill any liquids on any of the computer equipment or electrical outlets.**

5. Using the syringe put 10 cc of glucose solution into one of the test tubes.

6. Using the syringe put 10 cc of yeast solution into the same test tube. Secure the test tube in a clamp connected to a ring stand.

7. Lower test tube and clamp into a polystyrene cup filled with warm water to stabilize the temperature. Let it sit for a few minutes to allow the system to come to equilibrium. See the diagram below:

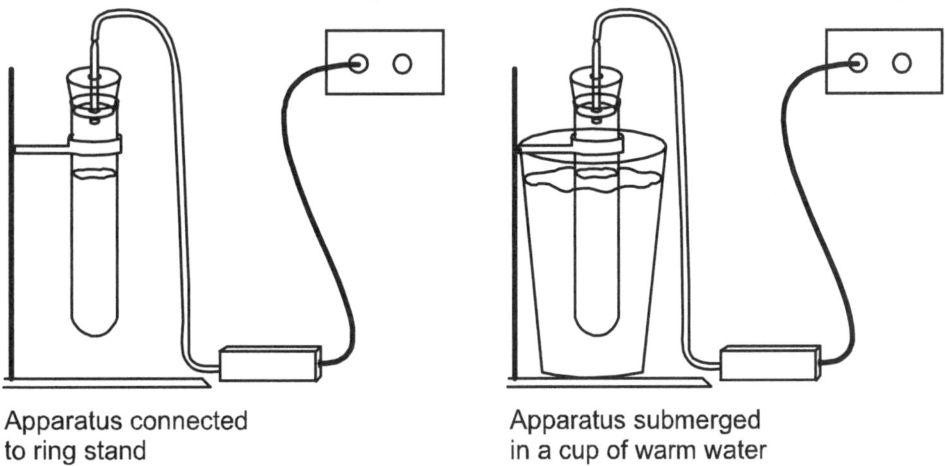

Apparatus connected to ring stand

Apparatus submerged in a cup of warm water

8. Now put the stopper that is connected to the pressure probe into the test tube. Open and close the valve. The pressure reading at this time should be around 760 mm Hg.

9. Click **Collect**. The experiment should run for 15 minutes. At the end of 15 minutes, the experiment will end and the **Stop** button will automatically become a **Collect** button.

10. When the experiment is complete, pull down the **Analyze menu** and highlight **Statistics**. This will display the minimum or initial pressure and the maximum or final pressure. Record this information in your data table on the student answer page.

11. Pull down the **Data Menu** and click on **Store Latest Run**. This will allow you to compare this run to the subsequent runs of the experiment. The red line should become a thinner red line.

12. Repeat the experiment, but this time use sucrose as your sugar. Be sure to add your yeast cells. Repeat steps 5-10. Be sure to record the pressures in your data table.

13. After you have finished, close all windows on the computer. Clean up your area and return your equipment to its original condition.

14. Complete the remaining blanks in your data table and answer the conclusion questions.

PART II

1. Answer the pre-lab questions.

2. In the space marked HYPOTHESIS on your student answer page formulate a hypothesis about the effect of enzyme specificity on the process of digestion.

3. Plug the pressure sensor into Port 1 of the serial box or Ch 1 of the LabPro interface box. Plug the gas pressure probe into channel 1 of the interface. There should piece of plastic tubing from the pressure probe. Some versions of certain pressure probes have valves for opening and closing the sensor. If the pressure probe has such a valve, ensure that it is open in accordance to the directions accompanying the probe.

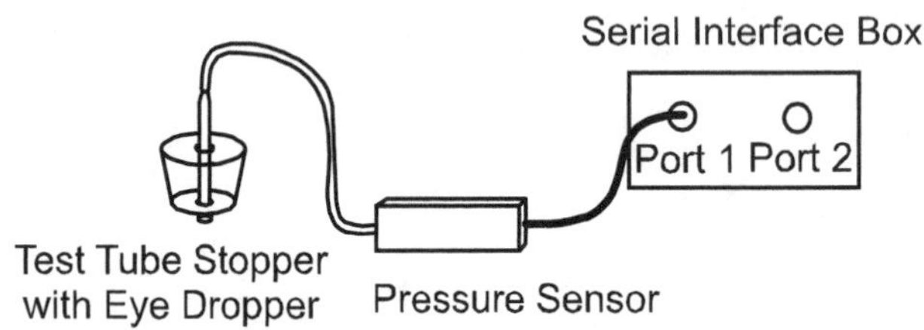

4. Turn on the computer. Click on the folder called **Experiment Templates**, and then open up **Enzyme Lab**. Logger Pro should open.
   - **CAUTION: Electricity is being used; take care not to spill any liquids on any of the computer equipment or electrical outlets.**

5. Using the syringe put 10 cc of lactose solution into one of the test tubes.

6. Using the syringe put 10 cc of yeast solution into the same test tube. Secure the test tube in a clamp connected to a ring stand.

7. Lower test tube and clamp into a polystyrene cup filled with warm water to stabilize the temperature. Let it sit for a few minutes to allow the system to come to equilibrium. See the diagram below:

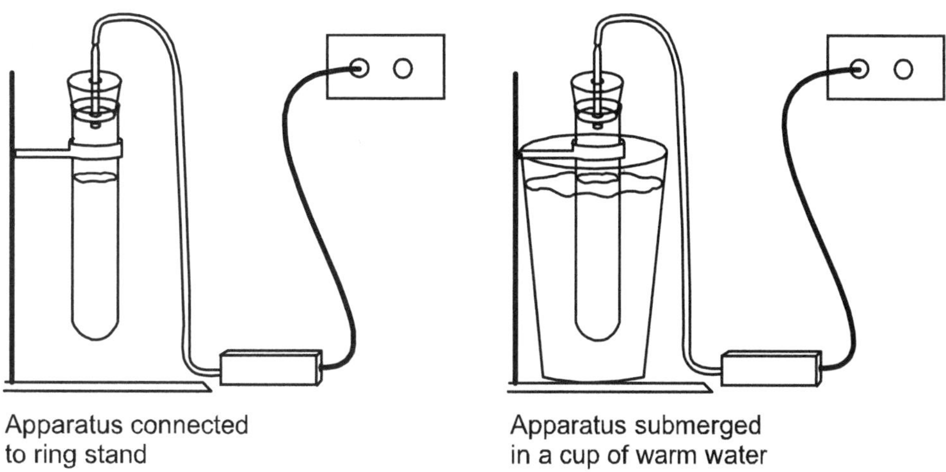

Apparatus connected to ring stand

Apparatus submerged in a cup of warm water

8. Now put the stopper that is connected to the pressure probe into the test tube. Open and close the valve. The pressure reading at this time should be around 760 mm Hg.

9. Click **Collect**. The experiment should run for 15 minutes. At the end of 15 minutes, the experiment will end and the **Stop** button will automatically become a **Collect** button.

10. When the experiment is complete, pull down the **Analyze menu** and highlight **Statistics**. This will display the minimum or initial pressure and the maximum or final pressure. Record this information in your data table on the student answer page.

11. Pull down the **Data Menu** and click on **Store Latest Run**. This will allow you to compare this run to the subsequent runs of the experiment. The red line should become a thinner red line.

12. Redo the experiment, but this time use sucrose as your sugar. Be sure to add your yeast cells. Repeat steps 5-10. Be sure to record the minimum and maximum pressures on your data sheet.

13. After you have finished close all windows on the computer. Clean up your area and return your equipment to its original condition.

14. Answer the fill out the data table and answer the questions for this experiment.

Name ______________________________

Period______________________________

Yeast Cells and Digestion of Nutrients
Examining Enzyme Specificity

HYPOTHESIS

DATA AND OBSERVATIONS

	Experiment	Minimum Pressure, mm Hg	Maximum Pressure, mm Hg	Total Pressure Change, mm Hg	Type of Saccharide
Part I	Glucose				
	Sucrose				
Part II	Lactose				
	Lactose/Enzyme				

PRE-LAB QUESTIONS

1. List four characteristics of enzymes.

2. What is cellular respiration?

3. Explain what must occur in order to use a disaccharide for cell respiration?

4. What is the molecular formula for sucrose and lactose?

5. How are sucrose and lactose alike and how are they different?

CONCLUSION QUESTIONS

1. How did you know that respiration was occurring?

2. Which was the best energy source for respiration?

3. Which disaccharide could the yeast cells respire and how is it that they were able to respire that disaccharide if yeast cells can only respire monosaccharides?

4. It is said that enzymes have specificity, meaning that enzymes only interact with one substrate. What evidence from this activity can justify this statement?

5. What is the purpose of the lactase in this experiment?

6. When most children are born, they make the enzyme lactase. What would be the advantage of children having the enzyme lactase?

7. As adults some people lose the ability to make lactase. How would this affect their diet and why does this not seem to effect their health?

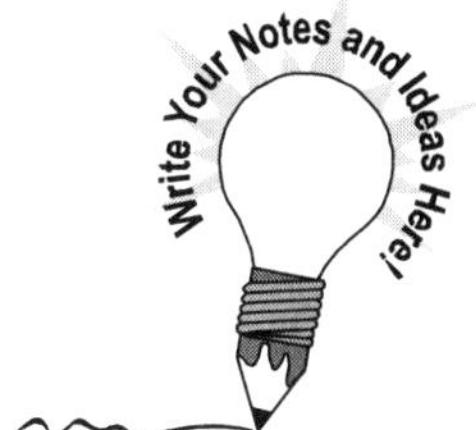
Write Your Notes and Ideas Here!

Circulatory System
Structure & Function of Vessels, Blood and Heart

OBJECTIVE
Students will identify structure to function relationships found in arteries, veins, human blood and frog blood. Students will also observe the structures of a vertebrate heart and relate structure to function.

LEVEL
Biology I

NATIONAL STANDARDS
UCP.1, UCP.2, UCP.5, C.1, C.5, E.1, E.2, F.1, G.1, G.2

TEKS
5(A), 10(A), 10(B)

CONNECTIONS TO AP
AP Biology:

III. Organisms and Populations B. Structure and Function of Plants and Animals 2. Physiological and behavioral adaptations

TIME FRAME
two 45 minute periods

MATERIALS
(For a class of 28 students working in pairs)

14 prepared slides of arteries
14 prepared slides of veins
14 prepared slides of human blood
14 prepared slides of frog blood
14 disposable pipets
14 metric rulers
14 microscopes
fresh dog blood sample (approx. 3 mL)
14 cover slips
14 glass slides
labeled preserved or fresh mammalian heart
14 pair latex gloves

TEACHER NOTES
Prepared slides of arteries and veins may be purchased from scientific supply companies. Some companies offer slides that have the artery and vein preserved on the same slide which may be more cost effective. Likewise, the human blood samples and frog blood samples may be purchased from a scientific supply company. The frog blood provides an important comparison because frog blood cells contain a nucleus while human cells do not. Fresh samples of dog blood can be obtained from a local veterinarian. Since each lab group is only using one drop of the sample, a 3 mL sample will provide an ample volume. The sample needs to contain heparin to prevent clotting. The vials used by the veterinarians when collecting blood samples typically contain heparin. The sample can be stored in the

refrigerator for several days prior to using. To alleviate any question of contamination or concern with students touching blood samples, you can wear gloves and prepare the slides for the students.

Prior to this lab you will need to obtain a preserved or fresh mammalian heart. Preserved pig, sheep or cow hearts can be purchased from a scientific supply company. These hearts can be reused for this activity several times if stored in an airtight container with preservative solution. Fresh pig, sheep, and/or cow hearts can be purchased at a local butcher shop. You will need to call in advance to request an entire heart since most butchers remove the vessels and atria when preparing the hearts for sale.

To prepare the heart for display you should make a top to bottom cut along the frontal plane of the heart. This cut will separate the anterior portion from the posterior portion of the heart and reveal the internal structures. All of the structures that need to be labeled for this lab can be shown on the posterior portion of the heart. See the illustration below.

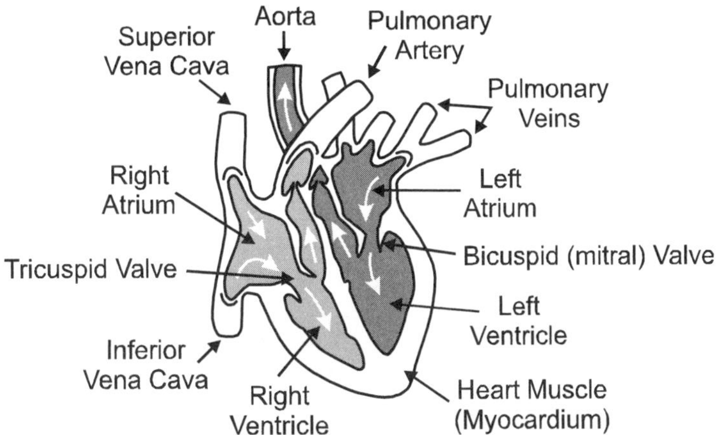

Using pins, label the following parts of the heart: right atrium, left atrium, right ventricle, left ventricle, tricuspid valve and bicuspid valve. This heart should be displayed during the lab activity. You will need to instruct your students regarding the order in which they should come up to view the dissected heart. One suggestion is to give each lab group a number and have them take turns observing the heart in numerical order. As an alternative, you may want to purchase enough hearts for each group to have a labeled heart at their lab table.

POSSIBLE ANSWERS TO THE CONCLUSION QUESTIONS AND SAMPLE DATA

PART 1: VESSEL STRUCTURE

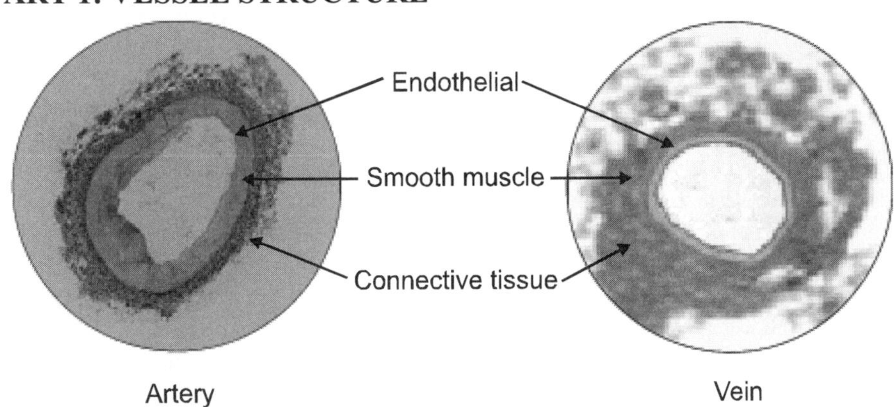

Artery Vein

PART II: BLOOD CELLS

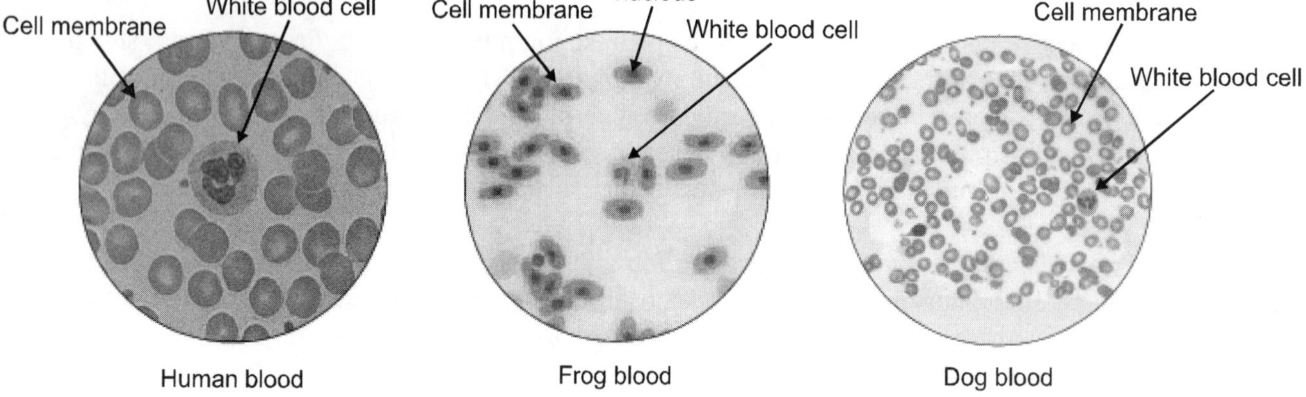

PART III:

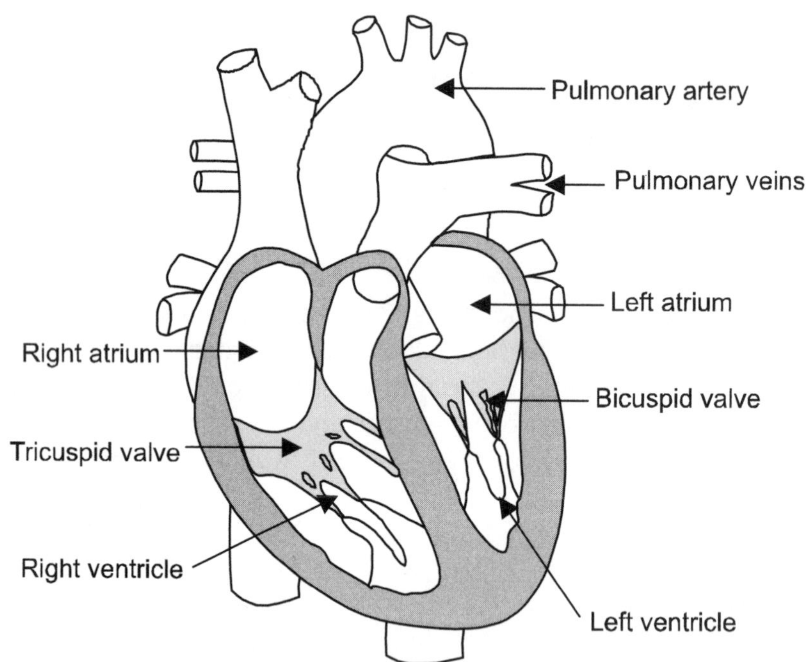

Table 1: Observations/Descriptions	
Part I	**Vessel Structure**
Artery	Thick muscle wall, small inner diameter
Vein	Thin muscle wall, large inner diameter
Part II	**Blood Cells**
Human Blood	Lots of small red circular cells, (may occasionally see a white blood cell)
Frog Blood	Lots of small red cells with darker colored nucleus. (Occasionally a white blood cell)
Dog Blood	Many small red circular cells. (may occasionally see white blood cells)
Part III	**Heart Structure**
Ventricle Wall	Thickness ____________
Artium Wall	Thickness ____________
Tricuspid Valve	Three flaps, several stringy fibers attached
Bicuspid Valve	Two flaps, several stringy fibers attached

Table 2: Structure and Function	
Structure	**Function**
Thick wall of artery	Provides strength/support to transport blood that is under pressure
Valve of vein	Prevents back flow, keeps blood moving toward the heart
Surface of red blood cell	Increased surface area allows for increased oxygen carrying capacity
Thick wall of ventricle	Provides the power to move blood from heart to the rest of the body
Thin wall of atrium	Contracts to move blood to lower ventricle chamber

1. Describe how arteries and veins differ in structure and function.
   - arteries have thick walls and a small inner diameter and function to carry blood away from the heart.
   - veins have thin walls, a large inner diameter, contain valves and function to carry blood to the heart.

2. An aneurysm is a weak or thin spot in the wall of an artery. Considering the function of an artery, why do you suppose this change in the structure of the artery can be a dangerous health threat?
   - Blood in the artery is under high pressure. The pressure could cause the weak, thin spot in the wall of the artery to rupture causing a bleeding stroke if this occurs in the brain.

3. Each of the red blood cells of the frog has a nucleus while human and dog red blood cells lack nuclei. What cellular process would the frog red blood cells be able to perform that human and dog blood cells would not be able to perform?
   - Frog red blood cells can go through mitosis and reproduce themselves while human and dog red blood cells cannot.

4. Describe two ways that the structure of the heart allows it to function efficiently as a blood pump.
   - thick walled ventricles have the strength to pump blood long distances.
   - the heart valves allows for one way flow of blood.

5. Mitral stenosis is a specific type of heart murmur caused when the biscuspid valve (mitral valve) does not open completely, reducing the volume of blood passing through the valve. Which 2 chambers of the heart would be most directly affected by this change in volume?
   - The left ventricle would have a decrease in volume. The left atrium would have an increase in volume due to retention.

6. Arrange the following structures of the heart in the order they would be encountered by a drop of blood flowing through the heart as it enters from the vena cava: tricuspid valve, bicuspid valve, left ventricle, left atrium, right ventricle, right atrium.
   - right atrium, tricuspid valve, right ventricle, left atrium, biscuspid valve, left ventricle.

7. Sickle cell anemia is a mutation that causes red blood cells to take on a narrow sickle shape rather than the normal biconcave shape. What impact would this structural mutation have on the function of the blood cell?
   - The change in shape will reduce the surface area of the cell reducing the amount of oxygen the cell can carry.

REFERENCES

Marieb, Elaine N. *Human Anatomy and Physiology*. Redwood City: Benjamin/Cummings, 1989.

Wallace, Robert A., Gerald Sanders, and Robert Ferl. *Biology*. New York: HarperCollins, 1996.

Circulatory System
Observing Structure & Function of Vessels, Blood and Heart

The circulatory system serves as the body's transport system, delivering essential chemicals to cells throughout the entire organism. Structure and function relationships exist throughout the entire system. Each component of the circulatory system is designed to function in a specific role within the system and within the body.

The structure of the heart allows it to be an efficient pump, providing the power to move blood from one area of the body to another. The mammalian heart, for example, consists of four chambers which collectively function to move blood to the lungs and the entire body. The chambers are divided into the right atrium and ventricle and the left atrium and ventricle. The two halves of the heart are separated by a septum, a thick muscular wall which prevents the flow of blood between the two atria or the two ventricles. Structure and function relationships can also be seen in the valves of the heart. The flap-like, one-way flow structure of the valves allows for the forward movement of blood through the heart while preventing any back flow of blood. The pathway blood takes through the heart as well as the location of the chambers of the heart are illustrated in Figure 1.

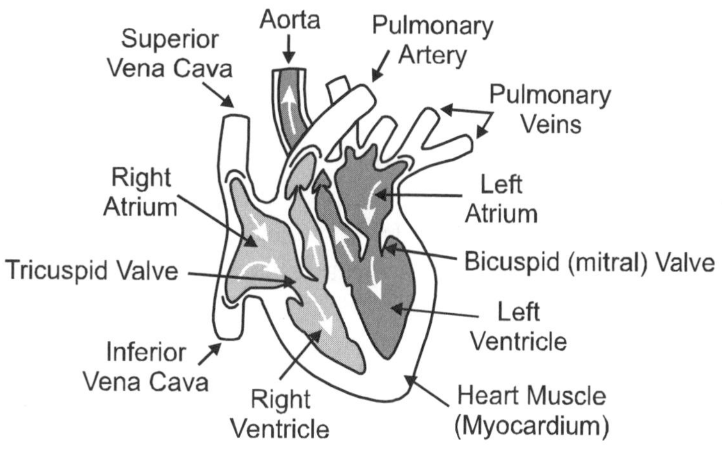

Fig. 1

The heart pumps blood in two phases, called the systolic and diastolic phases. In the systolic phase, the ventricles contract, and pump blood into the arteries. In the diastolic phase occurs as the ventricles relax and blood flows into them from the atria. The pressure exerted on the vessels by this pumping action is referred to as blood pressure and can be measured using a sphygmomanometer.

Similarly, structure and function relationships are clearly present in the blood vessels of the circulatory system. The vessels include the arteries, veins and capillaries. Arteries and veins have the similar function of serving as passageways for blood flow through the body but each type of vessel is specifically suited to perform a unique role within the circulatory system. The force created by the contraction of the heart muscles requires that the arteries that transport blood away from the heart are built with thick, elastic walls that can withstand this pressure. The veins, which carry blood toward the heart, have comparatively thin walls as well as valves. The valves of the veins prevent backflow of blood that is moving under lower pressure toward the heart. See Figure 2. The capillaries serve as the exchange site between the circulatory system and the tissues of the body. Capillary vessels are made of thin, single cell walls that allow for rapid diffusion of substances.

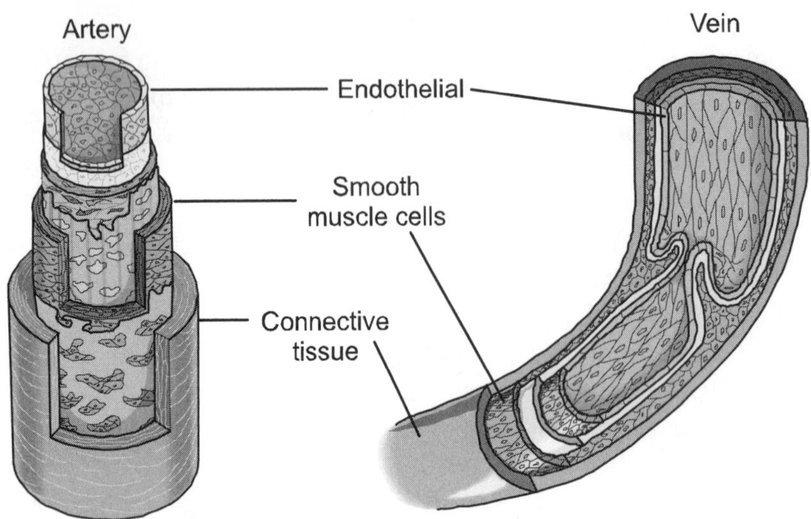

Fig. 2

Blood is a connective tissue that serves as a fluid transport medium which circulates through the cardiovascular system bringing needed substances such as sugars, amino acids, and oxygen to tissues. Additionally, this connective tissue matrix functions to remove waste materials such as carbon dioxide and nitrogenous wastes from the tissues. Blood is made of two main parts, the liquid plasma and the blood cells which are called formed elements. A variety of substances are carried as solutes in the watery solvent plasma. The formed elements, which include red blood cells (erythrocytes), white blood cells (leukocytes) and platelets (thrombocytes), each play specific roles in the system. The platelets help in the formation of blood clots while the white blood cells are involved in immune responses. The red blood cells, the most numerous of the types of cells found in the blood, provide a vivid example of correlation between structure and function in the circulatory system. Red blood cells in the human system are biconcave in structure as shown in Figure 3. This means that both sides of the disk shaped cell are sunken in toward the center of the cell. This biconcave structure results in an increase surface area which allows blood cells to more efficiently perform their function of carrying oxygen.

Fig. 3

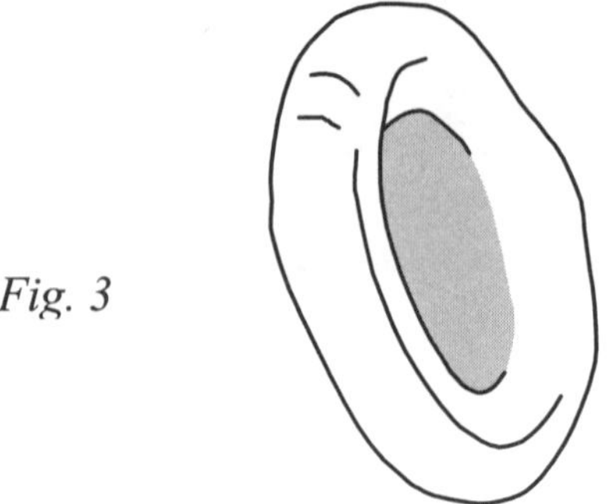

PURPOSE

In this activity you will relate structure to function as you observe a mammalian heart, slides of arteries and veins, and frog and mammalian blood samples.

MATERIALS

1 prepared slide of an artery
1 prepared slide of a vein
1 prepared slide of human blood
1 prepared slide of frog blood
1 disposable pipet
metric ruler
1 microscope
1 drop of dog blood sample
1 cover slip
1 glass slide
access to a labeled preserved or fresh mammalian heart
latex gloves

Safety Alert

1. Wear gloves when handling any blood samples in the laboratory setting.
2. Avoid excessive contact with tissue preservatives when using preserved specimen.

PROCEDURE

PART I: VESSEL STRUCTURE

1. Obtain a microscope and prepared slides of arteries and veins.

2. Place the prepared slide of the artery on the stage of the microscope and using the course adjustment knob bring the artery into view. Using the fine adjustment, focus the slide on low power.

3. Make a sketch of the artery in the space provided on the student answer page. Label the endothelium, smooth muscle, and connective tissues.

4. Describe the structure of the artery in the table on the student answer page.

5. Place the prepared slide of the vein on the stage of the microscope and using the course adjustment knob bring the vein into view. Using the fine adjustment know, focus the slide on low power.

6. Make a sketch of the vein in the space provided on the student answer page. Label the endothelium, smooth muscle, and connective tissues.

7. Describe the structure of the vein in the table on the student answer page.

PART II: BLOOD CELLS

1. Obtain prepared slides of human blood and frog blood.

2. Place the prepared slide of the human blood on the stage of the microscope and using the course adjustment knob bring the blood into view. Using the fine adjustment, focus the slide on low power. Switch to the high power objective and refocus using the fine adjustment knob.

3. Make a labeled sketch of the human blood cells in the space provided on the student answer page.

4. Place the prepared slide of the frog blood on the stage of the microscope and using the course adjustment knob bring the blood into view. Using the fine adjustment, focus the slide on low power. Switch to the high power objective and refocus using the fine adjustment knob.

5. Carefully observe the cells. Note any similarities and differences you may see in the frog blood compared to the human blood. For example, look to see if there are organelles present within the frog cells that are not present in the human cells. Record your observations in the space provided on the student answer page.

6. Make a labeled sketch of the frog blood cells in the space provided on the student answer page.

7. Obtain a clean glass slide and a cover slip. Using a disposable pipet, place a drop of dog blood on the center of the glass slide. Lower the coverslip over the blood sample.

8. Place the sample of dog blood on the stage of the microscope and using the course adjustment knob bring the blood into view. Using the fine adjustment, focus the slide on low power. Switch to the high power objective and refocus using the fine adjustment knob.

9. Carefully observe the cells. Note any similarities or difference that you observe in comparison to the human and frog blood samples. Record your observations in the space provided on the student answer page.

10. Make a labeled sketch of the dog blood cells in the space provided on the student answer page.

PART III: HEART STRUCTURES

1. Observe the mammalian heart. Locate a ventricle and observe the muscular wall. Label the right and left ventricles on heart diagram on the student answer page.

2. Use a ruler to measure the thickness of muscle of the ventricle wall. Record the value in the space provided on the student answer page.

3. Locate an atrium and observe the wall. Label the right and left atria on the heart diagram.

4. Using the ruler, measure the thickness of the wall of the atrium. Record the value in the space provided on the student answer page.

5. Observe the structure of the tricuspid and bicuspid valves that separate the atria from the ventricles. Label these valves on the heart diagram and write a brief description of the structure of these valves on your student answer page.

6. Describe the function of each of the structures listed in Table 2 on the student answer page.

7. Complete the conclusion questions.

Name ______________________________

Period ______________________________

Circulatory System
Observing Structure & Function of Vessels, Blood and Heart

DATA AND OBSERVATIONS

PART 1: VESSEL STRUCTURE

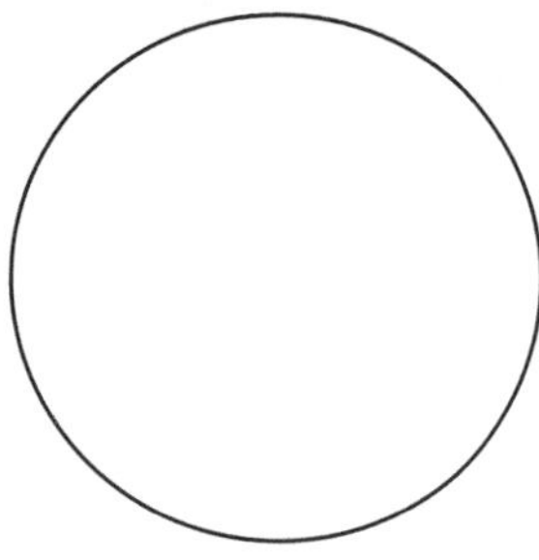

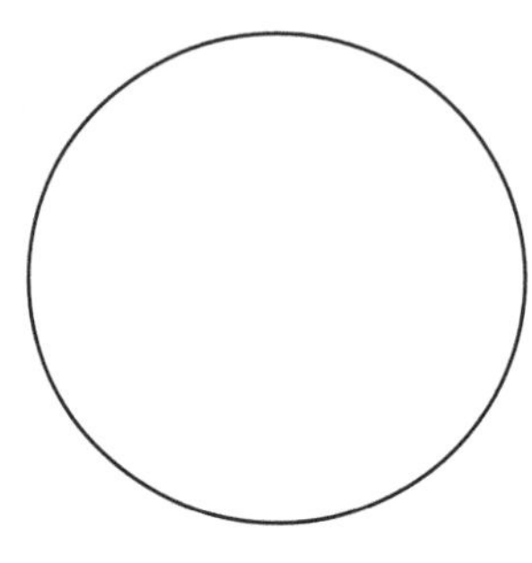

________________ ________________

PART II: BLOOD CELLS

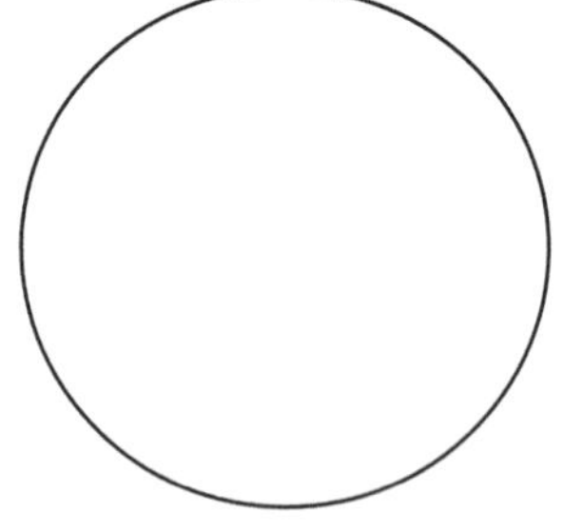

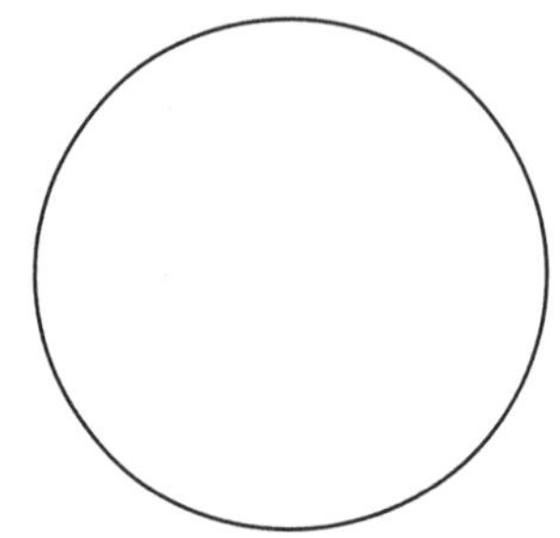

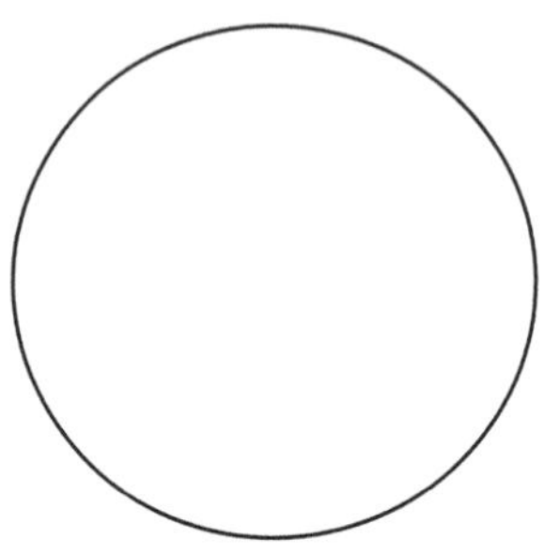

________________ ________________ ________________

PART III:

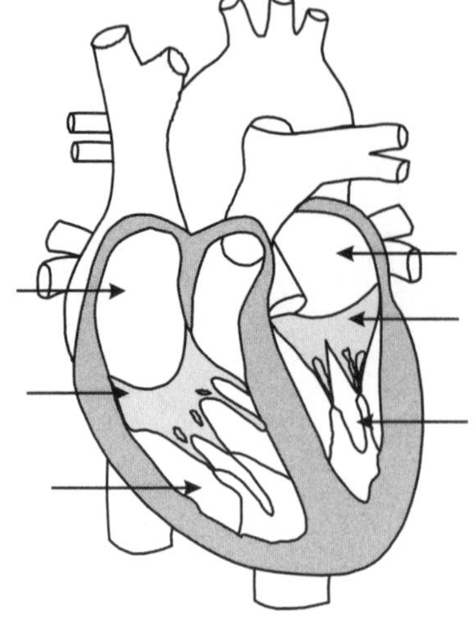

Table 1: Observations/Descriptions	
Part I	**Vessel Structure**
Artery	
Vein	
Part II	**Blood Cells**
Human Blood	
Frog Blood	
Dog Blood	
Part III	**Heart Structure**
Ventricle Wall	Thickness ____________
Artium Wall	Thickness ____________
Tricuspid Valve	
Bicuspid Valve	

ANALYSIS

Table 2: Structure and Function	
Structure	**Function**
Thick wall of artery	
Valve of vein	
Surface of red blood cell	
Thick wall of ventricle	
Thin wall of atrium	

CONCLUSION QUESTIONS

1. Describe how arteries and veins differ in structure and function.

2. An aneurysm is a weak or thin spot in the wall of an artery. Considering the function of an artery, why do you suppose this change in the structure of the artery can be a dangerous health threat?

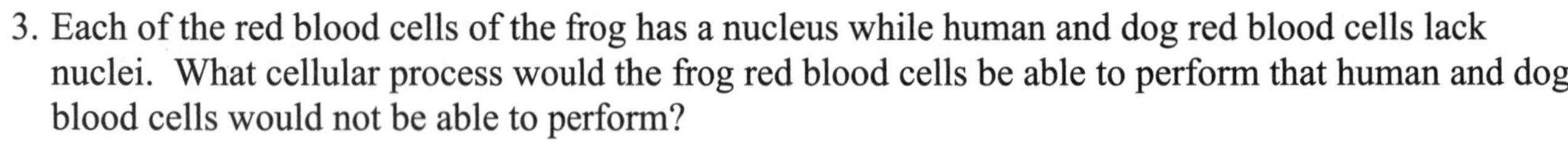

3. Each of the red blood cells of the frog has a nucleus while human and dog red blood cells lack nuclei. What cellular process would the frog red blood cells be able to perform that human and dog blood cells would not be able to perform?

4. Describe two ways that the structure of the heart allows it to function efficiently as a blood pump.

5. Mitral stenosis is a specific type of heart murmur caused when the biscuspid valve (mitral valve) does not open completely, reducing the volume of blood passing through the valve. Which two chambers of the heart would be most directly affected by this change in volume?

6. Arrange the following structures of the heart in the order they would be encountered by a drop of blood flowing through the heart: tricuspid valve, bicuspid valve, left ventricle, left atrium, right ventricle, right atrium.

7. Sickle cell anemia is a mutation that causes red blood cells to take on a narrow sickle shape rather than the normal biconcave shape. What impact would this structural mutation have on the function of the blood cell?

Urinalysis
Investigating the Structures and Functions of the Excretory System

OBJECTIVE
Students will observe the structure of the vertebrate kidney. Students will perform a simulated urinalysis on three synthetic urine samples to diagnose disorders.

LEVEL
Biology I

NATIONAL STANDARDS
UCP.1, UCP.2, UCP.5, C.1, C.5, E.1, E.2, F.1, G.1, G.2

TEKS
10(A), 10 (B)

CONNECTIONS TO AP
AP Biology:

III Organisms and Populations B. Structure and Function of Plants and Animals 2. Structural, physiological and behavior adaptations

TIME FRAME
90 minutes

MATERIALS
(For a class of 28 working in pairs)

14 sheep kidneys
14 dissecting trays
14 probes
14 scalpels
56 disposable medicine cups
14 marking pens
Biuret solution (50 mL)
14 disposable plastic pipets
500 mL synthetic urine samples 1-4
56 pH test strips
56 glucose test strips
56 ketone test strips
14 test tubes

TEACHER NOTES
Preserved sheep or pig kidneys can be purchased through scientific supply companies. If the students who use them first cut them properly, the specimen can be re-used in subsequent classes.

Synthetic urine solutions should be prepared as follows:

Sample	To simulate	Distilled water	Sodium Chloride	Food coloring	Urea	Glucose	Albumin	Acetone	pH
1	diabetes	500 mL	.5 g	1 drop	2.0 g	6 g	-	-	Use 1 M HCl to adjust to pH 6
2	Severe anemia	500 mL	.5 g	1 drop	2.0 g	-	5 g	-	Add NaOH raise pH to 8
3	High protein diet	500 mL	.5 g	1 drop	2.0 g	-	-	15 mL	Use 1 M HCl to adjust to pH 6
4	Normal	500 mL	.5 g	1 drop	2.0 g	-	-	-	Use 1 M HCl to adjust to pH 6

Artificial urine samples should be labeled, covered and stored in the refrigerator. Samples can be stored for several weeks.

Biuret solution may be purchased from scientific supply companies. Biuret solution may be prepared by dissolving 1.5 g copper (II) sulfate in 250 mL of distilled water, then adding 6 g potassium sodium tartrate. Stir until dissolved. Boil 450 mL distilled water and allow it to cool. Add 300 mL of 10% NaOH to the cooled water. Add the two solutions together.

POSSIBLE ANSWERS TO THE CONCLUSION QUESTIONS AND SAMPLE DATA

DATA AND OBSERVATIONS

Description of external anatomy of kidney

Smooth surface
Curved outer edge
Curved inner edge
Bulging round sides

Diagram of external kidney

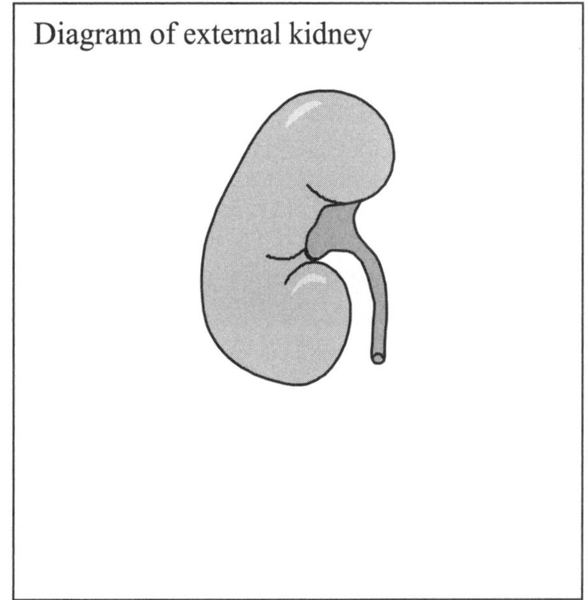

Description of internal kidney

Light edges
Darker middle area
Appears to be in sections
Organized appearance

Labeled diagram of internal kidney

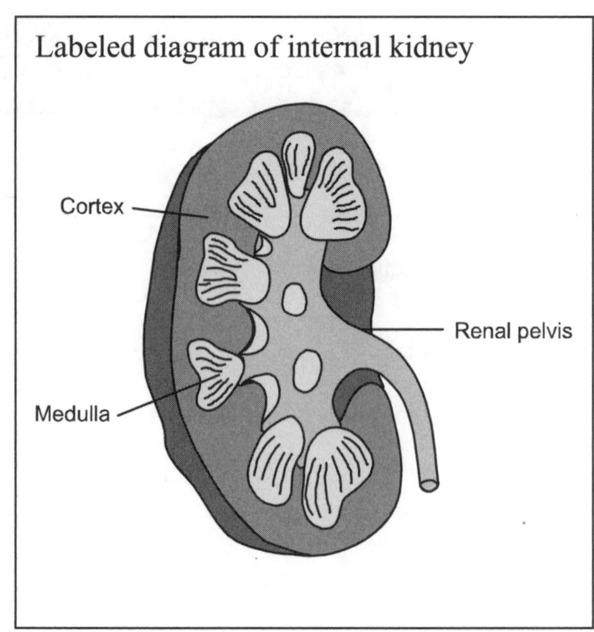

PART II: URINALYSIS

Data Table 1				
Sample	pH	Glucose	Ketones	Protein
Urine Sample 1	6	yes	no	no
Urine Sample 2	8	no	no	yes
Urine Sample 3	6	no	yes	no
Urine Sample 4	6	no	no	no

ANALYSIS

Based on the data collected for each urine sample, identify a possible medical cause or explanation for the results obtained.

Sample	Possible Cause/Explanation
Urine Sample 1	diabetes mellitus
Urine Sample 2	severe anemia
Urine Sample 3	starvation or high protein diet
Urine Sample 4	normal

CONCLUSION QUESTIONS

1. How does the structure of the kidney allow it to perform its function of removing waste from the blood stream?
   - each kidney contains 1 million nephrons which filter the blood

2. List, in order of occurrence, the structures a drop of urine would pass through from its formation to its elimination from the body.
   - nephron in kidney, ureter, urinary bladder, urethra

3. Approximately 125 mL of plasma are filtered by the paired kidneys per minute. How many liters of plasma can be filtered in a single day? Show you work in the space below.
   - $\frac{125\,\text{mL}}{\cancel{\text{min}}} \times \frac{60\,\cancel{\text{min}}}{\cancel{\text{hr}}} \times \frac{24\,\cancel{\text{hr}}}{\text{day}} = 180{,}000\,\text{mL/day} = 180\,\text{L/day}$

4. Normal humans contain two kidneys. However, people can survive with a single kidney. What would be the advantage of having paired kidneys?
   - In case one gets damaged a second one is available to perform the life sustaining function of filtration.

5. Describe the relationship between the circulatory system and the excretory system in humans.
   - The renal artery of the circulatory system delivers the blood to the kidney for filtration. The pressure of the blood forces the plasma into the nephron. The renal vein carries the cleaned blood away from the kidney.

6. Blood plasma contains glucose. Normal urine does not. Explain what happens in the kidneys to cause this difference.
   - The kidneys return the glucose to the blood stream.

7. Explain why doctors may request urine samples as a part of annual physical exams.
   - the contents of urine discovered during urinalysis can indicate health problems

8. What are some examples of health problems that can be detected through the use of urinalysis?
   - diabetes, anemia, starvation, urinary tract infections, kidney stones.

REFERENCES

Marieb, Elaine N. *Human Anatomy and Physiology*. Redwood City: Benjamin/Cummings, 1989.

Shmaefsky, Brian R. "Artificial Urine for Laboratory Testing". National Association of Biology Teachers online How-To-Do-It-Archives. http://www.nabt.org/sup/resources/urine.asp

Tortora, Gerard and Sandra Reynolds Grabowski. *Principles of Anatomy and Physiology*. New York: HarperCollins College Publishers, 1992.

Urinalysis
Investigating the Structures and Functions of the Excretory System

Living cells produce a variety of metabolic wastes such as carbon dioxide, salt and urea. These wastes must be removed from the cells and eliminated from the body in order to maintain a constant internal environment or homeostasis. The removal of these metabolic wastes is performed by the excretory system in the process of excretion. Excretory waste products can be eliminated through the skin, the lungs and the kidneys. The primary components of the human excretory system consists of a pair of kidneys connected to the urinary bladder by the ureters. The urinary bladder stores the urine until it is excreted from the body by traveling through the urethra. See Figure 1.

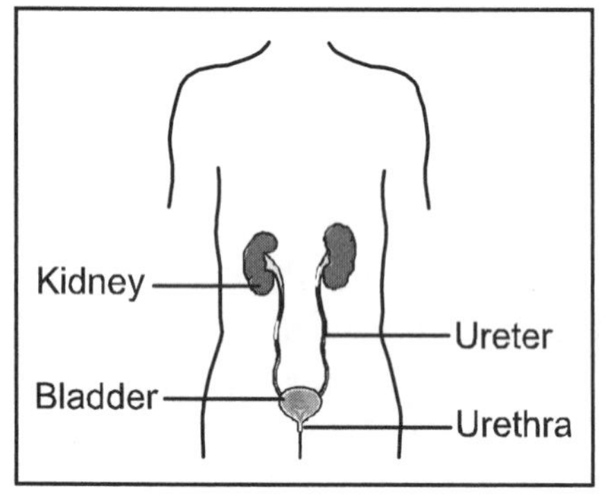

Figure 1: Excretory system

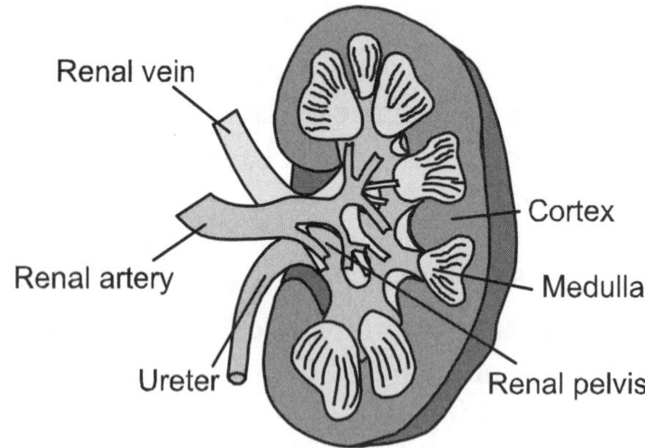

Figure 2: Kidney

The structure of the kidney allows it to perform its function of filtering the blood to remove excess urea, water, and wastes. Blood is brought into the kidney by the renal artery. See Figure 2. Once in the kidney, the blood is filtered by functional units called nephrons. Each kidney has approximately 1 million nephrons that serve as tiny filters that capture the waste found in the blood. Blood pressure forces the fluid of the blood or plasma into the nephrons. This filtration process cleanses the blood by removing the waste products such as urea, excess salts, and excess water. The useful portion of the filtrate, which includes glucose, is then reabsorbed and returned to the circulatory system through the renal vein. The waste products that have been removed from the blood remain inside the nephron and are combined with water to form urine. Urine is then moved to the bladder where it is temporarily stored. The urine will eventually be eliminated from the body through the process of urination.

The urine formed during the excretion process is often reflective of the health of the organism. Normal urine has a pH of 6-7, a slight odor, light yellow color and contains a variety of chemicals such as urea, salt, creatine, potassium, and other electrolytes. However, high levels of certain substances may indicate health problems or conditions. For example, glucose in the urine may be a sign of diabetes mellitus. A pH above 7 along with protein in the urine may be a sign of severe anemia. High ketone levels in the urine may be caused from starvation or high protein diets. Urinary tract infections produce cloudy urine.

Crystals and high calcium levels in urine may be symptoms of kidney stones. Therefore, analysis of urine contents or urinalysis is a common diagnostic test requested by doctors.

PURPOSE

In this investigation you will observe the physical features of a vertebrate kidney and perform urinalysis on artificial urine samples.

MATERIALS

- sheep kidney
- dissecting tray
- probe
- scalpel
- 4 disposable medicine cups
- marking pen
- 14 test tubes (20mm x 150mm)
- disposable plastic pipet
- 4 protein test strips
- 4 pH test strips
- 4 glucose test strips
- 4 synthetic urine samples
- 14 dropper bottles of Biuret solution

Safety Alert

1. Goggles and aprons should be worn during this activity.
2. Avoid prolonged contact with preservative solutions.
3. Be careful when using sharp instruments such as scalpels. Always cut away from yourself.

PROCEDURE

PART I: KIDNEY DISSECTION

1. Place a preserved sheep kidney on a paper towel in a dissecting tray.

2. Observe the external structure of the kidney. Touch the surface of the kidney with the probe. Is it soft or tough? Write a description of the external anatomy of the kidney in the space provided on the student answer page.

3. Using a scalpel, cut the kidney in half horizontally, producing to halves as shown here.

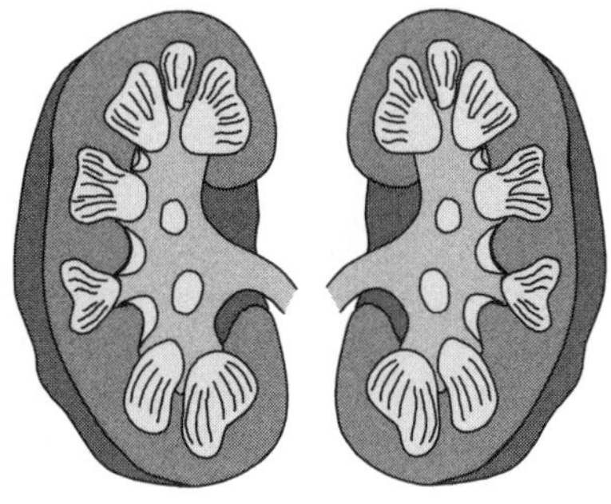

4. Observe the internal structure of the kidney. Locate the outer edge of the kidney called the cortex. Note the distinct color change between the outer and inner section or medulla. Locate the renal pelvis where urine accumulates. Describe the shape appearance of the kidney in the space on your student answer page.

5. Prepare a sketch of the kidney in the space provided on the student answer page. Label the cortex, medulla, and renal pelvis.

6. Return the kidney to its storage container. Rinse and return your tray, scalpel, and forceps.

PART II: URINALYSIS

1. Place 10 mL of urine sample 1 into a medicine cup. Label the cup using the marking pen.

2. Test the pH of the sample using a strip of pH paper. Record the pH in Data Table 1.

3. Test the sample for the presence of glucose by placing a glucose test strip in the urine sample. Wait one minute and interpret the results using the color code chart for the test strip. Record the results in Data Table 1.

4. Test the sample for the presence of ketones by placing a ketone test strip in the urine sample. Wait 15 seconds and interpret the results using the color code chart for the test strip. Record the results in Data Table 1.

5. Test the sample for the presence of protein using the Biuret test. Use a disposable pipet to transfer 3 mL of the urine sample into a test tube and add 10 drops of Biuret solution. A brownish purple or pink color indicates the presence of proteins in the urine. Record the results in Data Table 1.

6. Repeat steps 7 through 11 for each of the three remaining urine samples.

7. Clean your lab station and return supplies as directed by your teacher.

8. Based on the data collected for each urine sample, identify a possible medical cause or explanation for the results obtained.

9. Answer the conclusion questions on the student answer page.

Name ____________________

Period ____________________

Urinalysis
Investigating the Structures and Functions of the Excretory System

DATA AND OBSERVATIONS

Description of external anatomy of kidney	Diagram of external kidney

Description of internal kidney	Labeled diagram of internal kidney

PART II: URINALYSIS

Data Table 1 - Urinalysis				
Sample	pH	Glucose	Ketones	Protein
Urine Sample 1				
Urine Sample 2				
Urine Sample 3				
Urine Sample 4				

ANALYSIS

Based on the data collected for each urine sample, identify a possible medical cause or explanation for the results obtained.

Sample	Possible Cause/Explanation
Urine Sample 1	
Urine Sample 2	
Urine Sample 3	
Urine Sample 4	

CONCLUSION QUESTIONS

1. How does the structure of the kidney allow it to perform its function of removing waste from the blood stream?

2. List, in order of occurrence, the structures a drop of urine would pass through from its formation to its elimination from the body.

3. Approximately 125 mL of plasma are filtered by the paired kidneys per hour. How many liters of plasma can be filtered in a single day? Show you work in the space below.

4. Normal humans contain two kidneys. However, people can survive with a single kidney. What would be the evolutionary advantage of having paired kidneys?

5. Describe the relationship between the circulatory system and the excretory system in humans.

6. Blood plasma contains glucose. Normal urine does not. Explain what happens in the kidneys to cause this difference.

7. Explain why doctors request urine samples as a part of annual physical exams.

8. What are some examples of health problems that can be detected through the use of urinalysis?

Chicken Leg Dissection
Observing Structure and Function

OBJECTIVE
Students will dissect a chicken leg to observe the tissues and organs. Students will have the opportunity to make careful observations.

LEVEL
Biology I

NATIONAL STANDARDS
UCP.1, UCP.2, UCP.5, C.5, G.1, G.2

TEKS
Biology 5(A), 5(C), 10(A)

CONNECTIONS TO AP
AP Biology:

III Organisms and Populations 2. Structure and Function of Plants and Animals 2. Structural, physiological, and behavioral adaptations

TIME FRAME
20 minutes

MATERIALS
(For a class of 28 working in pairs)

14 forceps
14 scalpels
14 scissors
paper towels
14 dissecting trays
14 dissecting pins
14 probes
14 fresh chicken legs

TEACHER NOTES
This activity can be used to introduce the study of the organ systems. The hierarchy of structure can be explored through this dissection. As an introductory or exploratory lesson, the activity is heavily dependent upon the students' observations.

The legs can be bought in bulk and frozen until needed for this activity. The wing of the chicken could serve as an appropriate substitute for the leg if it is more economically feasible at the time of purchase.

Students may prefer to wear gloves during this dissection activity.

You may want to conduct this dissection on a disposable surface given that there are no preservatives in the tissue.

POSSIBLE ANSWERS TO THE CONCLUSION QUESTION AND SAMPLE DATA

Tissue Observed	Description
Skin	1. lighter in color that the other tissues 2. rough on outer surface with occasional raised areas 3. smoother inner surface
Tendon	Tough, light whitish color, extends from the end of the muscle
Muscle	Diagram
Connective Tissue	Thin, white, fibrous, stringy covering the muscle
Blood Vessel	Reddish, thin, tubes that run along the bone
Nerve	Thin, pale stringy fiber that runs along the bone

1. Arrange the following into a descending hierarchy (from largest to smallest): Muscle, bundle of muscle fiber tissues, nucleus of muscle cell, chicken, muscle cell.
   - Chicken, muscle, muscle fiber tissues, muscle cell, nucleus of muscle cell

2. Which tissues observed in the chicken leg would belong to the following systems:

System	Example of a structure found in chicken leg	Function in the leg
Muscle System	Muscle	Contracts for movement
Integumentary System	Skin	Protects
Nervous System	Nerves	Brings messages to muscle
Circulatory System	Artery or vein	Delivers nutrients
Skeletal	Bone	Supports organism

REFERENCES

Campbell, Neil and Jane Reece. *Biology*. New York: Addison Wesley Longman, 2002. pp. 4, 835-837

Marieb, Elaine. *Human Anatomy and Physiology*. Redwood City: Benjamin/Cummings, 1989. Chapter 4.

Modern Biology Laboratories. Austin: Holt, Rinehart, Winston, 1989.

Chicken Leg Dissection
Observing Structure and Function

INTRODUCTION
Every cell in an organism is both an independent unit and an interdependent part of a larger grouping of cells. In living organisms cells join together in organized relationships to form *tissues*. Tissues that work together to perform related functions are called *organs*. In the chicken's leg the muscle fibers or cells are bundled together to form muscle tissues which make up the larger organ, the muscle. *Organ systems* are formed by a group of organs that work together to perform a special function. The muscles of the leg are part of the organ system called the muscle system.

Additional organ systems are found in the leg as well. For example, the skin of the leg is a component of the integumentary system of the bird. The blood vessels found in the leg are part of the circulatory system. The bones of the leg are components of the skeletal system. This hierarchy of organization from cells to tissues, to organs, and organ systems culminates in the functioning organism.

The leg of a chicken demonstrates the relatedness of structure and function. Each part is built for the specific role it plays in the movement of the leg. Additionally, the interrelatedness of various organ systems can be seen among the tissues found in the leg. For example, the skin serves to protect the contracting muscles which are surrounded by supporting connective tissue. These muscles are connected to the bones by ligaments and tendons. Together, the muscles, tendons, and ligaments work to allow the bones of the leg to move. The movement of the leg is controlled by the impulses received from the nervous system by way of the nerves. The muscles are provided with the needed energy and waste disposal by the permeable vessels of the circulatory system. Working together the organ systems allow the leg to function.

PURPOSE
In this exploratory lab activity, you will dissect a chicken leg to locate and observe tissues, organs and organ system components.

MATERIALS
- forceps
- scalpel
- scissors
- paper towels
- dissecting tray
- dissecting pins
- probe
- fresh chicken leg

Safety Alert
1. Take care when using sharp instruments by making cuts away from the body.
2. Wash you hands thoroughly after touching the specimen.

PROCEDURE

1. Obtain a chicken leg and place the specimen on a paper towel in your dissecting pan.

2. Examine the tough tissue covering the outside of the leg. This tough tissue, the skin, has an outer layer referred to as the epidermis.

3. Lift up the skin and gently cut away any of the fibrous connective tissue that may be holding it in place. Remove all of the skin from the leg.

4. Observe the skin you have removed. Compare the outer surface of the skin to the inner surface of the skin. Record three observations you make about the skin in the space on the answer page. The yellow masses found on the inside surface of the skin are fat tissue.

5. Observe the tough white tissue that is found at both ends of the muscle. It extends from the muscle ends to the bone. This tissue is a tendon. Describe the tendon in the space on your answer page.

6. With a scalpel, carefully cut out a muscle, with its tendons and place it in the dissecting pan. Make a diagram of the muscle and its tendons and label each.

7. Observe the thin white tissue that covers the muscle. This is connective tissue. Describe this connective tissue in the space on your answer page.

8. Remove all the muscles as you carefully look for the blood vessels. The vessels will be thick, red threadlike strands near the bones. Also look for the nerves, white threadlike strands that are found between the muscles nearest the bones. Compare the nerves to the blood vessels. Write your description of the vessels and nerves on the answer page.

9. Gather all tissues and dispose of them as instructed by your teacher. Clean up your tools and work area.

Name ____________________________

Period ____________________________

Chicken Leg Dissection
Observing Structure and Function

DATA AND OBSERVATIONS

Tissue Observed	Description
Skin	1. 2. 3.
Tendon	
Muscle	Diagram
Connective Tissue	
Blood Vessel	
Nerve	

CONCLUSION QUESTIONS

1. Arrange the following into a descending hierarchy (from largest to smallest): Muscle, bundle of muscle fiber tissues, nucleus of muscle cell, chicken, muscle cell.

2. Which tissues observed in the chicken leg would belong to the following systems:

System	Example of a structure found in chicken leg	Function in the leg
Muscle System		
Integumentary System		
Nervous System		
Circulatory System		
Skeletal		

3. The functioning leg of a chicken shows how body systems are interdependent. Explain how each system works together with the other systems to allow the chicken to walk.

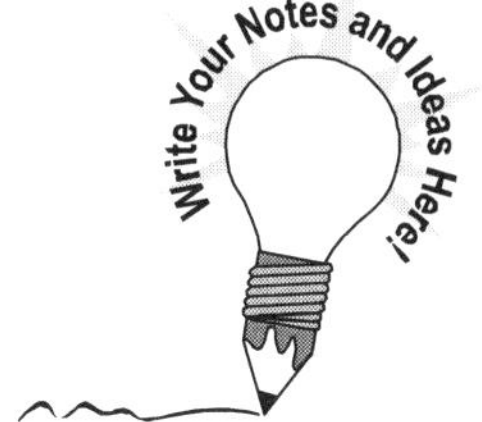
Write Your Notes and Ideas Here!

Kermit Versus Mickey Mouse
Determining the Q_{10} of an Endothermic and Exothermic Organism

OBJECTIVE
Students will explain the effect of temperature on endotherms and ectotherms. Students will analyze and graph respiration data as a function of temperature and determine the Q_{10} value for those organisms.

LEVEL
Biology I

NATIONAL STANDARDS
UCP.2, UCP.3, C.5, C.6, E.1, E.2, G.1, G.2

TEKS
2 (C), 9 (B), 11 (A)

CONNECTIONS TO AP
AP Biology:

III. Organisms and Population B. Structure and Function Plant and Animals 2. Structural, physiological, and behavioral adaptations

TIME FRAME
Time 30-50 minutes

MATERIALS
28 TI-83 graphing calculators

TEACHER NOTES
This activity is an exercise in analyzing data. If you have respirometers and it is allowed, you may want to do the experiment itself. Some states have regulations against experimentation involving vertebrates. This activity can be used to supplement a unit on cell respiration, the respiratory system, or bioenergetics. The students should know how to properly graph data. Discussing the following points will be helpful to the students:

1. The relationship between the amount of oxygen consumed and time is linear.

2. The data points do not all lie on the best fit line. There is some variation above and below.
   - This would account for the fact that the organisms are not perfectly still and any movement can affect the oxygen intake.
   - The syringe is an adequate way to measure the amount of oxygen consumed but not the most sensitive of devices.

3. It is important that the amount of oxygen consumed is divided by the mass of the animals.
   - This is because the frog is twice as large as the mouse and one would expect that a frog would consume more oxygen than a mouse all other factors being equal. However, not all factors are equal because the mouse is an endotherm and the frog is an ectotherm.

4. The data table has an average rate of respiration. This is determined by taking the total amount of oxygen consumed and dividing it by the total amount of time that has elapsed.

5. Q_{10} is a concept used in chemistry and applied to chemical reactions. It can be applied to ectotherms because the environmental temperatures affect the rates of the chemical reactions, the sum of which is their metabolism.

6. The line of best fit as determined by a graphing calculator is a better analyzing tool than averaging the rate of respiration. Averaging the rate of respiration only takes into consideration the beginning and end points and does not average all of the data.

7. The slope of the regression line, "a" can be found as the coefficient to x in the regression equation, $y = ax + b$. The slope is the rate of oxygen consumption per gram of body mass. (Point out that for *any* graph having time on the *x*-axis, the slope of the line is equal to rate.) You might want to compare this value to the value determined by averaging the end points. The values are similar but not exactly the same.

ANSWERS TO PRE-LAB QUESTIONS

1. Ectotherm/poikilotherm
   - An ectotherm is an organism whose temperature varies with the environment. Some modification of the temperature can occur through behavior.

2. Endotherm/homeotherm
   - An endotherm is an organism whose temperature is constant regardless of the environmental temperature. The temperature is regulated by the organism through its physiology.

3. Q_{10}
   - Q_{10} is a measurement of what happens to the reaction rate of an organism's metabolism if the temperature is increased by 10° Celsius. If the rate doubles then Q_{10} is equal to 2 and if it triples then it is equal to 3.

4. What is the advantage of being an endotherm?
   - The advantage of endothermy is that fluctuations in the environmental temperature do not affect the metabolism of the organism.

5. What is the disadvantage of being an endotherm?
   - The disadvantage to endothermy is that it requires a large energy input in the form of food.

6. What is the advantage of being an ectotherm?
   - The advantage of ectothermy is that energy requirements for survival are not nearly as great as endotherm.

7. What is the disadvantage of being an ectotherm?
   - The disadvantage of being an ectotherm is that fluctuations in environmental temperature can affect the metabolism of the animal.

POSSIBLE ANSWERS TO THE CONCLUSION QUESTIONS AND SAMPLE DATA

Summary Table				
Organism	**Temperature (°C)**	**# Oxygen Consumed, cc**	**Average Rate Respiration Oxygen, cc/minute**	**Average Rate Respiration/gram body mass cc/g/min**
Mouse Warm	20	8.5	0.85	0.043
Mouse Cold	10	13.5	1.35	0.068
Frog Warm	20	9.5	0.95	0.024
Frog Cold	10	5.5	0.55	0.014

	Mouse Mass 20 g Room Temperature 20° Celsius			Mouse Mass 20 g Cold Temperature 10° Celsius		
Time	**Syringe Reading**	**# O_2 Consumed**	**# O_2 Consumed per gram**	**Syringe Reading**	**# O_2 Consumed**	**# O_2 Consumed per gram**
0.0	20.0	0.0	0.00	20.0	0.0	0.00
0.5	18.0	2.0	.100	19.0	1.0	.050
1.0	18.0	2.0	.100	18.5	1.5	.075
1.5	17.5	2.5	.125	18.0	2.0	.100
2.0	17.5	2.5	.125	17.0	3.0	.150
2.5	17.0	3.0	.150	16.5	3.5	.175
3.0	16.5	3.5	.175	16.0	4.0	.200
3.5	16.0	4.0	.200	15.0	5.0	.250
4.0	15.5	4.5	.225	14.5	5.5	.275
4.5	15.0	5.0	.250	14.0	6.0	.300
5.0	15.0	5.0	.250	13.5	6.5	.325
5.5	14.5	5.5	.275	12.5	7.5	.375
6.0	14.5	5.5	.275	11.5	8.5	.425
6.5	14.0	6.0	.300	11.0	9.0	.450
7.0	13.5	6.5	.325	10.5	9.5	.475
7.5	13.5	6.5	.325	10.5	9.5	.475
8.0	13.0	7.0	.350	9.5	10.5	.525
8.5	12.5	7.5	.375	9.0	11.0	.550
9.0	12.0	8.0	.400	8.5	11.5	.575
9.5	12.0	8.0	.400	7.5	12.5	.625
10.0	11.5	8.5	.425	6.5	13.5	.675

	Frog Mass 40 g Room Temperature 20° Celsius			Frog Mass 40 g Cold Temperature 10° Celsius		
Time	**Syringe Reading**	**# O_2 Consumed**	**# O_2 Consumed per gram**	**Syringe Reading**	**# O_2 Consumed**	**# O_2 Consumed per gram**
0.0	20.0	0.0	0.0	20.0	0.0	0.0
0.5	19.5	0.5	.13	20.0	0.0	0.0
1.0	18.0	2.0	.50	19.5	0.5	.0125
1.5	17.0	3.0	.75	19.0	1.0	.025
2.0	17.0	3.0	.75	18.5	1.5	.0375
2.5	16.5	3.5	.88	18.5	1.5	.0375
3.0	16.0	4.0	.10	18.0	2.0	.05
3.5	15.5	4.5	.113	18.0	2.0	.05
4.0	15.0	5.0	.125	18.0	2.0	.05
4.5	15.0	5.0	.125	17.5	2.5	.0625
5.0	14.5	5.5	.138	17.5	2.5	.0625
5.5	14.0	6.0	.150	17.0	3.0	.075
6.0	13.0	7.0	.175	16.5	3.5	.0875
6.5	12.5	7.5	.188	16.5	3.5	.0875
7.0	12.5	7.5	.188	16.0	4.0	.1
7.5	12.5	7.5	.188	16.0	4.0	.1
8.0	12.0	8.0	.200	15.5	4.5	.1125
8.5	11.5	8.5	.213	15.5	4.5	.1125
9.0	11.0	9.0	.225	15.0	5.0	.125
9.5	10.5	9.5	.238	15.0	5.0	.125
10.0	10.5	.95	.238	14.5	5.5	.1375

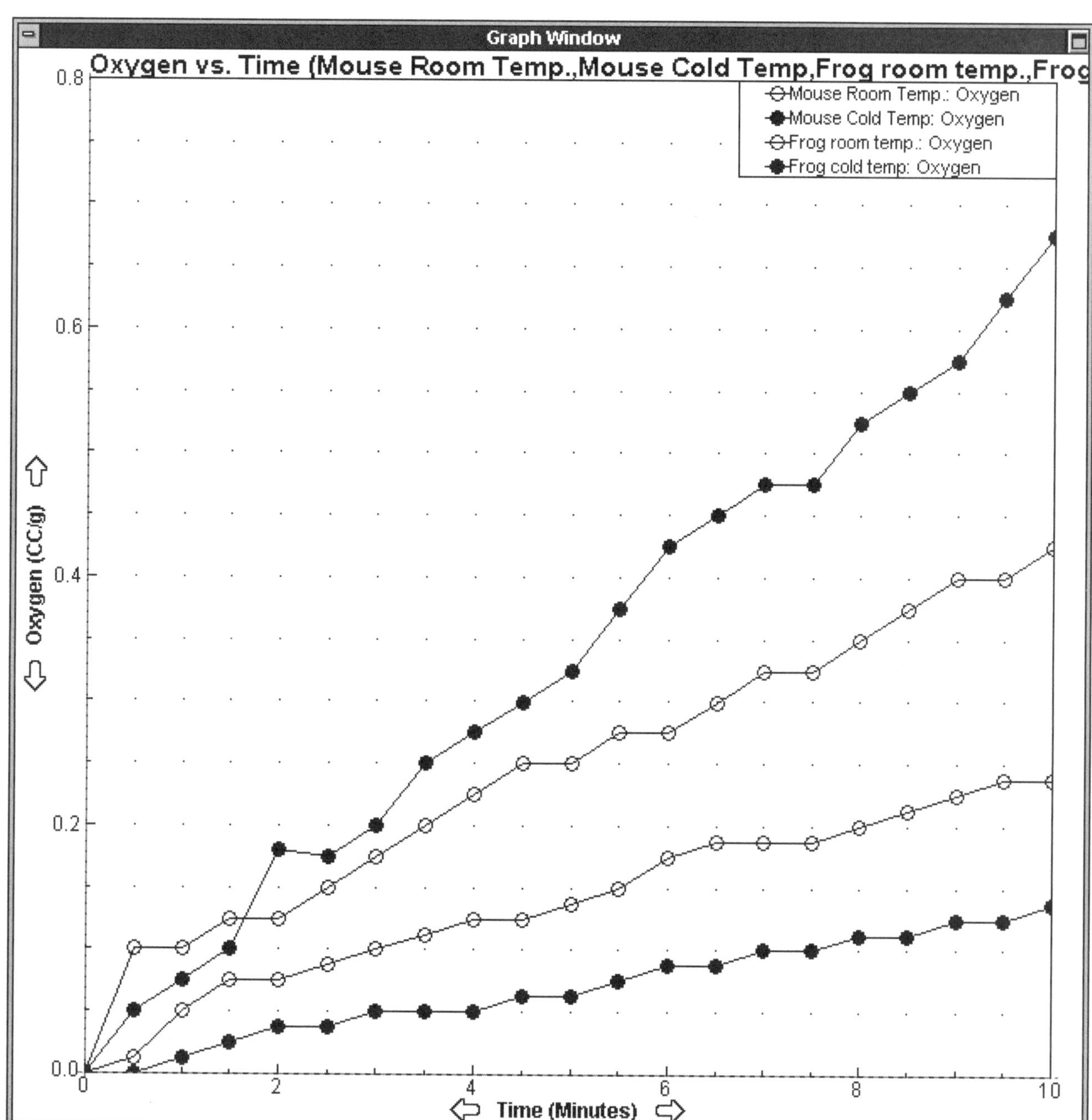

TEACHER PAGES

Below are the graphs that can be generated if students are using the graphing calculator.
Figure 1 shows the data and best fit lines for the mouse at both 10°C and 20°C.
Figure 2 shows the data and best fit lines for the frog at both 10°C and 20°C.
Figure 3 shows all four lines together.

Figure 1

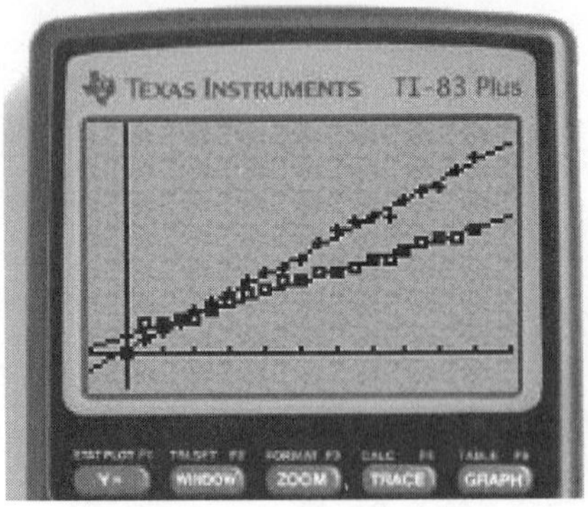

Figure 2

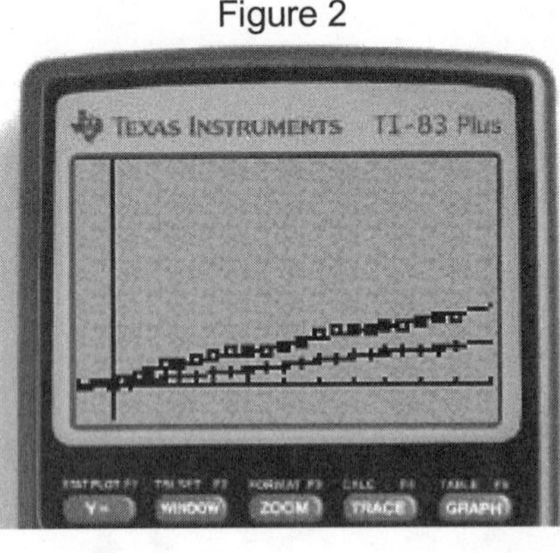

Figure 3

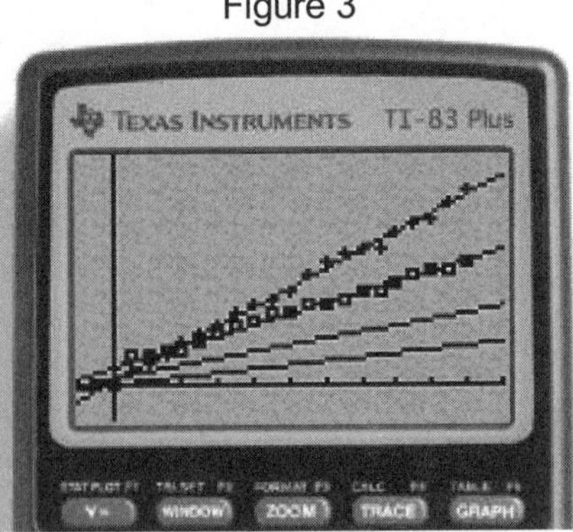

1. What happened to rate of respiration for the frog when the temperature was lowered?
   - The rate of respiration decreased when the temperature was lowered for the frog.

2. What happened to rate of respiration for the mouse when the temperature was lowered?
   - The rate of respiration increased when the temperature was lowered for the mouse.

3. The following is the formula for Q_{10}. Determine the Q_{10} for the frog and the mouse. How did the value for Q_{10} for the frog compare to that of the mouse? Explain why the values were so different.

$$Q_{10} = \frac{\text{(Rate of respiration at the higher temperature)}}{\text{(Rate of respiration at the lower temperature)}}$$

   - The Q_{10} value for the frog was 1.7, which means the rate of the chemical reactions increased with an increase in temperature. It almost doubled. The Q_{10} value for the mouse was .63. Q_{10} is not a valid measurement for endotherms because their metabolism is constant regardless of a change of temperature.

Mouse

$$Q_{10} = \frac{0.043\,\text{cc/min/g}}{0.068\,\text{cc/min/g}} = 0.63$$

Frog

$$Q_{10} = \frac{0.024\,\text{cc/min/g}}{0.014\,\text{cc/min/g}} = 1.71$$

4. Explain why oxygen is needed for the body.
   - Oxygen is needed for the cellular respiration.

5. Using the relationship that for every 1 L of oxygen consumed for respiration, approximately 4.83 kcal of energy are released, determine the metabolic rate in kcal/hr for both the mouse and frog at both temperatures. Use the average rate of respiration from you summary table for each organism and temperature. Be sure to show your work.

Mouse at 20°C

$$\frac{4.83\,\text{kcal}}{1\,\cancel{\text{L}}}\times\frac{8.5\,\text{m}\cancel{\text{L}}}{10\,\cancel{\text{min}}}\times\frac{1\,\cancel{\text{L}}}{1000\,\text{m}\cancel{\text{L}}}\times\frac{60\,\cancel{\text{min}}}{1\,\text{hr}}=0.25\,\text{kcal/hr}$$

Mouse at 10°C

$$\frac{4.83\,\text{kcal}}{1\,\cancel{\text{L}}}\times\frac{13.5\,\text{m}\cancel{\text{L}}}{10\,\cancel{\text{min}}}\times\frac{1\,\cancel{\text{L}}}{1000\,\text{m}\cancel{\text{L}}}\times\frac{60\,\cancel{\text{min}}}{1\,\text{hr}}=0.39\,\text{kcal/hr}$$

Frog at 20°C

$$\frac{4.83\,\text{kcal}}{1\,\cancel{\text{L}}}\times\frac{9.5\,\text{m}\cancel{\text{L}}}{10\,\cancel{\text{min}}}\times\frac{1\,\cancel{\text{L}}}{1000\,\text{m}\cancel{\text{L}}}\times\frac{60\,\cancel{\text{min}}}{1\,\text{hr}}=0.28\,\text{kcal/hr}$$

Frog at 10°C

$$\frac{4.83\,\text{kcal}}{1\,\cancel{\text{L}}}\times\frac{5.5\,\text{m}\cancel{\text{L}}}{10\,\cancel{\text{min}}}\times\frac{1\,\cancel{\text{L}}}{1000\,\text{m}\cancel{\text{L}}}\times\frac{60\,\cancel{\text{min}}}{1\,\text{hr}}=0.16\,\text{kcal/hr}$$

6. The frog was twice the size of the mouse, so one might expect that the frog would consume more oxygen because of its larger size. Adjust the answers that were calculated in question number five to compensate for that by dividing by the mass of the organism.

Mouse at 20°C

$$\frac{0.25\,\text{kcal/hr}}{20\,\text{g}}=0.013\,\text{kcal/hr/g}$$

Mouse at 10°C

$$\frac{0.39\,\text{kCal/hr}}{20\,\text{g}}=0.020\,\text{kcal/hr/g}$$

Frog at 20°C

$$\frac{0.28\,\text{kcal/hr}}{40\,\text{g}}=0.007\,\text{kcal/hr/g}$$

Frog at 10°C

$$\frac{0.16\,\text{kcal/hr}}{20\,\text{g}}=0.004\,\text{kcal/hr/g}$$

7. What happened to the metabolic rate of the frog and mouse when the temperature of the environment was lowered? What explanation can you give for any observed differences?
   - The metabolic rate of the mouse increased when the temperature was lowered. This is a physiological response in order to generate more heat to keep the internal temperature constant. The metabolic rate of the frog decreased as the overall internal temperature of the frog decreased. This is a matter of chemical kinetics since all of its chemical reactions slowed down.

REFERENCES

Campbell, Neil, Lawrence G. Mitchell, and Jane B. Reece. *Biology*. New York: Addison Wesley Longman, 1999. pp. 784-787

Schmidt-Nielsen, Knut. *Animal Physiology*. Cambridge, UK: Cambridge University Press, 1997. pp. 218-222

Kermit Versus Mickey Mouse
Determining the Q_{10} of an Endothermic and Exothermic Organism

Metabolism is the sum total of the chemical reactions occurring in an organism. Animals consume oxygen and use it to "burn" or oxidize high energy organic compounds such as carbohydrates or fats to make ATP. As a by-product of this process another gas, carbon dioxide, is released. Over sixty percent of the energy released during the process of cellular respiration is released as heat energy. Some animals conserve this heat energy so that their body temperature remains constant regardless of the environmental temperature. These animals are called endotherms or homeotherms. A more general term for an endothermic animal is a "warm-blooded" animal. Mammals, birds, and other animals such as bees are endotherms.

Animals that release their heat energy to the environment are called ectotherms or poikilotherms. A "cold-blooded" animal is the more general term. Ectothermy means the animal's body temperature is equal to that of the environment. This means that these animals' metabolisms are influenced by environmental temperature. Ectotherms are sluggish when it is cold and can move quickly when it is warm. The behavior of ectotherms can modify their internal temperature. For instance, a lizard can sun itself, or bask, when it is cold and increase its temperature or move to a wet environment when it is hot to lower its internal temperature.

The metabolism of an ectotherm decreases when it is cooler and increases when it is warmer. This is a disadvantage to ectotherms because when the temperature drops, the ectotherm responds more slowly. However, the advantage of being an ectotherm is that they do not require as much food. Endotherms, on the other hand, have the advantage that their metabolic rate stays constant, and they do not get "sluggish" in cold weather. The disadvantage of, being an endotherm is that it requires a tremendous amount of energy and thus food, to maintain that constant body temperature. For example, an average human at rest at 20° C requires 1300-1800 kilocalories (kcal) of food energy per day, whereas an alligator of approximately the same size, at the same temperature requires only 60 kilocalories of food per day.

An animal's metabolic rate is the total amount of energy it uses per unit time. The metabolic rate of an animal can be measured several ways. One way to measure metabolic rate is to measure the animal's heat loss per unit of time. Heat is lost from an animal as it uses chemical energy. Another way to measure metabolic rate is to determine the amount of oxygen consumed by an animal as a result of cellular respiration. This can be done with a respirometer. It is estimated that for every liter of oxygen consumed by an organism, respiration releases approximately 4.83 kilocalories of energy.

In chemistry, a measurement of a rate of a chemical reaction and its relationship to temperature is called Q_{10}. Q_{10} is the ratio of the rate of a chemical reaction at one temperature to the rate of that same chemical reaction at a second temperature.

$$Q_{10} = \frac{\text{(Rate of respiration at the higher temperature)}}{\text{(Rate of respiration at the lower temperature)}}$$

It is usually studied in 10° increments. Therefore if the temperature of an organism goes from 15° to 25° C and its metabolism doubles, then Q_{10} is equal to 2. Similarly, if the metabolism triples then Q_{10} is equal to 3.

PURPOSE

In this activity you will determine the metabolic rate per gram of body mass for an endotherm and an ectotherm. You will also calculate their respective Q_{10} values.

MATERIALS

TI-83 graphing calculator or computer with graphing software

PROCEDURE

In this activity, you will analyze data that was collected during an experiment. This experiment was performed on an endotherm, a mouse, and an ectotherm, a frog. The data in this activity was collected using a respirometer which was set up as shown below. The container was tightly sealed in order to measure the amount of oxygen consumed by the organism. At the beginning of the experiment, the syringe contained 20 cc of oxygen gas. The syringe measures the amount of oxygen the animal consumes. The soda lime in the respirometer combines with the carbon dioxide produced as the animal respires forming a solid. This means that the only gas influencing the pressure in the container is oxygen. The colored water will move toward the respirometer as the animal inside begins to consume oxygen. Pushing the plunger on the syringe will return the water to it original position. This also will measure how much oxygen the animal is consuming.

The mouse and frog were weighed and their masses are recorded in the data table.

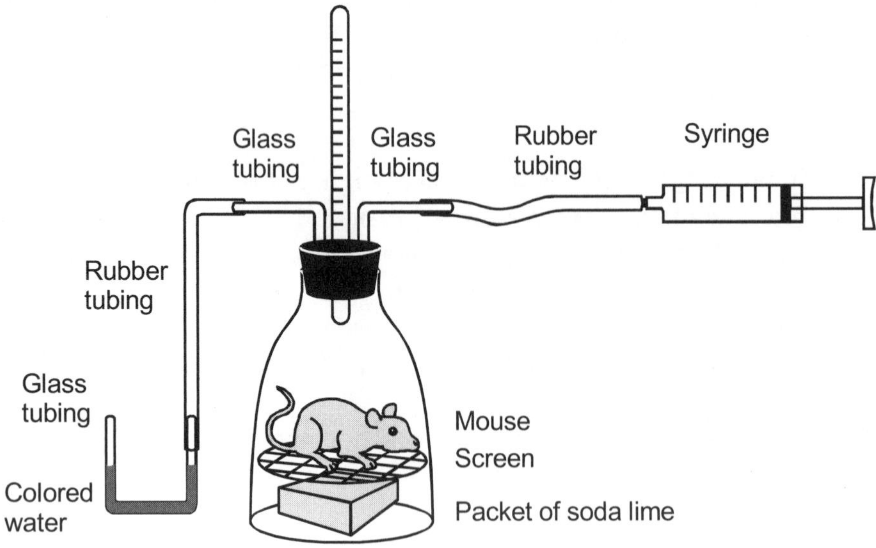

The reading on the syringe is recorded every 30 seconds for 10 minutes. There were experiment was done four times. Once with the mouse at room temperature and a second time with the frog at room temperature. The third and fourth times the respirometer is put into a resealable gallon bag filled with ice. The temperature of the respirometer is brought down to 10° C. The experiment was repeated with the mouse and then with the frog at this cooler temperature.

The readings from the syringe were recorded on the data table. This data is found on your student answer sheet.

1. Answer the pre-lab questions on the student answer sheet.

2. Determine the cumulative readings in the third column by subtracting the syringe reading from 20 cc. This is the amount of oxygen contained in the syringe.

3. The frog and mouse have different masses. The amount of oxygen consumed should be converted to the amount of oxygen consumed per gram of body mass to provide a more accurate comparison. To determine this value divide the #O_2 in cc consumed values by the mass of the animal for each time point recorded. Record these values in column four, the #O_2 in cc consumed per gram.

4. Construct a graph that illustrates the amount of oxygen consumed per gram of body mass for each organism over time. The graph should have four lines, one for each run of the experiment. Be sure to give the graph a descriptive title and correctly label the axes and lines.

5. To determine the average rate of respiration over this 10 minute interval, divide the final value of #O_2 consumed by ten minutes. Now, to determine the average rate of respiration per gram of body mass of the organism, divide your calculated average rate of respiration by the mass of the frog or mouse. Record these values in the summary table provided on your student answer page.

6. Determined the Q_{10} value for both organisms. Completely explain your results.

   ***Optional** - These calculations can be done on a TI-83 calculator by doing the following:

1. Turn your calculator on, ON, and press CLEAR to clear the screen. To make a data table press STAT, then select EDIT (Figure 1) and press ENTER. Notice that there are columns, or lists, for recording data.

2. To clear a list that might have data in it, put the cursor at the very top of the list so that the name of the column is highlighted. Press CLEAR followed by the ▼.

3. Now enter the time in L1 starting at 0 for the first entry and ending at 100 percent for the last entry. In L2 record the corresponding measurement on the syringe.

4. To determine the amount of oxygen used per gram of body mass, move the cursor to the left move the cursor up so that it is on L3 and press ENTER then enter the equation (20-L2)/20 by pressing (, 2 , 0 , − , 2nd 2 [L2],) , ÷ , 2 , 0 ENTER (Figure 2).

Figure 1

Figure 2

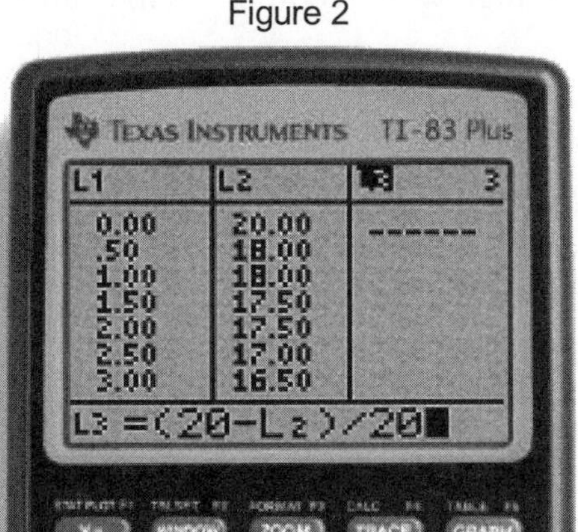

- Repeat this for the next three sets of data. Use L2 for the syringe readings and be sure to remove the previous data or overwrite the data present in L2. Put the 2nd, 3rd, and 4th sets of data in L4, L5, L6 respectively. Be sure when working with the frog data, you divide by 40g instead of 20g.
- Your lists should contain the following information:

L1	L2	L3	L4	L5	L6
Time	Syringe readings for appropriate trial	#O2 cc/g for warm mouse (20-L2)/20	#O2 cc/g for cold mouse (20-L2)/20	#O2 cc/g for warm frog (20-L2)/40	#O2 cc/g for cold frog (20-L2)/40

5. To view a graph of the mouse at 20° C and 10° C, press 2nd , Y= , ENTER . At this time make sure put your cursor on PLOT 1 and press ENTER and move the cursor down to ON and press ENTER . Both PLOT 1 and ON should be highlighted. All other plots should be inactivated. Highlight the scatter graph (the first of graph displayed) and press ENTER .

6. Highlight the Xlist and press 2nd , 1 [L1]. Highlight the Ylist and press 2nd , 3 [L3].

7. Highlight the box symbol (for the mark) and press ENTER . (Figure 3)

Figure 3

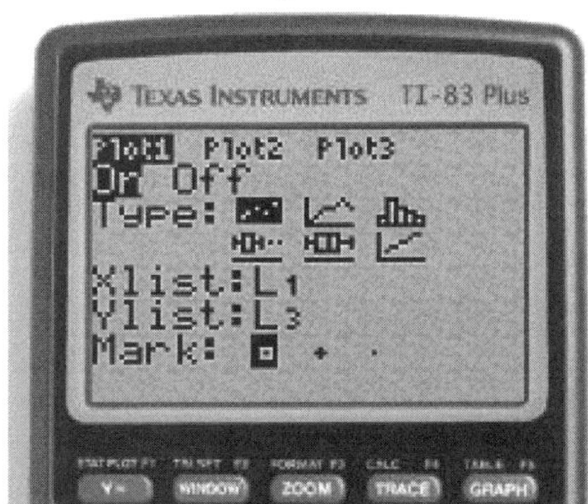

Figure 4

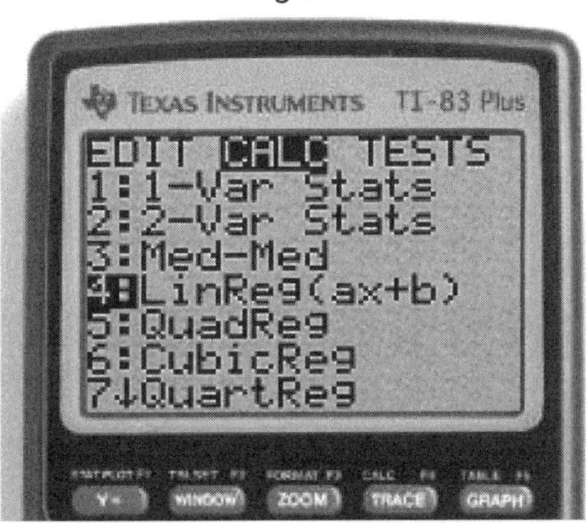

8. To activate a second line or graph a second set of data, put the cursor on PLOT 2 and press ENTER then move the cursor down to ON and press ENTER. Both PLOT 2 and ON should be highlighted. All other plots should be inactivated. Highlight the scatter graph (the first of graph displayed) and press ENTER.

9. Highlight the Xlist and press 2nd, 1 [L1]. Highlight the Ylist and press 2nd, 4 [L4].

10. Highlight the cross-hairs symbol (for the mark) and press ENTER.

11. Press ZOOM, then press 9. A graph should appear that will automatically adjust the axis's so that they fit the window. It should display the amount of oxygen consumed per gram of mouse tissue versus time.

    Examine the graph and notice that the relationship between time and the amount of oxygen consumed per gram of body mass is a linear relationship. While it is a linear relationship, notice that not all the points make a perfectly straight line. In analyzing data such as this, investigators draw a line of best fit. It is a line in which equal numbers of points are above the line and equal numbers of points are below the line. With the *y*-axis of the graph being oxygen consumption per gram and the *x*-axis of the graph being time, the slope of this line represents the rate of oxygen consumption per gram of body mass. By using all of the data points rather than just the initial and final data points, the slope calculation is a much more accurate representation of the rate of oxygen consumption. To make a line of best fit, do the following

12. To make the regression line or best-fit line, press STAT, and then press ► so that the cursor is on **CALC**. Press 4 so that LinReg (ax+b) is chosen. (Figure 4)

13. The blinking cursor is asking what lists the linear regression line is for, so press 2nd, 1 [L1], ,, 2nd, 3 [L3], so that list 1 and list 3 are selected (Figure 5). Press ENTER and the linear equation for the data points in L1 and L3 should appear. The numerical coefficient for X is the rate respiration per gram of body mass for a mouse at 20° C (Figure 6).

Figure 5

Figure 6

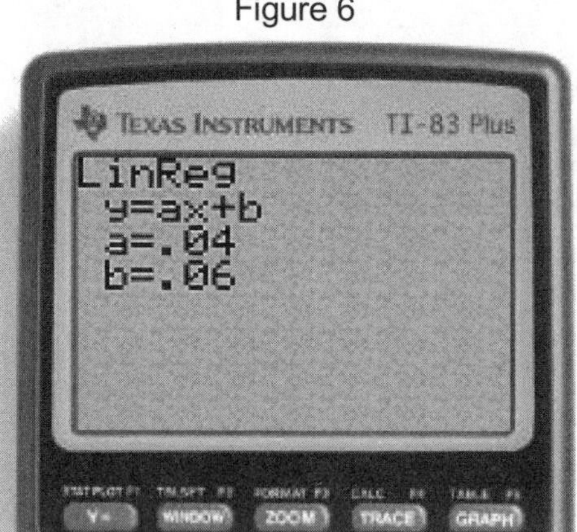

14. Now press Y= and move the cursor down so that it is at Y1=. (Figure 7) It should be blinking. Make sure that no other equations or numbers are there or in any other equation. Clear them out if there is anything else present. This is asking what equation Y is equal to. To paste an equation there do the following:
   a. Press VARS and 5. (Figure 8)
   b. Press ▶ so that the cursor highlights **EQ**. (Figure 9)
   c. Press 1 or **RegEQ**.and press ENTER. (Figure 10)
   d. Now the regression line should be on the graph.
   e. Press GRAPH. If the axis need to be adjusted press ZOOM, 9.

Figure 7

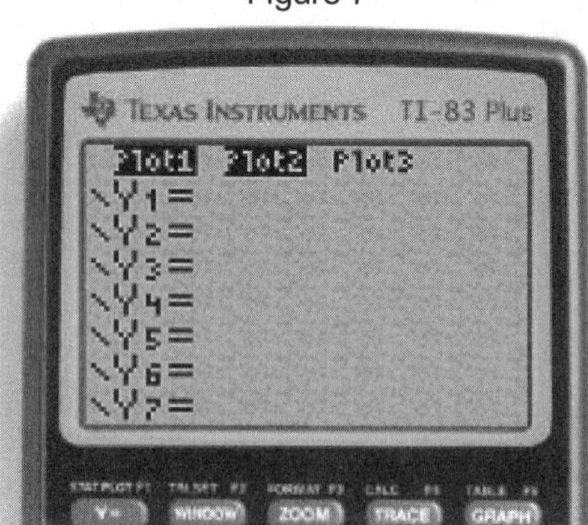

Figure 8

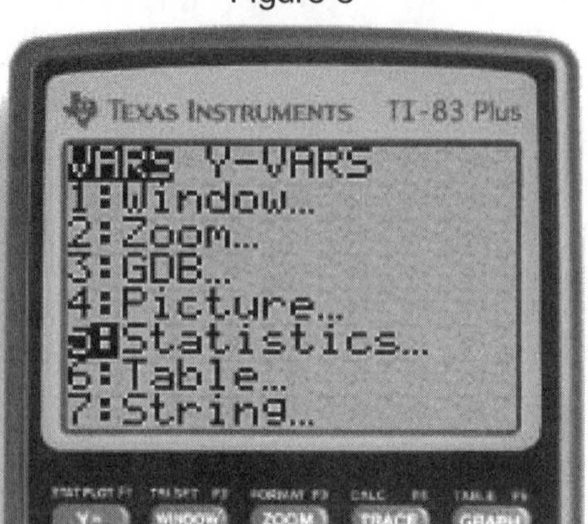

Figure 9

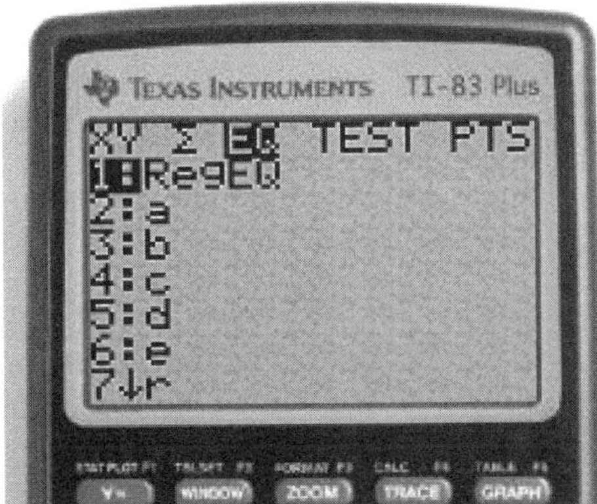

Figure 10

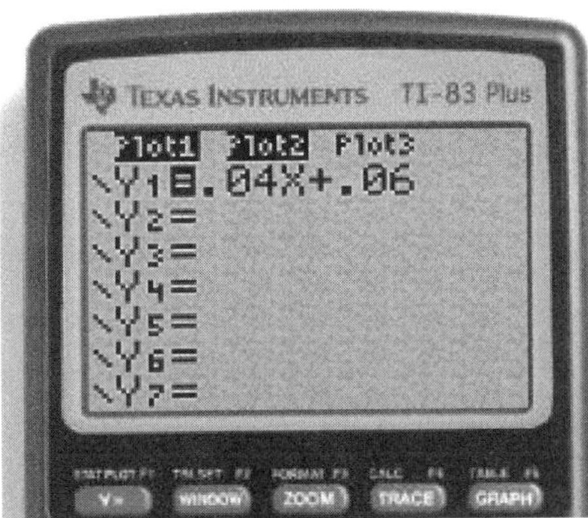

15. To make a regression line for the second set of data displayed on the graph (mouse at 10° C) repeat steps 12-14 but make the following changes:
    a. On step 13, instead of using L3 use L4 [2nd], [4] [L4].
    b. On step 14, paste the equation on Y2= instead of Y1=.
    c. Now two regression lines should appear. One line represents the rate of respiration for the mouse per gram of body mass at 20° C and the other line is the same rate but at 10° C (Fig. 11).

Figure 11

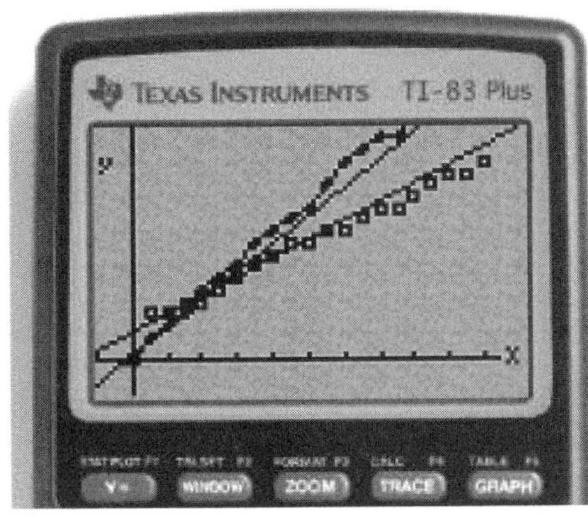

16. To display the data collected for the frog experiment, repeat steps 5-15 but make the following changes:
    a. Step # 6 change to [2nd], [5] [L5].
    b. Step # 9 change to [2nd], [6] [L6].
    c. Step # 13.change (L3) to [2nd], [5] [L5] so that list 1 and list 5 are selected.
    d. Step # 15a when redoing this step for the second regression line for the frog in the cold environment, instead of using L3 use L6 [2nd], [6] [L6].
    e. Now two regression lines should appear. One line represents the rate of respiration for the frog per gram of body mass at 20° C and the other line is the same rate of respiration at 10° C.

Name ______________________________

Period______________________________

Kermit Versus Mickey Mouse
Determining the Q_{10} of an Endothermic and Exothermic Organism

DATA AND OBSERVATIONS

	Mouse Mass 20 g Room Temperature 20º Celsius			Mouse Mass 20 g Cold Temperature 10º Celsius		
Time	**Syringe Reading**	**# O_2 Consumed**	**# O_2 Consumed per gram**	**Syringe Reading**	**# O_2 Consumed**	**# O_2 Consumed per gram**
0.0	20.0			20.0		
0.5	18.0			19.0		
1.0	18.0			18.5		
1.5	17.5			18.0		
2.0	17.5			17.0		
2.5	17.0			16.5		
3.0	16.5			16.0		
3.5	16.0			15.0		
4.0	15.5			14.5		
4.5	15.0			14.0		
5.0	15.0			13.5		
5.5	14.5			12.5		
6.0	14.5			11.5		
6.5	14.0			11.0		
7.0	13.5			10.5		
7.5	13.5			10.5		
8.0	13.0			9.5		
8.5	12.5			9.0		
9.0	12.0			8.5		
9.5	12.0			7.5		
10.0	11.5			6.5		

	Frog Mass 40 g Room Temperature 20° Celsius			Frog Mass 40 g Cold Temperature 10° Celsius		
Time	**Syringe Reading**	**# O_2 Consumed**	**# O_2 Consumed per gram**	**Syringe Reading**	**# O_2 Consumed**	**# O_2 Consumed per gram**
0.0	20.0			20.0		
0.5	19.5			20.0		
1.0	18.0			19.5		
1.5	17.0			19.0		
2.0	17.0			18.5		
2.5	16.5			18.5		
3.0	16.0			18.0		
3.5	15.5			18.0		
4.0	15.0			18.0		
4.5	15.0			17.5		
5.0	14.5			17.5		
5.5	14.0			17.0		
6.0	13.0			16.5		
6.5	12.5			16.5		
7.0	12.5			16.0		
7.5	12.5			16.0		
8.0	12.0			15.5		
8.5	11.5			15.5		
9.0	11.0			15.0		
9.5	10.5			15.0		
10.0	10.5			14.5		

Summary Table				
Organism	**Temperature (°C)**	**# Oxygen Consumed, cc**	**Average Rate Respiration # Oxygen cc/minute**	**Average Rate Respiration/gram body mass**
Mouse Warm				
Mouse Cold				
Frog Warm				
Frog Cold				

PRE-LAB QUESTIONS

Define the following:

1. Ectotherm/poikilotherm

2. Endotherm/homeotherm

3. Q_{10}

4. What is the advantage of being a homeotherm?

5. What is the disadvantage of being a endotherm?

6. What is the advantage of being an ectotherm?

7. What is the disadvantage of being an ectotherm?

CONCLUSION QUESTIONS

1. What happened to the rate of respiration for the frog when the temperature was lowered?

2. What happened to the rate of respiration for the mouse when the temperature was lowered?

3. The following is the formula for Q_{10}. Calculate the Q_{10} for the frog compared and the mouse. How did the value for Q_{10} for the frog compare to that of the mouse? Explain why the values were so different.

$$Q_{10} = \frac{\text{(Rate of respiration at the higher temperature)}}{\text{(Rate of respiration at the lower temperature)}}$$

4. Explain why oxygen is needed for the body.

5. If 1 L of oxygen consumed for respiration, releases approximately 4.83 kcal of energy from food, then determine the metabolic rate in kcal/hr for both the mouse and frog at both temperatures. Be sure to show your work.

6. The frog was twice the size of the mouse, so one might expect that the frog would consume more oxygen because of its larger size. Adjust the answers that were calculated in question number five to compensate for that by dividing by the mass of the organism.

7. What happened to the metabolic rate of the frog and mouse when the temperature of the environment was lowered? What explanation can you give for any observed differences?

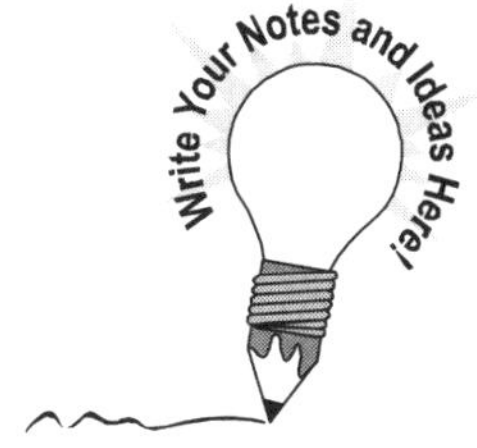
Write Your Notes and Ideas Here!

Specific Immune Response
Modeling the Immune System

OBJECTIVE
Students will test for antibody-antigen interaction using prescribed techniques. The students will explain the structure and specificity of antibodies. Then, they will model the immune response using models, text, and diagrams.

LEVEL
Biology I

NATIONAL STANDARDS
UCP.1, UCP.2, UCP.5, C.1, C.5, F.1, G.1, G.2

TEKS
1(A), 2(B), 2(C), 2(D), 10(A), 11(D)

CONNECTIONS TO AP
AP Biology:

III. Organisms and Populations B. Structure and Function of Plants and Animals 2. Structural, physiological and behavioral adaptation

TIME FRAME
Part I 30 minutes, 1 hour developing time.
Part II 50 minutes.

MATERIALS
For a class of 28 working in groups of 4

7 mL disposable plastic pipets
7 30 mL dropping bottles of solution A antigen (NaCl)
7 30 mL dropping bottles of solution A antibody ($AgNO_3$)
7 30 mL dropping bottles of unknown antigen
7 beakers (150 mL) of water to clean pipets
42 small Petri dishes (60 x 15 mm) with poured agar or agarose
7 Pasteur pipets or disposable plastic pipets for filling wells
7 30 mL dropping bottles of solution B antigen (KF)
7 30 mL dropping bottles of solution B antibody ($La(NO_3)_3$)
7 permanent markers
28 pairs of gloves

Part II

7 loose leaf rings
model pieces
resealable gallon size plastic bags

Safety Alert
1. CAUTION: All of the salts should be treated as tissue irritants and toxic by ingestion.
2. CAUTION: Eye/skin contact: flush with running water for 10 minutes. Do not ingest.

TEACHER NOTES

PART I

This lab uses chemical precipitation reactions to simulate the antigen-antibody reaction that occurs in vertebrates. There are two antigen-antibody combinations that will produce visible precipitates in Petri dishes containing agar. The "A" reaction uses silver nitrate (antibody A) and sodium chloride (antigen A) to give the following products:

silver nitrate + sodium chloride ⟶ silver chloride (precipitate) + sodium nitrate

The "B" reaction uses lanthanum nitrate (antibody B) and potassium fluoride (antigen B) to give the following products:

lanthanum nitrate + potassium fluoride ⟶ lanthanum fluoride (precipitate) + potassium nitrate

Both the silver chloride and lanthanum fluoride precipitates will form a white line in the agar to represent the formation of the antigen-antibody complex. The silver chloride line will darken upon exposure to ultraviolet light.

The specificity of the immune response is simulated because lanthanum does not react with chloride to form a precipitate and silver does not react with fluoride to form a precipitate. Therefore only the correct antibody-antigen combination will precipitate.

All the solutions are stable indefinitely at room temperature and can be used for several years once made. The silver nitrate should be stored in opaque, amber, or foil wrapped bottle due to its photo reactivity. To prevent contamination of the solutions, tie a disposable thin stem or graduated pipet to the neck of the bottle with a length of string about 30 cm long. Secure a small test tube to the side of the bottle with a rubber band or two and place the pipet into the test tube which acts as a holder. Instruct students to never lay the pipet on the countertop, but rather return it to the test tube after each use.

To prepare the solutions:

Antigen (AG) Antibody (AB)	add	to	dilute to
AB A	6.80 g $AgNO_3$	100 mL	200 mL (0.2 M)
AG A	23.38 g NaCI	100 mL	200 mL (0.4 M)
AB B	83.0 g $La(NO_3)_3 \bullet 5H_2O$	100 mL	200 mL (1 M)
AG B	116 g KF	100 mL	200 mL (10 M)

In addition to the above reagent solutions, each student will receive an unknown. Prepare and label the unknowns as follows:

- unknown AG #1 is water
- unknown AG # 2 is a combination of AG A and AG B made by adding 10 mL of .4 M NaCl and 10 mL of 1 M KF
- unknown AG #3 is AG B or 20 mL of 1 M KF
- unknown AG # 4 is AG A or 20 mL of .4 M NaCl

The agar/agarose plates are 2% agar/agarose plates and poured into small Petri dishes measuring 60 x 15 mm.

To prepare 450 mL of agar/agarose:

- **Note**: Agar is much less expensive than agarose.
- Mix 9 g of agar or agarose into 450 mL of distilled water in 2 L beaker. Heat the solution in a microwave for 4 -5 minutes, monitoring and stirring the solution each minute until it comes to a boil. The solution should be clear.
- **Caution: Use hot pads to handle this solution – it is very hot and will cause burns.**
- Dispense 10 mL of agar or agarose into each Petri dish. Put the lids on and allow the plates to solidify for 10-15 minutes. Turn upside down so condensation does not collect on the gels.
- Each group will need 6 plates for a total of 42 plates per class. These gels can be prepared in advance and stored for up to two weeks in a sealed plastic bag.

The antibody solutions are always placed in the center well and the antigen solutions are placed in the wells on the periphery.

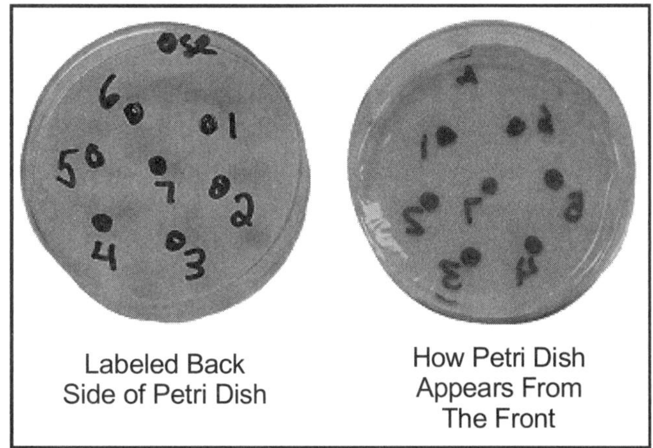

Labeled Back Side of Petri Dish

How Petri Dish Appears From The Front

PART II—MODEL BUILDING
This simulation uses models to demonstrate the immune response. Six events are used in this lesson. They include:

2. Recognizing Self
3. Revenge of the Monocytes
4. Cloning an Army of T-cells
5. Cytotoxic Attack
6. Cloning an Army of B-cells
7. The Glue Needed for Dinner

Each of the 6 simulated events includes a textual description, diagrams, and models. It is recommended that these items be copied onto colored paper (see below) and laminated before the models are cut. To make a manageable instruction booklet, trim the laminated text portions, then punch a hole in the upper left hand corner and secure the pages in order with a loose-leaf ring.

The colors for the model pieces should be:

T-Cells — blue and green
B-Cells — pink
Normal cells — yellow
Infected cells — red
Antigens
Antibodies

Once the models are cut, they can be stored in a resealable gallon-sized plastic bag. The first year this is done, you may want to enlist the help of your classes to cut the laminated paper models. Once they are laminated and cut, they will last for years.

When the text instructs the students to re-label a cell, the label is provided and should be taped onto the cell. The tape can later be removed easily without harming the model. You may want to use a water soluble pen for this part. The ink can be removed with water.

You may want to go though the simulation with your students for the first time. Be sure to identify each part with your students. Ask the students to remove the models from the bag and arrange them in an order that is meaningful to them. Working in a group of four, they should go through the simulation three times. The first time they do the simulation, the students should use the models, text, and diagram. The second time they do it, the students should use only the models and text. The third time they try it, the students should use only the models. Students should help each other as they try to explain the immune response to one another. Be sure to monitor the students and check for understanding.

1. "Recognizing Self"

During fetal development, T-cells match up with their own body cells. This is a match between the MHC receptor and the MHC protein on the body cell. Once the match is made, the T-cells become MHC restricted. Sometimes the match is between the T-cell and other leukocytes, like a monocyte, rather than a normal cell. Match the T-cells up with other cells and now label them MHC restricted and virgin-T cells. Make sure the correct labels end up on the correct T-cells.

1. Recognizing Self

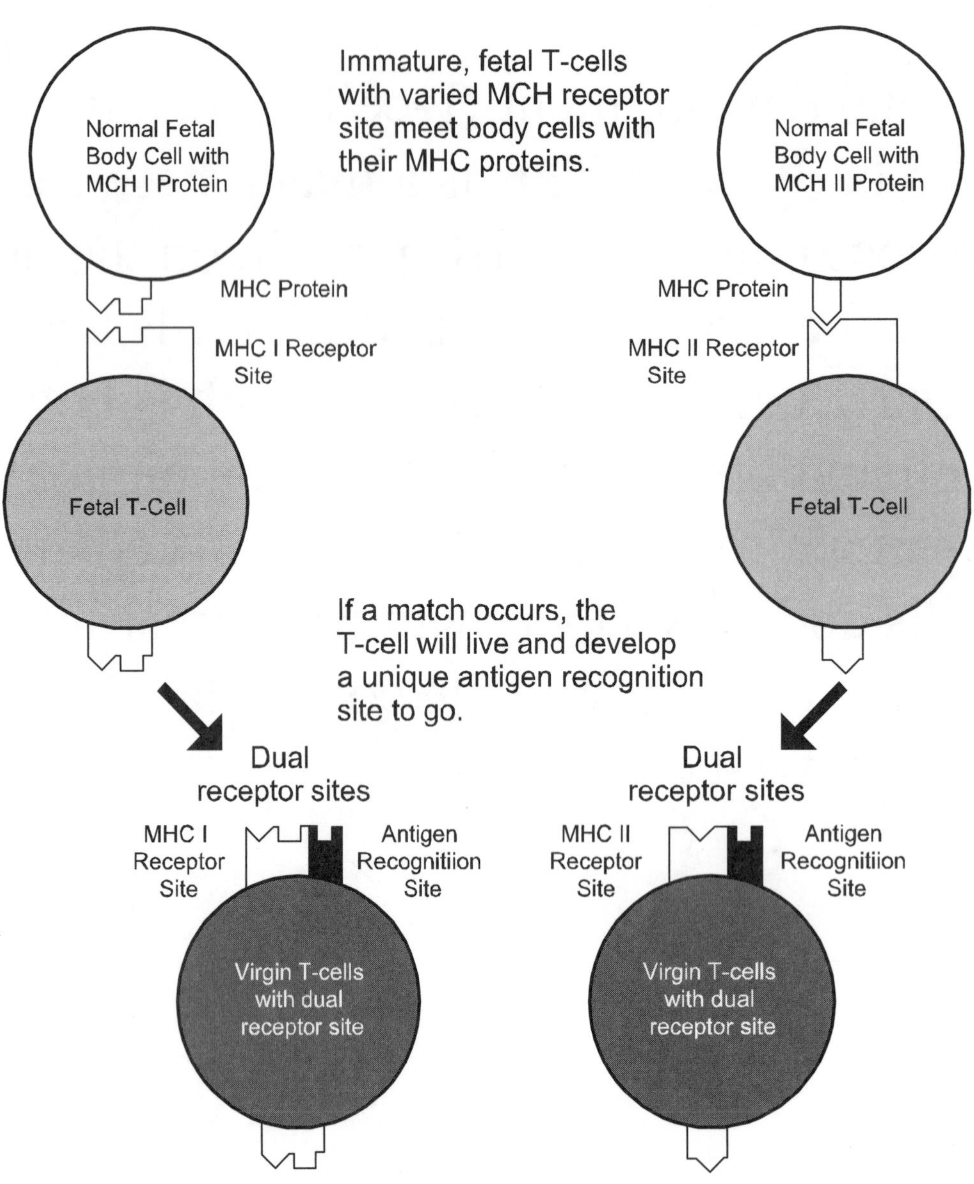

1. Models for recognizing self

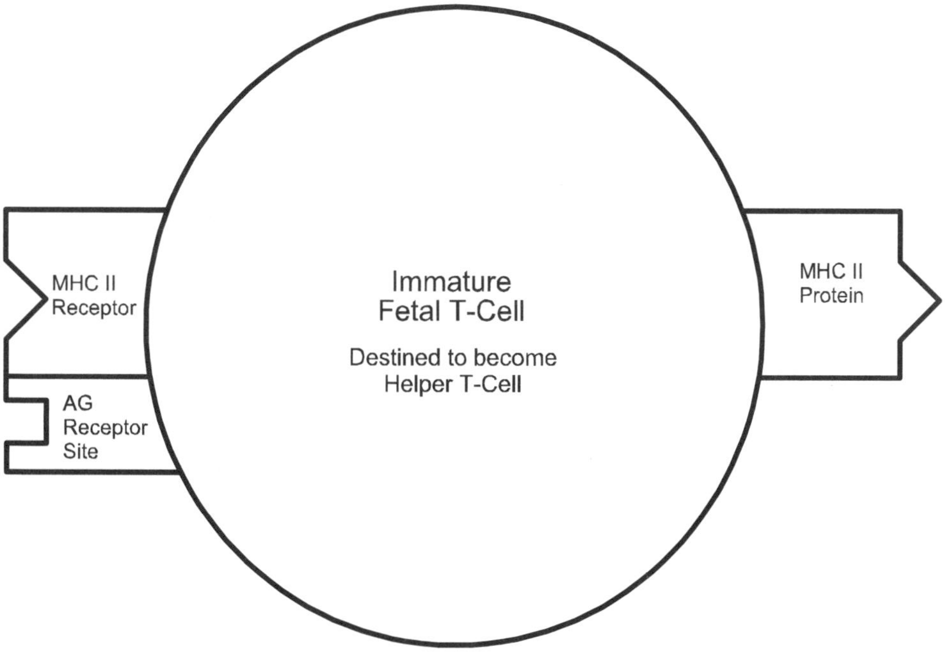

MHC II Receptor

AG Receptor Site

Immature Fetal T-Cell

Destined to become Helper T-Cell

MHC II Protein

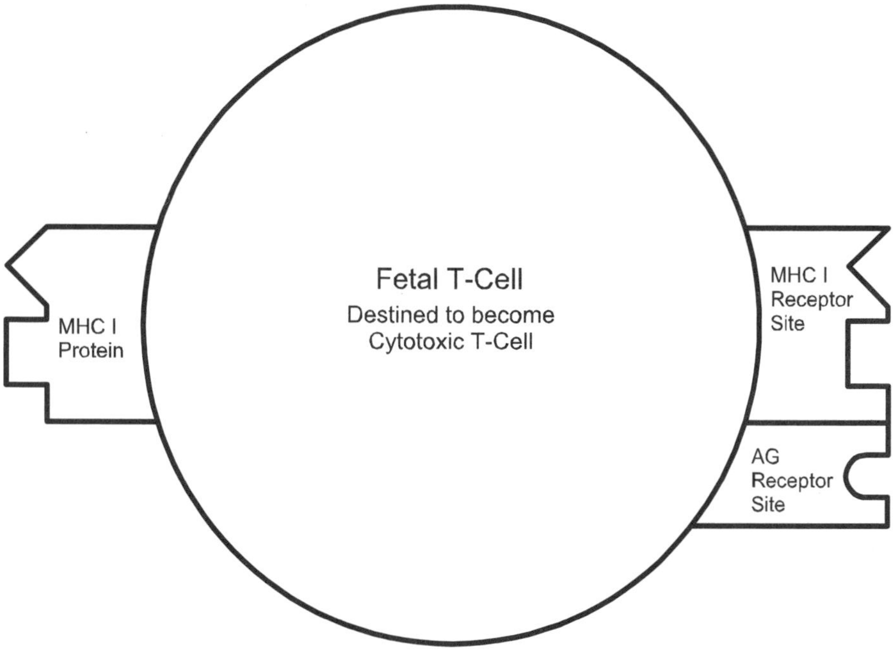

MHC I Protein

Fetal T-Cell

Destined to become Cytotoxic T-Cell

MHC I Receptor Site

AG Receptor Site

1. Models for recognizing self

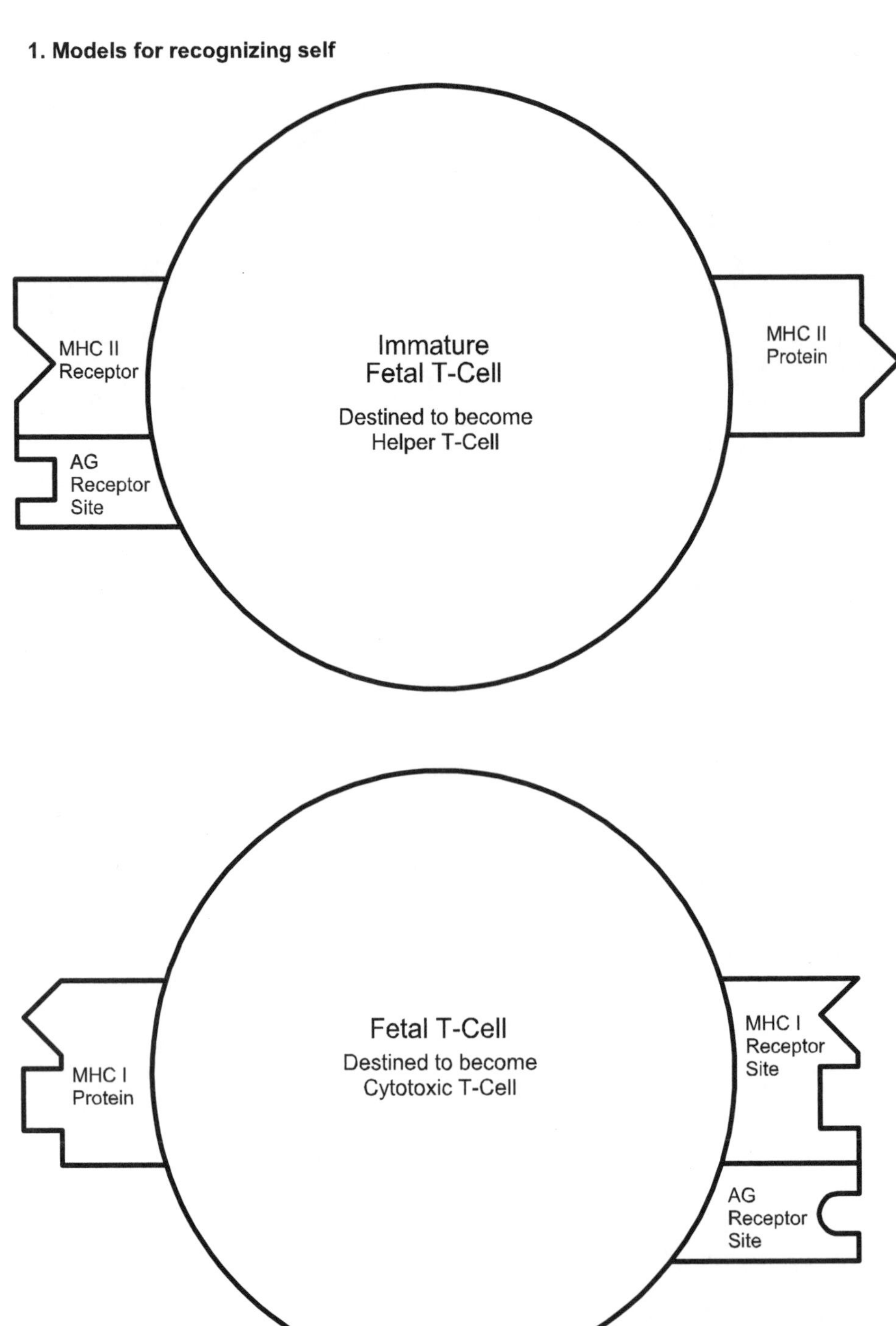

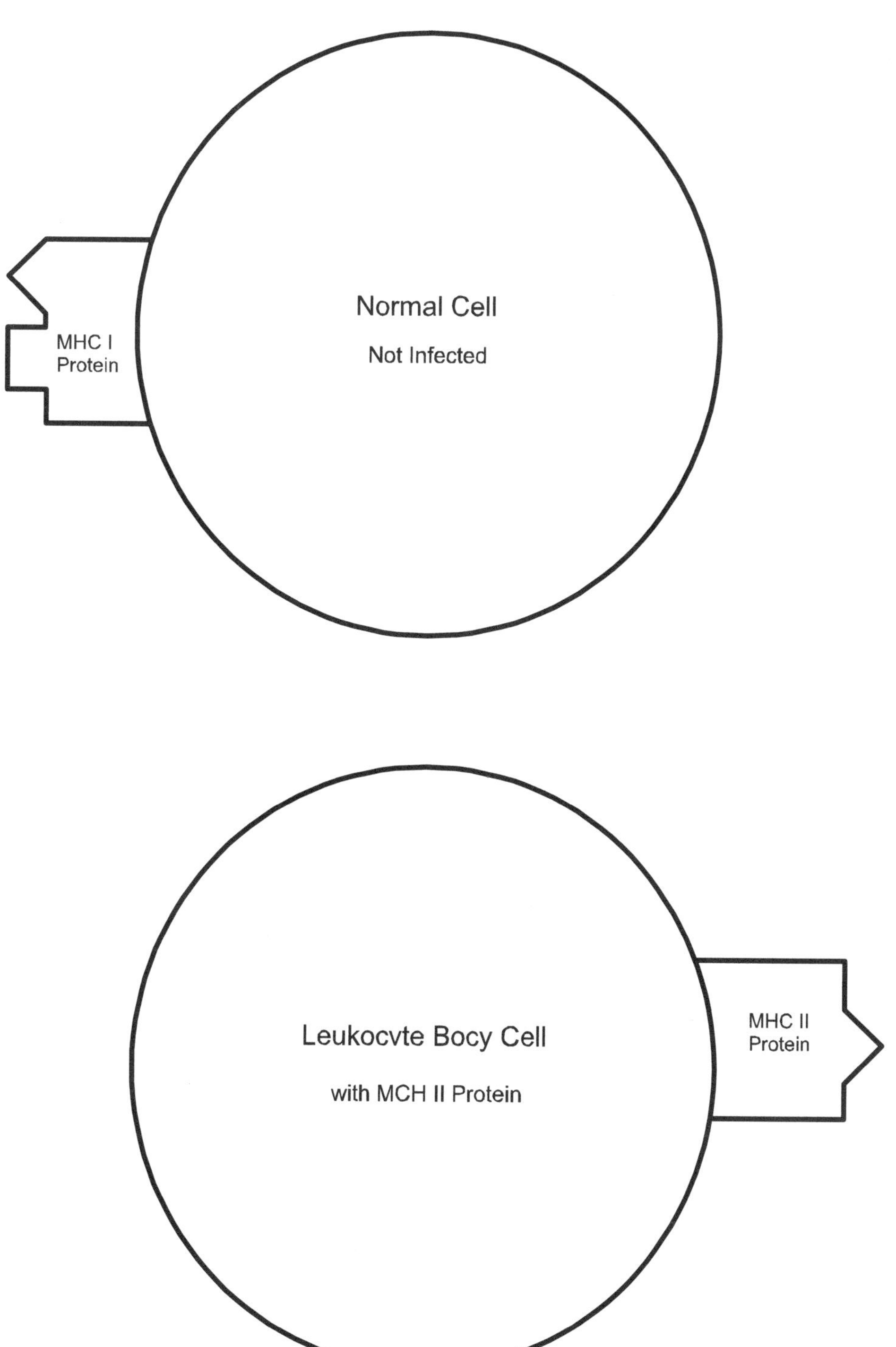
MHC I
Protein
Normal Cell
Not Infected
Leukocvte Bocy Cell
with MCH II Protein
MHC II
Protein

MHC Restricted
Virgin T-Cell

Destined to become
Cytotoxic T-Cell

MHC Restricted
Virgin T-Cell

Destined to become
Helper T-Cell

2. "Revenge of the Monocytes"

One of the first events to happen when the body is being infected by pathogens is the body's dispersal of monocytes. Once the monocytes arrive at the site of infection they are transformed into macrophages. Macrophages have both MHC I and MHC II proteins. These voracious macrophages begin to engulf the pathogens and as it does so, it begins to place antigens on the surface of its cell membranes next to the MHC I and II proteins. Find the monocyte and label it as a macrophage since it undergoes the transformation. Also find the antigen #1 and place it next to the MHC I protein and find antigen #2 and place it next to the MHC II protein.

2. Revenge of the monocytes

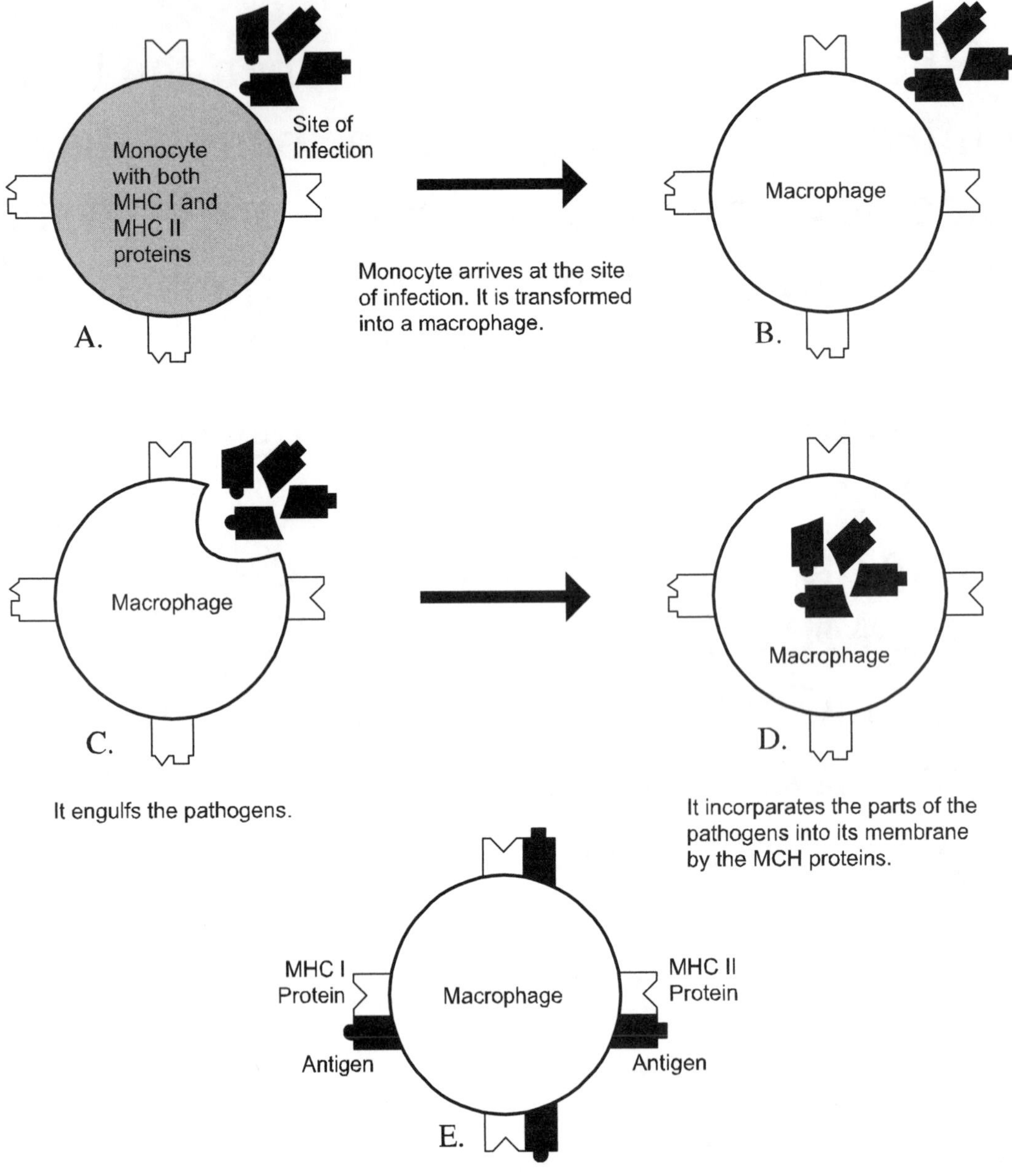
Monocyte
with both
MHC I and
MHC II
proteins
Site of
Infection
A.
Monocyte arrives at the site
of infection. It is transformed
into a macrophage.
Macrophage
B.
Macrophage
C.
It engulfs the pathogens.
Macrophage
D.
It incorparates the parts of the
pathogens into its membrane
by the MCH proteins.
MHC I
Protein
Antigen
Macrophage
MHC II
Protein
Antigen
E.
Antigen presenting macrophage.
Looking for a virgin T-cell to activate.

2. Revenge of the monocytes

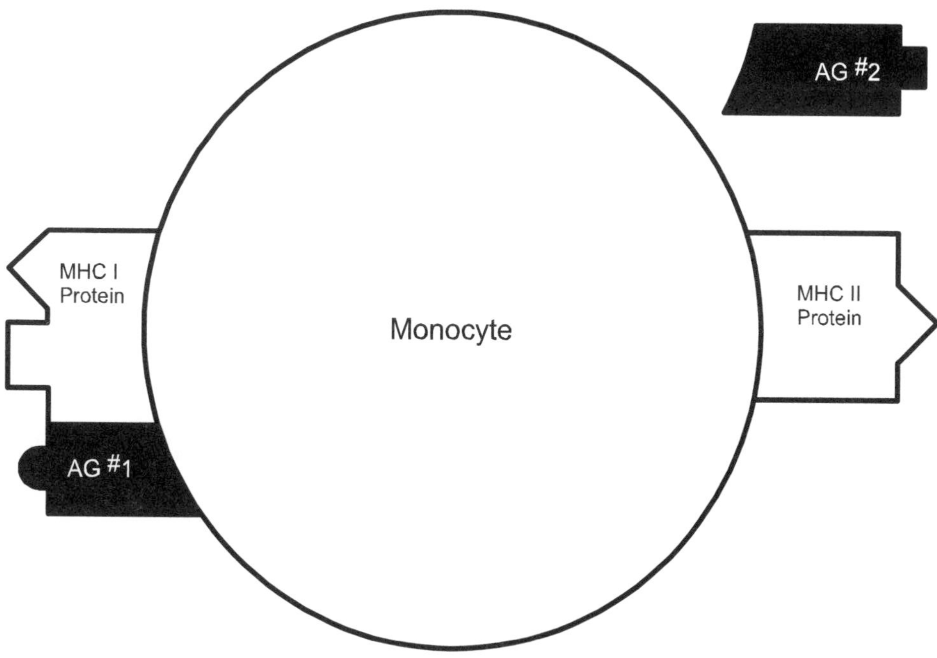

2. Revenge of the monocytes

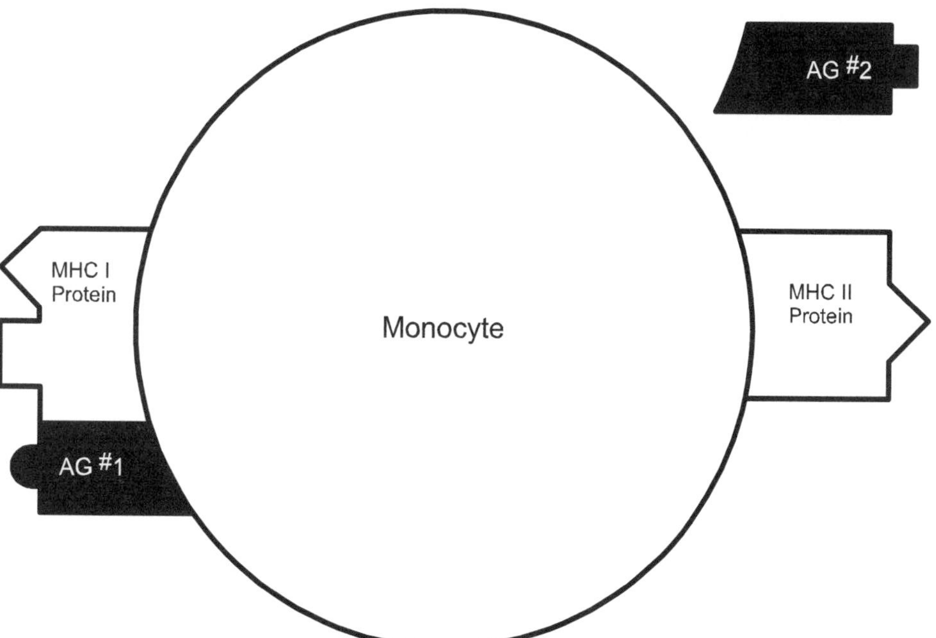

Macrophage
was once a monocyte

3. Clonal Selection or "Cloning an Army of T-cells"

Now the macrophage is an antigen-presenting macrophage. The antigen-presenting macrophage begins to "present" the antigens to the T-cells and tries to find a match. It must match both the MHC I protein and the antigen receptor site. If a match occurs, that particular T-cell is "selected" and the macrophage begins to secrete a substance called interleukin. Interleukin stimulates the T-cell to undergo mitotic divisions. The T-cell is "cloned" as it replicates itself during the process of mitosis. If the T-cell has a MHC I protein, it is destined to become a cytotoxic T-cell or if it has a MHC II protein, it is destined to become a helper T cell to be used in the humoral response. This process is called "clonal selection". Make a match between the macrophage and the T-cells. Re-label the T-cells as they are selected and then cloned. Note which ones are destined to become cytotoxic T-cells and which ones are to become helper T-cells.

3. Cloning an army of T-cells

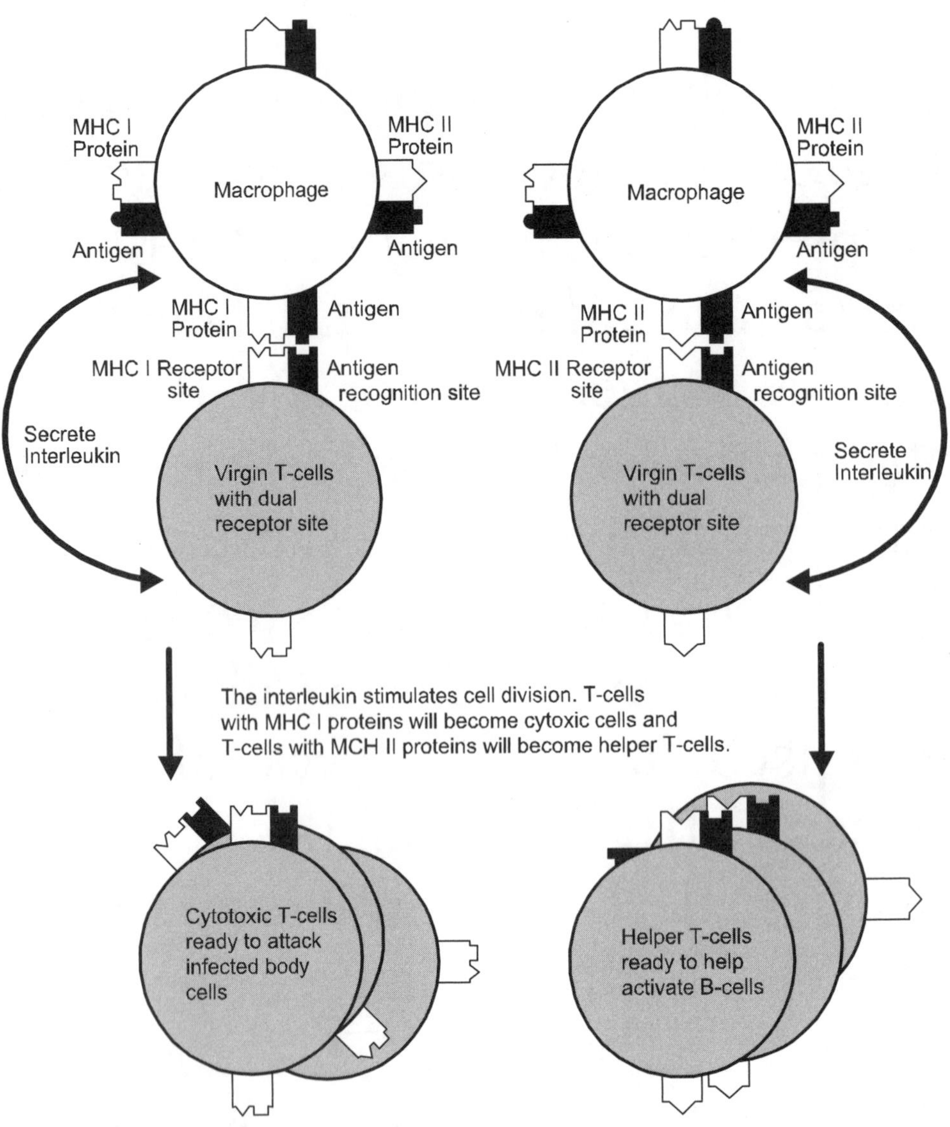

These T-cells with the MHC I protein will become cytotoxic cells. Their MHC I and antigen receptors will bind with infected body cells and kill them.

The helper T-cells will be used in the humoral response.

TEACHER PAGES

Models needed for 3. Cloning an army of T-cells.

Activated Cytotoxic T-Cell

On a mission to kill infected cells

Activated Helper T-Cell

On a mission to help B-cells to become activated

Activated Macrophage

Was once a monocyte

4. "Cytotoxic Attack"

Once the cytotoxic T-cells are cloned, the cloned cells begin to roam the body looking for infected cells. When a normal cell becomes infected with a pathogen, it is not unusual for parts of that pathogen to remain on the surface of the cell's membrane and become an antigen. With this tag, infected cells are differentiated from uninfected cells. Find a normal, uninfected cell. Notice that it only has the MHC I protein. Find the infected normal cell. Notice that it has the pathogen antigen on its surface and the MHC I protein. Now try to match the cytotoxic T-cell with the infected and uninfected cells. The match for both the MHC I protein and its antigen receptor site occurs only on the infected cell. The cytotoxic cell pokes holes into the infected cell. Water rushes in and lyses the infected cells, killing them. The cytotoxic cell will disengage and continue on its mission to try to find another match and destroy another infected cell

4. Cytotoxic T-cell Attack

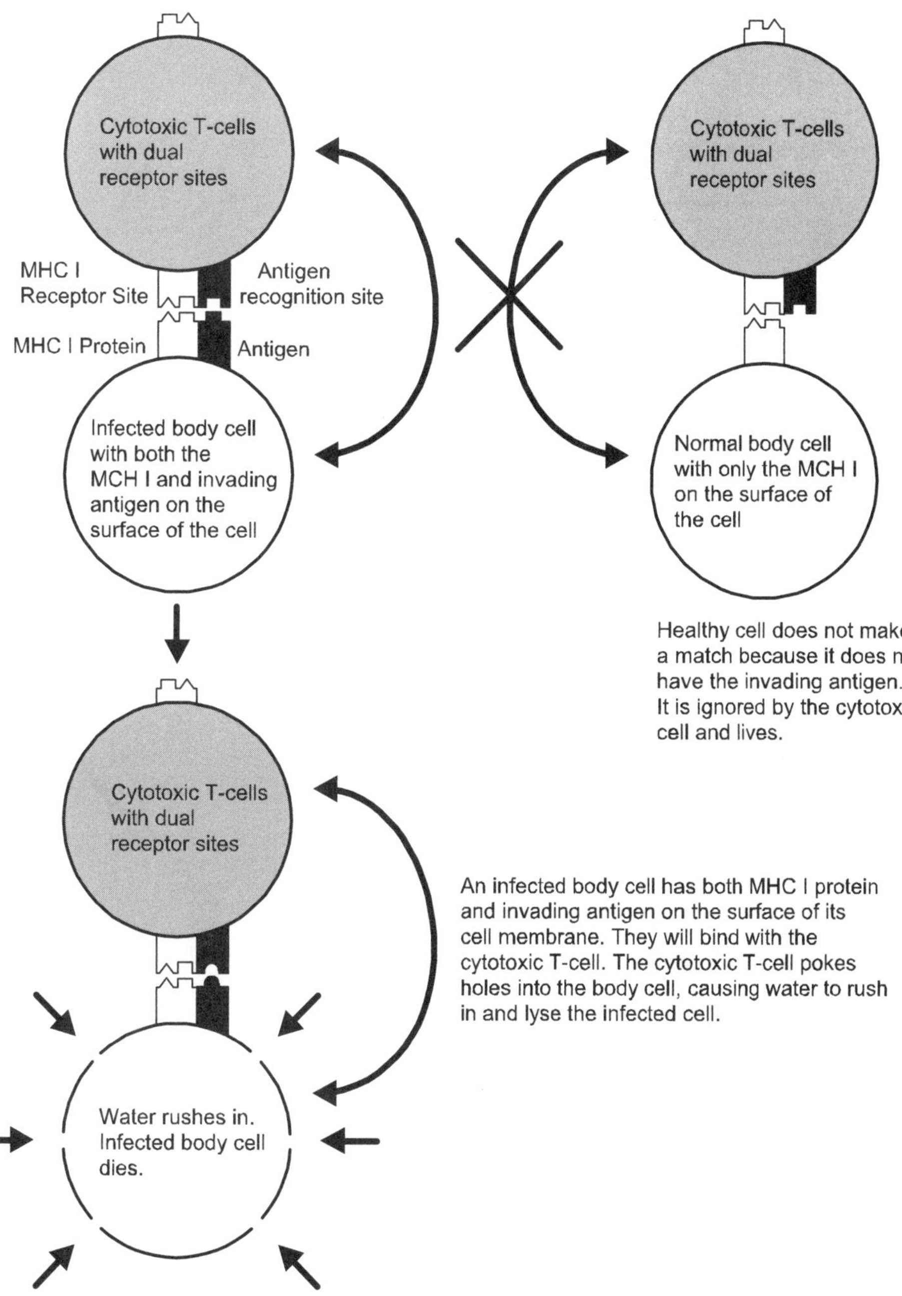

Healthy cell does not make a match because it does not have the invading antigen. It is ignored by the cytotoxic cell and lives.

An infected body cell has both MHC I protein and invading antigen on the surface of its cell membrane. They will bind with the cytotoxic T-cell. The cytotoxic T-cell pokes holes into the body cell, causing water to rush in and lyse the infected cell.

4. Models Needed for Cytotoxic Attack

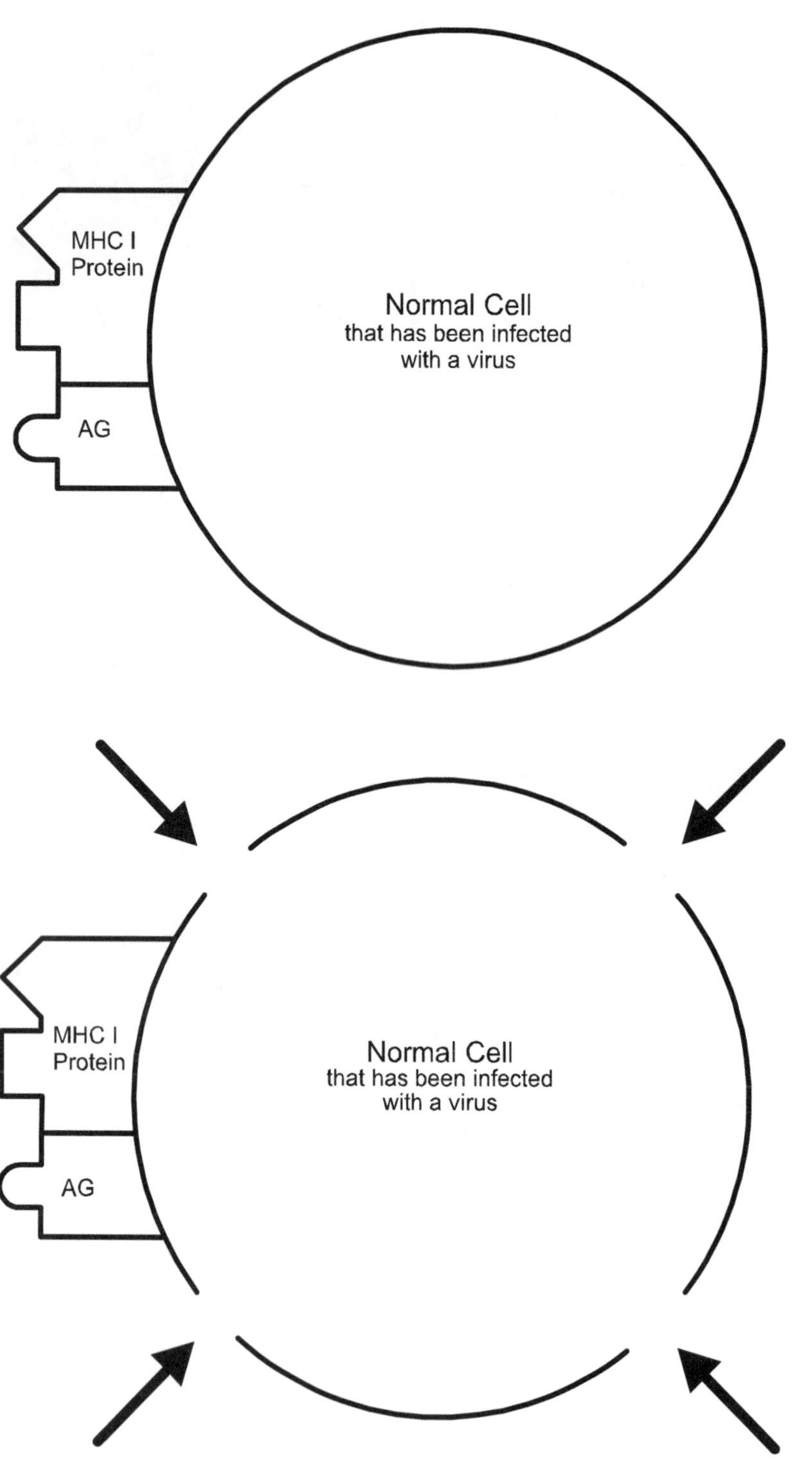

4. Models Needed for Cytotoxic Attack

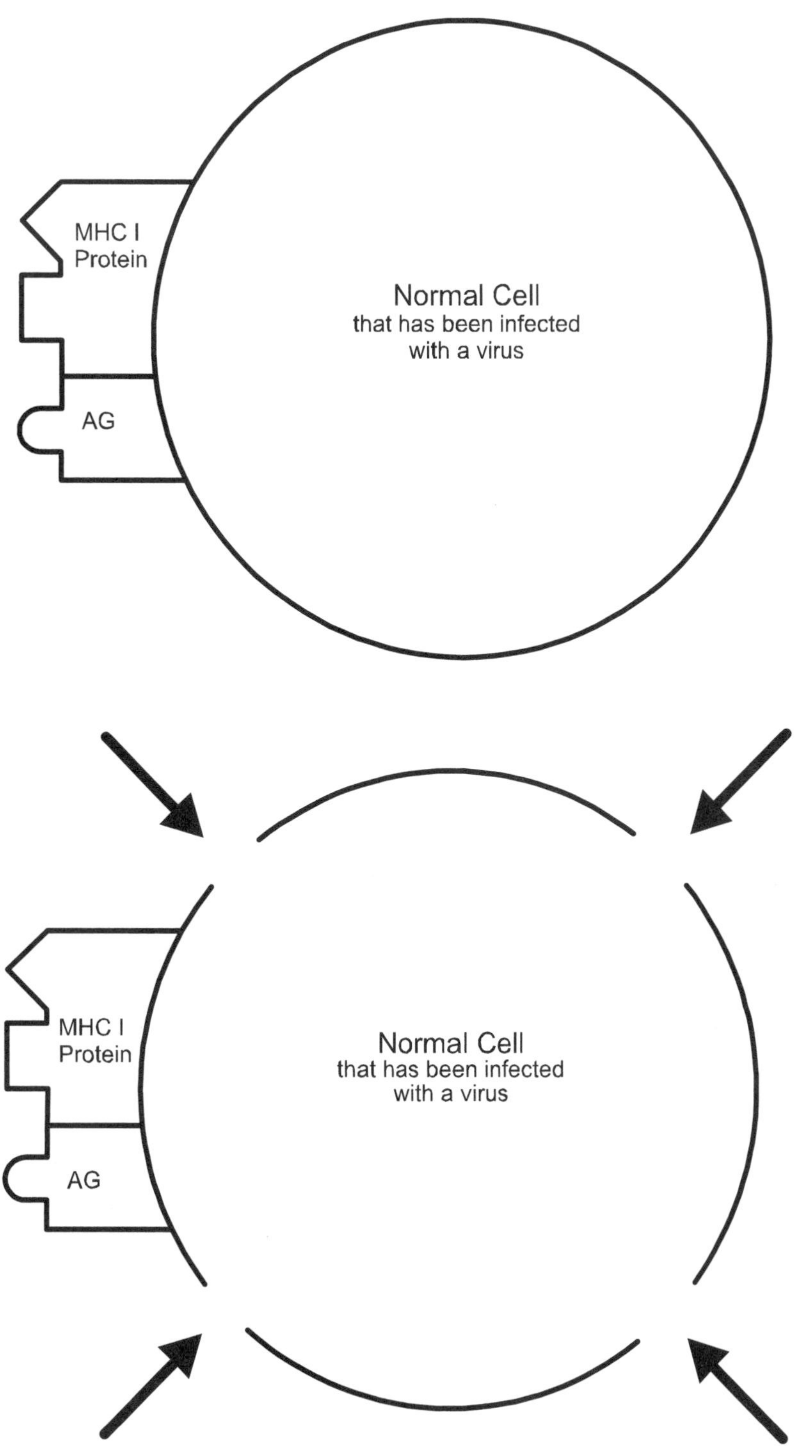

5. Humoral Response or "Cloning an Army of B-Cells"

The humoral response includes the selecting and cloning of the B-cells. This happens when a free-floating antigen encounters a B-cell that has an antibody on its cell membrane that is specific for that particular antigen. Once the antibody has bonded with the antigen, the antigen is placed next to the MHC II surface protein. In order to complete the activation of the B-cell, the helper-T cell is needed. Helper T-cells have receptor sites for MHC II proteins and antigens. These helper T-cells can now make a match between the B-cell's MHCII protein and the captured free-floating antigen. Once the binding between the two cells occurs, the helper T-cell will secrete interleukin much like the macrophage. This causes the B-cell to undergo mitosis and produce plasma B-cells. Re-label the B-cells as plasma B-cells.

5. Cloning an Army of B-cells

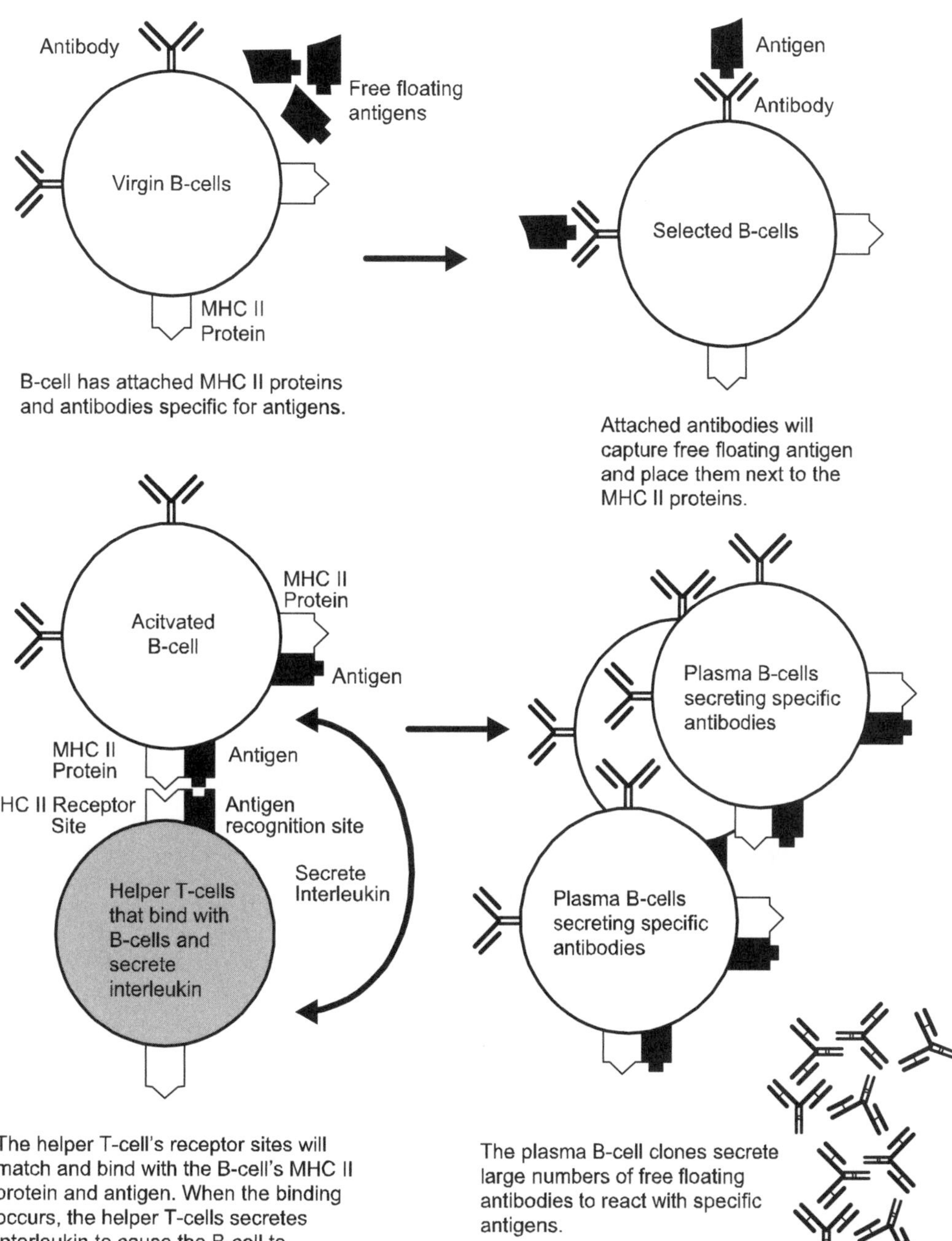

The helper T-cell's receptor sites will match and bind with the B-cell's MHC II protein and antigen. When the binding occurs, the helper T-cells secretes interleukin to cause the B-cell to replicate and form plasms B-cells.

The plasma B-cell clones secrete large numbers of free floating antibodies to react with specific antigens.

Models for #5.
Cloning an Army of B-cells

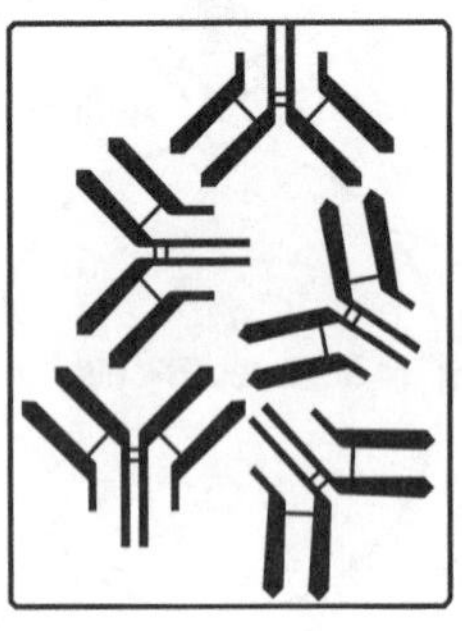

Activated B-Cell
Plasma B-Cell
Will secrete large amounts of antibodies for specific antigens

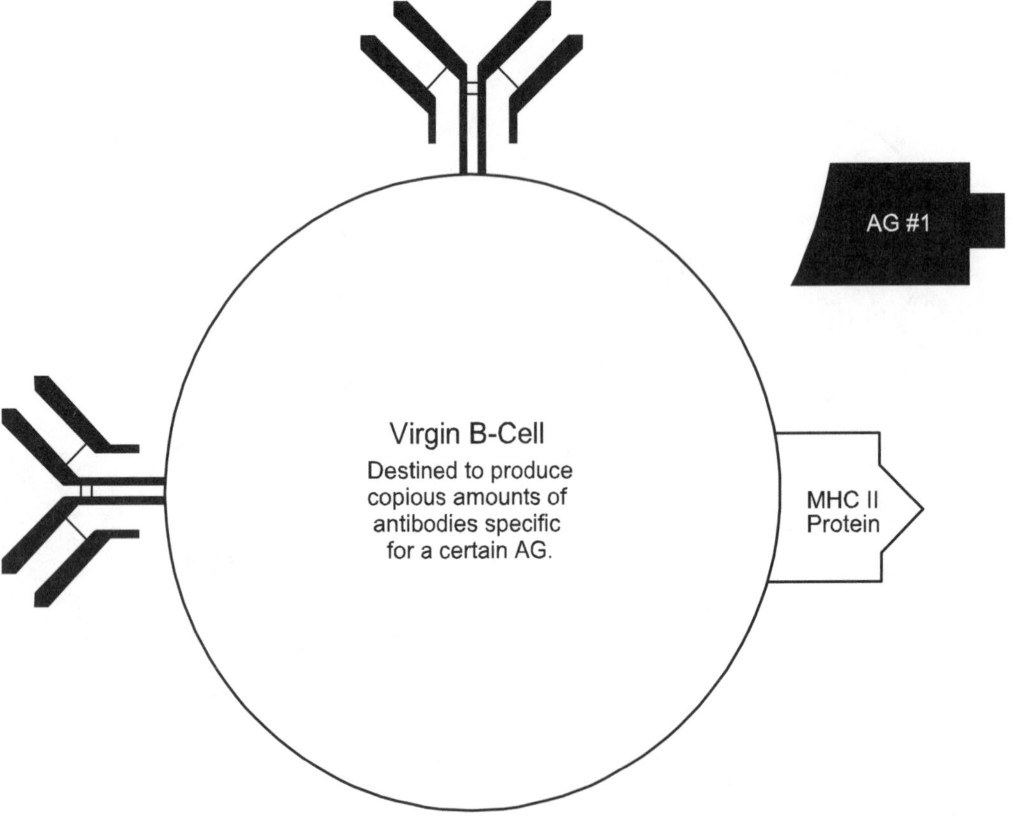

6. "The Glue Needed for Dinner"

Now the plasma cells will start secreting copious amounts of specific antibodies. These free- floating antibodies are specific for the invading antigen or pathogen. One way antibodies work is by binding with at least two antigens. This allows the antibodies and antigens to form clumps that the macrophages can clean up by phagocytosis.

6. Models needed for the glue needed for dinner

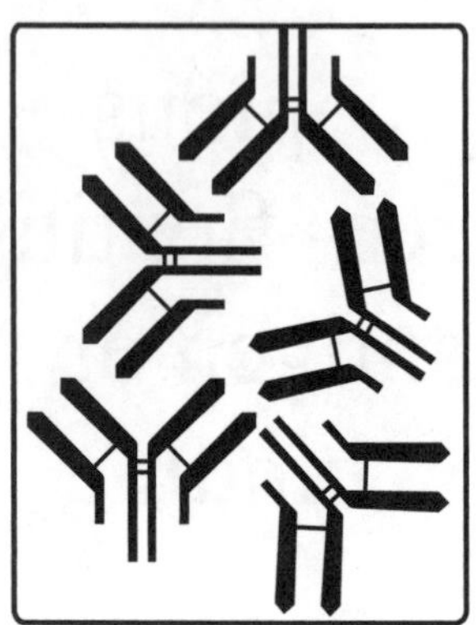

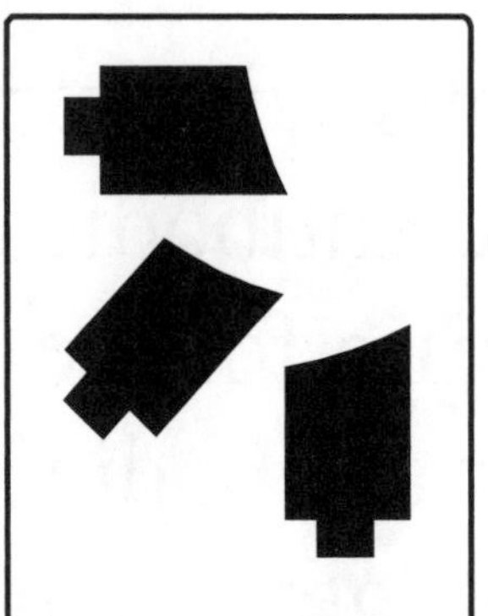

POSSIBLE ANSWERS TO THE CONCLUSION QUESTION AND SAMPLE DATA

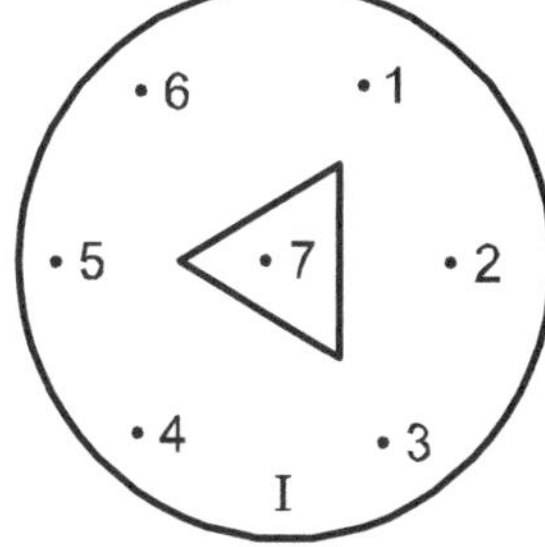

Antigen(s) used A
Antibody(s) used A
Reaction(+,-) +

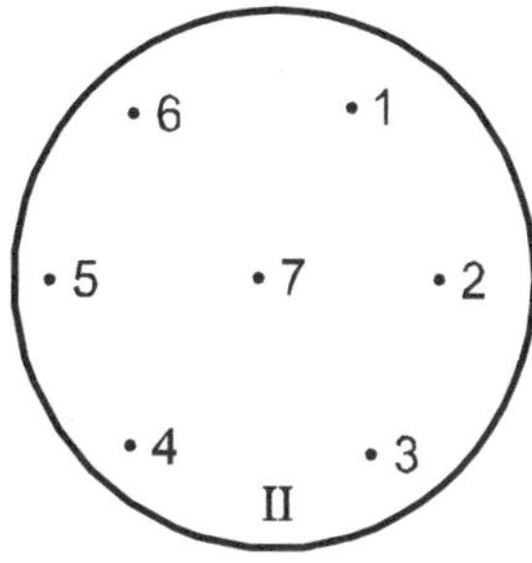

Antigen(s) used B
Antibody(s) used A
Reaction(+,-) –

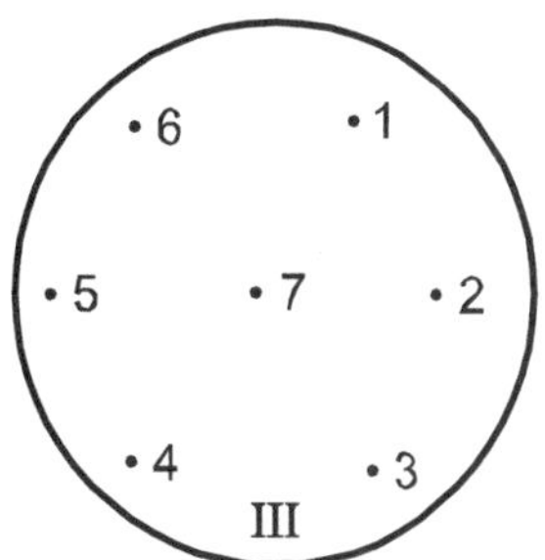

Antigen(s) used A
Antibody(s) used B
Reaction(+,-) –

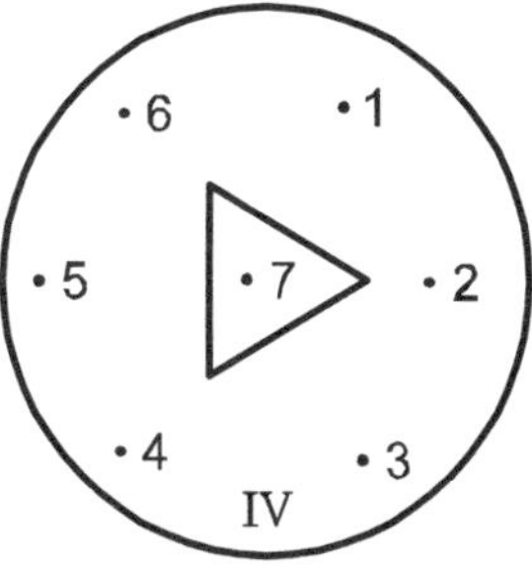

Antigen(s) used B
Antibody(s) used B
Reaction(+,-) +

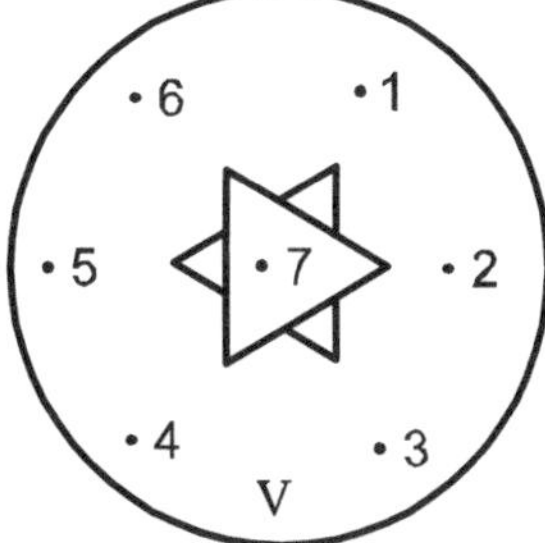

Antigen(s) used AB
Antibody(s) used AB
Reaction(+,-) +

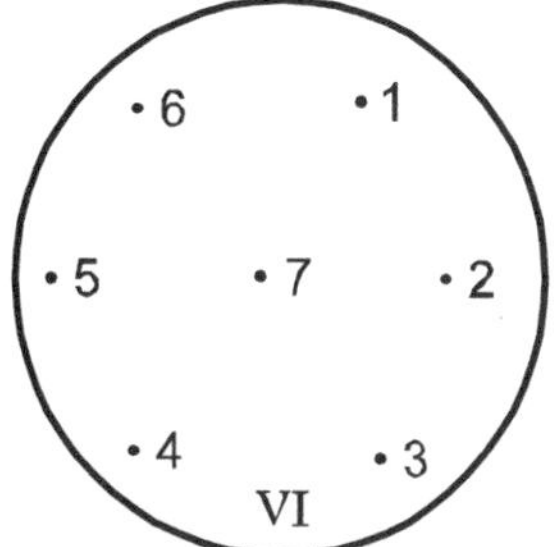

Antigen(s) used _____
Antibody(s) used _____
Reaction(+,-)

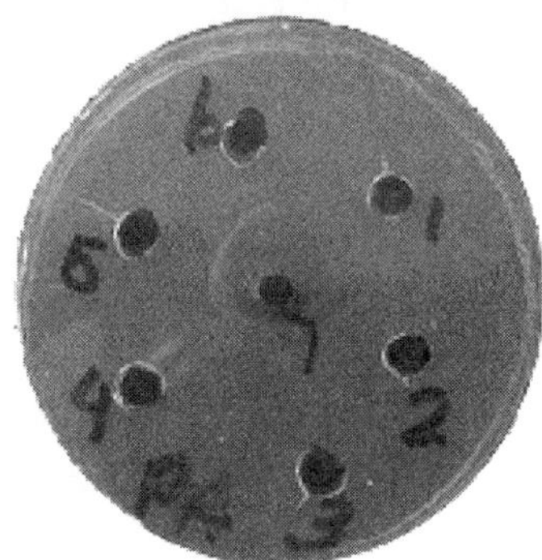

Plate I
Antibody A
reacting with antigen A

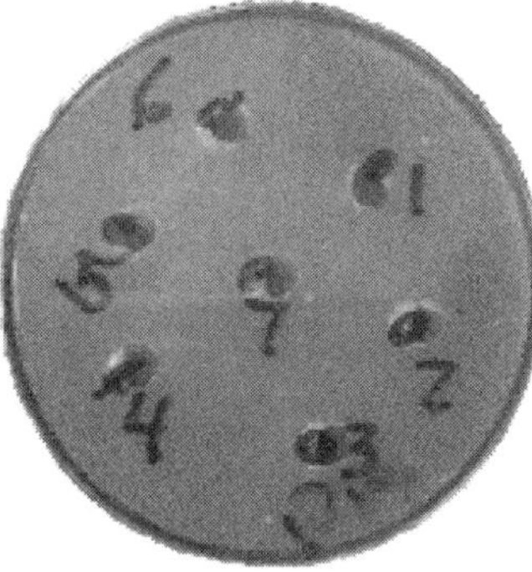

Plate II
Antibody A
reacting with antigen B
(no reaction)

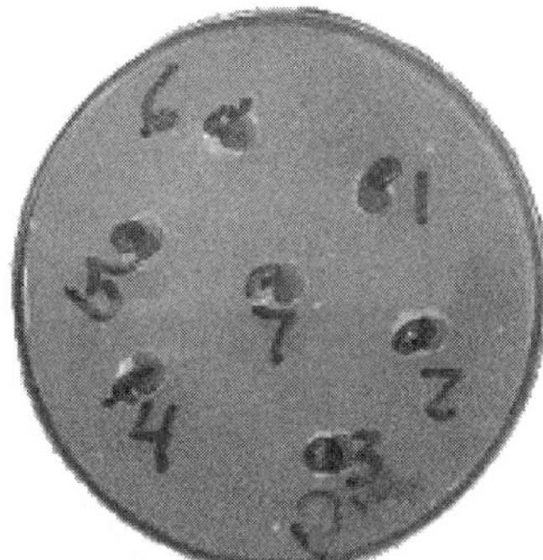

Plate III
Antibody A
reacting with antibody B
(no reaction)

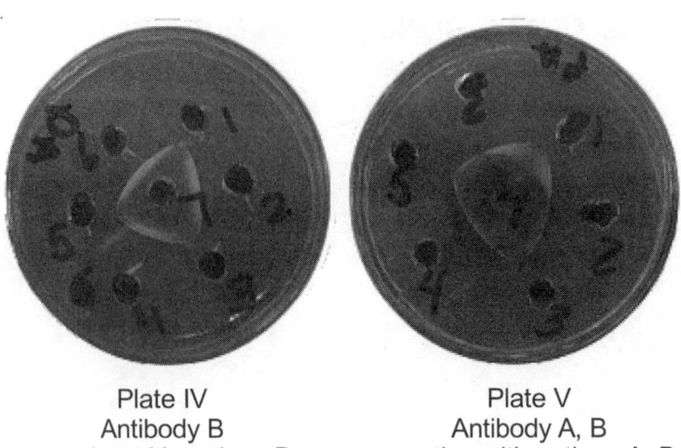

Plate IV
Antibody B
reacting with antigen B

Plate V
Antibody A, B
reacting with antigen A, B

PART I

1. On what plates do you see evidence of antibody-antigen interaction?
   - There is the formation of a white precipitate line on the gel, indicating antigen-antibody complexes are formed. This is indicated on the answer diagram above.

2. What evidence do you see that there is antibody specificity?
   - Antigen A only reacts with antibody A and not antibody B. Antigen B only reacts with antibody B and not antibody A.

3. Explain how antibodies work in the immune system.
   - Antibodies are proteins which have two antigen-specific receptor sites. When an antibody encounters an antigen it can bind to it making an antibody-antigen complex that a macrophage can engulf.

4. Explain how antibodies could be used in medicine as a diagnostic tool for pregnancy or diseases such at AIDS.
   - If there were antibodies created that were the result of a particular antigen, they could be used later to test for the presence of that antigen in a tissue or fluid like plasma.

PART II

1. What is the role of the macrophage in both the specific and nonspecific immune response?
   - In the nonspecific response, a macrophage engulfs any foreign particle the same way. It does not differentiate between invaders. In the specific immune response, it becomes an antigen-presenting macrophage that is used to activate T-cells.

2. What is the physical difference between helper T-cells and cytotoxic T-cells?
   - Helper T-cells bear a MHC II protein and cytotoxic T-cells bear a MHC I protein.

3. What does the term "clonal selection" mean in immunology?
   - It is the process by which one T-cell or B-cell is selected for its specificity to a particular antigen. Once it is selected, it is then cloned to form an army of T-cell and B-cell lymphocytes to fend off a pathogen.

4. If the AIDS virus attacks helper T-cells, how does that affect the humoral response in the immune system?
   - Helper-T cells are responsible for selecting B-cells which are vital to the humoral response in the production of free-floating antibodies.

TEACHER PAGES

REFERENCES

American Phytopathological Society. <http://www.apsnet.org/education/K-12PlantPathways/TeachersGuide/Activities/AntigenAntibody.html>. "Antigen-Antibody Testing", (viewed October 1, 2003)

Ferl, Robert, Gerald Sanders, and Robert Wallace. *Biology the Science of Life.* New York: Harper Collins Publisher, 1991. pp. 980-1007

Greenberg, Jon, Revision Editor. *Biology, a Molecular Approach.* Chicago: Everyday Learning, 2001. pp. 603-629

Specific Immune Response
Modeling the Immune System

In our efforts to maintain homeostasis and fend off nasty pathogens, vertebrates have evolved two lines of defense. The first line of defense is called the *nonspecific defense* because it does not distinguish one infectious agent from another. It includes the physical barrier of the skin, mucus secretions, phagocytic cells and antimicrobial proteins. The second line of defense is the immune system, which is classified as the *specific defense response*. It is called the specific defense response because it responds in a particular way to a specific pathogen, toxin, or foreign molecule.

The immune system is a very elegant and intricate system. The two special types of cells involved in the immune response are called *T-cell lymphocytes* and *B-cell lymphocytes*. Both arise in the bone marrow. The T-cells mature in the thymus and are larger than B cells. The B-cells remain in the bone marrow to mature and have a large amount of rough endoplasmic reticulum for the production of antibodies. There are two distinct responses to pathogens. The first is the *cell-mediated immune response* which involves the use of cytotoxic T-cells, suppressor-T-cells and memory-T-cells and helper-T-cells. The second part of the immune response is called the *humoral response* or chemical response. This involves the helper-T-cells and the production of very specific antibodies by B-cell lymphocytes.

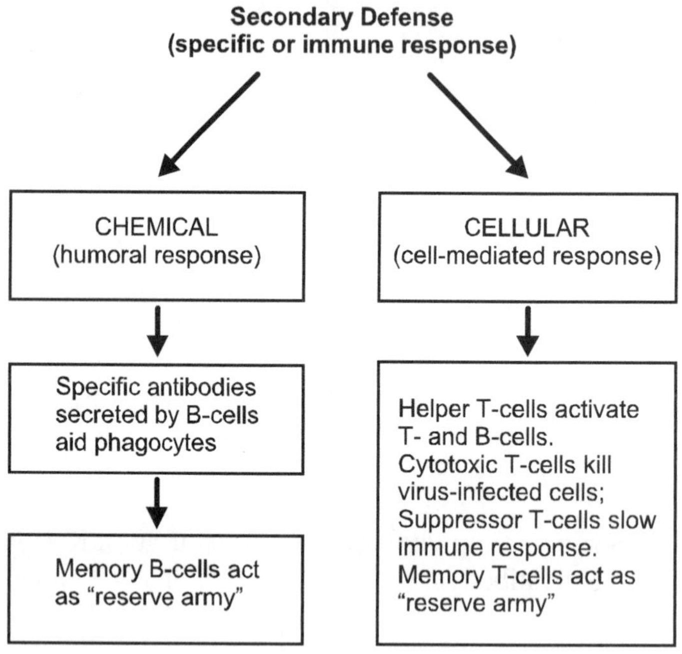

An *antibody* is a protein that can combine with a substance that is foreign to your body. This foreign substance can be a virus, bacteria, or a foreign molecule like a protein or large carbohydrate. These foreign substances are collectively called *antigens*. Antigens stimulate the production of antibodies by B-cells. A typical antibody can combine with two antigens. As this reaction happens, the antibody-antigen complex comes out of solution and, forms a precipitate. A special white blood cell or macrophage will engulf the antigen-antibody complex. An antibody is a protein comprised of four polypeptide chains. Two are larger or heavier chains that are identical to one another and two smaller or lighter chains that are also identical to one another. Each of the 4 chains contains an area called the *constant region* and an area called the *variable region*. The variable region is the antigen-binding site and is different for each antibody.

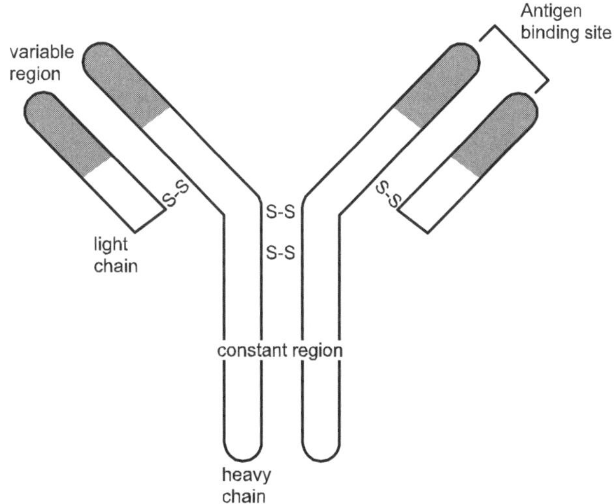

PURPOSE

This lesson has two parts. The first part is a lab that demonstrates the interaction of antibodies and antigens and their specificity. The second part is a simulation of the immune response.

MATERIALS

6 petri dishes with poured agar
Pasteur pipettes for filling wells
solution of B antigen
solution of B antibody
permanent marker
5 mL graduated disposable plastic pipet
solution of A antigen
solution of A antibody
solution of unknown antigen
beaker of water to clean pipet

PROCEDURE

PART I

1. Obtain six Petri dishes with poured agar. Label each plate a different Roman numeral, numbering from I-VI. Make the numbers small.

2. To make wells in the agar, obtain a 5 mL graduated disposable plastic pipet and cut the end off at the second gradation. This should leave an approximately 2mm diameter opening.

3. Center the Petri dish on the pattern below. The pattern should be visible through the gel.

4. Compress the bulb of the pipet as completely as possible.

5. Press the tip of the pipet into the gel, going all the way to the bottom of the gel layer.

6. Release the compression on the bulb. This should pull the gel plug out of the well and into the pipet.

7. Several wells can be cut before cleaning the pipette. To clean the pipet, draw water into it and forcefully expel the water into a waste container. This should carry the gel pieces out of the pipet.

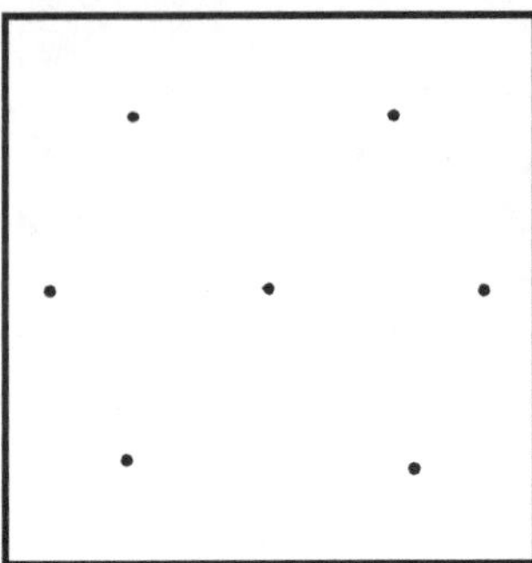

8. Label the wells with a permanent marker on the back of the Petri dish as follows:

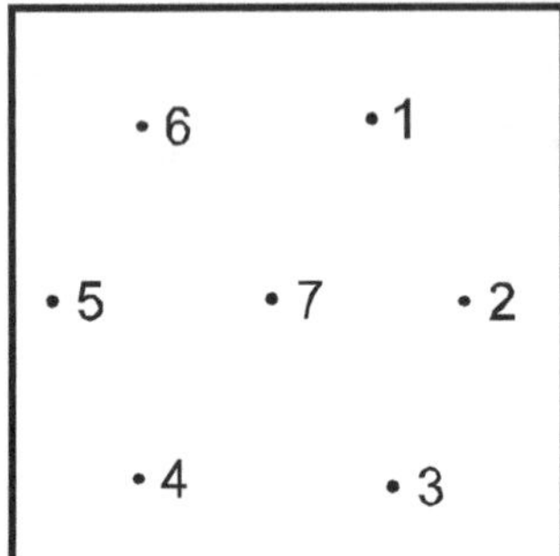

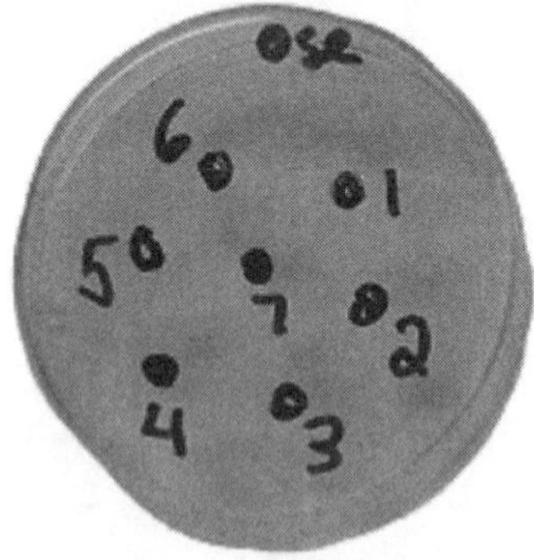

Labeled Back Side of Petri Dish

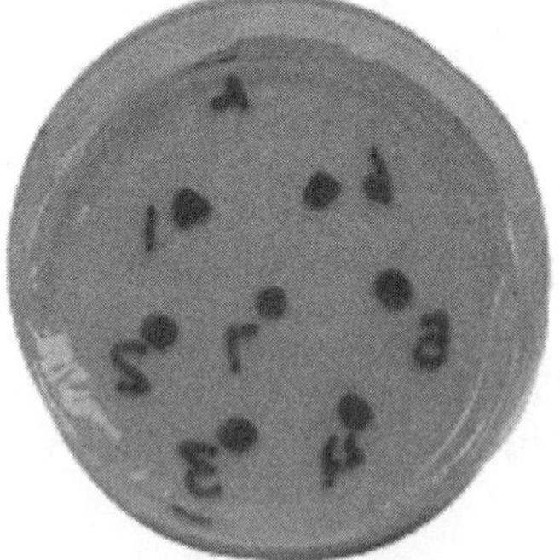

How Petri Dish Appears From the Front

9. The chart below shows the correct placement of antigens (AG) and antibodies (AB) into the wells.

Well Number	Plate I	Plate II	Plate III	Plate IV	Plate V	Plate VI
1	AG A	-	AG A	-	AG A	AG A
2	-	AG B	-	AG B	AG B	AG B
3	AG A	-	AG A	-	AG A	AG A
4	-	AG B	-	AG B	AG B	AG B
5	AG A	-	AG A	-	AG A	AG A
6	-	AG B	-	AG B	AG B	AG B
7	Antibody A	Antibody A	Antibody B	Antibody B	Antibody A & B	Unknown Antibody

10. When you are ready to load your wells, obtain the antigen and antibody solutions as your teacher directs. Avoid contamination of the solutions by using only the attached pipet and ensuring that the pipet is returned to its correct location without touching the countertop or any other surfaces.

11. To load the antigen or antibody into the well, first steady your hand by placing your elbow on the table. Place the tip of the pipet in contact with the bottom of the well and then slowly release a small amount of solution. Usually 1-2 drops will fill the well.

12. Allow the plate to remain still for at least 30 minutes. After 30 minutes you may begin to observe white lines of precipitation indicating a reaction is occurring.

13. Sketch the lines found on each plate in the data table.

14. Clean your workspace and dispose of the plates as your teacher instructs.

PART II

1. Obtain a package of models. The package should contain:
   - T-Cells which are blue and green
   - B-Cells which are pink
   - Normal cells which are yellow
   - Infected cells which are red
   - Antigens
   - Antibodies
   - Assorted additional labels

2. Each member of the group should read about the six major events of the immune response. Next, do the simulations using the models supplied while reading the accompanying text and examining the diagrams. There are six major events. Once you have gone through the entire set of simulations, try them without the diagrams. The third time, try it without the diagrams or the text, use only the models. Explain every step with either a classmate or your teacher checking for understanding.

THE IMMUNE RESPONSE—SIX MAJOR EVENTS

1. "Recognizing Self"
   - Every human (unless an identical twin) is unique and their cells are tagged with special proteins called major histocompatibility proteins. For each individual these proteins differ. There are three major classes of MHC proteins. All of our nucleated cells with the exception of monocytes, T-cells, and B-cells have MHC I proteins. Monocytes have both Class I and Class II T-cells can have either Class I or Class II MHC proteins. Find the cell that is labeled "Normal Cell Not Infected" and notice the MHC protein tagging the cell. Now look at all the cells and determine what sort of MHC protein they have.
   - Look at the T-cell notice that in addition to having either of MHC I or MHC II protein, it also has two receptor sites. One is for a MHC I protein and the other is for an antigen. These are dual receptor sites. During fetal development, the T-cells mature in the thymus and as a part of this process, the T-cell must make a match with the body's own MHC proteins. If they do not, the T-cell will simply die. This how T-cells recognize the body's own cells and thus do not attack them. This process is called recognizing "self". Once the T-cells make a match they are termed MHC restricted and are virgin T-cells. Find event #1 and simulate the process of T-cell maturation or "Recognizing Self".
   - Tape the MCH Restricted Virgin T-Cell label onto the appropriate cell.

CELL MEDIATED RESPONSE

2. "Revenge of the Monocytes"
   - One of the first events occuring when the body is being infected by pathogens is the body's dispersal of monocytes. Monocytes are leukocytes involved in both the specific and nonspecific response. Once they arrive at the site of infection, the monocytes are transformed into macrophages. These macrophages have both MHC I and MHC II proteins. These voracious macrophages begin to engulf the pathogens and as it does so, it begins to place antigens on the surface of its cell membrane. Find event #2 and simulate the process of monocyte transformation or the "Revenge of the Monocytes".
   - The humoral response includes the selecting and cloning of the B-cells. This happens when a free floating antigen encounters a B-cell that has an antibody on its cell membrane that is specific for that particular antigen. Now, once the antibody has bonded with the antigen, the antigen is placed next to the MHC II surface protein. In order to complete the activation of the B-cell, the helper-T cell is needed. Remember back in the clonal selection process, T-cells that had a MHCII protein were. Tape the "Activated Macrophage was once a monocyte" onto the appropriate cell during step D of this simulation.

3. "Cloning an Army of T Cells"
   - Now the macrophage is an antigen presenting macrophage. The antigen-presenting macrophage begins to "present" the antigens to the T-cells and tries to find a match. It must match both the MHC I protein and the antigen receptor site. If a match occurs, that particular T-cell is "selected" and the macrophage begins to secrete a substance called interleukin. Interleukin stimulates the T-cell to undergo mitotic divisions. The T-cell is "cloned". If the T-cell has a MHC I protein, it is destined to become a cytotoxic T-cell or if it has a MHC II protein it is destined to become a helper T cell to be used in the humoral response. This process is called "clonal selection". Find event #3 and simulate the process of clonal selection for T-cells or "Cloning an Army of T Cells".
   - Tape the "Activated "Cytotoxic T-Cell" and "Activated Helper T-Cell" to the appropriate cell during the final step of this simulation.

4. "Cytotoxic Attack"
   - Once the cytotoxic T-cells are cloned, the cloned cells begin to roam the body looking for infected cells. When a normal cell becomes infected with pathogen, it is not unusual for parts of that pathogen to remain on the surface of the cell's membrane and become an antigen. This is analogous to someone removing their shoes before entering a house and leaving them outside, thus marking the house with their presence. With this tag, infected cells are different from uninfected cells. Cytotoxic T-cells begin roaming the body seeking a match for both its MHC I protein and its antigen receptor site. A healthy cell only has a MHC I protein and is ignored by the cytotoxic cell, but an infected cell has both the antigen and MHC I protein and makes a match. The cytotoxic cell pokes holes into the infected cell. Water rushes in and lyses the infected cell. The cytotoxic cell continues on its way. Find event # 4 and simulate the process of "Cytotoxic Attack".

HUMORAL RESPONSE

5. "Cloning an Army of B-Cells"
   - Destined to become helper T-cells instead of cytotoxic cells. Helper T-cells have receptor sites for MHC II proteins and antigens. These helper T-cells can now make a match between the B-cell's MHCII protein and the captured free-floating antigen. Once the binding between the two cells occurs, the helper T-cell will secrete interleukin much like the macrophage. This causes the B-cell to undergo mitosis and produce plasma B-cells. Find event #5 and simulate the process of clonal selection for B-cells or "Cloning an Army of B-Cells".
   - Tape the antibodies inside the appropriate cell.

6. "The Glue Needed for Dinner"
   - Now the plasma cells will start secreting copious amounts of specific antibodies. It is estimated that a plasma B-cell can secrete up to 2,000 antibody molecules per second during its life of several days. These are free floating antibodies are specific for the invading antigen or pathogen. Antibodies work by being able to bind with at least two antigens. This allows the antibodies and antigens to form clumps that the macrophages can clean up by phagocytosis. Find event #6 and simulate the process of antigen-antibody binding for the formation of clumps that are readily engulfed by phagocytes or "The Glue Needed for Dinner".

Name ______________________________

Period ______________________________

Specific Immune Response
Modeling the Immune System

DATA AND OBSERVATIONS

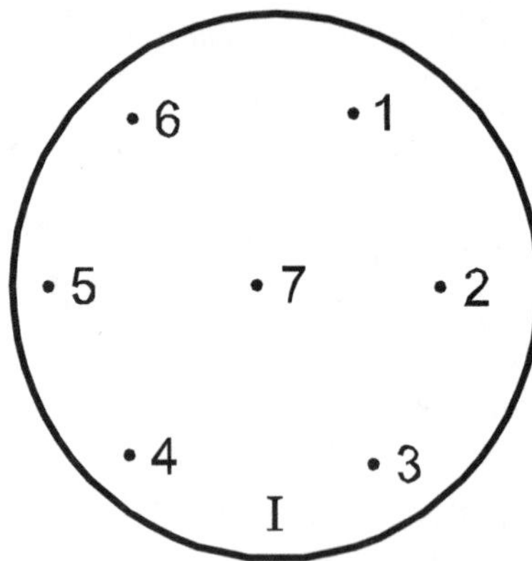

Antigen(s) used _____
Antibody(s) used _____
Reaction(+,-)

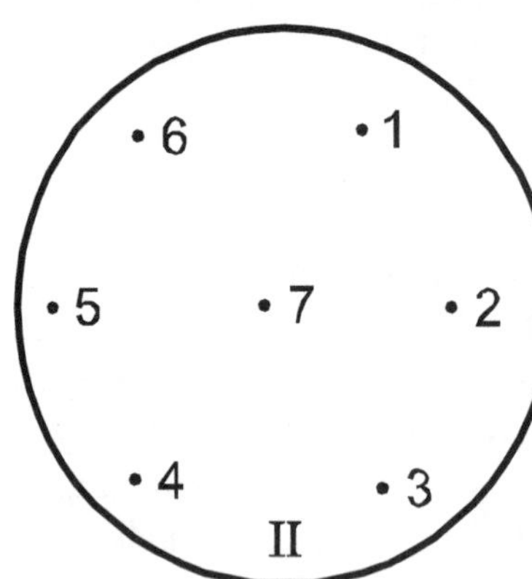

Antigen(s) used _____
Antibody(s) used _____
Reaction(+,-)

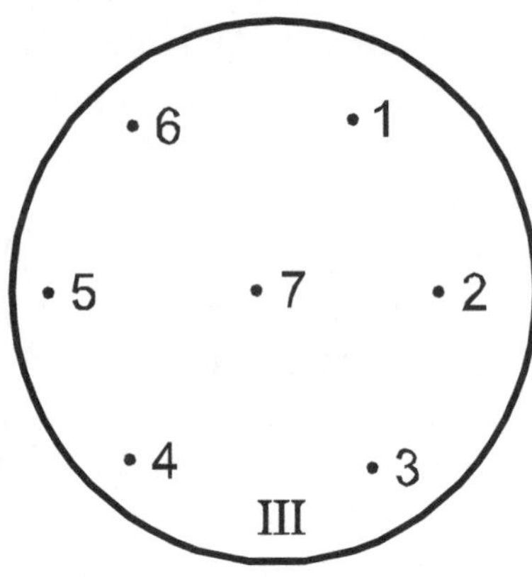

Antigen(s) used _____
Antibody(s) used _____
Reaction(+,-)

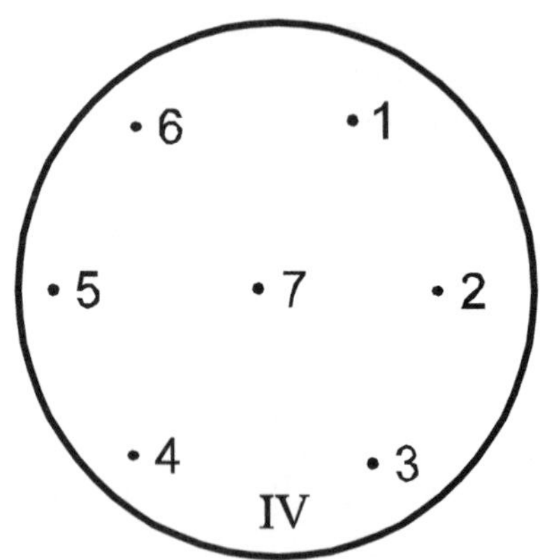

Antigen(s) used _____
Antibody(s) used _____
Reaction(+,-)

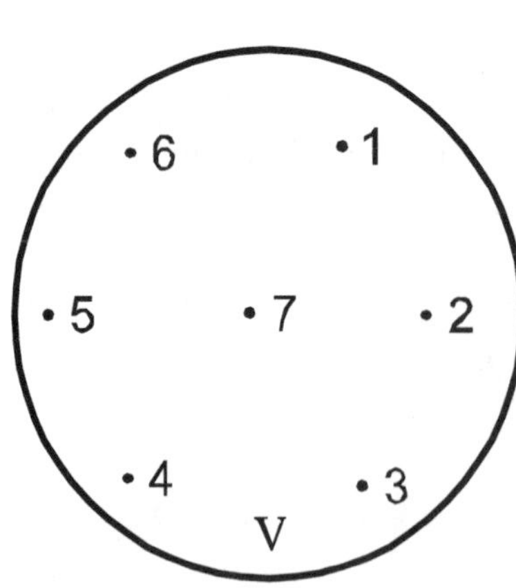

Antigen(s) used _____
Antibody(s) used _____
Reaction(+,-)

• 6 • 1
• 5 • 7 • 2
• 4 • 3
VI

Antigen(s) used _____
Antibody(s) used _____
Reaction(+,-)

CONCLUSION QUESTIONS

PART I

1. On what plates do you see evidence of antibody-antigen interaction?

2. What evidence do you see that there is antibody specificity?

3. Explain how antibodies work in the immune system.

4. Explain how antibodies could be used in medicine as a diagnostic tool for pregnancy or diseases such at AIDS.

PART II

1. What is the role of the macrophage in both the specific and nonspecific immune response?

2. What is the physical difference between helper T-cells and cytotoxic T-cells?

3. What does the term "clonal selection" mean in immunology?

4. If the AIDS virus attacks helper T-cells, how does that affect the humoral response in the immune system?

Write Your Notes and Ideas Here!

Making Sense of It All
Exploring the Nervous System and Senses

OBJECTIVE
Students will research the components of the brain and neurons. Students will investigate human sense of smell, sense of taste, and sensory fatigue.

LEVEL
Biology I

NATIONAL STANDARDS
UCP.1, UCP.2, UCP.5, C.6, G.1, G.2

TEKS
2(C), 10(A)

CONNECTIONS TO AP
AP Biology:

III. Organisms and Populations B. Structure and Function of Plants and Animal 2. Physiological and behavioral adaptations

TIME FRAME
90 minutes

MATERIALS
(For a class of 28 working alone in parts I and II, in pairs in Part III, IV and V)

- textbook or internet access
- 35 empty film canisters with lids
- 2 kitchen sponges
- colored toothpicks (five different colors)
- food extracts; vanilla, almond, maple, orange and onion
- 35 cotton balls
- 56 brads
- brown paper lunch sack
- 10 candies
- dime
- nickel
- 14 metric rulers

TEACHER NOTES

The diagram tables in Part I stress the relationship of structure and function. They are designed to be completed outside the classroom prior to the completion of Parts II-V.

Preparation of smell canisters for Part II:

Cut a kitchen sponge into pieces small enough to fit in the bottom of an empty film canister. Place the sponge pieces into 35 film canisters. Add several drops of vanilla extract to 7 of the canisters and then a small ball of cotton to hide the color of the extract. Replace the cap and set aside. Use the same process to prepare 7 canisters with almond extract, 7 with onion juice, 7 with orange extract, and 7 with maple extract for a total of 35 smell canisters. The canisters need to be inconspicuously labeled. One way to label them is to set up a color code system using colored toothpicks. For example, place yellow toothpicks in the vanilla canisters, red toothpicks in the almond canisters, etc. The toothpicks will need to be broken in half to fit inside the canister underneath the concealing cotton ball.

You can substitute other food extracts in this activity. Avoid cloves because it can desensitize the nose.

Place 6 of each type of smell canister (for a total of 30) in one box prior to the class. Randomly arrange them in the box.

Before distributing the canisters instruct the students to only open them for short periods of time and then promptly replace the lids. Also remind them to not reach inside the container.

Set aside one of each type of smell canister to serve as "home" base for each of the smells. On the day of the activity, place the "home" canisters on a numbered piece of paper in random locations around the room. The students will gather at these locations so pick places that have space enough for up to 6 students to stand.

As you conduct the activity, allow students to search for their family members and homes for several minutes. Encourage stragglers to make a decision and when most have moved to a "home" or "abandoned" location, call time. Tell them to discuss and record group responses to the questions in step 8 as you make your way around to each group to check for accuracy. (Remind them that there is nothing wrong with them if they can't distinguish the smells.) Take class counts of abandoned and misplaced students.

At the end of this activity, sort the canisters and store each smell in separate plastic bags.

Part III: Skittles™, Starbursts™, and other flavored bite-sized candies work well for this.

Part IV Makes a nice data collection activity to be done at home. Students can select a family member to serve as the subject.

Part V: Other objects may be substituted for the coins.

POSSIBLE ANSWERS TO THE CONCLUSION QUESTIONS AND SAMPLE DATA

Structure and Function of a Neuron

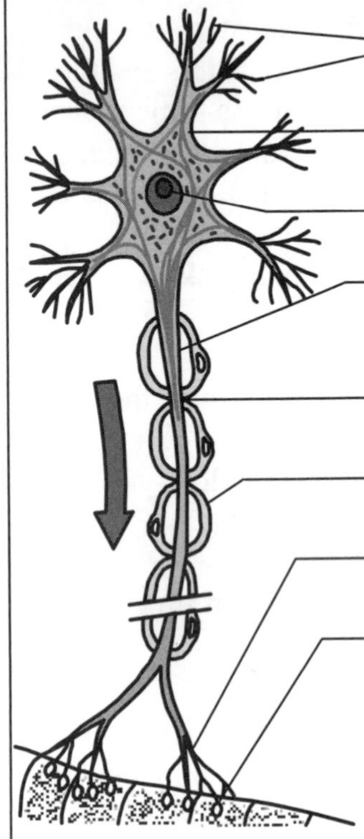

Neuron component	Function
dendrites	Receive stimulus
cell body	Collect impulses from dendrite
nucleus	Regulates neuron activity
axon	Fibrous process that conducts impulse away from cell body
node	Conducting space between Schwann cells
myelin sheath	Insulating protein layer around axon
axon terminal	Ends of the axon, contains neurotransmitters
synapse	Gap between neurons where neurotransmitters are released

Structure and Function of Brain Components		
	Brain Component	**Function**
	Frontal lobe of cerebrum	Associated with reasoning, planning, speech, movement, emotions, and problem solving
	Parietal lobe of cerebrum	Associated with movement, orientation, recognition, perception of stimuli
	Occipital lobe of cerebrum	Associated with visual processing
	Pituitary gland	Produces hormones
	Pons	Connects cerebrum with cerebellum
	Medulla oblongata	Controls involuntary functions such as breathing and heartbeat.
	Cerebellum	Regulates movement and muscle coordination
	Spinal cord	Pathway of signal relay connect brain to peripheral nerves

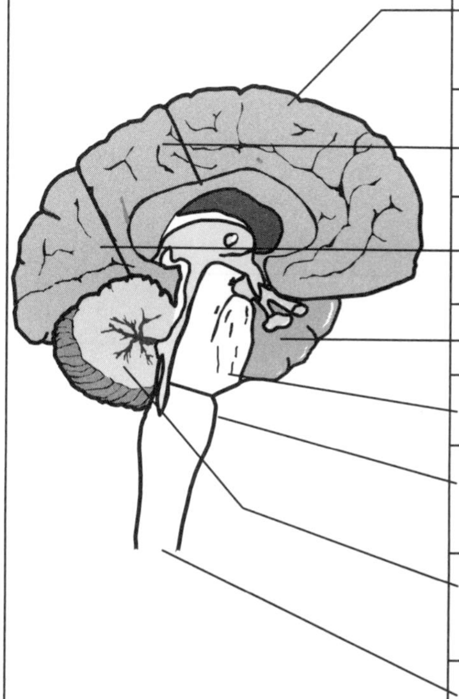

Data Table 2	
Number of Family Members	6
Description of Family Scent	Sweet, cake-like smell, vanilla, pleasant, familiar, not everyone agrees.
Number of abandoned members	0
Number of misplaced members	1

Data Table 3: Sense of Taste and Smell				
	Trial	Color of Candy	Description of taste	Flavor Identification Correct/Incorrect
Partner #1	1	red	sweet	incorrect
	2	purple	sweet	incorrect
	3	green	sour or sweet	incorrect
	Control	yellow	lemony	correct
Partner #2	1	purple	sweet	incorrect
	2	green	sweet	incorrect
	3	green	sour	incorrect
	Control	purple	grape	correct

Data Table 4: Ability to Distinguish Touch				
	Back of Hand	Palm	Tip of middle finger	Tip of thumb
2 cm brad tips	yes	no	yes	yes
1 cm brad tips	no	no	yes	yes
0.5 cm brad tips	no	no	yes	no
0 cm (single) brad tip	yes	yes	yes	yes

Data Table 5: Sensory Fatige		
	Partner #1 Fatigue Time	Partner #2 Fatigue Time
Nickel	15 seconds	17 seconds
Dime	9 seconds	12 seconds

CONCLUSION QUESTIONS

1. What is the role of a neuron?
   - conduct impulses

2. Identify the following as belonging to the central or peripheral nervous systems:
   a. avagus nerve (peripheral)
   b. brain (central)
   c. chemoreceptors of tongue (peripheral)
   d. pressure receptors of skin (peripheral)
   e. spinal cord (central)

3. If a person exhibits movement disorders as the result of a brain injury which part of the brain would you suspect had been damaged? Why?
   - cerebellum. It is responsible for movement and motor coordination.

4. Based on the functions of the brain, why do you think damage to the medulla oblongata often results in death?
   - The medulla oblongata controls the heartbeat and breathing so if it is damaged and these events are interrupted and it can be lethal.

5. In Part II of this activity, was your family able to correctly identify your canister smell? Explain.
   - Answers will vary but often the orange, maple and vanilla extracts are easy for the students to name.

6. Were there variations in the ability of your family members to smell the odors in the canisters? Explain your answer.
   - Yes. Some people were better at distinguishing the smells.
   - Students will likely name students with strong sense of smell and those with weak sense of smell.

7. Which smells were most difficult to distinguish? Why do you think this is so?
   - The vanilla and almond extracts have similar smells and are sometimes difficult to distinguish.

8. What would be the evolutionary advantage in humans of having a keen sense of smell? List two advantages.
   - To recognize foul odors caused by contamination of food or by spoiled food.
   - To recognize dangers in the environment such as smoke, poisonous gases.
   - Helps make consumption of food more positive, thus encouraging eating.
   - To recognize family members. (babies can smell their mothers when they enter the room even if they can't see them, etc.)

9. Write a conclusion statement describing the relationship between smell and taste in Part III of this activity.
   - Breathing allowed us to smell the flavor of the candy in addition to tasting its sweetness.

10. Did you and your partner have the same sensitivity to touch as measured in Part IV of this activity? Explain.
    - The sensitivity will vary slightly among students but the tips of the fingers will typically be more sensitive than the back and palm of the hand.

11. How does information from the sensory receptors in the skin get to the brain?
    - Stimuli is picked up by the sensory receptors and travels down the axon of the receptor to the spinal cord and then to the brain.

12. What area of the hand was most sensitive to touch? What would be an evolutionary advantage of this area being more sensitive?
    - The tips of the finger and thumb.
    - This allows us to be able to pick up objects, avoid dangerously hot objects and reduces the chances of damage to the hand.

13. Did you and your partner experience sensory fatigue in the same amount of time? Explain your answer.
    - The amount of time required for fatigue to set in will vary by a few seconds from person to person.

14. Sensory fatigue can happen with a variety of our senses such as smell and touch. Under what conditions is sensory fatigue beneficial? Under what conditions would it be harmful?
    - Sensory fatigue is beneficial when our skin is constantly exposed to an object like our clothing articles. Olfactory fatigue can allow us to tolerate unpleasant odors.
    - Sensory fatigue could be harmful if the object touch our body is harmful or if the odor was dangerous.

REFERENCES

Ackerman, Diane. *A Natural History of the Se*nses. New York: Vintage Books, 1995.

Lawrence Hall of Science. *Learning About Learning*. Berkley: University of California.

Marieb, Elaine N. *Human Anatomy and Physiology*. Redwood City: Benjamin/Cummings, 1989.

Making Sense of It All
Exploring the Nervous System and Senses

Have you ever watched a dog sniff the ground in search of a ball that was clearly in view? Have you ever smelled a box of crayons and remembered your first grade classroom? Does your house smell different than your friend's? These smells or olfactions play an important role in the survival of species. The sense of smell is just one of the senses afforded by the complex nervous systems found among members of the kingdom Animalia.

Nervous systems are formed from specialized cells that conduct signals rapidly through the long cell extensions that make up nerves. The nerve cells communicate with each other by secreting specific excitatory and inhibitory molecules. In sense organs, specialized cells detect light, sound, and specific chemicals and enable animals to monitor what is going on in the world around them.
The nervous system functions to coordinate and control the functions of the body. Additionally, the nervous system allows the organism to detect and respond to stimuli. The human nervous system is composed of the central and peripheral nervous systems. The central nervous system contains the brain and spinal cord while the peripheral nervous system is made up of the nerves and ganglia.

The functional unit of the nervous system is the neuron. Neurons are specialized cells that conduct impulses from one part of the body to another. Neurons have extensions called dendrites which receive impulses and axons which transmit impulses. The long extensions of the neurons bundle together forming nerves.

Scattered throughout the body are specialized neurons that react to environmental stimuli such as temperature changes, light, chemicals, pressure, sound and motion. The skin, nose, eyes, ears, and mouth are sensory organs which contain high concentrations of the sensory neurons. The sensory neurons allow organisms to monitor the world around them as they detect stimuli and relay sensory information to the central nervous system.

PURPOSE
In this activity you will research the structure of the neuron and the brain and investigate the senses of smell, touch, taste and pressure.

MATERIALS

- textbook or internet access
- small canister
- brown paper lunch sack
- 10 candies
- 4 brads
- metric ruler
- nickel
- dime

Safety Alert

1. Report any food allergies to your teacher prior to beginning this activity.

PROCEDURE

PART I

1. Use a textbook, the websites shown below, or other resources to label the structure and identify the function of the components of a typical neuron shown on the student answer page. Use the following terms to label the neuron: synapse, dendrites, nucleus, axon, cell body, node, axon terminals, Schwann cells, myelin sheath.

   http://www.enchantedlearning.com/subjects/anatomy/brain/Neuron.shtml
   http://www.botany.uwc.ac.za/sci_ed/grade10/mammal/nervous.htm
   http://www.howstuffworks.com/brain1.htm

2. Use a textbook, the websites shown below, or other resources to label the structures and identify the functions of the brain structures shown on the student answer page.

   http://www.enchantedlearning.com/subjects/anatomy/brain/label/lateralbrain/labelanswers.shtml
   http://science.howstuffworks.com/brain2.htm

PART II: SENSE OF SMELL

1. The object of this activity is to use your sense of smell to find all other members of the class whose canister smell matches yours. You may not use your sense of hearing during this activity. This means that you may not speak to the other students. You are to rely only on your sense of smell. Obtain an odor canister from your teacher. Open it and briefly smell its contents. Do not touch the inside of the canister.

2. Silently move around the room to locate all of the other members of your "family" by smelling other student canisters. How many family members did you find? Record the number of members in your family on the student answer page.

3. If you are unable to find any canisters that smell like yours, move to the area of the room labeled "abandoned family members".

4. Once you have located your "family", use your sense of smell to locate your "home" canister by smelling the various "home" canisters located around the room.

5. When you and your "family" have found your "home", signal your teacher to come check your group's accuracy.

6. Discuss with your "family" members what smell is coming from your canisters. Describe your family's smell in the space provided on the data page. In your description include answers to questions such as: What does it smell like? Does everyone agree? Is the smell pleasant or unpleasant? Familiar or unfamiliar?

7. Send one of your family members to the abandoned family member station to determine how many, if any of your family members have ended up abandoned. Record the number of abandoned family members on the Data Table 2.

8. As your teacher instructs, determine the number of misplaced family members and record the number in Data Table 2.

PART III: THE SENSE OF TASTE

1. Formulate a hypothesis to test whether or not a person can distinguish among different flavors of candy while holding his/her nose. Write your hypothesis on the student answer page in the Part III answer box.

2. Place 8 various flavored candies in the brown paper sack.

3. Have your partner hold his/her nose, reach in the paper sack and select a candy without looking. Record the color of the candy in Data Table III.

4. Your partner should chew up the candy while continuing to hold their nose. Ask them to describe the taste and identify its flavor. Indicate whether they are correct or incorrect in Data Table 3.

5. Repeat steps 12 and 13 two additional times.

6. As a control trial, have your partner select a candy and chew it without holding their nose and without looking at the candy. Have them describe the taste and identify the flavor of the candy. Record the responses in Data Table 3.

7. Change roles with your partner and repeat steps 12 and 15.

PART V: MEASURING SENSITIVITY TO TOUCH

1. In this activity you will experiment to determine which portion of the hand is most sensitive to touch. Mechanoreceptors in our skin layer, can respond to pressure created by touch. The receptor then sends the impulse down its axon, to the spinal cord and eventually to the brain. Write a hypothesis that will test which area of the hand is most sensitive to touch.

2. Obtain 4 brads and adjust the legs of 3 brads so that they are different distances apart. The legs of the brads should be 2 cm, 1 cm and .5 cm apart. The legs of the fourth brad should not be bent leaving a single tip to touch the skin.

3. Have your partner rest their elbow on the table with their hand extended and their eyes closed.

4. Touch the back of their hand with a randomly selected brad and ask them to tell you if the brad has one tip or two. Do this for all four brads. In Data Table 4, record a yes if the response is correct and a no if it is incorrect.

5. Repeat step 20 on the tip of the middle finger, the tip of the thumb, and on the palm of your partner.

6. Switch roles with your partner and repeat steps 20 and 21 to collect data for your partner's Data Table 4.

PART V: SENSORY FATIGUE

In this activity you will measure sensory fatigue. Sensory fatigue often occurs in response to constant stimulation. When sensory fatigue begins it means that the receptors are not producing signals. In this way, our body disregards certain stimuli.

1. Obtain a nickel and a dime. Hold them in your hand for several seconds in order to warm them to body temperature.

2. Ask your partner to place their hand palm down on the lab table and look away from their hand.

3. Place the nickel in the center of the back of their hand and determine how many seconds pass until they can no longer feel the nickel. Record the time in Data Table 5.

4. Remove the nickel and replace it with the dime. Once again, determine how many seconds pass until they can no longer feel the dime. Record the time in Data Table 5.

Name ______________________________

Period ______________________________

Making Sense of It All
Exploring the Nervous System and Senses

DATA AND OBSERVATIONS

Structure and function of a Neuron

	Neuron component	Function

Structure and Function of Brain Components		
	Brain Component	Function
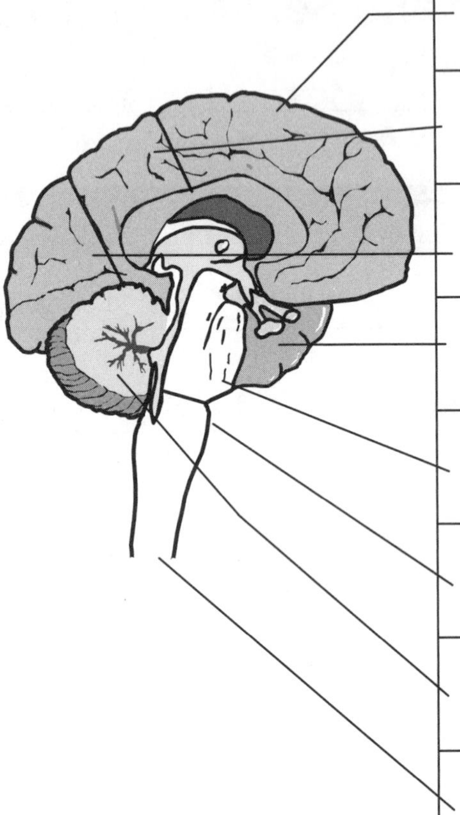		

Data Table 2	
Number of Family Members	
Description of Family Scent	
Number of abandoned members	
Number of misplaced members	

Data Table 3: Sense of Taste and Smell				
	Trial	Color of Candy	Description of taste	Flavor Identification Correct/Incorrect
Partner #1	1			
	2			
	3			
	Control			
Partner #2	1			
	2			
	3			
	Control			

Data Table 4: Ability to Distinguish Touch				
	Back of Hand	Palm	Tip of middle finger	Tip of thumb
2 cm brad tips				
1 cm brad tips				
.5 cm brad tips				
0 cm (single) brad tip				

Data Table 5: Sensory Fatigue		
	Partner #1 Fatigue Time	Partner #2 Fatigue Time
Nickel		
Dime		

CONCLUSION QUESTIONS

1. What is the role of a neuron?

2. Identify the following as belonging to the central or peripheral nervous systems:
   a. vagus nerve
   b. brain
   c. chemoreceptors of tongue
   d. pressure receptors of skin
   e. spinal cord

3. If a person exhibits movement disorders as the result of a brain injury which part of the brain would you suspect had been damaged? Why?

4. Based on the functions of the brain, why do you think damage to the medulla oblongata often results in death?

5. In Part II of this activity, was your family able to correctly identify your canister smell? Explain

6. Were there variations in the ability of your family members to smell the odors in the canisters? Explain your answer.

7. Which smells were most difficult to distinguish? Why do you think this is so?

8. What would be the evolutionary advantage in humans of having a keen sense of smell? List two advantages.

9. Write a conclusion statement describing the relationship between smell and taste in Part III of this activity.

10. Did you and your partner have the same sensitivity to touch as measured in Part IV of this activity? Explain.

11. How does information from the sensory receptors in the skin get to the brain?

12. What area of the hand was most sensitive to touch? What would be an evolutionary advantage of this area being more sensitive?

13. Did you and your partner experience sensory fatigue in the same amount of time? Explain your answer.

14. Sensory fatigue can happen with a variety of our senses such as smell and touch. Under what conditions is sensory fatigue beneficial? Under what conditions would it be harmful?

Planarian Behaviors
Investigating Geotaxis, Chemotaxis, and Phototaxis in Planaria

OBJECTIVE
Students will measure geotaxis, chemotaxis and phototaxis in planaria. Students will design and conduct an experiment to determine what type of taxis, if any, planaria will exhibit in response the presence of liver.

LEVEL
Biology I

NATIONAL STANDARDS
UCP.1, UCP.2, UCP.5, A.1, A.2, C.6, G.1, G.2

TEKS
2(A), 2(B), 2(C), 2(D), 11(B)

CONNECTIONS TO AP
AP Biology:

III. Organisms and Populations B. Structure and Function of Plants and Animals 3. Response to the environment

TIME FRAME
60 minutes

MATERIALS
(For a class of 28 working in groups of 4)

28 planaria
7 test tubes of culture water with stoppers
7 disposable pipets
7 strips of foil (5 cm x 5cm)
500 mL spring water
14 strips of 8 cm lengths of 5mm bore Tygon® tubing split in half length-wise
28 sodium chloride soaked filter paper strips
28 acetic acid soaked filter paper strips
timing device (seconds)
7 pieces of liver cut in .5cm^3
14 white sheets of paper

TEACHER NOTES
Planaria can be ordered from scientific supply companies. Planaria are typically sold in sample sizes of 12 to 15, however, due to damage or death of the specimen, you should order at least two cultures. The planaria can be reused by additional classes but will benefit from a rest period of 15 to 20 minutes.

As soon as your culture arrives, remove the cap to allow a fresh supply of air into the container. Leave the lids loosely sitting on top of the containers. If the water is cloudy when the specimens arrive, replace the water using only spring water, not distilled or drinking water. Spring water and drinking water can be purchased at a local grocery store. The optimum temperature for these flatworms is 60-65° F. If you wish to maintain your planaria culture upon completion of the lab, you will need to feed them weekly. They will eat small pieces of egg yolk, liver and tubifex worms. Leave the food in their water for 30 minutes and then replace the water with fresh spring water.

Depending on the size of the planaria in your culture, you may need to cut the tip off of the disposable pipets to make a larger opening so as to prevent damaging the planaria during transfer.

Clear plastic tubing with 5mm bore can be purchased at local plumbing supply stores or ordered from scientific supply companies. Cut 7 sections that are 8 cm long. Use sharp scissors to cut each 8cm section of tubing in half length-wise.

In advance, prepare the sodium chloride soaked filter paper strips by cutting filter paper into strips approximately 3mm x 5 mm. Soak the filter paper strips in a 10% sodium chloride solution. To prepare 10% sodium chloride, place 10 grams of sodium chloride in 90 mL of distilled water. Remove the strips from the sodium chloride solution and allow any excess solution to drain from the strips. Store the strips in a Petri dish or resealable plastic bag until ready to use.

In advance, prepare acetic acid soaked filter paper strips by cutting filter paper into strips approximately 3mm x 5 mm. Soak the filter paper strips in vinegar. Remove the strips from the vinegar and allow any excess solution to drain from the strips. Store the strips in a Petri dish or resealable plastic bag until ready to use.

As you begin this activity, demonstrate how to transfer the planaria from the culture to the troughs using a pipet. Encourage students to gently, slowly, release bulb pressure to pull the planaria into the pipet. You will also need to tell the students where to place planaria that have been used during this activity if you want to keep the used ones separate from the fresh supply.

POSSIBLE ANSWERS TO THE CONCLUSION QUESTIONS AND SAMPLE DATA

HYPOTHESIS 1

If a planarian is placed in a test tube of spring water then when the tube is inverted the planarian will show a positive geotaxis by moving to the bottom of the tube.

HYPOTHESIS 2

If planaria are exposed to sodium chloride and acetic acid then they will exhibit a negative chemotaxis.

HYPOTHESIS 3

If a planarian is placed in a tube with both light and dark areas, then the planarian will show a negative phototaxis by spending more time in the dark area.

DATA AND OBSERVATIONS

Planarian Geotaxis Observations		
	Observations in upright tube	**Observations in inverted tube**
Group 1	Swims in bottom area of tube	Swam toward the bottom
Group 2	Stays in the lower part of the tube	Moved toward the stoppered bottom end
Group 3	Sat at the bottom of the tube	Went down to middle of tube
Group 4	Moved little, stays in bottom	Swam to bottom then back up a little way

Planarian Chemotaxis Observations		
	Reactions to sodium chloride	**Reactions to acetic acid**
Minute 1 with one strip	Little response	Small reaction
Minute 2 with two strips	Moves around more	Avoids the strips
Minute 3 with three strips	Tends to stay away from the strips	Swims away from the acid
Minute 4 with four strips	Moved to the other side of the puddle	Stays on the side opposite the strips

Planarian Phototaxis Observations		
Time Elapsed	**Dark**	**Light**
0 sec		x
5 sec.		x
10 sec.	x	
15 sec.		x
20 sec.		x
25 sec.	x	
30 sec.	x	
35 sec.	x	
40 sec.	x	
45 sec.	x	
50 sec	x	
55 sec.	x	
60 sec.	x	

ANALYSIS

1. What is the stimulus for each type of taxis listed below?
   a. Geotaxis - gravity
   b. Chemotaxis - chemicals
   c. Phototaxis - light

2. Do planaria exhibit a positive or negative geotaxis? Explain your answer using the data you collected.
   - positive geotaxis. The planaria in most groups moved to the bottom half of the test tube when it was inverted.

3. Do planaria exhibit a positive or negative chemotaxis to sodium chloride? Explain your answer using the data you collected.
   - negative chemotaxis. The more sodium chloride the planarian was exposed to by the addition of strips the more it would try to avoid that area of the water.

4. Do planaria exhibit a positive or negative chemotaxis to acetic acid? Explain your answer using the data you collected.
   - negative chemotaxis. The more acetic acid the planarian was exposed to by the addition of strips the more it would try to avoid that area of the water.

5. What type of taxis did planaria(n) exhibit in the presence of liver? Explain your answer using the data you collected.
   - positive chemotaxis. The planarian moved toward the liver.

CONCLUSION QUESTIONS

1. What is the difference in a taxis and a kinesis?
   - A kinesis is random movement in unpredictable directions. A taxis is a movement toward or away from a specific stimulus.

2. What structural adaptations do planaria possess that allow them to perform a taxis response?
   - simple nervous system with brain, eyespots, and two parallel nerves

3. How could a negative chemotaxis be beneficial to a bacterium that is exposed to bleach?
   - The bacterium would move away from the bleach and not be killed by the chemical.

4. What type of taxis is represented in the following scenarios?
   a. An earthworm moves away from a bright light. (Negative phototaxis)
   b. The roots of a growing seedling turn downward.(Positive geotaxis)
   c. Brine shrimp in a Petri dish collect around a blue light source. (Positive phototaxis)
   d. A meal worm crawls toward a moist potato. (Positive chemotaxis)
   e. A snail crawls away from a patch of fertilizer in a flower bed. (Negative chemotaxis)
   f. The surface of leaf tilts toward the sunlight. (Positive phototaxis)

5. Explain the evolutionary advantage of possessing a nervous system that allows the organism to perform a taxis behavior.
   - Taxis behaviors can prevent damage or destruction of the organism or its tissues. This allows the organism to be more likely to live long enough to reproduce.

Sample Part IV Experiment

Hypothesis: If liver is placed in the water with a planarian, then the planarian will exhibit a positive chemotaxis and move toward it.

Procedure:

1. Obtain an 8 cm length of tygon tubing that has been cut in half length-wise. This piece of tubing will serve as a test trough in which the planarian will swim.

2. Use a disposable pipet, to transfer enough culture water to the central area of the piece of split tubing to make a 4 cm long water puddle.

3. Transfer one planarian with culture water into the center of the water puddle of the trough.

4. Use forceps to place a $0.5cm^3$ piece of liver in one end of the water.

5. Observe the planarian's activities for three minutes. During this 3 minute period note the location of the planaria every 30 seconds by placing an X in the data table under the liver/no liver column.

Sample data for liver experiment

Planarian Experiment Observations		
Elapsed time	**Liver side**	**No liver side**
30 sec.		x
1 min.		x
1 min. 30 sec.	x	
2 min.	x	
2 min. 30 sec.	x	
3 min.	x	

Sample Conclusion Statement:

Planaria show a positive chemotaxis in response to the food stimulus liver.

REFERENCES

Allen, Dorothea. *The Biology Teacher's Deskbook*. West Nyack: Parker Publishing, 1979.

Campbell, Neil and Jane B. Reece. *Biology*. San Francisco: Benjamin Cummings, 2002.

Klinckmann, Evelyn. *Biology Teachers' Handbook*. New York: Wiley and Sons, Inc., 1970. pp. 660-661

Planarian Behaviors
Investigating Geotaxis, Chemotaxis, and Phototaxis in Planaria

Living organisms are exposed to a variety of environmental changes during their lifetime. Changes in the environment can serve as external stimuli that result in the production of behavioral responses in the organisms. For example, a pill bug will move away from bright light. The light serves as a stimulus for the response, the movement away from the light. The movement of an organism in response to a stimulus can categorized as a kinesis or a taxis. A *kinesis* is a behavioral response that produces random movements when a stimulus is present. There is no clear movement toward or away from the stimulus. A *taxis*, on the other hand, is a behavioral response that produces movements either toward or away from a stimulus.

Taxis behaviors can be classified according to the stimulus producing the response. The presence of stimuli such as light, gravity, and chemicals can result in taxis behaviors. If an organism moves toward a particular stimulus, the movement is referred to as a positive taxis. Avoidance of or movement away from a stimulus is a negative taxis. A *phototaxis* is a response to a light stimulus. Earthworms have a negative phototaxis and tend to avoid bright light by moving away from it. A *geotaxis* is an organism's movement in response to the stimulus of gravity. Roots, for example, exhibit a positive geotaxis while stems exhibit a negative geotaxis. An organism performs a *chemotaxis* when it moves toward or away from a chemical.

The organisms used in this activity to study taxis and kinesis are planaria. These aquatic flatworms are simple animals belonging to the phylum Platyhelminthes. As Figure 1 illustrates, these worms have a simple nervous system and a small amount of cephalization or concentration of nervous tissue at the anterior region of the organism. The head of the planaria contains eyespots which are concentrations of nerve tissue or ganglion that allow them to detect light and dark. The planaria has a small brain beneath the eyespots. Connected to the brain are two parallel nerves that run the length of the body. Transverse nerves branch from the parallel nerves to form a ladder-like nervous system. The presence of this nervous system allows the planaria to detect and respond to stimuli in their environment.

PURPOSE

In this activity you will investigate geotaxis, chemotaxis and phototaxis in planaria. Additionally, you will design an experiment to determine the type of taxis a planarian will have in response to the presence of a potential food source, liver.

MATERIALS

4 planaria
test tube of culture water with stopper
disposable pipet
5 cm strip of foil
2 sheets of white paper
2 sections of 5mm bore Tygon® tubing cut in half length-wise
4 sodium chloride soaked filter paper strips
4 acetic acid soaked filter paper strips
timing device (seconds)
0.5cm^3 piece of liver
spring water (culture water)

> **Safety Alert**
> 1. Acetic acid can be an irritant, avoid eye contact.
> 2. Culture waters may contain microorganisms. Be sure to wash your hands thoroughly after any laboratory activity.

PROCEDURE

PART I: RESPONSE TO GRAVITY (GEOTAXIS)

1. In this activity you will determine the response of a planarian to being inverted in a test tube. Formulate a hypothesis to test what the planarian's response will be when the tube is inverted. Record your hypothesis in the space provided on the student answer page.

2. Obtain a test tube filled with spring water. As demonstrated by your teacher, use a disposable pipet to place a planarian in the test tube.

3. Insert a stopper into the mouth of the test tube. Be sure to insert the stopper firmly so that the test tube will not leak when inverted.

4. Holding the test tube upright, observe the activity of your planarian. Record your observations in Data Table 1.

5. Slowly invert the test tube and observe the planarian's reaction(s). Record your observations in Data Table 1.

6. Record the reactions observed by at least three other lab groups in Data Table 1.

7. Return your planarian to storage as directed by your teacher.

PART II: RESPONSE TO CHEMICALS (CHEMOTAXIS)

1. In this portion of the activity, you will determine planaria's responses to the presence of sodium chloride and acetic acid. Formulate a hypothesis to test what the planarian's response will be to sodium chloride and to acetic acid. Record your hypothesis in the space provided on the student answer page.

2. Obtain two 8 cm lengths of Tygon® tubing that have been cut in half length-wise. These pieces of tubing will serve as test troughs in which your planaria will swim.

3. Place both troughs on a sheet of white paper.

4. Using a disposable pipet, transfer enough culture water to the central area of both of the pieces of split tubing to make a 4 cm long water puddle.

5. Using a disposable pipet, transfer one planarian with culture water into the center of the water puddle of each trough.

6. Observe the general behavior of these flatworms for 1 minute. Record your observations in Data Table 2.

7. Use forceps to introduce a chemical into one of the planarian's environment by placing a 5mm strip of sodium chloride soaked filter paper into the edge of the water at one end of one trough. Use forceps to push the strip completely into the water. Observe the planarian's behavior for 1 minute. Record your observations in Data Table 2.

8. Add 3 additional pieces of sodium chloride filter paper one at a time into the same end of the trough. After each filter paper strip addition, observe the planarian's reaction for 1 minute and record your observations in Data Table 2.

9. In the second trough, place a strip of acetic acid soaked filter paper into the edge of the water at one end of one trough. Use forceps to push the strip completely into the water. Observe the planarian's response for 1 minute. Record your observations in Data Table 2.

10. Add 3 additional pieces of acetic acid filter paper one at a time into the same end of the trough. After each filter paper strip addition, observe the planarian's reaction for one minute and record your observations in Data Table 2.

11. Remove the planaria from the test troughs and return them to a location designated by your teacher.

12. Rinse test troughs to remove the contaminated water.

PART III: RESPONSE TO LIGHT (PHOTOTAXIS)

1. In this portion of the activity you will determine whether a planarian's response to light is a taxis or a kinesis. Formulate a hypothesis to test a planarian's response to the light.

2. Obtain an 8 cm length of Tygon® tubing that has been cut in half length-wise. This piece of tubing will serve as a test trough in which your planarian will swim.

3. Using a disposable pipet, transfer enough culture water to the central area of the piece of split tubing to make a 4 cm long water puddle.

4. Cover half of the water puddle with foil to create a dark environment. Do not allow the foil to touch the water.

5. Transfer one planarian with culture water into the center of the water puddle of the trough.

6. Observe the planarian's activities for one minute. Every five seconds during this one minute period note the location of the planaria by placing an X in the data table under the appropriate light or dark column.

PART IV: DESIGN AND CONDUCT A CHEMOTAXIS EXPERIMENT

1. Formulate a hypothesis to test the planarian's response to the presence of liver. Record your hypothesis in the space provided on the student answer page.

2. Design an experiment to test your hypothesis. Write your procedures in the space provided on the student answer page.

3. Conduct your experiment. Collect and record your data in data table that you design in the space provided on the student answer page.

Upon completion of your experiment, clean up your work area. Return your planaria to the storage area designated by your teacher.

Name ______________________________

Period ______________________________

Planarian Behaviors
Investigating Geotaxis, Chemotaxis, and Phototaxis in Planaria

HYPOTHESIS 1

HYPOTHESIS 2

HYPOTHESIS 3

DATA AND OBSERVATIONS

Data Table 1: Planarian Geotaxis Observations		
	Observations in upright tube	**Observations in inverted tube**
Group 1		
Group 2		
Group 3		
Group 4		

Data Table 2: Planarian Chemotaxis Observations		
Number of strips	**Reactions to sodium chloride**	**Reactions to acetic acid**
0		
1		
2		
3		
4		

Data Table 3: Planarian Phototaxis Observations		
Time Elapsed	**Dark**	**Light**
0 sec.		
5 sec.		
10 sec.		
15 sec.		
20 sec.		
25 sec.		
30 sec.		
35 sec.		
40 sec.		
45 sec.		
50 sec		
55 sec.		
60 sec.		

ANALYSIS

1. What is the stimulus for each type of taxis listed below?
   a. Geotaxis
   b. Chemotaxis
   c. Phototaxis

2. Do planaria exhibit a positive or negative geotaxis? Explain your answer using the data you collected.

3. Do planaria exhibit a positive or negative chemotaxis to sodium chloride? Explain your answer using the data you collected.

4. Do planaria exhibit a positive or negative chemotaxis to acetic acid? Explain your answer using the data you collected.

5. What type of taxis did planaria(n) exhibit in the presence of liver? Explain your answer using the data you collected.

CONCLUSION QUESTIONS

1. What is the difference in a taxis and a kinesis?

2. What structural adaptations do planaria possess that allow them to perform a taxis response?

3. How could a negative chemotaxis be beneficial to a bacterium that is exposed to bleach?

4. What type of taxis is represented in the following scenarios?
   a. An earthworm moves away from a bright light. ____________________
   b. The roots of a growing seedling turn downward. ____________________
   c. Brine shrimp in a Petri dish collect around a blue light source.____________
   d. A meal worm crawls toward a moist potato.________________
   e. A snail crawls away from a patch of fertilizer in a flower bed.___________
   f. The surface of leaf tilts toward the sunlight. __________________________

5. Explain the evolutionary advantage of possessing a nervous system that allows the organism to perform a taxis behavior.

Wonderful Pond Water
Measuring the Impact of Organisms on Their Environment

OBJECTIVE
Students will determine changes made in pH, temperature, and dissolved oxygen in pond water caused by organisms interacting with the environment. In addition, students will determine the gross and net productivity of pond water.

LEVEL
Biology I

NATIONAL STANDARDS
UCP.1, UCP.2, UCP.3, B.3, B.6, C.4, C.5, C.6, E.1, E.2, F.3, F.4, G.1, G.2

TEKS
2 (B), 2 (C), 2(D), 12(E)

CONNECTIONS TO AP
AP Biology:
III. Organisms and Population C. Ecology 2. Communities and ecosystems

TIME FRAME
30 min day 1
45 min day 2

MATERIALS
60 mL beaker
temperature probe or thermometer
LaMotte kit for testing dissolved water
fluorescent light
180 mL pond water
pH probe or universal paper
3 ea 60 mL water-sampling bottles

Safety Alert
1. The chemicals found in the LaMotte kit should be handled with extreme caution.
2. Avoid contact between reagent chemicals and skin, eyes, nose, and mouth. Do not ingest. Immediately run water over any skin that the liquid or chemical comes in contact with your skin for 10 minutes. Notify your teacher.

TEACHER NOTES

This laboratory activity can be used with a unit on ecology and the interaction of organisms with their environment. This can lead to discussions of succession. Students are also introduced to the concept of primary productivity in an aquatic ecosystem. The laboratory activity supports "Lab 12, Dissolved Oxygen and Aquatic Primary Productivity". This laboratory activity is found in the Advanced Placement Biology Lab Manual.

The pH of the pond water can be measured with a pH probe or with universal paper. There may be a change in pH in the dark bottle. This depends upon how many organisms are present.

The temperature of the pond water will not change significantly. This maybe an unexpected result for students as they assume there should be change, if a parameter is being tested.

There should be a change in the amount of dissolved oxygen. The amount of change depends on the pond water. The kit used in this experiment is LaMotte. There are other dissolved oxygen kits or other methods to measure dissolved oxygen. If you choose another kit or method consult the directions for determining dissolved oxygen.

LaMotte Co.
P.O. Box 239
802 Washington, Ave.
Chestertown, MD 21620

A disposable florescent light can be purchased at a department store. This can be taped to a box and the bottles can then be put under the light for 24-48 hours.

POSSIBLE ANSWERS TO THE CONCLUSION QUESTIONS AND SAMPLE DATA

	Temperature (°C)	pH	Dissolved Oxygen (ppm)
Water after 48 hrs. in light	22.3	6.5	7.2
Initial water sample	22.2	6.4	6.1
Difference	0.1	0.1	1.1
Water after 48 hrs. in the dark	22.3	5.2	0.9
Initial water sample	22.2	6.4	6.1
Difference	0.1	-1.2	-5.2

	Productivity (ppm)
Light bottle (ppm)	7.2 pm
Initial bottle (ppm)	6.1 ppm
Net productivity	1.1 ppm
Light bottle (ppm)	7.2pm
Dark bottle (ppm)	5.2 ppm
Gross productivity	2.0 ppm
Initial bottle (ppm)	6.1 ppm
Dark bottle (ppm)	5.2 ppm
Respiration (ppm)	-0.9 ppm

1. What cellular processes might cause changes in pH, temperature, and dissolved oxygen?
   - The metabolic activities of the organisms in the water might cause the changes. These include cellular respiration and photosynthesis.

2. What processes were occurring in the light bottle that is different from that in the bottle in the dark?
   - The process of photosynthesis is occurring in the light which does not occur in the dark bottle.

3. What evidence is there that organisms can change their environment?
   - There are changes in pH and dissolved oxygen.

4. In terms of net productivity, what does is it mean if the result is a positive number, zero, or a negative number?
   - If the net productivity is a positive number then the process of photosynthesis is greater than the process of respiration.
   - If the number is zero, then the process of photosynthesis is equal to the process of respiration.
   - If the number is less than zero than the rate of respiration is greater than the rate of photosynthesis.

5. Explain why it would be incorrect to report gross productivity with a negative number. In terms of gross productivity, what does is it mean if the result is a positive number? A zero?
   - Gross productivity is not a negative number because either photosynthesis is occurring or it is not resulting in zero. If it is a positive number, then photosynthesis is occurring and if it is zero, then photosynthesis is not occurring.

6. Explain why the change in dissolved oxygen should be a negative number when the bottle is in the dark. What does it mean if the change in dissolved oxygen for respiration is equal to zero?
   - The process of respiration removes carbon from the ecosystem and also will remove oxygen. This will result in a negative number. If the number is zero, then no respiration is occurring.

REFERENCES

Campbell, Neil. Jane Reece, Lawrence G. Mitchell. *Biology*. New York: Addison Wesley Longman, Inc., 1999. pp. 1131-1138

Wonderful Pond Water
Measuring the Impact of Organisms on Their Environment

All organisms interact with their environment. They can change the environment. This can lead to the process of succession. Succession is a replacement of one community by another in a progression to a climax community. For example, after a volcano erupts, it may eliminate the climax community as the hot, molten lava flows across the earth's surface. As the lava cools, a new, uninhabited layer of rock is formed. The first organisms to colonize the area may be mosses and lichens. These plants produce acids as a waste product. The acids slowly break down rocks forming soil. Once soil formation has begun, ferns may come in and colonize the area. Its rhizoids will help form more soil, and as they die and decompose, the soil may become richer and thereby suitable for different types of organisms. Through this example it is easy to see that organisms can have a significant impact on their environment.

There are two types of succession: primary and secondary. Primary succession is more severe than secondary succession and must start with the process of building soil. Examples of primary succession include environments that have glaciers and volcanoes. Secondary succession is less severe. It is the result of a disturbance to the community by events such as fire or tornado. The community is disrupted but the soil remains. The community recovers more quickly with secondary succession than primary succession.

As the process of succession occurs, there is an increase in the productivity of the ecosystem. *Gross productivity* is the total amount of chemical energy stored by the process of photosynthesis. In other words, the amount of carbon dioxide successfully turned into organic matter. Much of that energy is used by the producers to grow and maintain themselves. The heterotrophs will remove organic matter from the ecosystem as they eat the autotrophs. The remaining organic matter is the net productivity of the ecosystem.

In typical the pond water, there are autotrophs such as algae. These producers obtain their energy by photosynthesis.

$$6\ CO_2 + 6\ H_2O \longrightarrow C_6H_{12}O_6 + 6\ O_2$$

This process increases the amount of dissolved oxygen in the pond. The pH of the water could increase because a source of carbon dioxide comes from the carbonic acid found in the water.

The metabolic activities of both autotrophs and heterotrophs can affect the pH of the water. The pH of the water increases as carbonic acid is decomposed forming the carbon dioxide necessary for photosynthesis.

$$H_2CO_3 \longrightarrow H_2O + CO_2$$

This reaction removes acid from the water and increases the pH of the water.

The pond water could contain heterotrophs such as protozoans, small worms, or hydra. These organisms decrease the amount of dissolved oxygen because they obtain their energy from cellular respiration along with the autotrophs.

$$C_6H_{12}O_6 + 6\ O_2 \longrightarrow 6\ CO_2 + 6\ H_2O$$

This process would decrease the pH of the water because as carbon dioxide is produced and dissolves in the water, it converts to carbonic acid.

$$H_2O + CO_2 \longrightarrow H_2CO_3$$

There might also be a change in temperature due to the metabolic activities of the organisms contained in the pond water.

Changes in dissolved oxygen can also measure net productivity and gross productivity. If the dissolve oxygen is measured today and then measure 24 hours later, the change in dissolved oxygen is the net productivity. That is because both processes of photosynthesis and respiration were occurring in the water. To measure gross productivity, one could account for the process of respiration and subtract it from the net productivity. This leaves the process of only photosynthesis, which is the gross productivity. If a bottle of pond water is covered with foil and its initial oxygen is measured and then after 24 hours, the water's dissolved oxygen is measured again, there should be a decrease in the amount of dissolved oxygen. This is because photosynthesis has been halted and only the process of respiration is occurring.

Net productivity = Light bottle (after 24 hrs.) - Initial bottle

Gross productivity = Light bottle (after 24 hrs.) - Dark bottle

PURPOSE

The purpose of this lab is to take the measurement of several factors of pond water. After 48 hours, the factors will be measured again to determine if the organisms have changed their environment. The measurements to be taken are temperature, pH, and dissolved oxygen. In addition, the gross and net productivity of the pond water will be determined by measuring changes in dissolved oxygen.

MATERIALS

- 100 mL beaker
- temperature probe or thermometer
- LaMotte kit for testing dissolved water
- 250 mL pond water
- pH probe or universal paper
- 3 60 mL water sampling bottles

Safety Alert

1. The chemicals found in the LaMotte kit should be handled with extreme caution.
2. Avoid contact between reagent chemicals and skin, eyes, nose, and mouth. Do not ingest. Immediately run water over any skin that comes in contact with the liquid or chemical. Continue washing for 10 minutes. Call your teacher.

PROCEDURE

1. Obtain 60 mL of pond water. Measure its pH using either a pH probe or universal test paper. Record your results in data table 1 on the student answer page.

2. Measure the temperature using either a temperature probe or thermometer. Record this information in data table 1.

3. Obtain three water-sampling bottles and fill them completely leaving no air bubbles with pond water.

4. Determine the amount of dissolved water in one of the sampling jars using the instructions below. This value will be recorded as the initial amount of dissolved oxygen. The instructions for determining the amount of dissolved oxygen can be found on the lid of the LaMotte kit.
   a. Place the sampling bottle on several paper towels.
   b. Uncap the bottle.
   c. Add 8 drops of manganous sulfate.
   d. Add 8 drops of alkaline potassium iodide.
   e. Cap and gently shake the bottle. Allow settling.
   f. Uncap the bottle and add a scoop of sulfamic acid crystals.
   g. Cap and gently shake the bottle.
   h. Pour 20 mL into the titrator jar.
   i. Add 8 drops of starch indicator.
   j. Put the plastic lid on the titrator jar.
   k. Fill the glass syringe (titrator) with sodium thiosulfate to the zero mark.
   l. Put the syringe into the hole on the lid and drop the sodium thiosulfate into the titrator jar one drop at a time.
   m. After each drop gently swirl.
   n. There will be a point in which the solution will turn from purple to clear.
   o. Remove the titrator from the titrator jar and read the position of the plunger. This is the amount of dissolved oxygen in the solution in units of parts per million, or ppm. Record this data in data table 1.

5. Cover one of the remaining two water-sampling bottles with aluminum foil. Put both bottles under a light source for 24-48 hours.

6. After 24-48 hours, measure the pH and temperature of both bottles and record in Data Table 1.

7. Using the LaMotte kit, determine the amount of dissolved oxygen in both water samples and record them in Data Table 2. Determine net and gross productivity for the pond water as indicated on the data table.

Name ____________________

Period ____________________

Wonderful Pond Water
Measuring the Impact of Organisms on Their Environment

DATA AND OBSERVATIONS

Data Table 1			
	Temperature (°C)	**pH**	**Dissolved Oxygen (ppm)**
Water after 48 hrs. in light			
Initial water sample			
Difference			
Water after 48 hrs. in the dark			
Initial water sample			
Difference			

Data Table 2	
	Productivity (ppm)
Light bottle (ppm)	
Initial bottle (ppm)	
Net productivity	
Light bottle (ppm)	
Dark bottle (ppm)	
Gross productivity	
Initial bottle (ppm)	
Dark bottle (ppm)	
Respiration (ppm)	

CONCLUSION QUESTIONS

1. What cellular processes might cause changes in pH, temperature, and dissolved oxygen?

2. What processes were occurring in the light bottle that is different from that in the bottle in the dark?

3. What evidence is there that organisms can change their environment?

4. In terms of net productivity, what does is it mean if the result is a positive number, zero, or a negative number?

5. Explain why it would be incorrect to report gross productivity with a negative number. In terms of gross productivity, what does is it mean if the result is a positive number? A zero?

6. Explain why the change in dissolved oxygen should be a negative number when the bottle is in the dark. What does it mean if the change in dissolved oxygen for respiration is equal to zero?

Ecotones
Investigating Ecosystems using CBLs

OBJECTIVE
Students will investigate the physical differences between two ecosystems and the associated ecotone. Students will relate the physical parameters to plant populations in specific ecosystems.

LEVEL
Biology

NATIONAL STANDARDS
UCP.3, A.1, C.5, F.4

TEKS
1(A), 2(A), 2(B), 2(C), 2(D), 12(C), 12(E)

CONNECTIONS TO AP
AP Biology:

III. Organisms and Populations C. Ecology 2. Communities and ecosystems

TIME FRAME
3 class periods (up to 5 class periods with extensions)
1 class period for written observations and lab design
1 class period for data collection and analysis

MATERIALS
(For a class of 28 working in pairs)

14 meter sticks
100 meter tape
14 CBLs
14 temperature probes
Needed for extension
14 grids for transect

14 graphing calculators:
14 linking cords
14 light probes
14 relative humidity probes
14 soil pH test kits

TEACHER NOTES
This exercise is used to supplement a unit on ecology. It is designed to engage the students in fieldwork and familiarize them with the concept of an ecotone. An ecotone is transitional area found between two distinct plant communities. Ecotones may vary in scale from local such as the area between a field and a forest or on a larger scale like the forest and savannas. The ecotone between a grassland area and a forest area provides the best results, but other areas are also suitable.

Instructor should allow an extra day if students have little or no CBL experience. As this lab uses three different probes, it is not recommended for novice CBL users.

1. **Calculator Information**
   The lab protocol is based on using a LabPro® or CBL 2 (Calculator-Based Laboratory System). Students will need a TI 83+ or the TI 83, 85, 86, 89 or 92 can be easily used. Be aware that this lab can be adapted for a number of interface systems and calculators. Check with the individual manuals when making adaptations. The standard pressure probe that is needed for this lab comes from Vernier. These probes, calculators and interfaces can also be purchased from Vernier. The address is:

   Vernier Software Company
   13979 SW Millikan Way
   Beaverton, OR 97005-2886
   (503)-277-2299
   www.vernier.com

2. **Calculator Software Information**
   This activity uses DATAMATE as the data collection program. This program must be installed on the graphing calculators and can be downloaded free from Vernier. A TI-GraphLink cable is necessary for connecting the CBL2 or LabPro to a computer for download or upload processes. It is a good idea to check the Vernier site periodically for updates and update both the DATAMATE program and the operating system of your data collection devices.

Usually the students complete 6 graphs, but you may want to limit the number or type of graphs completed by the students. The following graphs can be constructed and examine the relationship between the following sets of data:

a. Distance vs. temperature
b. Distance vs. relative humidity
c. Distance vs. light intensity
d. Temperature vs. light intensity
e. Relative humidity vs. temperature
f. Light intensity vs. relative humidity

In discussing the data analysis, remind students that the graphs should include lines of best fit or linear regression lines. The points on the graph should be plotted as points and not connected points. The instructions include using the EVENTS WITH ENTRY mode in DATAMATE on the graphing calculator. This feature allows the students to analyze their data, and the program will automatically draw a linear regression line when analyzing the data. The data can be downloaded to a graphing program such as Graphical Analysis. Consult the instructions that accompany the software for downloading student data. Students can make a line of best fit using such program.

It should also be noted that while sample data is given below, the physical parameters for different ecotones vary and will not match the sample data below. Also the answers to the questions will vary depending upon the ecotone examined

SAMPLE DATA

distance meters	Temperature degrees C	light intensity lux	relative humidity %
0	34.7	84	67.0
10	33.6	79	67.7
20	31.9	78	67.0
30	31.5	70	68.8
40	31.4	68	66.3
50	30.8	45	67.9
60	30.1	10	62.8
70	29.9	11	64.4
80	29.5	13	55.8
90	29.5	16	52.1
100	29.5	15	48.6

Sample distance vs temperature graph.

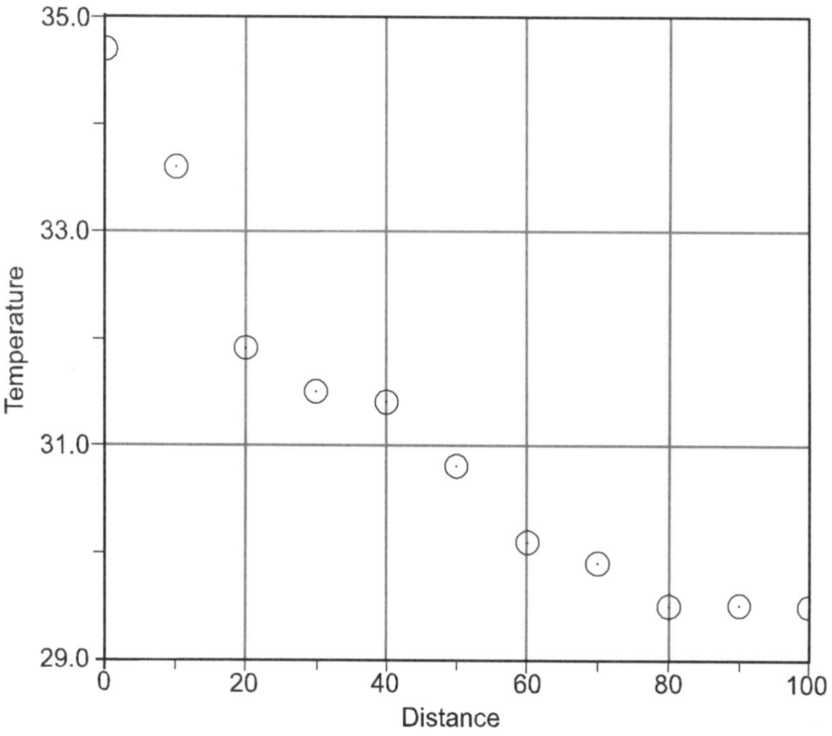

Sample distance vs light intensity graph.

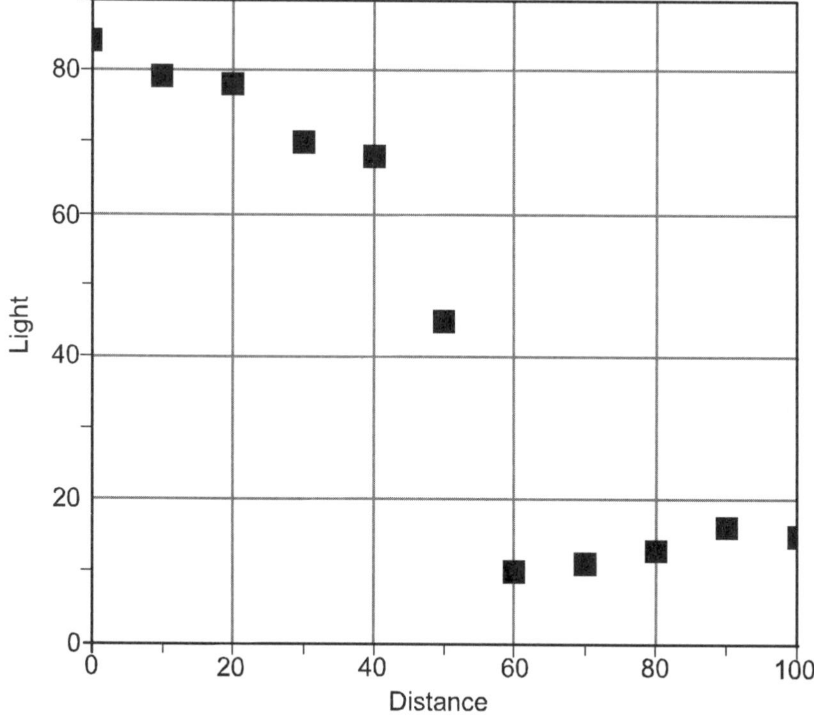

Sample distance vs relative humidity graph.

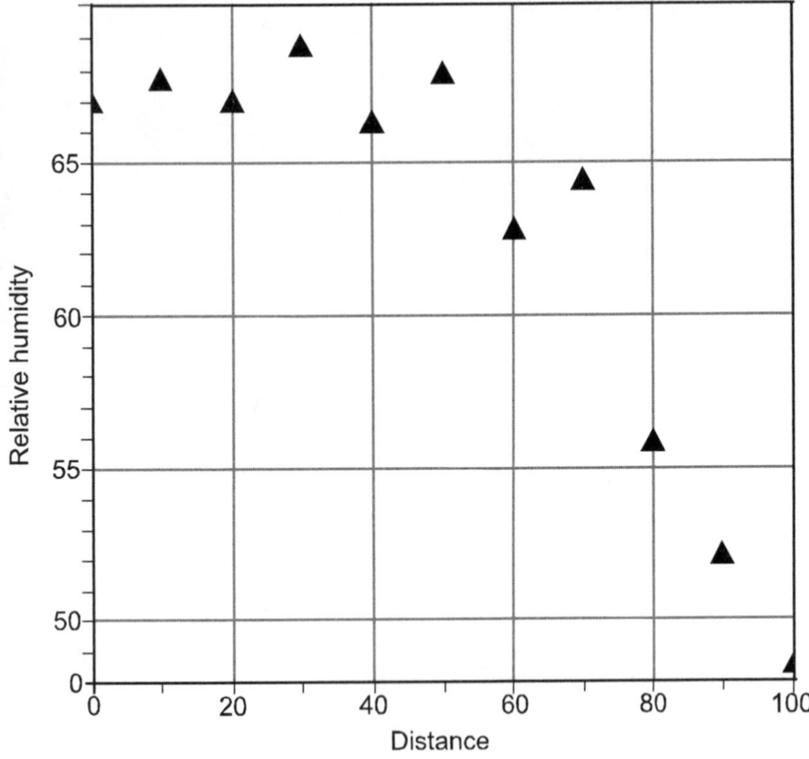

Sample temperature vs light intensity graph.

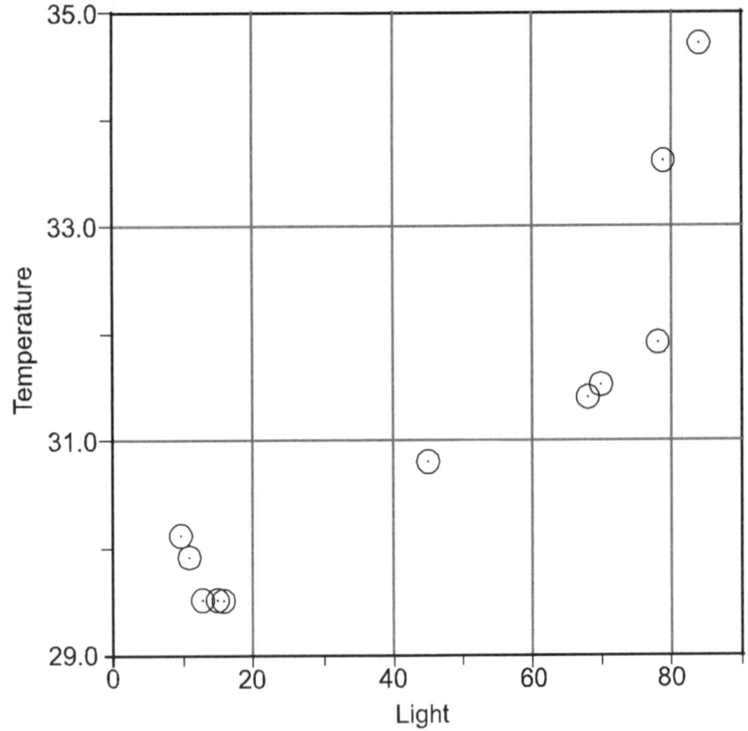

Sample light intensity vs relative humidity graph.

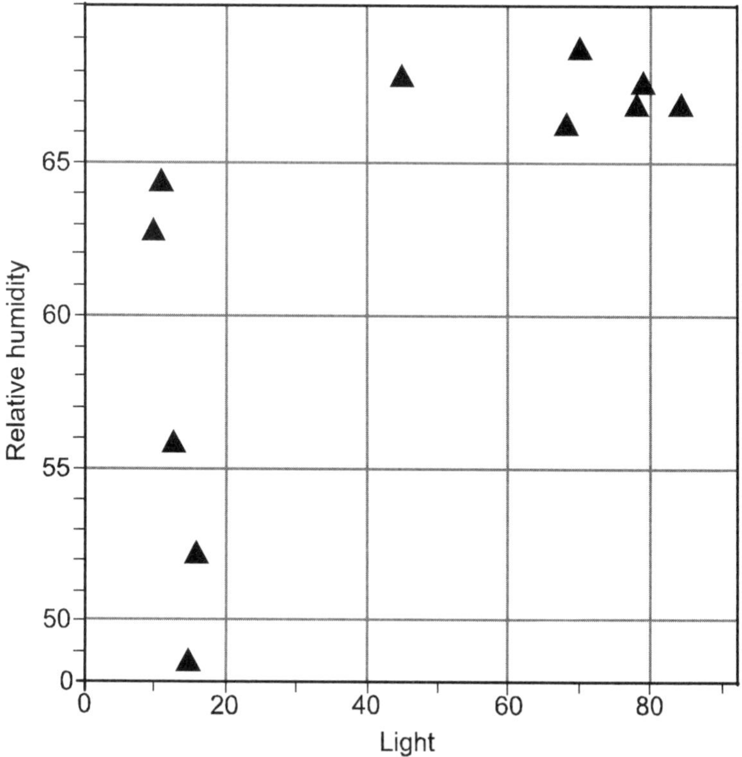

Sample relative humidity vs temperature graph.

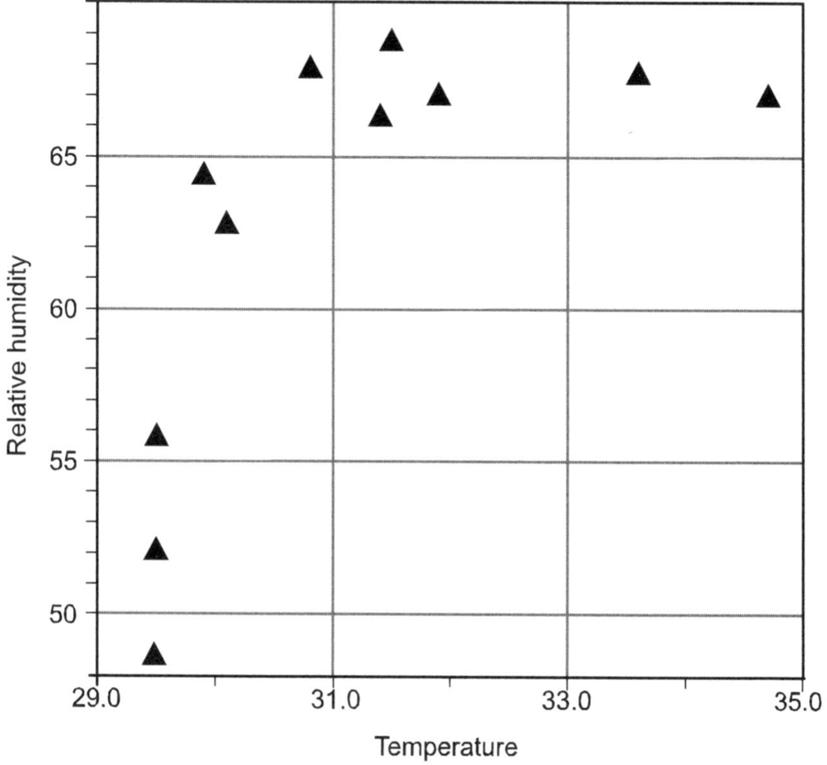

There are numerous alternatives and extensions possible with this lab. Possibilities include:

a. Complete soil analysis at each sampling location.
b. Complete species diversity study at each sampling site.
c. Complete species diversity in each ecosystem and in the ecotone.
d. Complete the study with each group at a different height. One group or class could collect data at 10 cm, others at 50 cm, 100 cm, 150 cm.
e. Collect data in a building, down hallways and up stairs.
f. Collect data in different rooms around campus.

ANALYSIS

For each graph produced, use your graphing software to provide a linear fit. Then answer the following questions:

1. Briefly discuss the change in temperature as you move from the field to the woods.

2. Temperature will decrease as you move from the field to the woods.

3. Briefly discuss the change in light intensity as you move from the field to the woods.

4. Light intensity will decrease as you move from the field to the woods.

5. Briefly discuss the change in relative humidity as you move from the field to the woods.

6. Humidity will increase as you move from the field to the woods.

7. Is there a relationship between temperature and light intensity?

8. Yes, as the light intensity increases, the temperature will also increase.

9. Is there a relationship between light intensity and relative humidity?

10. Yes, as the light intensity increases, the relative humidity will tend to decrease.

11. Is there a relationship between relative humidity and temperature?

    Yes, there is usually a relationship. If it has been dry, a temperature increase will lead to a decrease in relative humidity. If the soil is wet from a recent rain, a temperature increase will lead to an increase in relative humidity.

CONCLUSION QUESTIONS

1. Briefly describe the changes that occur in the plant communities as you move from the field ecosystem, through the ecotone, and into the woods.

   Student responses should reflect the types of plants (grasses, shrubs, trees) in each area, amount of groundcover in each area, total number of plants in each area, number of different species in each area. Students should recognize that the ecotone should have plants from both the field and the woods, but might also have some unique species.

2. Considering you observations and data, which of the three factors investigated (temperature, light intensity, relative humidity) seems to have the most impact on the type of plant life in the field? In the ecotone? In the woods? Be sure to support your decisions.

   Student answers will vary considerably. For example, amount of light penetration influences the amount of ground cover in the woods.

3. What others factors might also contribute to the types of plants found in each area?

   Student answers will vary considerably. Proximity to residential or agricultural areas, type of soil, depth of soil, proximity to natural water sources are some possibilities.

Ecotones
Investigating Ecosystems using CBLs

Environments with similar physical characteristics and climate often have similar plant life. This results in distinct regions of vegetation or biomes. Biomes are classified according to the dominant plant life found in particular area. The major biomes found on earth include tundra, taiga, deciduous forest, grasslands, tropical rain forest and desert. Very seldom will the boundary between two biomes be as clear-cut as a map may indicate. The reason for this is because the changes in climate patterns from one point to another are gradual. The place where two biomes overlap is called an ecotone and is a transition zone between the two biomes. An ecotone is may vary more in its physical parameters than either biome. For example there may be a gradual change in the pH of the soil in an ecotone between a forest and grasslands. Other factors that may vary include temperature, rainfall, relative humidity and other such factors. Ecotones may differ in scale. An example of a local ecotone is the land between a field and a stand of trees. On a larger scale, one can observe an ecotone found between the forest and a savanna.

PURPOSE

In this activity you will investigate the physical differences between two ecosystems and the associated ecotone. You will also relate the physical parameters to plant populations in specific ecosystems.

MATERIALS

meter stick
100 meter tape
CBL
temperature probe
Needed for extension
grid for transect

graphing calculator:
linking cords
light probe
relative humidity probe
soil pH test kits

Safety Alert

When doing field work, students must be aware of biting and stinging insects present in the study area.

If you have known allergies to outdoor allergens, notify your teacher.

PROCEDURE

PART I: OBSERVATIONS IN AN ECOTONE

1. Move to the grassland area to be studied as directed by your teacher. Once you arrive, select a spot where you may sit quietly and alone to make your initial observations of the area. You should make observations regarding the plants, animals and soil in the area. The list below indicates the type of information to include in your written observations. Your observations should be recorded in the space provided on the student answer sheet

    A. Plant Observations
      i. types of plant species in the area
      ii. typical height of plant species
      iii. type of distribution of plant species

    B. Animal observations
      i. tracks
      ii. sounds
      iii. scat (feces)
      iv. visual (birds, insects, reptiles)

    C. Soil characteristics
      Consider soil color, particle size, amount of organic debris, and look for soil organisms.

2. Move to the forest area to be studied. Make observations in this area following the instructions in step 1. Record your observations on the student answer sheet.

3. Move to the ecotone area located between the grassland and the forest areas. Make observations in this area following the instructions in step 1. Record your observations on the student answer sheet.

4. After completing written observations of the study areas, consider the changes that may occur as you move from the field ecosystem, through the ecotone and into the forest ecosystem. Formulate three hypotheses that answer the following questions and write them on the student answer sheet.

    A. What will happen to the temperature as you move from the field to the forest?

    B. What will happen to the light intensity as you move from the field to the forest?

    C. What will happen to the relative humidity as you move from the field to the forest?

PART II: CBL DATA COLLECTION

Working with a partner, configure the graphing calculator and CBL to take data on temperature, light intensity, and relative humidity by doing the following:

1. Slide the calculator and CBL or LabPro Interface in the bottom part of the cradle and it will click into place. Snap the calculator into the top portion of the cradle.

2. Plug the short black link cable into the link port on the bottom of the TI Graphing Calculator and the interface.

3. Plug following probes into following channels of the LabPro interface or a CBL 2.

channel 1	temperature probe
channel 2	relative humidity sensor
channel 3	light sensor

4. It will be easier to manage the probes if they are wrapped together with a rubber band. Turn on the calculator and press APPS for a TI 83+ or PRGM for the TI 83 then press the number key that precedes the DATAMATE program. At this time the interface should have automatically identified your temperature probe. It will display the correct temperature in the upper right hand corner. If the correct temperature is not displayed do the following:
   - Select SETUP from the MENU by pressing 1.
   - Select "CH1" from the MENU and press ENTER.
   - Press 1 for temperature.
   - Select the correct type of temperature probe and unit (Celsius) being used by pressing the number next to that probe.
   - Press 1 to indicate OK. This should return to SETUP screen.
   - Once the temperature probe is identified and measuring the temperature, continue activating the other probes by doing the following:
   - If the program is not at the SETUP screen, then select SETUP from the MENU by pressing 1.
   - Once at the SETUP screen, activate the relative humidity probe by selecting "CH2" from the MENU and press ENTER. Then press 7 for MORE, and then 7 again for MORE and 7 for MORE, and then 4 for REL HUMIDITY PCT. This should now return to the SETUP screen.
   - Once at the SETUP screen again, activate the light probe by selecting "CH3" from the MENU and press ENTER. Then press 7 for MORE, and then 5 for light. Now select LIGHT 6000 (LX) as the unit by pressing 2. This should now return to the SETUP screen.

- At the SETUP screen, select MODE and press ENTER. The SELECT MODE screen will appear. Now select EVENTS WITH ENTRY by pressing 3. This option will allow the distance to be correlated with the various measurements taken. This should now return to the SETUP screen.
- At the SETUP screen select OK by pressing 1.

5. Now begin taking data by selecting START by pressing 2. Hold all three probes 50 cm above the ground as measured by the meter stick unless specified differently by your teacher. Be sure the light probe is pointed down toward the ground for every measurement. Allow the three probes to stabilize. Then press ENTER. The calculator will ask for a value to be entered. Enter the distance value. For example the first distance value will be "0" because this is the first data point and you have not moved. Then press ENTER.

6. Now move five meters toward the forest, repeat the step above but this time enter "5" as the distance value this is because you have moved a distance of five meters from your original spot. Continue in the manner, recording readings every five meters until you are 50 meters into the forest. At this time you should have 20 readings, one made for every five meters. Your total distance moved should be approximately one hundred meters.

7. Stop taking readings by pressing STO→.

8. Return your equipment to its storage position and place it in the location indicated by your teacher.

9. Complete the analysis and conclusion questions on the student answer page.

Name ______________________________

Period ______________________________

Ecotones
Investigating Ecosystems using CBLs

HYPOTHESES

A.

B.

C.

DATA AND OBSERVATIONS

PART I

Complete your written observations in the space provided below or attach observations.

Grassland Observations:

Forest Observations:

Ecotone Observations:

PART II GRAPHS

1. After completing data collection, make a separate data table for your data set. You may do this by hand or you may use Graphical Analysis, Logger Pro, or Excel to make your data table.

2. Complete the following graphs using the data collected. You may do this by hand or with the computer.

   a. Distance vs temperature

   b. Distance vs light intensity

   c. Distance vs relative humidity

   d. Temperature vs light intensity

   e. Light intensity vs relative humidity

   f. Relative humidity vs temperature

ANALYSIS

For each graph produced, use your graphing software to provide a linear fit. Then answer the following questions:

1. Briefly discuss the change in temperature as you move from the field to the woods.

2. Briefly discuss the change in light intensity as you move from the field to the woods.

3. Briefly discuss the change in relative humidity as you move from the field to the woods.

4. Is there a relationship between temperature and light intensity?

5. Is there a relationship between light intensity and relative humidity?

6. Is there a relationship between relative humidity and temperature?

CONCLUSION QUESTIONS

1. Briefly describe the changes that occur in the plant communities as you move from the field ecosystem, through the ecotone, and into the woods.

2. Considering you observations and data, which of the three factors investigated (temperature, light intensity, relative humidity) seems to have the most impact on the type of plant life in the field? In the ecotone? In the woods? Be sure to support your decisions.

3. What others factors might also contribute to the types of plants found in each area?

Write Your Notes and Ideas Here!

Assessment

Assessment Foreword

Assessment in the foundational science courses is a critical component in the development of a successful AP program. Assessment can be used as a tool for measuring student understanding, measuring program success, and building students' test taking skills for use in a variety of settings. Well written, properly implemented assessment items play a valuable role in preparing students for success in subsequent AP courses and, ultimately, successful performance on AP exams.

Effective science programs expose students to a variety of assessment measures well in advance of the AP experience. For example, in foundational science courses, student performance can be measured through the use of laboratory practicals, laboratory reports, multiple choice questions, open-ended questions, free response items and other assessment tools. Formal and informal assessment should occur regularly and vary in complexity. Students should be exposed to questions of similar format and rigor as those that are used on the AP exams. Specific attention needs to be given to the development of test taking skills that will allow students to confidently approach a variety of multiple choice question styles and produce thorough and logical free responses.

Collaboration with members of a vertical team allows for a progression in the development and sophistication of test-taking skills. A cohesive science vertical team can implement strategies to ensure that students have sufficient exposure and opportunities to master these skills.

The assessment section of the *Laying the Foundation* series is designed to provide background information on the AP exams in scie33ce, offer samples of appropriate questions for use in the foundational courses, and suggest strategies that can be used to build student skills necessary for different question types. The types of multiple choice and free response items typically found on the exams are identified and described. Similar questions are presented at a level appropriate for use in foundational first year science courses. Additionally, this section contains a sample unit assessment and sets of multiple choice questions that can be used to assess student understanding of selected activities found within this book.

Hopefully, this section provides sufficient insight to allow you to confidently select or construct assessment items of the appropriate level of rigor and format to empower students.

AP TEST STRATEGIES AND INFORMATION

Course	Section	# of Questions	Relative Points	Time Allowed	Formula Sheet Provided?	Calculator Allowed
AP Biology	Multiple Choice	120 * will be 100 in 2004	60%	90 minutes	No	No
	Free Response (Problem/Essay)	4 (1 on molecules and cells, 1 on heredity and evolution, 2 on organisms and populations) At least one is lab-based.	40%	90 minutes	No	No
AP Chemistry	Multiple Choice	75	45%	90 minutes	No	No
	Free Response	2 mathematical problems (1 required; choose 1 of 2 others)	55%	40 minutes	Yes	Yes
		4 1 set of net ionic equations, 3 essay (2 mandatory, at least one of which is lab-based; choose 1 of 2 others)		50 minutes	Yes	No
AP Environmental Science	Multiple Choice	100	60%	90 minutes	No	No
	Free Response	4 (1 data, 1 document-based, 2 synthesis)	40%	90 minutes	No	No
AP Physics B	Multiple Choice	70	50%	90 minutes	Yes	Yes
	Free Response	7 (At least one lab-based)	50%	90 minutes	No	
AP Physics C (Electricity and Magnetism)	Multiple Choice	35	50%	45 minutes	No	No
	Free Response	3 (At least one lab-based)	50%	45 minutes	Yes	Yes
AP Physics C (Mechanics)	Multiple Choice	35	50%	45 minutes	No	No
	Free Response	3 (At least one lab-based)	50%	45 minutes	Yes	Yes

Overview of the AP Biology Exam

Description

***Multiple Choice Section**

Number of questions – 100
Relative points – 60%
Time Allowed – 90 minutes
No formula sheet provided
No calculator allowed

***Free Response Section**

Number of questions – 4
- Topic breakdown – 1 on molecules and cells, 1 on heredity and evolution, 2 on organisms and populations.

Relative points – 40%
Time Allowed
- 10 minute planning time
- 90 minutes of writing time

No formula sheet provided
No calculator allowed

The multiple choice portion of the exam is graded by machine while the free response portion is graded by a group of trained "readers" consisting of college professors and high school AP biology teachers. Each free-response question is scored based on a standard that is developed from input provided by not only the developers of the question but also the chief reader, question leaders, table leaders and graders. For a complete description of the grading process go to AP Central at http://apcentral.collegeboard.com and follow the exam links to "exam scoring".

The scoring of the free response section is based on a positive point system in which the student starts out with zero points and collects up to 10 points by writing correct statements in response to the prompt. Points are not deducted for incorrect or inaccurate statements. Students need acclimation to this positive point grading process. This process has a liberating effect in comparison to the process of deducting points for mistakes. The positive point system encourages students to write more generously and share the details of their understanding of a concept.

Strategies for Developing Test Taking Skills

Success on the Advanced Placement exam in biology is dependent not only on the student's understanding of the content but also upon the student's test taking skills. This section specifically addresses developing multiple choice testing skills and describes the attributes of the free response segment of the test. The information in this section is supported by the foundational lesson IX, "Essay Writing Skills, Developing a Free Response," which is designed to develop essay writing skills.

Students who know what types of questions to expect on the exam and how to approach these questions will perform more successfully. You can help your students develop these skills during the first year course by exposing them to a variety of types of multiple choice questions and periodically giving attention to test taking strategies. The skills and confidence your students develop under your guidance will serve them throughout their lives. The following strategies are offered to assist you in this skill development process.

Strategies you can implement to develop multiple choice test taking skills:

1. Teach students how to approach difficult multiple choice questions by encouraging them to
   a. First read the entire question rather than simply scanning the words.
   b. Think about what the question is asking and then think of an answer before reading the choices. This will make it easier to recognize the correct answer when it is encountered.
   c. Eliminate obvious wrong answers.
   d. Make an educated guess if one or two of the choices can be eliminated.

2. Provide frequent situations in which students are timed as they answer multiple choice questions. This is particularly important for students who have grown accustom to state level tests that have no time limitations.

3. Allow students the opportunity to bubble answers on an answer document during a timed test. Students should be taught to answer a question and immediately bubble the answer on the answer sheet rather than waiting to bubble at the end of the test.

4. Use multiple choice questions as warm-ups to provide skill development opportunities in situations outside the normal testing environment.

5. Allow the students opportunities to witness your approach to difficult multiple choice questions by modeling your thought processes aloud. This metacognition process allows students the opportunity to witness effective, logical, and mature thinking. It also helps them to see that answers can be derived rather than memorized.

6. Include multiple choice items on major tests that are based on or specifically related to the lab activities performed in your course. This will encourage students to pay attention to both content and process during the lab experiences.

7. Inform students about the penalty for guessing that is often used on standardized tests, including the AP exams. Have students calculate what their test score would be on any given test if you were to deduct ¼ point penalty for each wrong answer.

8. Include material and multiple choice questions from previous “units” or topics on your tests. This helps motivate students to retain the information rather than simply learn it “for the test”.

9. Give students feedback regarding their performance on multiple choice questions as quickly as possible. Prompt feedback allows students the opportunity to rethink the question and learn from their mistakes.

10. Expose your students to a variety of multiple choice question styles. Several types of multiple choice questions are described in the following section.

Examples of the Various Types of Multiple Choice Questions Found on the AP Biology Exam

EXCEPT QUESTIONS

Multiple choice questions that contain "EXCEPT" are sometimes difficult for students because they have to look for the answer that contains the **wrong** information. Since they have been trained to look for correct information in most questions, searching for the **wrong** information can be challenging. Help your students overcome this by including "EXCEPT" questions on your quizzes and tests.

Example from the 1999 AP Biology Exam:

Nuclear divisions in which the chromosome number is reduced from 2*n* to *n* is part of the life cycle of all of the following organisms EXCEPT

(A) molds
(B) ferns
(C) insects
(D) bacteria
(E) protozoans

Answer: D

Example suitable for use in a first year course:

The process of meiosis occurs in all of the following organisms EXCEPT

(A) fungi
(B) plants
(C) animals
(D) bacteria
(E) protists

Answer: D

CLASSIFICATION QUESTIONS

In classification type questions students are given a set of answers that are to be used to answer several questions. Students need practice with this type of question because frequently the answers can be used more than once or not at all. Students must be taught to **avoid** the tendency to think that if there are five questions following the answer choices that all five answers must be used. Frequently on the AP Biology exam one or more of the answer choices in an answer set will not be used at all.

Example from the 1999 AP Biology Exam:

<u>Questions 87-91</u>

(A) Annelida
(B) Mollusca
(C) Arthropoda
(D) Echinodermata
(E) Chordata

87. Bilaterally symmetrical; deuterostome; dorsal hollow nerve cord
88. Coelomate; exoskeleton; jointed appendages
89. Pharyngeal slits; endoskeleton derived from mesoderm; ventral heart
90. Internal calcareous skeleton; deuterostome; water-vascular system
91. Closed circulatory system; protostome; many body segments

Answers: 87. E, 88. C, 89. E, 90. D, 91. A

Example suitable for use in a first year course:

<u>Questions 1-5</u>

(A) Annelida
(B) Mollusca
(C) Arthropoda
(D) Echinodermata
(E) Chordata

1. Segmented worms such as an earthworm
2. Includes classes such as Insecta and Crustacea
3. Members of this phylum have jointed appendages and exoskeletons
4. Includes organisms with a dorsal notochord such as lamprey and perch
5. Phylum containing starfish and sea urchin

Answers: 1. A, 2. C, 3. C, 4. E, 5. D

TIERED-STEM QUESTIONS WITH MULTIPLE ANSWERS

Students may struggle with tiered-stem, multiple choice questions because they require more involved thought processes than do standard multiple choice questions. In these questions students are required to think about several items simultaneously. Exposure and practice with tiered-stem questions will help students develop confidence.

Example from the 1999 AP Biology Exam:

18. In a mesophyll cell of a leaf, the synthesis of ATP occurs in which of the following?
    I. Ribosomes
    II. Mitochondria
    III. Chloroplasts

    (A) I only
    (B) II only
    (C) III only
    (D) II and III only
    (E) I, II, and III

Answer: D

Example suitable for use in a first year course:

1. Which of the following cell organelles typically contain DNA?
    I. Nucleus
    II. Ribosomes
    III. Chloroplasts
    IV. Mitochondria

    (A) I only
    (B) I and II
    (C) III only
    (D) II and III
    (E) I, III, and IV

Answer: E

LAB SET QUESTIONS

Students need extensive practice answering multiple choice questions that are based on experimental data or scenarios describing experimental procedures. This type of question can be used to assess science process skills as well as understanding of the scientific basis for collected data. Students will be expected to interpret diagrams, data tables, and graphs. Additionally, they will be expected to apply their understanding of the biological concept to the data recorded and recognize acceptable explanations of the trends observed.

Example from the 1999 AP Biology Exam:

Question 114 refers to an experiment in which a dialysis-tubing bag is filled with a mixture of 3% starch and 3% glucose and placed in a beaker of distilled water, as shown below. After 3 hours, glucose can be detected in the water outside the dialysis-tubing bag, but starch cannot.

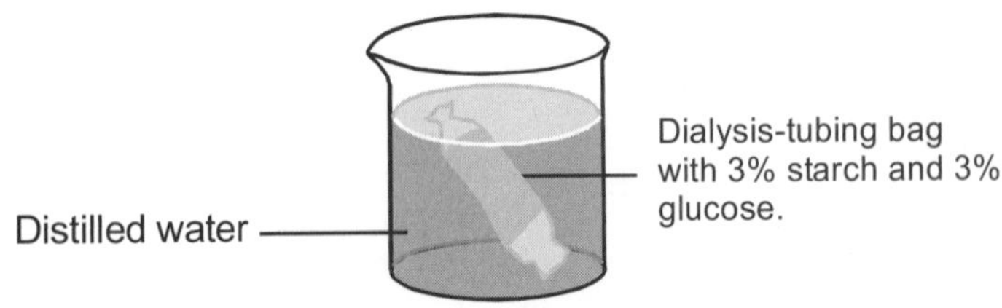

114. From the initial conditions and results described, which of the following is a logical conclusion?
    (A) The initial concentration of glucose in the bag is higher than the initial concentration of starch in the bag.
    (B) The pores of the bag are larger than the glucose molecules but smaller than the starch molecules.
    (C) The bag is not selectively permeable.
    (D) A net movement of water into the beaker has occurred.
    (E) The molarity of the solution in the bag and the molarity of the solution in the surrounding beaker are the same.

Answer: B

Example suitable for use in a first year course:

Question 1 refers to an experiment in which a dialysis-tubing bag is filled with a mixture of 3% starch and 3% glucose and placed in a beaker of distilled water, as shown below. After 3 hours, glucose can be detected in the water outside the dialysis-tubing bag, but starch cannot.

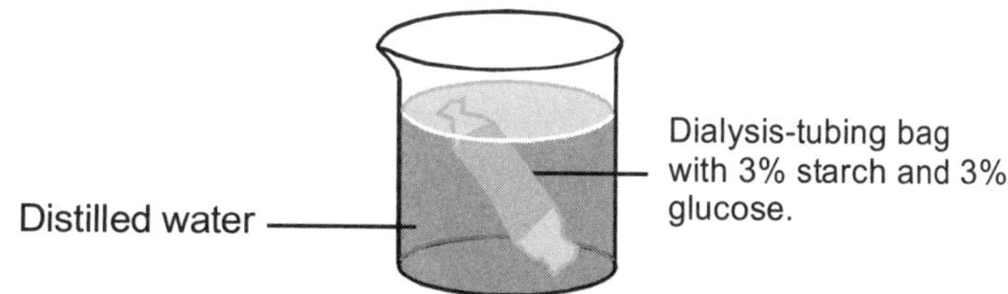

1. Which of the following statements is true based on the results described?
   (A) The bag is permeable to starch.
   (B) The distilled water caused the bag to rupture.
   (C) The pores in the bag are larger than the starch molecules.
   (D) The bag is permeable to glucose.
   (E) The bag does not allow water to move through it.

Answer: D

Free Response

In order to develop strong free response skills, students will need exposure to this type of question in the first year biology course as well as the AP Biology course. The foundation lesson IX, "Essay Writing Skills, Developing a Free Response" provides classroom strategies for developing skills in this area. The free response prompts are frequently broad and sweeping and thus require the students to consider an expansive scope of course content. The breadth of the questions makes them challenging for students. In this section we will look at examples of two types of free response questions encountered on the AP Biology Exam and explore how those types of questions may look in the first year course.

I. THEMATIC CONTENT BASED QUESTIONS

The College Board suggests the use of unifying themes to tie together the expansive content of the course. The themes used in the AP Biology course outline are frequent components in the free response prompts. The themes include science as a process, evolution, energy transfer, continuity and change, relationship of structure to function, regulation, interdependence in nature, and science, technology, and society. The following example shows how the themes are used in the prompts for the free response items:

Example from the 2002 AP Biology Exam:

3. The complexity of structure and function varies widely across the animal kingdom. Despite this variation, animals exhibit common processes. These include the following.
    - transport of materials
    - response to stimuli
    - gas exchange
    - locomotion

    a. Choose <u>two</u> of the processes above and for each, <u>describe</u> the relevant structures and how they function to accomplish the process in the following phyla.
        Cnidaria (e.g., hydra, jellyfish)
        Annelida (e.g., earthworm)
        Chordata (e.g., mouse)

    b. Explain the adaptive (evolutionary) value(s) of the structural examples you described in part a.

Example suitable for use in a first year course:

As animals became more complex, there was a selection pressure for a more efficient circulatory system. Compare and contrast the circulatory system for any two animals listed below and explain which animal has the more efficient system. Be sure to include a comparison of their hearts, effectiveness of gas exchange and any adaptations the system has to make it more efficient.

a. fish
b. grasshopper
c. mouse
d. snake

II. LABORATORY AND EXPERIMENT BASED QUESTIONS

Typically, at least one of the free response questions on the AP Biology exam is based on a laboratory or experimental activity. Often the lab based prompt has connections to one of the twelve labs in the AP Biology Lab Manual. In these questions the students are frequently asked to demonstrate science process skills such as graphing, making inferences, predicting experimental outcomes, and critiquing experimental design.

Example from the 2002 AP Biology Exam:

4. The following experiment was designed to test whether different concentration gradients affect the rate of diffusion. In this experiment, four solutions (0%NaCl, 1%NaCl, 5%NaCl, and 10%NaCl) were tested under identical conditions. Fifteen milliliters (mL) of 5%NaCl were put into a bag formed of dialysis tubing that is permeable to Na^+, Cl^-, and water. The same was done for each NaCl solution. Each bag was submerged in a separate beaker containing 300 mL of distilled water. The concentration of NaCl in mg/L in the water outside each bag was measured at 40-second intervals. The results from the 5% bag are shown in the table below.

CONCENTRATION IN mg/L of NaCl OUTSIDE THE 5% NaCl BAG

Time (seconds)	NaCl (mg/L)
0	0
40	130
80	220
120	320
160	400

a. On the axes provided, graph the data for the 5% NaCl solution.
b. Using the same set of axes, draw and label three additional lines representing the results that you would predict for the 0%NaCl, 1%NaCl, and 10%NaCl solutions. Explain your predictions.
c. Farmlands located near coastal regions are being threatened by encroaching seawater seeping into the soil. In terms of water movement into or out of plant cells, explain why sea water could decrease crop production. Include a discussion of water potential in your answer.

Example suitable for use in a first year course:

A student performs a laboratory experiment with eggs, by first removing the calcium shells with vinegar. This leaves the eggs with a tough, rubbery but porous membrane. The eggs are then weighed. The student makes a number of different corn syrup solutions with varying percentages of corn syrup. She submerges a different egg into each of the different percent corn syrup solutions and allows them to sit for 24 hours. After 24 hours, the student removes the eggs and reweighs them. Analyze the student's data by completing the data table and graphing the % change in mass versus the percentage of corn syrup used to submerge the egg.

Percent of syrup	0%	10%	20%	30%	40%	50%
Original mass (g)	89	81	82	76	62	55
Final Mass (g)	78	77	86	89	82	81
Change in mass						
Percent change in mass						

Using the principles of osmosis, explain the results the student obtained. Determine from the graph what percent of corn syrup is considered isotonic with the egg and explain how you would confirm that predicted data point.

Finally, the student places her egg in distilled water for 24 hours and noticed no change in mass. Explain why "water-proof" eggs would be an important adaptation for birds.

The thematic content questions and the experiment based questions require the students to think across the "unit boundaries". The students are required to weave together content from all parts of the course curriculum to demonstrate a foundational understanding of major concepts. This level of thinking requires practice and incremental skill development. In addition to presenting the concepts of the course, you should provide multiple opportunities for students to develop their free response skills.

The AP level questions, for the most part, will not be written at a level appropriate for the first year course. The implication is that you will need to modify the AP level prompts or write your own prompts. In either case you should provide the students with prompts that require them to make choices, have multiple parts in the answer, incorporate the unifying themes and require students to make connections among a range of items.

Tips for streamlining the grading process as it relates to free response questions are given in the teacher section of the foundation lesson on free responses. Refer to that lesson to glean time saving strategies that will enable you to effectively incorporate these assessment items without being overwhelmed by the task of grading.

You can have a strong, positive impact on your students test taking skills through the intentional incorporation of these assessment strategies. The next two parts of the assessment section provide you with a sample unit test incorporating the various types of questions that are written at a level appropriate for first year biology as well as eight sets of assessment questions related to activities presented in this book. Use the questions to serve as a resource as you apply the test building strategies presented here.

Major Test: Photosynthesis

Multiple Choice

Directions: Select the best answer choice for each item. Place your answer choice in the space provided.

____ 1. Which of the following structural hierarchies is arranged in the correct order from largest to smallest?

a. chloroplast, mesophyll tissue, mesophyll cell, leaf, thylakoid membrane
b. leaf, chloroplast, mesophyll cell, mesophyll tissue, thylakoid membrane
c. leaf, mesophyll tissue, mesophyll cell, thylakoid membrane, chloroplast
d. leaf, mesophyll tissue, mesophyll cell, chloroplast, thylakoid membrane

____ 2. A plant leaf was partially covered with foil, as shown in the diagram below. The plant was then exposed to light for 48 hours. Which picture best represents the expected results after the leaf has been boiled and stained with iodine?

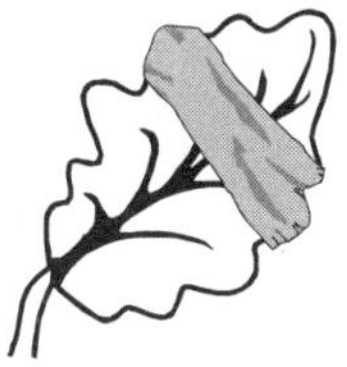

a. 
b. 
c. 
d.

____ 3. A product of the dark reactions of photosynthesis is

a. 3-carbon compound (PGAL)
b. oxygen
c. carbon dioxide
d. ATP

____ 4. The light independent reactions of the Calvin cycle take place in

a. cristae folds
b. stoma of the leaf
c. thylakoid membrane
d. stoma of the chloroplast

____ 5. All of the following are true regarding the dark reactions of photosynthesis EXCEPT
a. The dark reactions use ATP from the light reactions.
b. The dark reactions can occur in sunlight, shade or darkness.
c. The dark reactions use glucose as a reactant.
d. The dark reactions transfer energy to the bonds of organic compounds.

____ 6. Which letter in the schematic diagram represents oxygen given off during the light reactions?

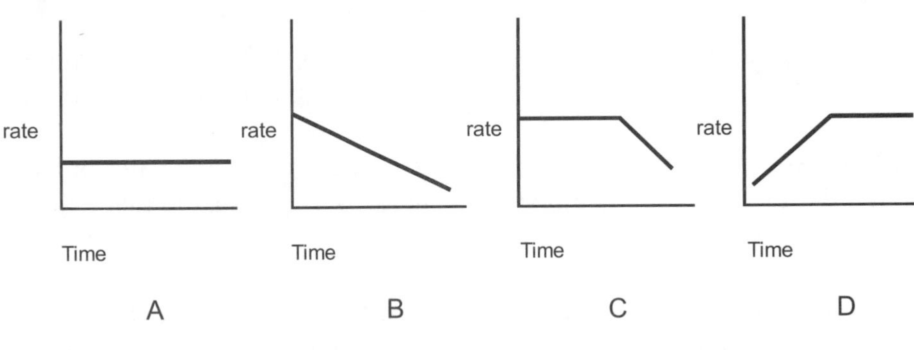

a. A
b. B
c. C
d. D

____ 7. The ultimate source of energy on Earth is
a. heat
b. solar
c. chemical
d. mechanical

____ 8. Carbon dioxide enters the leaves through the
a. stoma
b. epidermis
c. xylem
d. phloem

____ 9. Which of the following light reaction products is/are used by the light independent reactions?
a. Oxygen
b. ATP
c. NADPH
d. B and C

____ 10. Energy conversions occur during photosynthesis. Which statement most accurately describes the energy conversions?
a. Heat energy is converted to light energy.
b. Chemical energy is converted to light energy.
c. Mechanical energy is converted to light energy.
d. Light energy is converted to chemical bond energy.

____ 11. Which of the following is not an autotroph?
a. an oak tree
b. Bermuda grass
c. mushroom
d. cactus

____ 12. When light strikes the chlorophyll molecules in a leaf the electrons are excited to a higher energy level and then
a. release oxygen
b. enter an electron transport chain
c. attach to water molecules
d. give off solar energy

____ 13. Which letter in the diagram shown below represents carbon dioxide?

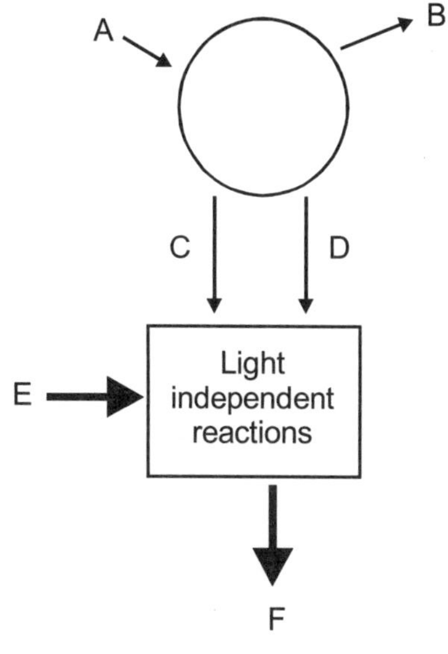

a. B
b. D
c. E
d. F

____ 14. Which letter on the diagram above represents oxygen?
a. A
b. B
c. C
d. F

____ 15. In the diagram above, which arrow indicates water?
a. A
b. B
c. C
d. D

Consider this diagram in response to questions 16-20.

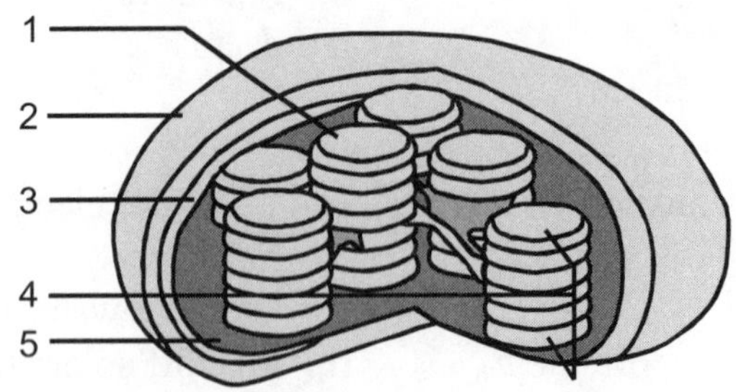

____ 16. Which number indicates the granum of the chloroplast?
a. 1
b. 2
c. 3
d. 4

____ 17. Which number indicates the outer membrane of the chloroplast?
a. 1
b. 2
c. 3
d. 4

____ 18. Which number represents the stroma of the chloroplast?
a. 2
b. 3
c. 4
d. 5

____ 19. Which number indicates the place where the light independent reactions occur?
a. 2
b. 3
c. 4
d. 5

____ 20. Which number indicates a thylakoid?
a. 1
b. 2
c. 3
d. 4

____ 21. Which of the following conclusion statements is supported by the graph below?

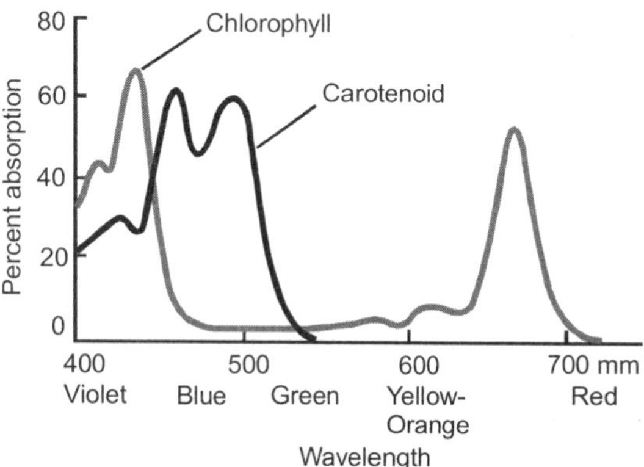

a. The green wavelength of light is strongly absorbed by chlorophyll.
b. The blue wavelength of light is reflected by carotenoid.
c. Red and blue wavelengths of light are absorbed by chlorophyll.
d. Yellow wavelengths of light are reflected and absorbed equally well by carotenoid.

____ 22. Which of the following statements is supported by the results obtained during the *Light Reactions Of Photosynthesis* lab that we conducted in our class?
a. Chlorophyll, alone, can perform the light reactions in the presence of light.
b. Chlorophyll can perform the light reactions without a light source.
c. An intact chloroplast in the presence of light can perform the light reactions.
d. An intact chloroplast without light can perform the light reactions.

____ 23. Oxygen that is released from plants comes from ______________.
a. Carbon dioxide
b. Glucose
c. PGAL
d. Water

____ 24. The purpose of the Calvin cycle, or light independent reactions is to ________________.
a. make ATP
b. make PGAL
c. make NADPH
d. release oxygen gas

____ 25. Which of the following has the most energy?
a. Glucose
b. ATP
c. NADP
d. PGAL

____ 26. All of the following statements are true EXCEPT?

a. Under extremely hot conditions C3 photosynthesis is more efficient than the C4 photosynthetic pathway.
b. C4 plants are more likely to be found in warmer climates.
c. C4 plants have two different types of chloroplasts.
d. C4 plants have two different types of chloroplasts.

____ 27. The diagram shown below shows a section of leaf from which type of plant?

a. CAM plant
b. C3 plant
c. C4 plant
d. Cannot be determined

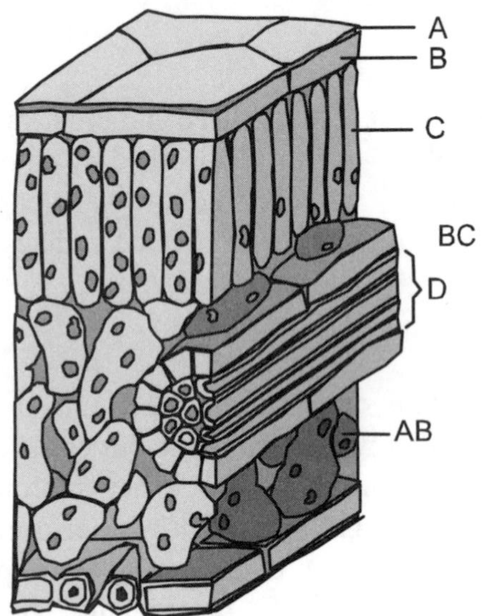

____ 28. The structure labeled A in the diagram above is the

a. upper epidermis.
b. lower epidermis.
c. cuticle.
d. vein.

____ 29. The structure labeled D in the diagram above functions to

a. regulate gas exchange
b. make the leaf water proof
c. perform photosynthesis
d. deliver water and other inorganic nutrients.

____ 30. The structure labeled C in the diagram above is the

a. upper epidermis.
b. lower epidermis.
c. palisade mesophyll.
d. vein.

Read the following description and use the information to answer the questions.

A botanist was studying how various factors affected the amount of photosynthesis occurring in plants. The various factors included the effect of light color, temperature, plant part, and plant species. This was done by measuring changes in the amount of carbon dioxide either consumed or produced. One hundred plants were placed in 5 containers of equal volume which were then sealed. The amount of carbon dioxide present in the containers at the beginning of the experiment was 250 mL. At the end of two days, the amount of carbon dioxide in the containers was measured and the results are tabulated below: Assume that the experimental conditions not listed are identical in all five containers.

Container	plant	plant part	light color	Temp (C°)	CO^2 (mL)
1	myrtle	leaf	red	15	100
2	myrtle	leaf	red	27	50
3	myrtle	stem	blue	27	200
4	oak	root	blue	27	300
5	oak	leaf	orange	27	150

____ 31. On the basis of the data presented in the table, one could properly compare the amount of carbon dioxide used per day at two different temperatures by comparing which containers?

a. 1 and 2
b. 1 and 3
c. 2 and 3
d. 4 and 5

____ 32. In which container was photosynthesis occurring most quickly?

a. 1
b. 2
c. 3
d. 4

____ 33. In which container was photosynthesis taking place most slowly?

a. 2
b. 3
c. 4
d. 5

____ 34. In which container was photosynthesis not occurring?

a. 2
b. 3
c. 4
d. 5

Consider the graph here in response to questions 35 and 36.

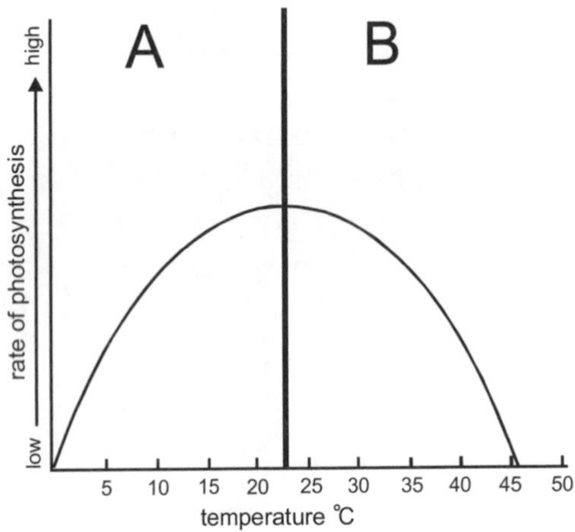

____ 35. Which of the following statements best explains part A of the graph?

a. The molecules are moving faster.
b. More photosystems are becoming activated.
c. Photorespiration is occurring more quickly than photosynthesis.
d. The photosynthesis enzymes are being denatured.

____ 36. Which of the following best explains part B of the graph?

a. The molecules are moving faster.
b. More photosystems are becoming activated.
c. Photorespiration is occurring more quickly than photosynthesis.
d. The photosynthesis enzymes are being denatured.

____ 37. Which of the following statements best explains the results shown in the graph below?

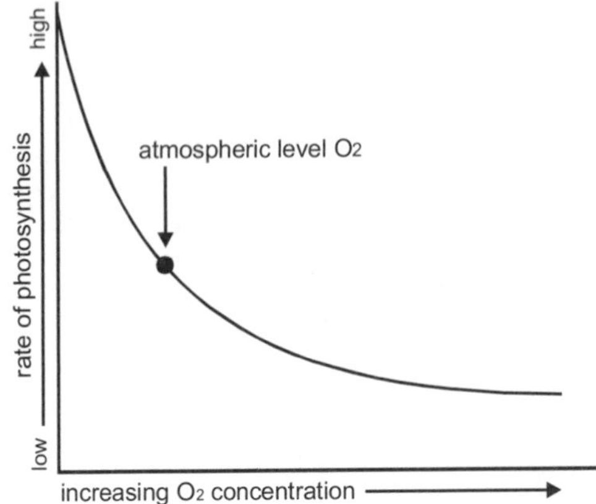

a. The molecules are moving faster.
b. More photosystems are becoming activated.
c. Photorespiration is occurring more quickly than photosynthesis.
d. The photosystems have become saturated.

____ 38. The leaf cross section shown below most likely came from which of the following types of plants?

a. C3
b. C4
c. CAM
d. Cannot be determined.

____ 39. Which of the following kingdoms contain members capable of performing photosynthesis?

I. Fungi
II. Plantae
III. Animalia
IV. Eubacteria
V. Archaebacteria
VI. Protista

a. I, II, III, IV, V, VI
b. II, III, IV, V, VI
c. II, IV, V, VI
d. I, II, IV, VI

____ 40. Which of the following kingdoms contain members capable of using the products of photosynthesis?

I. Fungi
II. Plantae
III. Animalia
IV. Eubacteria
V. Archaebacteria
VI. Protista

a. I, II, III, IV, V, VI
b. II, III, IV, V, VI
c. II
d. I, II, IV, VI

Free Response Essay

21. Chloroplasts removed from leaves of spinach are able to undergo photosynthesis given the right conditions. Describe an experiment that could be used to determine the effect of light on the rate of photosynthesis in spinach chloroplasts. In your description be sure to (a) include a control, (b) identify the dependent and independent variables, (c) provide a description of the procedures to be followed, (d) explain what results are expected and (e) give an explanation of the results.

Photosynthesis
Answer Section

Multiple Choice

1. ANS: D
2. ANS: C
3. ANS: A
4. ANS: D
5. ANS: C
6. ANS: D
7. ANS: B
8. ANS: A
9. ANS: D
10. ANS: D
11. ANS: C
12. ANS: B
13. ANS: C
14. ANS: B
15. ANS: A
16. ANS: D
17. ANS: B
18. ANS: D
19. ANS: D
20. ANS: A
21. ANS: C
22. ANS: C
23. ANS: D
24. ANS: B
25. ANS: A
26. ANS: A
27. ANS: B
28. ANS: C
29. ANS: D
30. ANS: C
31. ANS: A
32. ANS: B
33. ANS: B
34. ANS: C
35. ANS: A
36. ANS: D
37. ANS: C
38. ANS: B
39. ANS: C
40. ANS: A

Essay

ANS:

(a) Control - test tube with DPIP, phosphate buffer, and water.

(b) Dependent variable = color change of DPIP from blue to clear as the result of light reactions
Independent variable = the time intervals in which readings are taken

(c) In three test tubes, place 1 mL of phosphate buffer, 1 mL of distilled water and 1 mL of DPIP. Label the tubes 1-3. Add three drops of chloroplast solution to tubes 1 and 2. Tube 3 will not receive chloroplasts and will serve as a control. Write down the colors of the three tubes in data table. Wrap foil around tube 2 so that light cannot enter. Place all three tubes in front of a light source. Wait 1 minute and compare the colors again. Continue for a total of 15 minutes.

(d) At the end of 15 minutes the solution in tube 1 will have lost most of its blue color, tube 2 will appear almost the same color as it was initially, and tube 3 will remain unchanged.

(e) Tube 1 will change colors because DPIP has accepted electrons during the light reactions to form DPIPH which is colorless. Tube 2 will not change much because it has not been exposed to enough light to stimulate photosynthesis, and Tube 3 will not change because it lacks the chloroplasts needed to perform the light reactions to change DPIP.

Data Collection Devices
Determining the Amount of Energy Found in Food

Multiple Choice Questions:

Given the following information, answer the questions below. The student performed a calorimeter lab to determine the amount of Kcal/gram of peanut and walnut. The student used 10 grams of water in the test tube.

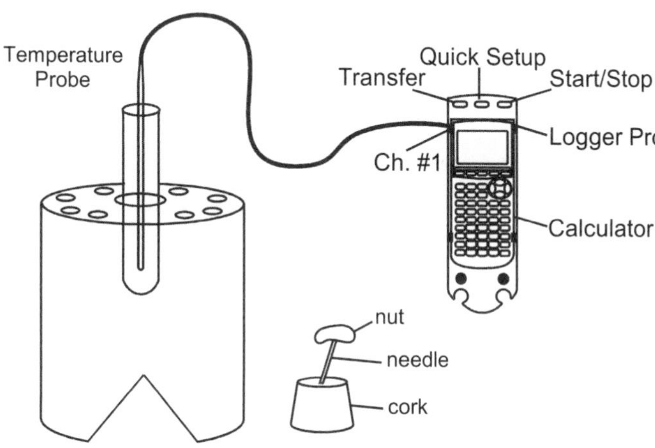

Calorimeter set-up with probe

Type of Nut	Mass of Nut	Beginning Temp.	Final Temp.	Calories	Kilocalories	kcal/gram
Peanut	0.2 g	15	95			
Walnut	0.1 g	15	65			

1. The number of calories produced by the peanut is
   A) 80 B) 50 C) 800 D) 500 E) 0.8

2. The number kilocalories produced by the walnut is
   A) .5 B) 0.4 C) 4.0 D) 5.0 E) 0

3. The number of kilocalories/gram of walnut is
   A) 0.5 B) 0.4 C) 5.0 D) 4.0 E) 8.0

4. If the actual value for the peanut is 6.2 kilocalories/gram, what was the percent error?
   A) 35% B) 19% C) 43% D) 29% E) 100%

5. The reason the experimental value and the actual value are not the same is
   A) the experimenter is not very careful with his measurements
   B) there is energy lost as the experimenter ate most of the nuts
   C) the experimenter destroyed energy during the chemical reaction
   D) not all the heat energy produced went into the test tube

Answer Key: (Nuts and Calories)

1. c
2. b
3. c
4. a
5. d

Larger Is Not Always Better
Examining Cell Size and Rates of Diffusion

Multiple Choice Questions:

three agar cubes of different sizes are shown below. The cubes have been made with phenolphthalein. Phenolphthalein is pink but when mixed with an acid it turns clear. The cubes were submerged in acid for ten minutes. The acid diffused into the cubes. After ten minutes the cubes were removed from the beakers and cut in half to see how far the acid had diffused. The results are shown below. Answer the following questions about the experiment.

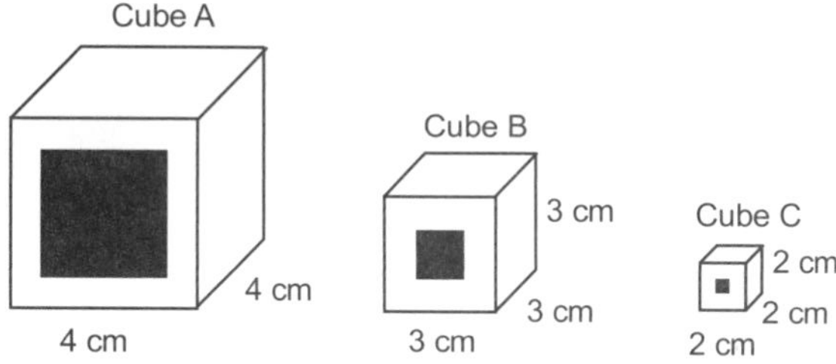

1. The surface area of cube B is
   A) 54 cm^2 B) 27 cm^2 C) 9 cm^2 D) 6 cm^2

2. The surface area to volume ratio of cube B is
   A) 3/2 B) 2/3 C) 2/1 D) 1/2

3. The cube with the greatest surface area is
   A) cube A B) cube B
   C) cube C D) cannot be determined with the information given

4. The cube with the greatest surface area to volume ratio is
   A) cube A B) cube B
   C) cube C D) cannot be determined with the information given

5. One reason the above experiment demonstrates the necessity for small cell size is that
   A) as the volume of the cell increases, its surface area increases much more quickly.
   B) as the volume of the cell increases, its surface area increases much more slowly.
   C) as the volume of the cell increases, its surface area increases at the same rate.
   D) the information presented has no implication for the reason why cells remain small.

Answer Key: (Larger Is Not Always Better)

1. a
2. c
3. a
4. c
5. b

McMush Lab
Testing for the Presence of Macromolecules

Multiple Choice Questions:

Questions 1-4

(A) Lugol's iodine
(B) Benedicts Solution
(C) Biuret's Solution
(D) Sudan III

1. Myra's task during a lab experiment was to determine whether or not a food sample contained fat. Which of the solutions should Myra use to detect fats?

2. Urinalysis involves testing urine for the presence of specific chemicals. One chemical that is present in the urine of diabetics is glucose. Which solution could be used to determine whether or not glucose is present in the urine?

3. Plants store the energy that has been captured during photosynthesis in starch molecules. Which solution listed above could be used to test for the presence of starch in the plant tissues?

4. Which solution listed above could detect the presence of the following compound?

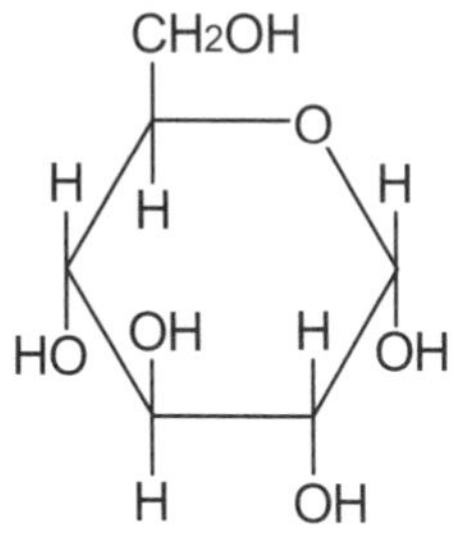

CH_2OH
O
H H H
HO OH H OH
H OH

5. Which of the following would be considered a source of error in the McMush lab?
   A) The McMush sample cooled down as it sat at room temperature.
   B) Test tubes were re-used and may have contained contaminants.
   C) Several lab groups conducted the protein test at the same time.
   D) Lab group 2 used test tubes of a different size than those used by lab group

Answer Key: (McMush Lab)

1. d
2. c
3. a
4. b
5. b

Plasmolysis
Comparing *Elodea* and Onion Cell Plasmolysis

Multiple Choice Questions:

Questions 1-5:

(A) The cells will experience a net loss of water.
(B) The cells will experience a net gain in water.
(C) The cells will experience no net change in the amount of water.
(D) The cells will experience a loss of water initially and then a rapid gain in water.

1. When onion cells are placed in a 9% salt water solution.

2. When red blood cells are placed in distilled water.

3. When a model cell made of dialysis tubing is filled with distilled water and placed in a 1M sucrose solution.

4. When a slide containing an Elodea leaf is flooded with distilled water.

5. When a model cell made of dialysis tubing is filled with 0.5 M glucose and placed in a 0.5M sucrose solution.

Consider the diagram shown below. The solution in the tube consists of starch molecules in water. The two sides of the "U" tube are separated by a semipermeable membrane.

6. Which of the following statements best explains the rising of water in the right side of the "U" tube?

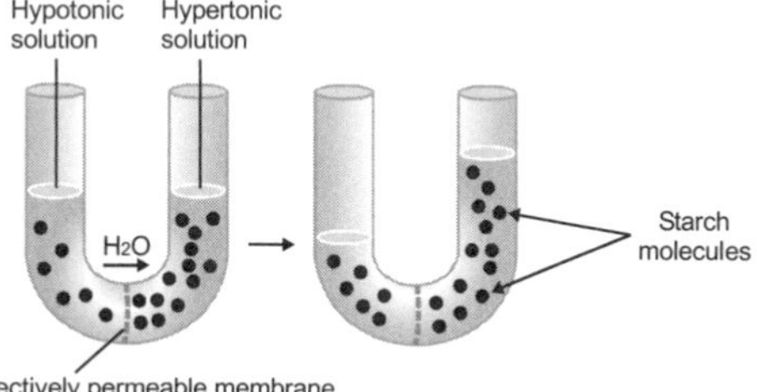

A) The starch molecules soak up water and swell causing water to rise.
B) The starch breaks down into glucose releasing water during the process. The release of water raises the level in the right side of the tube.
C) Osmotic pressure formed by osmosis pushes water into the right side causing the level to rise.
D) The water molecules on the right side of the tube reproduce and grow, raising the water level.

7. The starch molecules do not cross the membrane because:
   A) The membrane uses energy to keep the starch molecules from crossing over.
   B) The starch molecules are too large to pass through the membrane openings.
   C) The current produced by the water passing through the membrane keeps the starch molecules from getting across.
   D) Starch is a sticky lipid (fat). It sticks to the sides of the "U" tube so that it cannot move across the membrane.

Answer Key: (Plasmolysis)

1. a
2. b
3. a
4. b
5. c
6. c
7. b

Proteins, the Essence of Life
Simulating the Process of Protein Synthesis

Multiple Choice Questions:

Below is a mRNA that has been transcribed from a DNA gene. Under the mRNA is the amino acid sequence that is coded for by mRNA.

DNA Gene	TAC TTC AAA CCG CGT AAC ACT ATG AAC TTT GGC GCA TTC TGA
mRNA	AUG AAG UUU GGC GCA UUG UGA
Amino Acids	MET–LYS–PHE–GLY–ALA–LEU STOP

A mutation occurs in the gene. Adenine has been substituted for guanine at codon # 4. The new gene looks like this:

DNA Gene	TAC TTC AAA *ACG CGT AAC ACT ATG AAC TTT GGC GCA TTC TGA

1. The new mRNA that would result from this mutation would be
   A) AUG AAG UUU GGC GCA UUG UGA
   B) ATG AAC TTT GGC GCA TTC TAA
   C) AUG AAG UUU UGC GCA UUG UGA
   D) ATG AAC TTT GGC TCA TTC TAA

2. The above mutation is called a(n)
   A) frame shift mutation.
   B) point mutation.
   C) addition.
   D) deletion.

3. The above would probably result in
   A) The amino acid sequence remaining the same.
   B) The amino acid sequence remaining the same with only one amino acid being substituted for another.
   C) The amino acid sequence being changed from the beginning of the gene.
   D) The amino acid sequence being changed from the place of the mutation onward.

4. The above DNA gene is coding for a protein's
   A) quaternary structure.
   B) tertiary structure.
   C) secondary structure.
   D) primary structure.

Answer Key: (Proteins the Essence of Life)

1. c
2. b
3. b
4. d

Transpiration
Investigating Water Movement and Evaporation in Monocot and Dicot Plants

Multiple Choice Questions:

1. All of the following statements are true regarding the results of the transpiration lab EXCEPT
   A) Transpiration occurs more quickly in broad leafs than thin leafs.
   B) Monocot plants typically have a higher transpiration rate than dicots.
   C) Water exits the plant leaves through the stoma during transpiration.
   D) Transpiration functions to cool plant tissues.

2. In which of the following tissues is water conducted up the plant stem and into the leaf tissues during the transpiration lab?
   A) Phloem
   B) Xylem
   C) Epidermis
   D) Mesophyll

3. Why was it necessary to apply a thin layer of mineral oil to the water in the transpiration lab?
   A) To make it easier to insert the plant stem into the barrel of the syringe
   B) To make the water line visible while taking readings during the experiment.
   C) To help the plant stay in the center of the syringe barrel.
   D) To prevent the water from evaporating during the experiment.

4. If the leaves of a dicot plant were sprayed with water and covered with a plastic bag, which of the following is most likely to occur?
   A) The rate of transpiration will increase.
   B) The rate of transpiration will decrease.
   C) The rate of transpiration will increase initially and then decrease.
   D) The rate of transpiration will not be affected.

5. All of the following are true about water in the process of transpiration EXCEPT
   A) During adhesion, water molecules form hydrogen bonds with other substances.
   B) Capillary action moves water upward in a thin tube such as xylem tissue.
   C) During cohesion, water molecules form hydrogen bonds with carbon dioxide.
   D) Water moves from an area of high water concentration to an area of low water concentration.

Answer Key: (Transpiration)

1. b
2. b
3. d
4. b
5. c

Circulation System
Examining Vessels, Blood and Heart Structures

Multiple Choice Questions:

Consider the following diagram of the heart for questions 1-5:

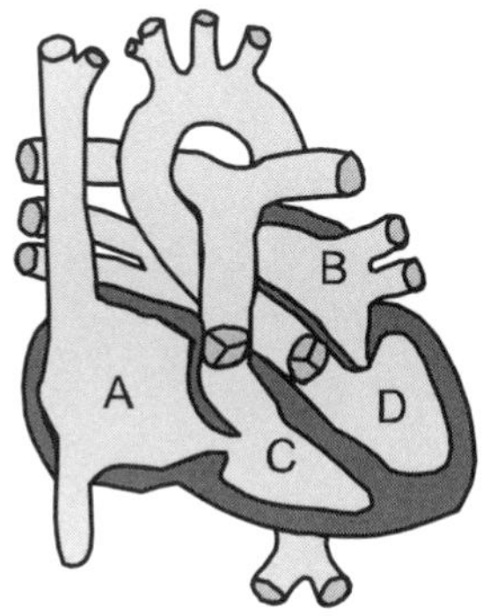

1. Which letter indicates the chamber of the heart that receives blood from the lungs?

2. Which letter indicates the chamber of the heart that receives deoxygenated blood from the body?

3. All of the following statements are true regarding veins EXCEPT
   A) Blood in veins travels toward the heart.
   B) Venous blood contains lower amounts of oxygen than arterial blood.
   C) Veins contain valves.
   D) The walls in veins are thicker, containing more connective tissue than artery walls.

4. When comparing dog blood with frog blood, which of the following differences will be observed?
   A) Frog blood cells have a slightly greenish tint while dog blood cells are dark red.
   B) Frog blood cells are convex, bulging outward in shape while dog blood cells are round and concave on both sides.
   C) Frog blood cells are much higher in number and larger than dog blood cells.
   D) Frog blood cells contain nuclei while dog blood cells lack nuclei.

5. Which of the following structure/function sets is incorrectly paired?
   A) Concave red blood cell/carry oxygen
   B) Thick muscular wall of left ventricle/pump blood to body
   C) Thin walled atrium/receive blood from the ventricle
   D) Tricuspid valve/regulate blood flow from right atrium to ventricle

Answer Key: (Circulation System)

1. b
2. a
3. d
4. d
5. c

Kermit versus Mickey Mouse
Determining the Q_{10} of an Endothermic and Exothermic Organism

Multiple Choice Questions:

A student was comparing the rates of respiration of frogs and mice by measuring the amount of oxygen being consumed. He obtained the results below:

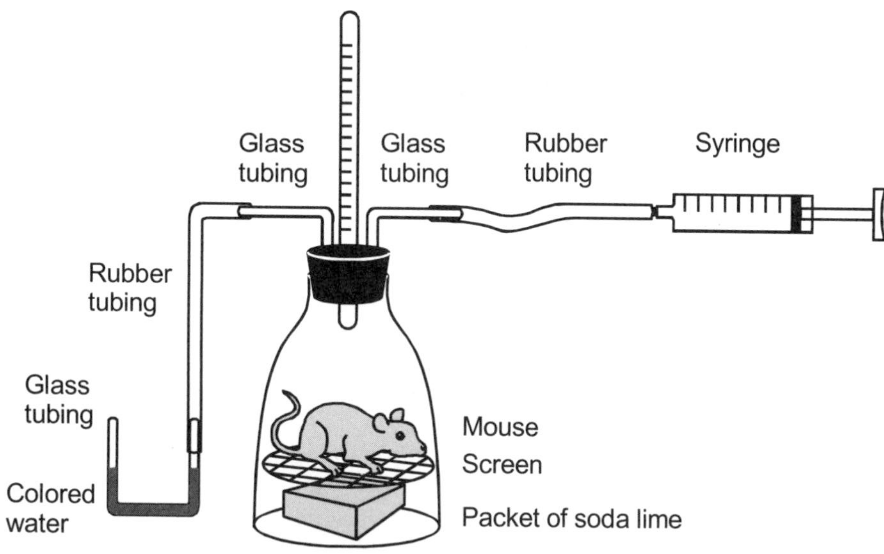

time minutes	mouse cc oxygen	frog cc oxygen
0.00	0.00	0.0
0.50	2.00	0.0
1.00	4.00	0.0
1.50	6.00	.5
2.00	8.00	.5
2.50	10.0	.5
3.00	12.0	1
3.50	14.0	1
4.00	16.0	1
4.50	18.0	1.5
5.00	20.0	1.5

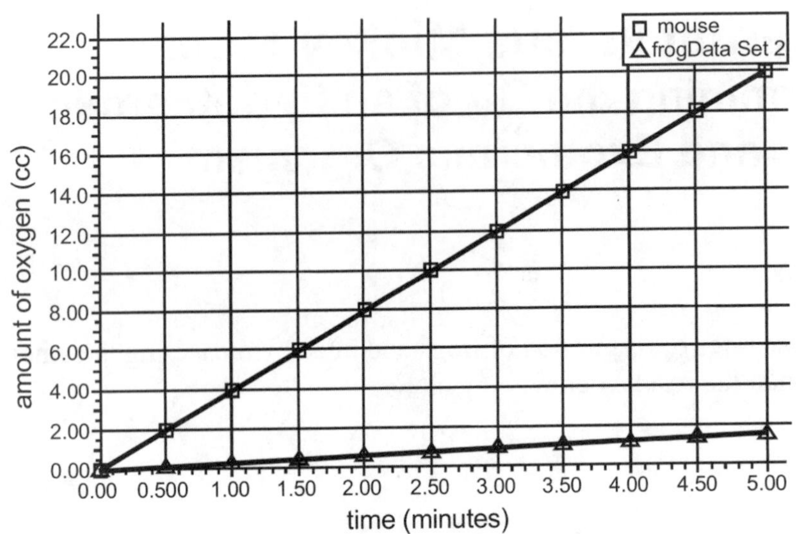

1. Which organism respired at the fastest rate?
   A) the mouse
   B) the frog
   C) both respired at the same rate
   D) can not be determined from the information provided

2. At three minutes, the frog used
   A) 1 cc
   B) 12 cc
   C) 0 cc
   D) 10 cc

3. At what time did the mouse use 8 cc of oxygen
   A) 0 min
   B) 1min
   C) 1.5 min
   D) 2 min

4. The rate of respiration for the mouse was
   A) 20 cc/min
   B) 10 cc/min
   C) 4 cc/min
   D) 0.3 cc/min

5. The rate of respiration for the frog was
   A) 20 cc/min
   B) 10 cc/min
   C) 4 cc/min
   D) 0.3 cc/min

6. If the frog weighed 10 grams and the mouse weighed 4 grams, then the rates of respiration per gram would be _______ for the frog and _______ for the mouse
   A) 0.3 cc/min/gram   4 cc/min/gram
   B) .03cc/min/gram   1 cc/min/gram
   C) 1.5 cc/min/gram   20 cc/min/gram
   D) 0.5 cc/min/gram   10 cc/min/gram

7. The reason that one animal respired more than the other was
   A) the mouse is an endotherm and the frog is an ectotherm
   B) the mouse is an ectotherm and the frog is an endotherm
   C) the mouse was larger than the frog and respired more
   D) the frog was larger than the mouse and respired more

Answer Key: (Kermit vs. Mickey Mouse)

1. a
2. a
3. d
4. c
5. d
6. b
7. a

Appendixes

A Brief History of Science

LEVEL

All levels of science

NATIONAL STANDARDS

Science in Personal and Social Perspectives; History and Nature of Science

OBJECTIVE AND INTRODUCTION

Science is a human endeavor, and the discoveries in science, whether accidental or deliberately pursued, always occur within the contexts of culture and social environment, curiosity and necessity, and the availability of technology. The following chart which chronicles some of the major developments in science and technology over thousands of years is not meant to be complete, but is intended to convey how some of the scientific concepts were discovered and how they developed from one generation to the next. The discoveries which are highlighted were chosen because of their direct relevance to the content typically covered in middle school and high school science courses.

It should also be noted that even though modern science is often partitioned into narrow, specific areas of concentration, as science continues to progress we continue to see how one science is dependent on another. For example, the discovery of the structure of the DNA molecule is certainly one of the most important discoveries of the modern era, and could not have been possible without the cooperation and contributions of physicists, chemists, and biologists. If one of the sciences doesn't have any events highlighted during a particular time period in the chart, it should not be assumed that there were no significant developments during that time period. Often progress in one area of science ultimately reveals itself in a major development in another area of science.

It is important to help the students realize that the discoveries listed on this chart did not happen overnight. Scientists struggled for years, decades, centuries, and sometimes millennia to grasp an understanding of the difficult riddles the natural world presents us. Science teachers should continually remind students that because these concepts took considerable time and effort to discover and understand, it will likely take time and effort for the students to understand them.

Perhaps this chart can help teachers put the science they are exploring with students into perspective as it relates to time, culture, and available technology. If you like to have the students write reports on scientists and their discoveries, you might choose a particular time period or topic and have the students do further research and present their findings in a creative way, such as posters, timelines, oral and written reports, or a Power Point presentation.

The primary sources for this chart can be found at http://www.sciencetimeline.net.

	10000 BC - 800 BC	*800 BC - 400 BC*	*400 BC - 200 BC*
Biology	10,000 BC - 6500 BC Animals were probably first domesticated. 2000 BC Egyptians considere the souring of wine comparable to the souring of milk. 1600 BC Egyptian papyrus list many diagnoses of head and neck injuries and their treatment. 1000 BC Horse breeders experiment with cross-breeding of horses and donkeys.	580 BC Thales of Miletus suggests that water is the fundamental component to all life. 510 BC Almaeon of Crotona locates the seat of perception in the brain by dissection. 500 BC Xenophanes examines fossils and speculates on the evolution of the earth. 400 BC Hippocrates of Cos, maintains that diseases have natural causes.	250 BC Erasistratus of Alexandria dissects the brain and distinguishes between the cerebrum and the cerebellum.
Physics	4800 BC Astronomical calendar stones used in Egypt. 3300 BC Numerals first used in Sumerian and Egyptian hieroglyphics. 3200 BC First evidence of wheeled vehicles in Uruk. 1600 BC Documents maintain the Earth was a globe and the Earth circled the Sun. 1500 BC Babylonians understand right-triangle relationships.	From 747 BC, a continuous record of solar and lunar eclipses was kept in Mesopotamia. 585 Thales predicts and eclipse 530 BC Pythagoras discovers musical intervals in strings depends on length and tension. 425 BC Herodotus writes the first scientific history. 400 BC Arrow-shooting catapult developed at Syracuse.	400 BC Babylonian astronomers can predict the occurence of lunar eclipses. 370 BC Eudoxus of Cnidus invents a model of concentric spheres by which he was able to predict the motions of the moon, sin, and planets. 335 BC Aristotle writes *Physics*, which becomes the standard for science for 2000 years. 300 BC Euclid writes *Elements*, providing the basis for geometry. 260 BC Aristarchus of Samos suggests the sun-centered model of the universe, and calculates the Earth-Sun distance to the Earth-moon distance; Archimedes formulates buoyancy principles.
Chemistry	4000 BC Copper smelting is introduced in Mesopotamia. 2500 BC Smelting of bronze in Sumeria. 1200 BC Smelting of iron in Armenia.	450 BC Empedocles of Agrigento divides matter into the four elements: earth, water, air, fire. 440 BC Leucippus of Miletus suggests the existence of atoms.	250 BC 'Zero' appears in the Babylonian place-value system.

	200 BC - 200 AD	*200 - 1000*	*1000 - 1300*
Biology	1st Century AD Pedanius Dioscorides publishes recommendations as to the medicinal use of specific plant extracts. 170 Claudius Galen uses pulse-taking as a diagnostic, performs numerous animal dissections, and writes treatises on anatomy.	900 Abu Bakr al-Razi, distinguishes smallpox from measles in the course of writing several medical books in Arabic.	1200 Medical doctors, especially in Italy, begin writing case-histories, describing the symptoms and courses of numerous diseases. 1266 Hugh and Theodoric Borgogoni advocate putting surgical subjects to sleep with narcotic-soaked sponges.
Physics	134 BC Hipparchus of Rhodes measures the year with great accuracy and builds the first comprehensive star chart with 850 stars and a luminosity scale. 45 BC Sosigenes designs the calendar adopted by Julius Caesar. 100 AD Hero of Alexandria explains that the four elements consist of atoms. 141 AD Claudius Ptolemy publishes *Almagest*, the standard book for astronomy for 1500 years.	517 John Philoponus determines that falling objects fall with the same acceleration. 530 Simplicius of Cilicia writes a commentary in Greek on Aristotle's writings on 'gravity'. 1000 Ibn al-Haitam, or al-Hazen, in *Opticae Thesaurus*, introduces the idea that light rays emanate in straight lines in all directions from every point on a luminous surface.	1054 Chinese astronomers at the Sung national observatory at K'ai-feng observe the explosion of a supernova in the Crab Nebulae, visible in daylight for twenty-three days. 1268 Roger Bacon publishes proposals for educational reform, arguing for the study of nature, using observation and exact measurement, and asserting that the only basis for certainty is experience, or verification.
Chemistry	1st century AD Titus Lucretius Carus maintains that the universe came into being through the working of natural laws in the combining of atoms.	800 Jabir ibn Hayyan, later known as Geber, bases his chemical system on sulfur and mercury. 850 Moors in Spain prepare pure copper by reacting its salts with iron, a forerunner of electroplating.	1100 Alchemists develop the art of distillation to the stage at which distillates could be captured by cooling in a flask. 1260 Albertus writes a book in which he geology into a coherent theory. He was the first to produce arsenic in a free form.

	1300 - 1400	*1400 - 1500*	*1500 - 1550*
Biology	1316 Mondino of Luzzi publishes *Anatomia*, introducing the practice of public dissections for teaching. 1360, Guy de Chauliac, recommends extending fractured limbs with pulleys and weights, and replacing lost teeth with bone fastened to the sound teeth with gold wire.	1410 Benedetto Rinio publishes an herbal which contains 450 paintings of plants, botanical notes, citations of authorities used, and the names of the plants in various languages. 1482 Leonardo da Vinci begins his notebooks on dissections of the human body, the impossibility of perpetual motion, dynamics, statics, and numerous machines.	1541Giambattista Canano publishes illustrations of each muscle and its relation with the bones. 1546 Fracastoro publishes the idea that diseases were caused by disease-specific seeds which could be contagious.
Physics	1304 Theodoric of Freiberg shows that rainbows could be explained through experiments with hexagonal crystals and spherical crystal balls. 1323 William Ockham introduces the distinction between 'being in motion' and 'being moved,' that is, as it is now called, between dynamic motion and kinematic motion. 1364 Giovanni di Dondi builds a complex clock which kept track of calendar cycles and computed the date of Easter by using various lengths of chain.	1420 Felipe Brunelleschi draws panels in scientifically-accurate perspective. 1437 Johann Gutenberg becomes the first in Europe to print with movable type cast in molds.	1543 Copernicus publishes *De revolutionibus orbium coelestium*, detailing the sun-centered model of the solar system. 1572 Tycho Brahe observes a supernova in the constellation Cassiopeia, now known as Tycho's star. 1583 Galileo Galilei discovers by experiment that the oscillations of a swinging pendulum take the same amount of time regardless of their amplitude. In 1590 Zacharias and Hans Janssen combines double convex lenses in a tube, producing the first telescope.
Chemistry	1300 Giles of Rome puts forward an atomic theory based on Avicebron's theory of matter.		Theophrastus Bombastus von Hohenheim (Paracelsus) suggests the chemical properties are combustibility, fluidity, and changeability, solidity, and permanence.

	1600 - 1625	*1625 - 1650*	*1650 - 1700*
Biology	1627 William Harvey confirms his observation that the blood circulates throughout the body.	1645 Marc Aurelio Severino discovers the heart of the higher crustacea., recognizes the respiratory function of fish gills, and recognizes the unity of vertebrates. 1650 Francis Glisson publishes an account of infantile ricketts.	1651 Harvey publishes the concept that all living things originate from eggs. 1652 Thomas Bartholin discovers the lymphatic system and determines its relation to the circulatory system. 1655 Thomas Sydenham promotes the idea that diseases are organisms inside a host. 1665 Robert Hooke names and gives the first description of cells. 1674 Anton van Leeuwenhoek reports his discovery of protozoa.
Physics	1600 William Gilbert, in *De Magnete*, holds that the earth behaves like a giant magnet with its poles near the geographic poles. 1604 Johannes Kepler and many other astronomers witness the outburst of a supernova in the constellation Serpens. 1605 Francis Bacon, with the *Advancement of Learning*, begins the publication of his philosophical works, in which he urges collaboration between the inductive and experimental methods of proof. 1609 Kepler publishes his 1st and 2nd laws of planetary motion. 1610 Galileo observes the moons of Jupiter, phases of Venus, craters on the moon. 1621 Willibrord Snell discovers the law of refraction.	1633 Galileo is placed under house arrest for his heliocentric views published in his book *Dialogue on the Two Chief World Systems.* 1638 Galileo publishes *Discourses on Two New Sciences*, outlining his theory of motion. 1644 Blaise Pascal builds a five digit adding machine. 1644 Evangelista Torricelli devises the mercury barometer and creates an artificial vacuum. 1648 Pascal shows that barometric pressure results from atmospheric pressure and that pressure applied to a confined fluid is transmitted equally to all areas and at right angles to the surface of the container.	1666 Isaac Newton discovers the essentials of calculus, the law of universal gravitation, and that white light is composed of all the colors of the spectrum. 1669 Newton circulates a manuscript containing the first notice of his calculus. 1676 Ole Roemer proves that light travels at a finite speed by repeated observations of eclipses of Jupiter's moon, Io. 1684 Gottfried Wilhelm von Leibniz publishes his system of calculus, developed independently of Newton. 1687 Newton publishes the *Principia*, a summary of his discoveries in motion, gravitation, and calculus. 1693 Edmund Halley discovers the formula for the focus of a lens. 1694 Rudolph Jakob Camerarious reports the existence of sex in flowering plants.

	1600 - 1625	*1625 - 1650*	*1650 - 1700*
Chemistry		1630 Jean Rey states that the slight increase in weight of lead and tin during their calcination could only have come from the air. 1644 Evangelista Torricelli devises the mercury barometer and creates an artificial vacuum. 1648 Jean Baptiste van Helmont concludes that plants derive their sustenance from water, demonstrates that physiological changes have chemical causes, coined the name 'gas' from the Greek *chaos*, distinguishes gases as a class with liquids and solids.	1661 Robert Boyle gives the first precise definitions of a chemical element, a chemical reaction, chemical analysis, made studies of acids and bases, and shows that pressure and volume of a gas are inversely proportional. 1670 Boyle produces hydrogen by reacting metals with acid. 1679 Denis Papin demonstrates the influence of atmospheric pressure on boiling points.

	1700 - 1750	*1750 - 1800*	*1800 - 1850*
Biology	1715 Thomas Fairchild produces the first artificial hybrid plant. 1745 Maupertius proposes the notion of descent from a common ancestor. 1749 Buffon begins the publication of the 44 volumes of *Histoire Naturelle*, in which he draws attention to vestigial organs and asserted that species are mutable. 1788 Jean Senebier demonstrates that it is light, not heat, from the sun that is effective in photosynthesis. 1791 Luigi Galvani shows that it is possible to control the motor nerves of frogs using electrical currents, i.e., that the nerves transmitted electricity.	1752 James Lind calls attention to the value of fresh fruit in the prevention of scurvy. 1753, Carl Linné publishes *Species plantarum*, in which he distinguished plants in terms of genera and species, and later applying the system to animals. 1762 Marcus Antonius Plenciz says that living agents are the cause of infectious diseases.	1800 Karl Friedrich Burdach introduces the term 'biology,' which replaces 'natural history,' which traditionally had three components, zoology, botany, and mineralogy. 1809 Jean-Baptiste Monet de Lamarck states that heritable changes in 'habits,' or behavior, could be brought about by the environment. 1820 Lamarck describes the origin of living things as a process of gradual development from matter. 1827 Robert Brown notices random movement of microscopic particles contained in the pollen from plants when suspended in fluid (Brownian movement). 1831 Brown discovers the cell nucleus in the course of a microscopic examination of orchids. 1833 Marshall Hall describes the mechanism by which a stimulus can produce a response independent of both sensation and volition, and coins the term 'reflex.' 1837 Heinrich Gustav Magnus determines that carbon dioxide released in the lungs had been carried there by blood and that more oxygen and less carbon dioxide was contained in arterial than in venous blood; René Dutrochet observes that chlorophyll is necessary for photosynthesis; Hugo von Mohl describes 'chloroplasts' as discrete bodies within the cells of green plants. 1838 Mattias Jakob Schleiden puts forward the theory that plant tissues are composed of cells, and recognizes the significance of the nucleus. 1839 Mohl describes the appearance of the cell plate between the daughter cells during cell division, or 'mitosis.' 1846 William Morton demonstrates the effective use of ether as an anesthesia. 1848 Louis Pasteur discovers molecular dissymmetry, or chirality, and coins the distinction between users and non-users of oxygen, 'aerobic' and 'anaerobic.' 1801 Thomas Young observes that light passing through a double-slit recombines to create light and dark areas, and measures the wavelength of light using this pattern.

	1700 - 1750	*1750 - 1800*	*1800 - 1850*
Physics	1704 Newton, in *Opticks*, presents his discoveries using light and elaborates his theory that it is composed of particles. 1705 Halley recognizes the orbit of the comet that bears his name and predicts its reappearance in 1758. 1718 Halley states that stars move, since they had changed position since Ptolemy's *Almagest*. 1738 Daniel Bernoulli asserts the principle that as the speed of a moving fluid increases, the pressure within the fluid decreases, inventing the kinetic theory of gases. 1746 Andreas Cunaeus invents the 'Leyden jar,' a form of capacitor. 1798 Cavendish constructs a torsion balance by which he measured the mean density of the Earth.	1751 Benjamin Franklin publishes *Experiments and Observations on Electricity* after several years of experiments. 1752 Thomas Melvill notices that the spectra of flames into which metals or salts have been introduced show bright lines characteristic of the metal or salt. 1756 Franz Ulrich Theodosius Aepinus, realizes that the causes of magnetic and electrical phenomena were extremely similar. 1759 The return of Halley's comet confirms Newton''s mechanics. 1759 Aepinus fathers the action-at-a-distance/localization of charge theory of electricity and magnetism. 1768 Euler proposes that the wavelength of light determines its color. 1783 Carnot specifies the optimal and abstract conditions for the operation for all sorts of actual machines. 1785 Charles Augustin de Coulomb formulates the inverse square law for the force between electric charges.	1807 Young coins the word 'energy' for the fundamental quantity created by the heat which moved particles in Bernoulli's kinetic theory. 1814 Joseph von Fraunhofer devises a primitive spectroscope by allowing light to pass through a narrow slit and then a prism. 1816 Augustin Jean Fresnel shows that diffraction, interference, and polarization can be explained in terms of the transverse wave theory of light. 1820 Hans Christian Ørsted initiates the study of electromagnetism by placing a needle parallel to a wire conducting electric current and discovering that this produces a magnetic field that curls around the wire. 1824 Sadi Carnot shows that even under ideal conditions a steam engine cannot convert into mechanical energy all the heat energy supplied to it. 1827 Georg Simon Ohm discovers that the ratio of the potential difference between the ends of a conductor and the current flowing through it is constant, and is the resistance of the conductor. 1831 Faraday discovers the means of producing electricity from magnetism, i.e., electromagnetic induction. 1841 Julius Robert Mayer, working with established experimental results, derives the general relationship between heat and work, which is the first law of thermodynamics, a form of the law of conservation of energy. 1842 Christian Doppler develops the theory that the frequency of energy in the form of the form of waves changes depending on the motion of either the sender or the receiver. 1843 James Prescott Joule demonstrates experimentally the equivalence of the heat produced and the mechanical work spent in the operation. 1846 Johann Gottfried Galle discovers the planet Neptune where Urbain Jean Joseph Le Verrier and, independently, John Couch Adams had predicted that a planet would be found.

	1700 - 1750	1750 - 1800	1800 - 1850
Physics (Continued)		1792 Volta discovers he could arrange metals in a series in such a way that chemical energy is converted into electrical energy.	1847 Hermann von Helmholtz formulates the law of the conservation of energy in an equation which expresses the most general form of the principle. 1850 Jean Foucault, using a rotating mirror, determines the speed of light in the air as 298,000 km/s.
Chemistry	1709 Gabriel Daniel Fahrenheit constructs an alcohol thermometer and, five years later, a mercury thermometer. 1742 Celsius develops the centigrade temperature scale which carries his name.	1754 Joseph Black heats calcium carbonate which separates into calcium oxide and carbon dioxide and then recombines back into calcium carbonate. 1757 Black discovers latent heat, distinguishing between heat and temperature. 1774 Priestly discovers sulphur dioxide, ammonia, and 'dephlogisticated air,' later named oxygen by Lavoisier. 1780 Lavoisier and Laplace develop a theory of chemical and thermal phenomena based on the assumption that heat is a substance, which they called 'caloric' and deduced the notion of 'specific heat.' 1787 Charles determines that the volume of a fixed mass of gas at constant pressure is proportional to its temperature. This was published by Joseph Louis Gay-Lussac in 1802. 1789 Lavoisier proves that mass is conserved in chemical reactions and created the first list of chemical elements.	1803 Dalton applies atomic theory to a table of atomic weights. 1808 Dalton publishes *A New System of Chemical Philosophy*, launching chemical atomic theory; Gay-Lussac ennunciates the 'Law of combining volumes,' which states that when gases combine they do so in small whole number ratios. 1811 Berzelius simplifies chemistry through his suggestion that they be represented by the first letter of each element's Latin name, with the addition of the second letter when necessary. Proportions in a compound were indicated with appropriate number as subscript. 1811 Amedeo Avogadro proposes that equal volumes of gases at the same temperature and pressure contain the same number of molecules. 1815 William Prout proposes that the atomic weights of elements are multiples of that for hydrogen. 1825 Faraday discovers benzene. 1834 Faraday states that the amount of chemical change produced is proportional to the quantity of electricity passed and the amount of chemical change produced in different substances by a fixed quantity of electricity is proportional to the electrochemical equivalent of the substance. 1835 Berzelius suggests the name 'catalysis' for reactions which occurred only in the presence of some third substance. 1839 Christian Swann discovers the existence of ozone. 1848, W. Thomson proposes what became known as the 'Kelvin scale,' after the title bestowed on him by the British government. 1850 Runge demonstrates the separation of inorganic chemicals by their differential adsorption to paper. This is forerunner of chromatographic separations.

	1850 - 1875	*1875 - 1900*	*1900 - 1925*
Biology	1852 Georges Newport observes the penetration of the vitelline membrane of a frog egg by sperm. 1857 Pasteur demonstrates that lactic acid fermentation is carried out by living bacteria; Albert von Kolliker describes what were later named 'mitochondria' in the nucleus of muscle cells. 1858 Darwin''s friends, arrange for the simultaneous announcement of Wallace's and Darwin's idea of natural selection. 1859, Darwin, in *Origin of Species* asserts all life had a common ancestor. 1862 Pasteur publishes the 'germ theory': Infection is caused by self-replicating microorganisms, and that attenuated viral cultures granted immunity. These beneficent antigens he named 'vaccines' in honor of Jenner and his vaccinia virus. 1865 O.F.C. Deiters proposes the image of the nerve cell which is accepted today: cell body with its nucleus, multiple, branching dendrites, and a single axon; Lister, using carbolic acid as antiseptic and sterilizing his instrument, proved the efficacy of antiseptic surgery. 1866 Gregor Mendel interprets heredity in terms of a pairing of dominant and/or recessive unit characters. 1871 Darwin, in *The Descent of Man*, suggests that there is no sharp discontinuity between the evolution of humans and animals.	1876 Robert Koch devises the method of employing aniline dyes to stain microorganisms, isolating pure cultures of bacteria and showing the bacterial origin of many infectious diseases. 1879 Walther Flemming names 'chromatin' and 'mitosis,' made the first accurate counts of chromosome numbers,and discerned the longitudinal splitting of chromosomes. 1883 Wilhelm Roux suggests that the filaments within the cell's nucleus carry the hereditary factors. 1885 Hertwig and Strasburger develop the conception that the nucleus is the basis of heredity. 1890 Hans Driesch separates two cells of a fertilized sea urchin egg by shaking with very different results than Roux: From a single cell arose an entire sea urchin; Richard Altmann reports the presence within cells of organisms which live as intracellular symbionts, later named mitochondria. 1894 H.J.H. Fenton discovers a reaction now considered to be one of the most important mechanisms of oxidative damage in living cell.	1900 Mikhail Tsvet discerns three green pigments, chlorophyll a, b, and c, differing in color, fluorescence, and spectral absorption. 1902 Karl Landsteiner found that human blood was one of four types, A, B, A-B, and O, thus making transfusions safe; Fischer proposes that proteins consist of chains of amino acids; Ivan Pavlov combines associative learning with reflex acts, postulating the existence of associated stimuli, or 'conditioned responses.' 1903 Tsvet develops methods in chromatography. 1905 Edmund Beecher Wilson discovers that the X chromosome is linked to the sex of the bearer. 1908 Godfrey Harold Hardy works out the equilibrium formula for a population heterogenous for a single pair of alleles. 1910 Konstantin S. Mereschovsky publishes an essentially modern view of the bacterial origin of what later came to be called eukaryotic cells. 1911 Alfred Henry Sturtevant, an undergraduate student of Morgan's, constructs the first rudimentary map of the fruit fly chromosome, establishing that genes are real. 1913 Lawrence Joseph Henderson proposes that the concept of fitness be extended to the environment. This has ramifications for the origin of life.

	1850 - 1875	*1875 - 1900*	*1900 - 1925*
Biology (Continued)	1873 Anton Schneider describes chromosomes during the process of mitosis during cell division.		1921 Victor Jollos hypothesizes that the disappearance of environmentally-induced acquired traits, even after hundreds of generations, indicates that their acquisition should be assigned to the cytoplasm rather than the nucleus; Muller raises the question of the relationship of genes to viruses, or 'naked genes'. 1922 Walter Garstang shows that phylogeny is not the cause but the product of different ontogenies. 1923 Robert Feulgen discovers a selective staining technique for DNA localization, which is still in use; Jean Piaget maintains that child development proceeds in the same sequence of genetically determined stages.
Physics	1851 Foucault demonstrates that a pendulum's swing, seen relative to the Earth, would gradually precess, evidence of the Earth's rotation. 1859 Kirchhoff proves a theorem about blackbody radiation, namely, the energy emitted E depends only on the temperature and the frequency of the emitted energy. 1861, Maxwell announces his discovery that some of the properties of the vibrations in the magnetic medium are identical with those of light, and predicts the speed of light theoretically; Anders Jonas Ångström, using a spectroscope, confirms the presence of hydrogen in the Sun.	1876 Alexander Graham Bell invents the telephone. 1879 Crookes attempts to determine the paths of the 'lines of molecular pressure,' or cathode rays, in an evacuated glass tube through which two electrodes are passed. 1879 Albert Michelson determines the speed of light to be 186,350 miles per second. 1881 Venn represents logical propositions diagrammatically.	1900 Planck introduces 'quantum theory' to explain a formula, E=hf, where E is energy, f is frequency, and h is a new constant; Rutherford identifies a third type of radiation, which he calls 'gamma radiation.' 1903 Orville and Wilbur Wright achieve flight in a manned, gasoline power-driven, heavier-than-air flying machine. 1904 Lorentz formulates the so-called 'Lorentz transformation,' which describes the increase in mass, the shortening of length, and the time dilation of a body moving at speeds close to that of light. 1904 Hantaro Nagaoka proposes a 'Saturn model' of the atom with a nucleus and many electrons in a ring around it.

	1850 - 1875	*1875 - 1900*	*1900 - 1925*
Physics (Continued)	1865 Maxwell publishes his four equations of electromagnetism based on the work of Coulomb, Gauss, Ampere, and Faraday. 1871 Crookes creates a vacuum of about one millionth of an atmosphere which made possible the discovery of X-rays and the electron.	1887 Michelson and Edward W. Morley, using an interferometer to investigate whether the speed of light depends on the direction the light beam moves, fail to detect the motion of the Earth with respect to the aether, thereby refuting the hypothesis that the aether exists; Heinrich Hertz produces electromagnetic radio waves. 1888 Nicola Tesla patents his invention of alternating electric current. 1892 Lorentz proposes a theory in which a body carries a charge if it has an excess of positive or negative particles, and an electric current in a conductor is a flow of particulate particles. 1895 Wilhelm Conrad Röntgen, using a Crookes' tube, observes a new form of penetrating radiation, which he named X-rays. 1897 Joseph John Thomson, using a Crookes' tube, demonstrates that cathode rays consisted of units of electrical current made up of negatively charged particles of subatomic size (electrons). 1899 Ernest Rutherford characterizes 'alpha rays' and 'beta rays'; Becquerel shows that radioactivity in uranium consists of charged particles that are deflected by a magnetic field.	1905 Albert Einstein publishes three papers describing his explanation of the photoelectric effect, Brownian movement, and his theory of special relativity. 1907 Einstein deduces the expression for the equivalence of mass and energy, $E=mc^2$. 1908 Robert Andrews Millikan determines the probable minimum unit of an electrical charge, that is, of an electron. 1909 Hans Geiger and E. Marsden, under Rutherford's direction, scatter alpha particles with thin films of heavy metals, providing evidence that atoms possess a discrete nucleus. 1911 Heike Kamerlingh Onmes discovers 'superconductivity,' the ability of certain materials at low temperatures to carry electric current without resistance; Einstein postulates that light is bent by gravity. 1911-13 Hertzsprung and Russell publish graphs plotting color or spectral class against the absolute magnitude of stars. These are now called HR diagrams and are the basis of the theory of stellar evolution. 1913 Niels Bohr, applying the Planck quantum hypothesis to Rutherford's atomic model, places electrons in discrete energy levels, and postulating the quantum model of the atom; Einstein and Marcel Grossman investigate curved space and time as it relates to a theory of gravity. Einstein contributed the physics and Grossman the mathematics.

	1850 - 1875	*1875 - 1900*	*1900 - 1925*
Physics (Continued)			1919 E. Rutherford discovers the proton, which contains the positive charge within the nucleus of an atom, and publishes the first evidence of artificially-produced splitting of atomic nuclei; Eddington and Frank W. Dyson measure the bending of starlight by the gravitational pull of the sun, thus confirming Einstein's general theory of relativity. 1920 E. Rutherford postulates the existence of the neutron, required in order to keep the positively-charged protons in the nucleus from repelling each other. 1922 Arthur Compton demonstrates an increase in the wavelengths of X-rays and gamma rays when they collide with loosely bound electrons, verifying the quantum theory since the effect requires the rays be treated as particles, not waves. 1923 Louis de Broglie hypothesizes that a moving electron particle has wave-like properties.
Chemistry	1855 David Alter described the spectra of hydrogen and other gases. 1858 Friedrich August Kekulé von Stradonitz suggests that carbon atoms are formed in chains. 1859 Robert Wilhelm Bunsen discovers that each element produces its own characteristic set of lines in the spectrum. 1866 Alfred Nobel patents dynamite in Sweden.	1879 Stefan conjectures that that the radiant energy emitted by an enclosure equivalent to a black body is proportional to the fourth power of the body's temperature. 1884 Jacobus van't Hoff explains the principle of equilibrium in chemical dynamics and osmotic electrical conductivity. 1894 Strutt and William Ramsay discover and isolate argon in the process of explaining the discrepancy between the weight of nitrogen obtained from the air and from ammonia.	1905 Arrhenius expresses concern about global warming as a result of burning fossil fuels. 1913 Frederick Soddy discovers that different forms of the same element were, in fact, groups of elements with the same chemical character, but varying in their masses (isotopes), and that radioactive decay is accompanied by the transmutation of one element to another. 1916 Gilbert Newton Lewis states that the chemical bond consists of two electrons held jointly by two atoms.

	1850 - 1875	*1875 - 1900*	*1900 - 1925*
Chemistry (Continued)	1869 Dmitri Mendeléev and, independently, Julius Lother Meyer formulate the 'Periodic law.' Mendeléev placed the chemical elements in seven rows in an order where those elements having similar chemical properties were aligned vertically. 1869 John Hyatt produces 'celluloid,' the first synthetic plastic to be put into wide use.	1896 Eduard Buchner discovers a chemical in yeast, which he called zymase. He noted that the crushed yeast, that is, cell-free yeast, fermented sugar. This observation opened the era of modern biochemistry. 1896 Antoine Henri Becquerel discovers radioactivity in uranium. 1897 Felix Hoffman synthesizes a form of acetysalicylic acid that enabled the mass production of aspirin two years later. 1898 Marie Sklodowska Curie and P. Curie discover and isolate radium and polonium, and clarify that radiation is an atomic property. M. Curie coins the term 'radioactive.' 1898 J. Thomson shows that neon gas consists of two types of charged electrons, or ions, each with a different charge, or mass, or both. This raised the possibility that varieties of a single element might exist with the same atomic number but differ in mass; Wien identifies a positive particle equal in mass to the hydrogen atom, which later was named the 'proton'; Ramsey and Morris Travers discover neon, krypton, and xenon; James Dewar liquefies hydrogen.	1925 Wolfgang Pauli puts forth the principle that no two electrons in the atom can be in the same quantum state.

	1925 - 1950	*1950 - 1975*	*1975 - 2000*
Biology	1928 Alexander Fleming discovers penicillin, a relatively innocuous antibiotic. 1929 It was found that deoxyribonucleic acid (DNA) is located exclusively in the chromosomes, whereas ribonucleic acid (RNA) is located mainly outside the nucleus; Fisher provides a mathematical analysis of how the distribution of genes in a population will change as a result of natural selection, and maintained that once a species' fitness is at a maximum, any mutation will lower it. 1930 Phoebus Aaron Levene elucidate the structure of mononucleotides and showed them to be the building blocks of nucleic acids. 1931 Harriet B. Creighton and Barbara McClintock, working with maize, and Curt Stern, working with Drosophila, provide the first visual confirmation of genetic 'crossing-over.' 1935, William Cumming Rose recognizes the essential amino acid 'threonine.' 1937, Krebs discovers the citrus acid cycle, also known as the tricarboxylic acid cycle and the Krebs cycle. 1938 Hans Spemann proposes the concept of cloning and insists that cell differentiation is the outcome of an orderly sequence of specific stimuli, namely, chemical inductive agents, which were predominantly cyto-plasmic in operation; Warren Weaver coins the term 'molecular biology.' 1940 Ernst Boris Chain and Howard Walter Florey extract and purify penicillin and demonstrate its therapeutic utility.	1953 James Watson and Francis Crick build a model of DNA showing that the structure is two paired, complementary strands, helical and anti-parallel, associated by secondary, noncovalent bonds. Maurice H. F. Wilkens' and Rosalind Franklin's X-ray crystallographs of DNA supported the discovery of the structure. 1954 Salk develops an injectable killed-virus vaccine against poliomyelytis, the incidence of which began to decline after mass immunization began the following year. 1968 Norman Geschwind and Walter Levitsky show that in male and female humans there are characteristic anatomical differences, e.g., the size of the planum temporale in the hemispheres of the brain. 1973 Mertz, Davis, Lobban, Berg, Boyer, Cohen, and Morrow, animal genes were spliced into the small rings of DNA, thus beginning recombinant cloning and launching of the biotechnology industry. 1975 E. M. Southern devises an extension of gel electrophoresis, known as 'Southern blotting,' which greatly aids cloning by enabling the identification and sizing of DNA fragments.	1977 Jack Corliss, in a diving bell 2600 meters below the surface of the Pacific Ocean, observes boiling, lightless deep-sea thermal vents with hundreds of species, including a nine-foot tube worm, most of them new to science. 1978 Mary Leaky announces the discovery of fossilized human footprints from about 3.5 million years ago. 1984 Richard Leaky and Alan Walker excavate a Homo erectus skeleton, dated 1.6 million years ago; Alec John Jeffreys discovers 'genetic fingerprinting,' the pattern of nonfunctional repetitions unigue to each individual's DNA. 1990 Teams led by Robin Lovell-Badge and Robin Goodfellow isolate the testis-determining factor gene SRY, the master switch for mammalian sex determination.

	1925 - 1950	*1950 - 1975*	*1975 - 2000*
Biology (continued)	1941 Astbury establishes that DNA has a crystalline structure. 1943 Thomas Francis and Jonas Edward Salk develop a formalin-killed-virus vaccine against type A and B influenzas. 1944 Oswald T. Avery, Colin MacLeod, and Maclyn McCarty establish that the material of heredity is deoxyribonucleic acid; Archer John Porter Martin and Richard Synge devise 'paper partition chromatography.' 1948 William Howard Stein and Stanford Moore isolate amino acids by passing a solution through through a chromatographic column filled with potato starch. 1949 Sven Furberg draws a model of DNA, setting sugar at right angles to base, with the correct three-dimensional configuration of the individual nucleotide; Frederick Sanger claims that proteins are uniquely specified, the implication being that, as there is no general law for their assembly, a code was necessary. 1950 Ernst L. Wynder and Evarts A. Graham publish a survey indicating a strong correlation between contracting lung cancer and smoking tobacco.		

	1925 - 1950	*1950 - 1975*	*1975 - 2000*
Physics	1926 Erwin Schrödinger initiates the development of the final quantum theory by describing wave mechanics, which predicted the positions of the electrons, vibrating as Bohr's standing waves. 1927 Heisenberg states that electrons do not possess both a well-defined position and a well-defined momentum simultaneously. 1927 George P. Thomson diffracts electrons by passing them in a vacuum through a thin foil, thus verifying de Broglie's wave hypothesis; Davisson and Germer measure the length of a de Broglie wave by observing the diffraction of electrons by single crystals of nickel. 1929 Robert van de Graaf develops an electro-static particle accelerator; Hubble observes that all galaxies are moving away from each other. 1930 Ernest O. Lawrence publishes the principle of the cyclotron which uses a magnetic field to curl the particle trajectory of a linear accelerator into into a spiral. 1931 Pauli, in order to solve the question of where the energy went in beta decay, predicts the existence of a 'little neutral thing,' the 'neutrino.' 1932 Irène Curie and Frédéric Joliot bombard nonradioactive beryllium with alpha particles, transmuting it briefly into a radioactive element; James Chadwick isolates the neutron, the first particle discovered with zero electrical charge. 1934 I. Curie and Joliot announce the discovery of "artificial radiation obtained by bombarding certain nuclei with alpha particles."	1950 Hoyle claims to have coined 'big-bang' for the primal fireball, disparaging the notion that such ever occurred. 1956 Leon Cooper shows that in superconductivity the current is carried in bound pairs of electrons, or 'Cooper pairs.' This led to the BCS theory of superconductivity the following year. 1957 John Backus leads the team which creates 'Fortran,' the Formula Translation language for the IBM 704 computer. 1957 The United States government forms the Advanced Research Agency, or ARPA, in response to the Soviet Union's Sputnik, the first artificial satellite. 1958, Jack Kilby builds the first integrated circuit. 1959, James A. Van Allen, Carl E. McIlwain, and George H. Ludwig establish the existence of geometrically trapped electrons and protons in two belts above the Earth, later called the Van Allen Belts. 1960 Theodore H. Maiman describes the first laser, which used a synthetic ruby rod as the lasing medium.	1978 Elementary particle physicists begin speaking of the 'Standard Model' as the basic theory of matter. 1979 The spacecraft Voyager 1 photographs Jupiter's rings, and subsequently visits Saturn, Uranus, and Neptune. 1983 Carlo Rubbia and Simon van der Meer, using the CERN particle accelerator, confirmed the existence of the Z and Ws particles. 1986 Johannes Georg Bednorz and Karl Alexander Müller find a new class of layered materials which superconduct at much higher temperatures than any which had been found previously. 1987 A supernova, SN 1987A, explodes in the Large Magellanic Cloud, and was the nearest supernova to have been observed since the invention of the astronomical telescope. 1990 NASAand the European Space Agency (ESA) launch the Hubble Space Telescope, or HST. Servicing missions were carried out in 1993, 1997, and 2002; Tim Berners-Lee and CERN, The European Organization for Nuclear Research, implemented a hypertext system for information access for physicists.

	1925 - 1950	1950 - 1975	1975 - 2000
Physics (Continued)	1935 IBM introduced a punch card machine with an arithmetic unit based on relays which could do multiplication. 1938, Otto Hahn and Lise Meitner, with their colleague Fritz Strassman, bombard uranium nuclei with slow neutrons. Meitner, interprets the results to be 'nuclear fission,' the term fission being borrowed from biology. 1942 Fermi creates the first controlled, self-sustaining nuclear chain reaction. 1945 The first atomic bombs are exploded over Hiroshima, Japan, then, three days later, over Nagasaki. 1946 John Mauchly and John Presper Eckert demonstrate ENIAC, or Electronic Numerical Integrator and Computer. Its components were entirely electronic.	1963 Murray Gell-Mann and, independently, George Zweig, invent the notion of a more fundamental particle than neutrons and protons which Gell-Mann named the 'quark.' 1965 Arno Allan Penzias and Robert Woodrow Wilson discover cosmic background radiation. The implication is that intergalactic space is above absolute zero, or about 3 degrees K, leading to a drastic shift of the consensus to favor acceptance of the big-bang cosmology. 1967 Steven Weinberg, and Abdus Salam complete the observation of Glashow that the weak and electromagnetic forces result from the same fundamental force. 1968 ARPA , under Lawrence G. Roberts, contracts with BBN to build ARPANET, the prototype of the computer internet. 1970 Stephen Hawking and Penrose prove that the universe must have had a beginning in time, on the basis of Einstein's theory of General Relativity, i.e., mathematically, the big-bang must have arisen from a singularity. 1972 Ray Tomlinson creates the first electronic mail program.	1992 the United States' COBE, or 'Cosmic Background Explorer,' astronomical satellite detects very small variations, or ripples or lumps, in the background cosmic radiation which are thought to be imprints of quantum fluctuations from the early universe, or, in other words, the seeds of later giant structures; CERN releases to the public their hypertext for physicists, naming it the World Wide Web. 1995 Michel Mayor and Didier Queloz detect the first extra-solar planet using the 'wobble technique.' 1997 Ian Wilmut and Keith Campbell clone a sheep, 'Dolly,' from adult cells.

	1925 - 1950	*1950 - 1975*	*1975 - 2000*
Chemistry	1927 Walter Heitler and Fritz London show that chemical bonding, the force which holds atoms together, is electrical, and a consequence of quantum mechanics. 1931 Pauling details the rules of covalent bonding. 1944 Seaborg proposed a second 'lanthanide group' as an addition to the periodic table of the elements, as well as existence of a similar series, 90 through 103, or 'actinide group.' 1950 Leo Rainwater combines the liquid drop and shell models of the atomic nucleus.	1950 Leo Rainwater combines the liquid drop and shell models of the atomic nucleus. 1963 Stephanie Louise Kwolek synthesizes polybenzamide, or PBA, a liquid crystalline polymer, used in lightweight body armor. 1969 Calvin publishes *Chemical Evolution* in which he gives several autocatalytic scenarios for the origin of life. 1970 Woodward and Hoffman, in *The Conservation of Orbital Symmetry*, design a set of rules for postulating the areas around atoms where it is most probable that electrons will be found.	1977 Mandelbrot publishes *The Fractal Geometry of Nature* in which complex curves are reduced to straight lines, or fractals, and undergo invariant scaling.

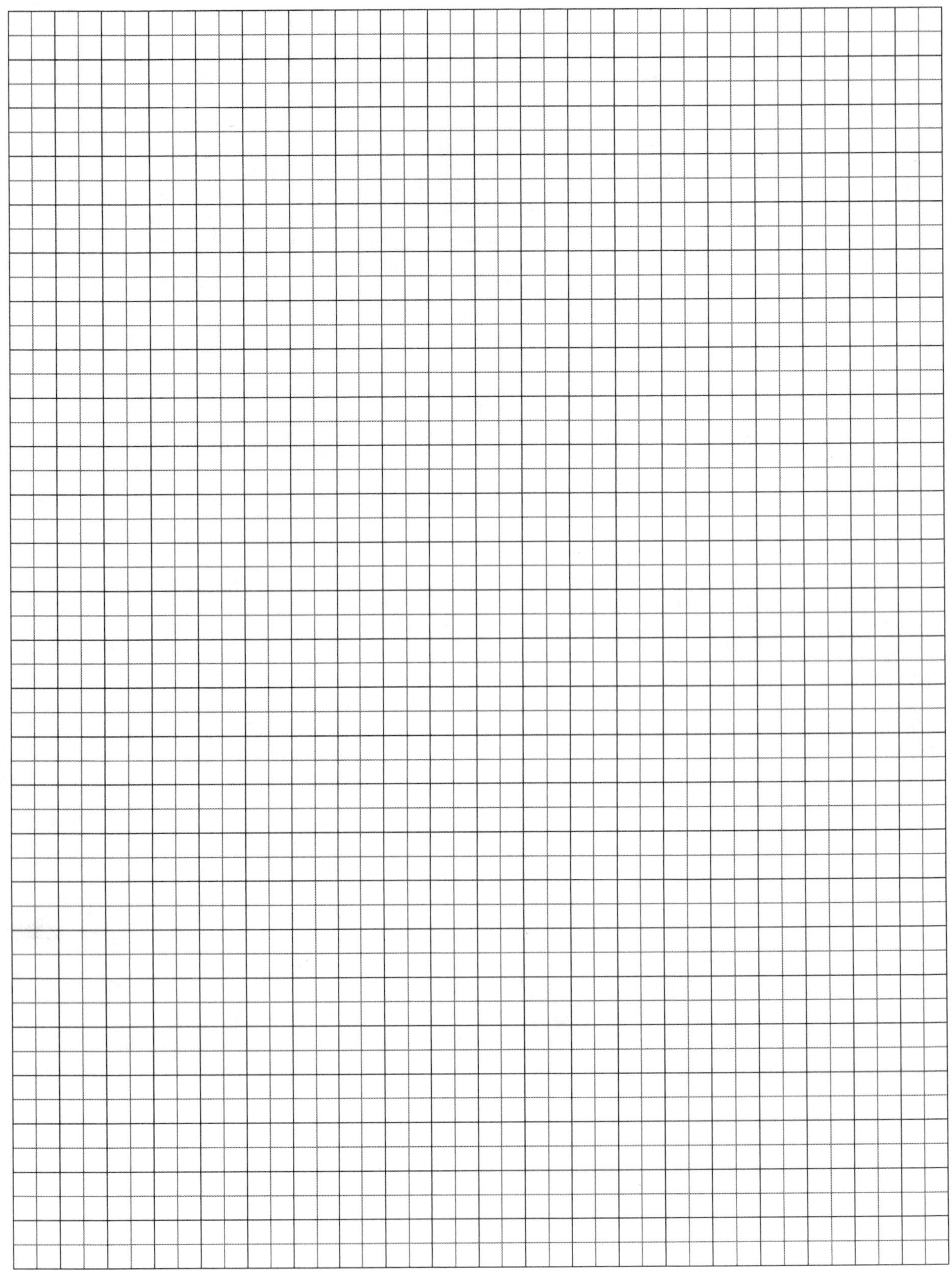

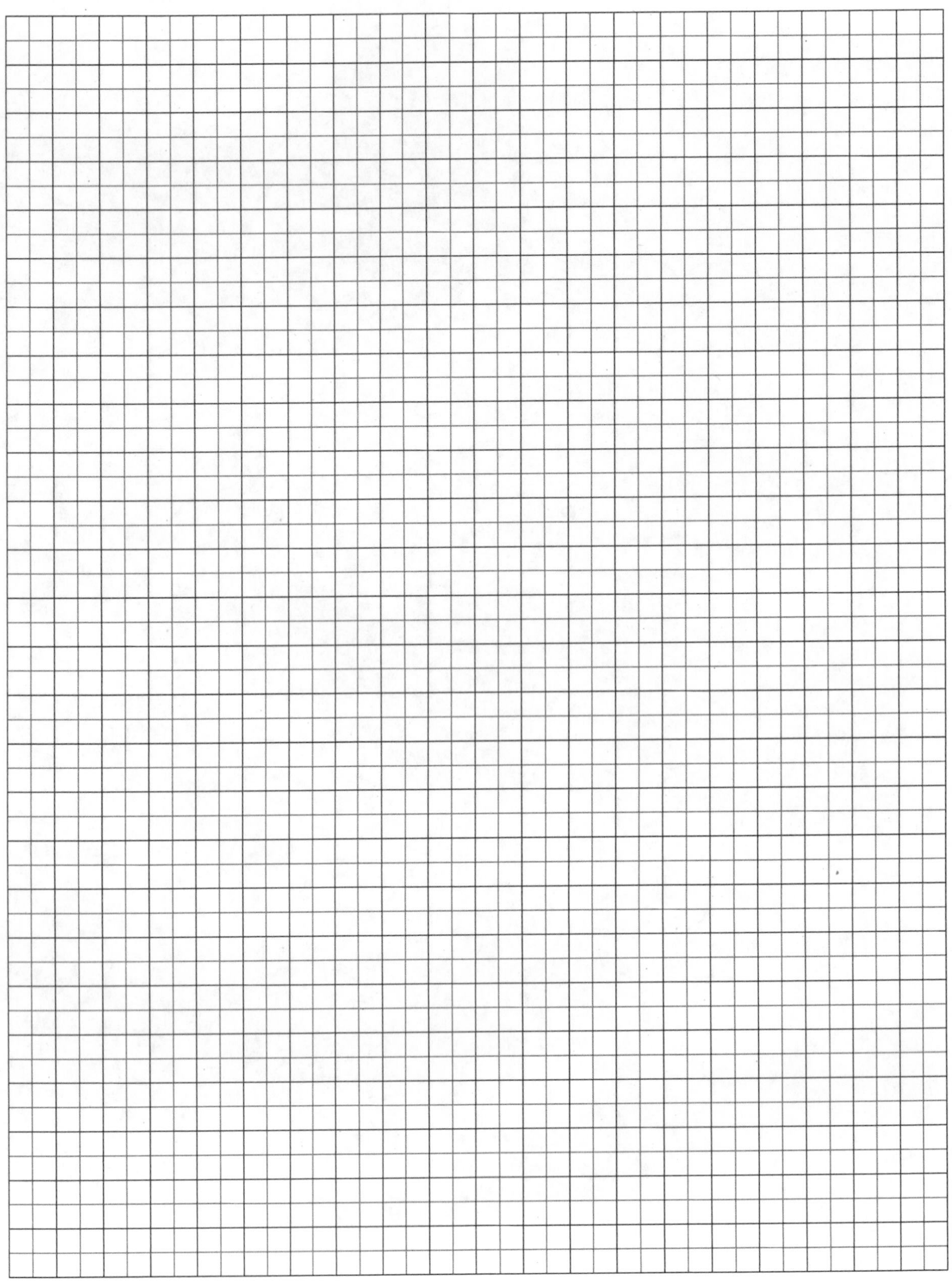